Indiana
Grade 8

interactive SCIENCE

AUTHORS

You're an author!

As you write in this science book, your answers and personal discoveries will be recorded for you to keep, making this book unique to you. That is why you are one of the primary authors of this book.

✎ **In the space below, print your name, school, town, and state. Then write a short autobiography that includes your interests and accomplishments.**

YOUR NAME

SCHOOL

TOWN, STATE

AUTOBIOGRAPHY

Your Photo

Acknowledgments appear on pages 540–544, which constitute an extension of this copyright page.

ISBN-13: 978-0-13-253478-9
ISBN-10: 0-13-253478-9
3 4 5 6 7 8 9 10 V011 15 14 13 12

ON THE COVER
Indianapolis 500 Race Cars
The Indy 500 race cars are going green with ethanol fuel made from plants! As spark plugs ignite compressed fuel, causing a chemical reaction, fire is a potential hazard. Racers traveling at 350 kilometers per hour fuel up with ethanol because it is less flammable and high performing.

Program Authors

DON BUCKLEY, M.Sc.
Information and Communications Technology Director, The School at Columbia University, New York, New York
Mr. Buckley has been at the forefront of K–12 educational technology for nearly two decades. A founder of New York City Independent School Technologists (NYCIST) and long-time chair of New York Association of Independent Schools' annual IT conference, he has taught students on two continents and created multimedia and Internet-based instructional systems for schools worldwide.

ZIPPORAH MILLER, M.A.Ed.
Associate Executive Director for Professional Programs and Conferences, National Science Teachers Association, Arlington, Virginia
Associate executive director for professional programs and conferences at NSTA, Ms. Zipporah Miller is a former K–12 science supervisor and STEM coordinator for the Prince George's County Public School District in Maryland. She is a science education consultant who has overseen curriculum development and staff training for more than 150 district science coordinators.

MICHAEL J. PADILLA, Ph.D.
Associate Dean and Director, Eugene P. Moore School of Education, Clemson University, Clemson, South Carolina
A former middle school teacher and a leader in middle school science education, Dr. Michael Padilla has served as president of the National Science Teachers Association and as a writer of the National Science Education Standards. He is professor of science education at Clemson University. As lead author of the *Science Explorer* series, Dr. Padilla has inspired the team in developing a program that promotes student inquiry and meets the needs of today's students.

KATHRYN THORNTON, Ph.D.
Professor and Associate Dean, School of Engineering and Applied Science, University of Virginia, Charlottesville, Virginia
Selected by NASA in May 1984, Dr. Kathryn Thornton is a veteran of four space flights. She has logged over 975 hours in space, including more than 21 hours of extravehicular activity. As an author on the *Scott Foresman Science* series, Dr. Thornton's enthusiasm for science has inspired teachers around the globe.

MICHAEL E. WYSESSION, Ph.D.
Associate Professor of Earth and Planetary Science, Washington University, St. Louis, Missouri
An author on more than 50 scientific publications, Dr. Wysession was awarded the prestigious Packard Foundation Fellowship and Presidential Faculty Fellowship for his research in geophysics. Dr. Wysession is an expert on Earth's inner structure and has mapped various regions of Earth using seismic tomography. He is known internationally for his work in geoscience education and outreach.

Instructional Design Author

GRANT WIGGINS, Ed.D.
President, Authentic Education, Hopewell, New Jersey
Dr. Wiggins is a co-author of the "Understanding by Design Handbook". His approach to instructional design provides teachers with a disciplined way of thinking about curriculum design, assessment, and instruction that moves teaching from covering the content to ensuring understanding.

The Association for Supervision of Curriculum Development (ASCD), publisher of the "Understanding by Design Handbook" co-authored by Grant Wiggins and registered owner of the trademark "Understanding by Design", has not authorized, approved or sponsored this work and is in no way affiliated with Pearson or its products.

Planet Diary Author

JACK HANKIN
Science/Mathematics Teacher, The Hilldale School, Daly City, California Founder, Planet Diary Web site
Mr. Hankin is the creator and writer of Planet Diary, a science current events Web site. He is passionate about bringing science news and environmental awareness into classrooms and offers numerous Planet Diary workshops at NSTA and other events to train middle and high school teachers.

ELL Consultant

JIM CUMMINS, Ph.D.
Professor and Canada Research Chair, Curriculum, Teaching and Learning department at the University of Toronto
Dr. Cummins focuses on literacy development in multilingual schools and the role of technology in promoting student learning across the curriculum. *Interactive Science* incorporates essential research-based principles for integrating language with the teaching of academic content based on his instructional framework.

Reading Consultant

HARVEY DANIELS, Ph.D.
Professor of Secondary Education, University of New Mexico, Albuquerque, New Mexico
Dr. Daniels is an international consultant to schools, districts, and educational agencies. He has authored or coauthored 13 books on language, literacy, and education. His most recent works are *Comprehension and Collaboration: Inquiry Circles in Action* and *Subjects Matter: Every Teacher's Guide to Content-Area Reading*.

REVIEWERS

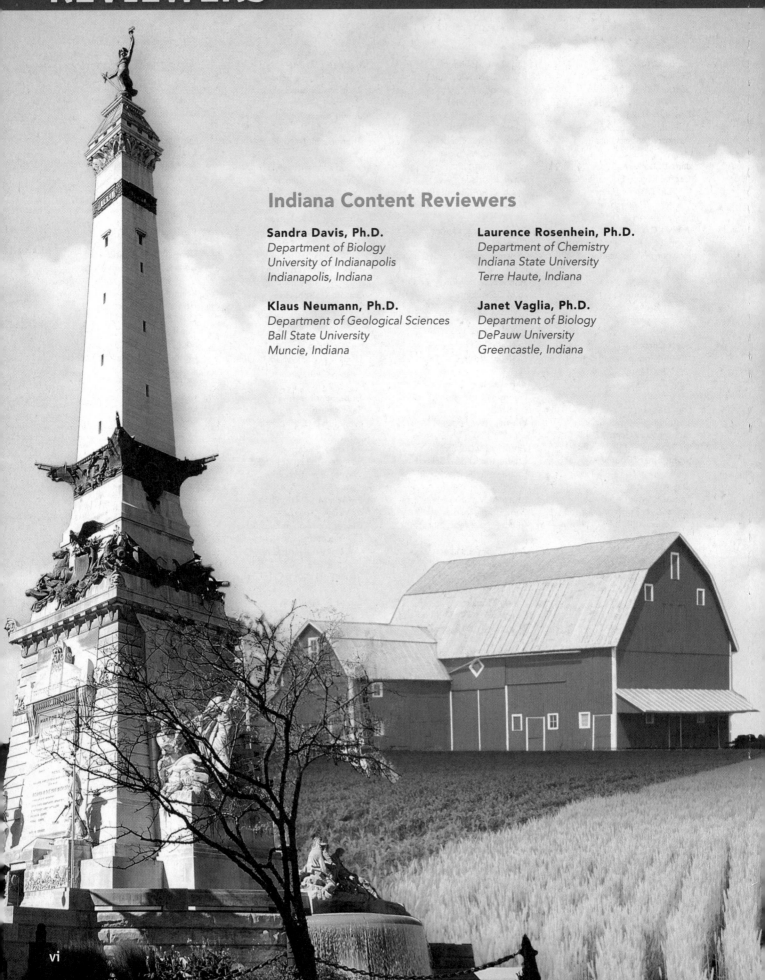

REVIEWERS

Indiana Content Reviewers

Sandra Davis, Ph.D.
Department of Biology
University of Indianapolis
Indianapolis, Indiana

Klaus Neumann, Ph.D.
Department of Geological Sciences
Ball State University
Muncie, Indiana

Laurence Rosenhein, Ph.D.
Department of Chemistry
Indiana State University
Terre Haute, Indiana

Janet Vaglia, Ph.D.
Department of Biology
DePauw University
Greencastle, Indiana

Built especially for

Indiana

Indiana Interactive Science covers 100% of Indiana's Academic Standards for Science without extraneous content. Built on feedback from Indiana educators, *Interactive Science* focuses on what is important to Indiana teachers and students, creating a personal, relevant, and engaging classroom experience.

Indiana K-8 Science Teacher Advisory Board

Jodi Allen
Glen Acres Elementary School
Lafayette, IN

Rick Dubbs
Monrovia Middle School
Monrovia, IN

Margaret Flack
Vincennes University-Jasper Campus
Jasper, IN

Michael Gibson
New Haven Middle School &
East Allen County School
New Haven, IN

Jill Hatcher
Spring Mill School
Indianapolis, IN

Jamie Hooten
Lincoln Elementary School, NLCS
Bedford, IN

Jamil Odom
Mary Bryan Elementary School
Indianapolis, IN

Mike Robards
Franklin Community Middle School
Franklin, IN

Richard Towle
Noblesville Middle School
Noblesville, IN

CONTENTS

Enter the Lab zone for hands-on inquiry.

Chapter Lab Investigation:
• Directed Inquiry: Become a Learning Detective
• Open Inquiry: Become a Learning Detective

Inquiry Warm-Ups: • How Does a Scientist Think? • Developing a Theory • What's the Question? • Posing Questions

Quick Labs: • Scientific Skills • Activities of Science • Scientific Thinking • Science and Its Methods • It Starts With a Question • How Can You Explain It? • Scientific Literacy Survey • Analyzing Claims • Sources of Information

my science online.com

Go to MyScienceOnline.com to interact with this chapter's content. Keyword: Using Scientific Inquiry

PLANET DIARY
• Using Scientific Inquiry

INTERACTIVE ART
• Inquiry Diagram

REAL-WORLD INQUIRY
• Where's the Evidence? • When Science Sparks Controversy

VIRTUAL LAB
• What Is Scientific Inquiry?

Enter the Lab zone for hands-on inquiry.

△ **Chapter Lab Investigation:**
  • Directed Inquiry: Selecting Models
  • Open Inquiry: Selecting Models

△ **Inquiry Warm-Ups:** • What Is Scientific Measurement? • How Do Math and Science Work Together? • What's in a Graph? • Models in Science • Can You Name the Safety Equipment?

△ **Quick Labs:** • Measuring With SI • A Unit of SI • Is It Accurate? • Math Tools in Science • Recognizing Trends • Working With Models • Characteristics of Systems • Be Prepared to Be Safe in the Field • How Would You Respond to These Emergencies?

my science online.com

Go to MyScienceOnline.com to interact with this chapter's content. **Keyword:** Mathematics and Models in Science

▷ **UNTAMED SCIENCE**
• Measuring Up

▷ **PLANET DIARY**
• Mathematics and Models in Science

▷ **INTERACTIVE ART**
• The Need for Numbers • Plotting a Line Graph • Modeling a System

▷ **VIRTUAL LAB**
• How Are Units Useful?

CONTENTS

Lab zone® Enter the Lab zone
for hands-on inquiry.

Chapter Lab Investigation:
• Directed Inquiry: Copper or Carbon? That Is the Question
• Open Inquiry: Copper or Carbon? That Is the Question

Inquiry Warm-Ups: • What's in the Box?
• What Is Easier? • Why Use Aluminum?
• What Are the Properties of Charcoal?

Quick Labs: • Visualizing an Electron Cloud
• How Far Away Is the Electron? • Classifying
• Using the Periodic Table • Expanding the
Periodic Table • Finding Metals • Carbon—A
Nonmetal • Finding Nonmetals

my science online.com

Go to MyScienceOnline.com to
interact with this chapter's content.
Keyword: **Elements and the Periodic
Table**

▷ PLANET DIARY
• Elements and the Periodic Table

▷ INTERACTIVE ART
• Periodic Table • Investigate an Atom

▷ VIRTUAL LAB
• Which Element Is This?

Chemical Reactions

Lab® zone Enter the Lab zone for hands-on inquiry.

Chapter Lab Investigation:
• Directed Inquiry: Shedding Light on Ions
• Open Inquiry: Shedding Light on Ions

Inquiry Warm-Ups: • Where's the Evidence? • What Are the Trends in the Periodic Table? • How Do Ions Form? • Covalent Bonds • Chemicals React • Lose Anything?

Quick Labs: • Element Chemistry • Ion Formation • Ionic Names and Formulas • Sharing Electrons • Molecular Compounds • Attraction Between Polar Molecules • Observing Change • Chemical Equation • Is Matter Conserved? • Chemical Reactions

my science online.com

Go to MyScienceOnline.com to interact with this chapter's content.
Keyword: Atoms and Bonding

> **UNTAMED SCIENCE**
• The Elements of Hockey

> **PLANET DIARY**
• Atoms and Bonding

> **INTERACTIVE ART**
• Periodic Table • Investigate Ionic Compounds • Table Salt Dissolving in Water • Changes in Matter • Conserving Mass • Chemical Reactions

> **ART IN MOTION**
• Bonding in Polar Molecules

> **VIRTUAL LAB**
• Will It React? • Energy In or Out

CONTENTS

 Lab zone® Enter the Lab zone for hands-on inquiry.

Chapter Lab Investigation:
• Directed Inquiry: Water From Trees
• Open Inquiry: Water From Trees

Inquiry Warm-Ups:
• Directed Inquiry: Modeling Ocean Currents
• Open Inquiry: Modeling Ocean Currents
• Where Does the Water Come From?
• Mapping Surface Waters • What Can You Learn Without Seeing? • Bottom to Top

Quick Labs: • Water, Water Everywhere
• Water on Earth • What Is a Watershed?
• Modeling How a Lake Forms • How Can Algal Growth Affect Pond Life? • Ocean Conditions
• The Shape of the Ocean Floor • Deep Currents

my science online.com

Go to MyScienceOnline.com to interact with this chapter's content.
Keyword: Fresh Water

> UNTAMED SCIENCE
• Water Cyclists

> PLANET DIARY
• Fresh Water

> INTERACTIVE ART
• Water Cycle • Ocean Floor

> ART IN MOTION
• How Does Groundwater Collect?
• Warming Sea

> REAL-WORLD INQUIRY
• Water Cycle, Interrupted

Lab zone ® **Enter the Lab zone for hands-on inquiry.**

Chapter Lab Investigation:
• Directed Inquiry: Heating Earth's Surface
• Open Inquiry: Heating Earth's Surface

Inquiry Warm-Ups: • How Long Will the Candle Burn? • Does Air Have Mass? • Is Air There? • Does a Plastic Bag Trap Heat? • What Happens When Air Is Heated? • Does the Wind Turn?

Quick Labs: • Breathe In, Breathe Out • What Is the Source of Earth's Energy? • Properties of Air • Soda Bottle Barometer • Effects of Altitude on the Atmosphere • Layers of the Atmosphere • Calculating Temperature Changes • How Does the Sun's Energy Reach Earth? • Measuring Temperature • Temperature and Height • Build a Wind Vane • Modeling Global Wind Belts

my science online.com

Go to MyScienceOnline.com to interact with this chapter's content.
Keyword: The Atmosphere

> INTERACTIVE ART
• Measuring Air Pressure • Global Winds

> ART IN MOTION
• Greenhouse Effect

> VIRTUAL LAB
• What Do Temperature and Volume Have to Do With Air Pressure?

CONTENTS

 Enter the Lab zone for hands-on inquiry.

Chapter Lab Investigation:
• Directed Inquiry: Reading a Weather Map
• Open Inquiry: Reading a Weather Map

Inquiry Warm-Ups: • Where Did the Water Go? • How Does Fog Form? • How Can You Make Hail? • How Do Fluids of Different Densities Move? • Can You Make a Tornado? • Predicting Weather

Quick Labs: • Water in the Air • Measuring to Find the Dew Point • How Clouds Form • Identifying Clouds • Types of Precipitation • Floods and Droughts • Tracking Air Masses • Weather Fronts • Cyclones and Anticyclones • Where Do Hurricanes Come From? • Storm Safety • Modeling Weather Satellites

my science online.com

Go to MyScienceOnline.com to interact with this chapter's content. Keyword: **Weather**

▷ **PLANET DIARY**
• Weather

▷ **INTERACTIVE ART**
• Water Cycle • Weather Fronts • Different Conditions, Different Storms

▷ **ART IN MOTION**
• How Does Precipitation Form?

▷ **REAL-WORLD INQUIRY**
• Predicting the Weather

 Enter the Lab zone for hands-on inquiry.

△ **Chapter Lab Investigation:**
• Directed Inquiry: Recycling Paper
• Open Inquiry: Recycling Paper

△ **Inquiry Warm-Ups:** • How Do You Decide?
• Using Resources • Doubling Time • What
Happened to the Tuna? • How Much Variety
Is There?

△ **Quick Labs:** • Environmental Issues
• Comparing Costs and Benefits • Natural
Resources • Human Population Growth
• Comparing Populations • Shelterwood
Cutting • Managing Fisheries • Modeling
Keystone Species • Grocery Gene Pool
• Humans and Biodiversity

my science online.com

Go to MyScienceOnline.com to
interact with this chapter's content.
Keyword: **Resources and Living Things**

▷ **UNTAMED SCIENCE**
• The Great Macaw Debate

▷ **PLANET DIARY**
• Resources and Living Things

▷ **INTERACTIVE ART**
• Logging Methods • Exploring
Environmental Impact

▷ **ART IN MOTION**
• Human Population Growth

▷ **VIRTUAL LAB**
• Is Variety the Spice of Life?

CONTENTS

Enter the Lab zone for hands-on inquiry.

Chapter Lab Investigation:
• Directed Inquiry: Waste, Away!
• Open Inquiry: Waste, Away!

Inquiry Warm-Ups: • How Does Mining Affect the Land? • What's in the Trash? • How Does the Scent Spread? • How Does the Water Change? • What Is the Greenhouse Effect?

Quick Labs: • Land Use • Modeling Soil Conservation • It's in the Numbers • Half-Life • How Acid Is Your Rain? • Analyzing Ozone • It's in the Air • Where's the Water? • Cleaning Up Oil Spills • Getting Clean • Greenhouse Gases and Global Warming

my science online.com

Go to MyScienceOnline.com to interact with this chapter's content. Keyword: Land, Air, and Water Resources

UNTAMED SCIENCE
• Manatee Survival

PLANET DIARY
• Land, Air, and Water Resources

INTERACTIVE ART
• Air Pollution • Match the Material

ART IN MOTION
• Greenhouse Effect

REAL-WORLD INQUIRY
• Mutation Mystery • Pollution and Solutions

Lab zone® **Enter the Lab zone for hands-on inquiry.**

Chapter Lab Investigation:
• Directed Inquiry: Please Pass the Bread
• Open Inquiry: Please Pass the Bread

Inquiry Warm-Ups: • Is It Living or Nonliving? • Can You Organize a Junk Drawer? • What Organism Goes Where? • Observing Similarities

Quick Labs: • React! • Compare Broth Samples • Classifying Seeds • Make a Classification Chart • Living Mysteries • Staining Leaves • Common Ancestors

my science online.com

Go to MyScienceOnline.com to interact with this chapter's content. Keyword: Introduction to Living Things

> **UNTAMED SCIENCE**
• What Can You Explore in a Swamp?

> **PLANET DIARY**
• Introduction to Living Things

> **INTERACTIVE ART**
• Redi's and Pasteur's Experiments
• Taxonomic Key

> **ART IN MOTION**
• Finding a Common Ancestor

> **VIRTUAL LAB**
• Classifying Life

CONTENTS

 Enter the Lab zone for hands-on inquiry.

Chapter Lab Investigation:
• Directed Inquiry: Nature at Work
• Open Inquiry: Nature at Work

Inquiry Warm-Ups: • How Do Living Things Vary? • How Can You Classify a Species? • Making a Timeline

Quick Labs: • Bird Beak Adaptations • Finding Proof • Large-Scale Isolation • Slow or Fast?

my science online.com

Go to MyScienceOnline.com to interact with this chapter's content. Keyword: Change Over Time

> **UNTAMED SCIENCE**
• Why Would a Fish Have Red Lips?

> **PLANET DIARY**
• Change Over Time

> **INTERACTIVE ART**
• What Is It Adapted To?
• Homologous Structures

> **ART IN MOTION**
• Rate of Evolution

> **REAL-WORLD INQUIRY**
• What Affects Natural Selection?

Enter the Lab zone for hands-on inquiry.

Chapter Lab Investigation:
• Directed Inquiry: Make the Right Call!
• Open Inquiry: Make the Right Call!

Inquiry Warm-Ups: • What Does the Father Look Like? • What's the Chance? • Observing Traits • Which Chromosome Is Which? • What Do Fingerprints Reveal?

Quick Labs: • Observing Pistils and Stamens • Inferring the Parent Generation • Coin Crosses • Patterns of Inheritance • Is It All in the Genes? • Chromosomes and Inheritance • Modeling Meiosis • Types of Reproduction • Selective Breeding

my science online.com

Go to MyScienceOnline.com to interact with this chapter's content.
Keyword: Genetics: The Science of Heredity

> **UNTAMED SCIENCE**
• Where'd You Get Those Genes?

> **PLANET DIARY**
• Genetics: The Science of Heredity

> **INTERACTIVE ART**
• Punnett Squares • Effects of Environment on Genetic Traits

> **ART IN MOTION**
• Mitosis or Meiosis • Genetic Engineering

interactive SCIENCE

This is your book.
You can write in it!

Get Engaged!

At the start of each chapter, you will see two questions: an Engaging Question and the Big Question. Each chapter's Big Question will help you start thinking about the Big Ideas of Science. Look for the Big Q symbol throughout the chapter!

WHAT CAN SHARKS TEACH THESE CAGED SCIENTISTS?

? What does it mean to think like a scientist?

Would you ever go diving in a shark cage? If you were a marine biologist, this might be part of your job. To learn more about sharks, marine biologists study them in their natural environment. These Galápagos sharks were observed swimming off the coast of Hawaii. Marine biologists have learned that a full-grown male Galápagos shark can grow to be 3.7 meters long and eat squid, octopus, and fish, including other sharks.

Infer What information could scientists learn by watching these sharks?

The scientists could estimate how old the sharks are and notice if they are males or females. They might also see how the sharks act around humans.

> UNTAMED SCIENCE Watch the **Untamed Science** video to learn more about science.

xxx   What Is Science?

Untamed Science™

Follow the Untamed Science video crew as they travel the globe exploring the Big Ideas of Science.

Interact with your textbook. **Interact with inquiry.** **Interact online.**

Build Reading, Inquiry, and Vocabulary Skills

In every lesson you will learn new ⤳ Reading and △ Inquiry skills. These skills will help you read and think like a scientist. Vocabulary skills will help you communicate effectively and uncover the meaning of words.

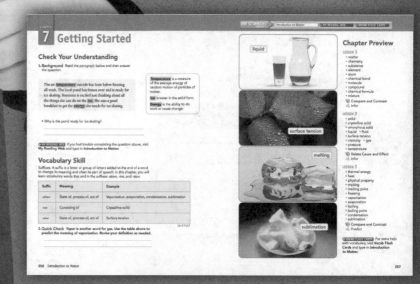

Go Online!

Look for the MyScienceOnline.com technology options. At MyScienceOnline.com you can immerse yourself in amazing virtual environments, get extra practice, and even blog about current events in science.

Master Indiana Standards

Indiana Academic Standards for Science are indicated every step of the way throughout your book.

Explore the Key Concepts.

Each lesson begins with a series of Key Concept questions. The interactivities in each lesson will help you understand these concepts and Unlock the Big Question.

MY PLANET DiARY
for Indiana

At the start of each lesson, My Planet Diary will introduce you to amazing events, significant people, and important discoveries in Indiana or help you to overcome common misconceptions.

Desertification If the soil in a of moisture and nutrients, the a advance of desertlike conditions fertile is called **desertification**

One cause of desertification is a period when less rain than droughts, crops fail. Without pl blows away. Overgrazing of gra cutting down trees for firewood

Desertification is a serious p and graze livestock where deser people may face famine and star central Africa. Millions of rural cities because they can no longer

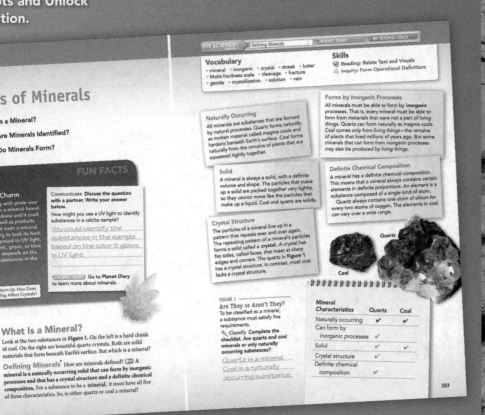

apply it!

Desertification affects many areas around the world.

1 Name Which continent has the most existing desert?

Africa

2 Interpret Maps Where in the United States is the greatest risk of desertification?

The western United S

3 Infer Is desertification a thr is existing desert? Explain. Circle your answer.

No; there are high-risk desert, such as along

4 CHALLENGE If an area is facin things people could do to possi

Sample: People could grow plants to provide

360 Land, Air, and Water Reso

Explain what you know.

Look for the pencil. When you see it, it's time to interact with your book and demonstrate what you have learned.

Elaborate further with the Apply It activities.

This is your opportunity to take what you've learned and apply it to new situations.

Lab Zone

Look for the Lab zone triangle. This means it's time to do a hands-on inquiry lab. In every lesson, you'll have the opportunity to do many hands-on inquiry activities that will help reinforce your understanding of the lesson topic.

Land Reclamation Fortunately, it is possible to replace land damaged by erosion or mining. The process of restoring an area of land to a more productive state is called **land reclamation**. In addition to restoring land for agriculture, land reclamation can restore habitats for wildlife. Many different types of land reclamation projects are currently underway all over the world. But it is generally more difficult and expensive to restore damaged land and soil than it is to protect those resources in the first place. In some cases, the land may not return to its original state.

FIGURE 4 ···

Land Reclamation
These pictures show land before and after it was mined.

✎ **Communicate** Below the pictures, write a story about what happened to the land.

Sample: Some trees were cut to make room for a mine. When the mining stopped, people replaced the soil and planted grass and trees. In time, the mine became a forest, but it is not the same as the original forest.

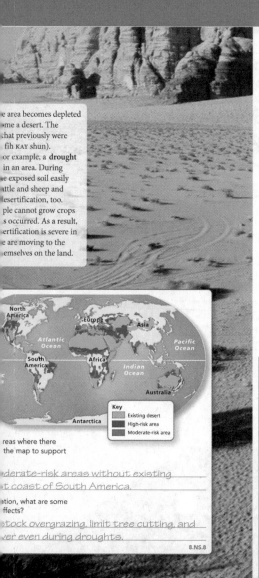

ve area becomes depleted
me a desert. The
chat previously were
fih KAY shun).

or example, a **drought**
in an area. During
ve exposed soil easily
attle and sheep and
desertification, too.
ple cannot grow crops
s occurred. As a result,
ertification is severe in
ve are moving to the
emselves on the land.

North America · Europe · Asia
Atlantic Ocean · Africa · Pacific Ocean
South America · Indian Ocean
Australia
Antarctica

Key
Existing desert
High-risk area
Moderate-risk area

reas where there
the map to support

derate-risk areas without existing
t coast of South America.

ation, what are some
ffects?

stock overgrazing, limit tree cutting, and
ver even during droughts.

8.NS.8

Lab zone ▸ Do the Quick Lab Modeling S...

📖 Assess Your Understanding

1a. Review Subsoil has (less/more) plant and animal matter than topsoil. 8.2.6

b. Explain What can happen to soil if plants are removed?
Soil particles can move, eroding the area.

c. Apply Concepts
that could prev
land reclam

Sample
might
other
farmin

got it? ··· 8.2.6

○ I get it! Now I know that soil management is important becau
ways, and poor management causes erosio
depletion, and desertification.

○ I need extra help with _See TE note._

Go to **MY SCIENCE COACH** online for help with this subject.

got it?

Evaluate Your Progress.

After answering the Got It question, think about how you're doing. Did you get it or do you need a little help? Remember, **MY SCIENCE COACH** is there for you if you need extra help.

Explore the Big Question.

At one point in the chapter, you'll have the opportunity to take all that you've learned to further explore the Big Question.

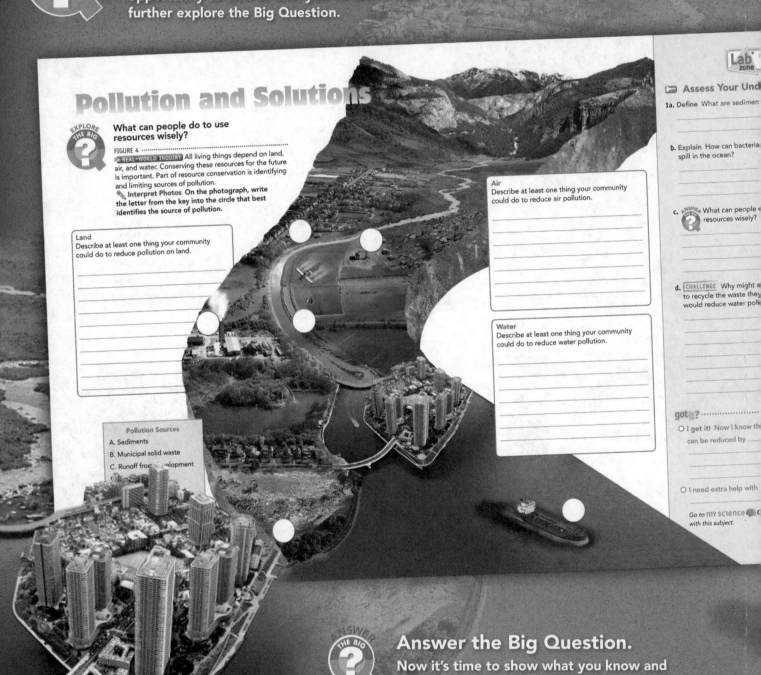

Pollution and Solutions

What can people do to use resources wisely?

FIGURE 4 ....

REAL-WORLD INQUIRY All living things depend on land, air, and water. Conserving these resources for the future is important. Part of resource conservation is identifying and limiting sources of pollution.

Interpret Photos On the photograph, write the letter from the key into the circle that best identifies the source of pollution.

Land
Describe at least one thing your community could do to reduce pollution on land.

Air
Describe at least one thing your community could do to reduce air pollution.

Water
Describe at least one thing your community could do to reduce water pollution.

Pollution Sources
A. Sediments
B. Municipal solid waste
C. Runoff from development

Lab zone

Assess Your Und

1a. Define What are sedimen

b. Explain How can bacteria spill in the ocean?

c. ANSWER What can people resources wisely?

d. CHALLENGE Why might a to recycle the waste they would reduce water poll

got it? ....

○ I get it! Now I know th can be reduced by

○ I need extra help with

Go to MY SCIENCE
with this subject.

Answer the Big Question.

Now it's time to show what you know and answer the Big Question.

Review What You've Learned.

Use the Chapter Study Guide to review the Big Question and prepare for the quizzes and exams.

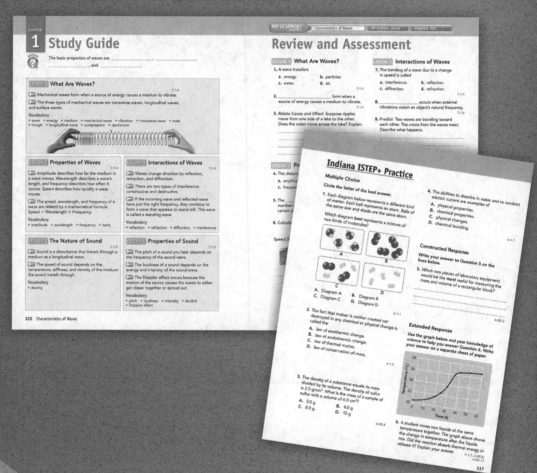

Practice Taking the ISTEP+.

Apply the Big Question and take a practice test in the ISTEP+ format.

INTERACT.... WITH YOUR TEXTBOOK....

Go to **MyScienceOnline.com** and immerse yourself in amazing virtual environments.

THE BIG QUESTION

Each online chapter starts with a Big Question. Your mission is to unlock the meaning of this Big Question as each science lesson unfolds.

VOCAB FLASH CARDS

Practice chapter vocabulary with interactive flash cards. Each card has an image, definitions in English and Spanish, and space for your own notes.

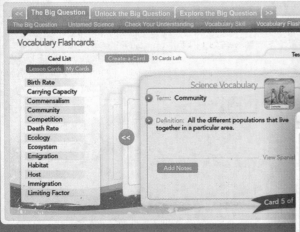

INTERACTIVE ART

At MyScienceOnline.com, many of the beautiful visuals in your book become interactive so you can extend your learning.

interactive SCIENCE
GO ONLINE

my science online.com ▸ Populations and Communities ▸ PLANET DIARY ▸ LAB ZONE ▸ VIRTUAL LAB

🔄 ➕ 🌐 http://www.myscienceonline.com/

▸ PLANET DIARY

My Planet Diary online is the place to find more information and activities related to lesson topics.

Elaborate | Evaluate

Everest

Tools
123

Still Growing! Mount Everest in the Himalayas is the highest mountain on Earth. Climbers who reach the peak stand 8,850 meters above sea level. You might think that mountains never change. But forces inside Earth push Mount Everest at least several millimeters higher each year. Over time, Earth's forces slowly but constantly lift, stretch, bend, and break Earth's crust in dramatic ways!

▸ Planet Diary Go to Planet Diary to learn more about forces in the Earth's crust.

Next
22 of 22
Back

▸ VIRTUAL LAB

Get more practice with realistic virtual labs. Manipulate the variables on-screen and test your hypothesis.

Find Your Chapter

1 Go to www.myscienceonline.com.

2 Log in with username and password.

3 Click on your program and select your chapter.

Keyword Search

1 Go to www.myscienceonline.com.

2 Log in with username and password.

3 Click on your program and select Search.

4 Enter the keyword (from your book) in the search box.

Other Content Available Online

▸ **UNTAMED SCIENCE** Follow these young scientists through their amazing online video blogs as they travel the globe in search of answers to the Essential Questions of Science.

▸ **MY SCIENCE COACH** Need extra help? My Science Coach is your personal online study partner. My Science Coach is a chance for you to get more practice on key science concepts. There you can choose from a variety of tools that will help guide you through each science lesson.

▸ **MY READING WEB** Need extra reading help on a particular science topic? At My Reading Web you will find a choice of reading selections targeted to your specific reading level.

? BIG IDEAS OF SCIENCE

Have you ever worked on a jigsaw puzzle? Usually a puzzle has a theme that leads you to group the pieces by what they have in common. But until you put all the pieces together you can't solve the puzzle. Studying science is similar to solving a puzzle. The big ideas of science are like puzzle themes. To understand big ideas, scientists ask questions. The answers to those questions are like pieces of a puzzle. Each chapter in this book asks a big question to help you think about a big idea of science. By answering the big questions, you will get closer to understanding the big idea.

✎ **Before you read each chapter, write about what you know and what more you'd like to know.**

Grant Wiggins, coauthor of *Understanding by Design*

BIGIDEA
Scientists use scientific inquiry to explain the natural world.

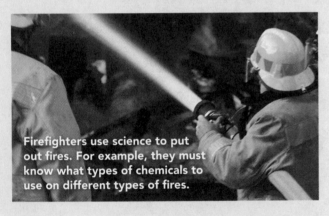

Firefighters use science to put out fires. For example, they must know what types of chemicals to use on different types of fires.

What do you already know about how science affects your everyday life? ✎ **What more would you like to know?**

_____

_____

_____

Big Question:

❓ How do science and society affect each other? Chapter 1

✎ **After reading the chapter, write what you have learned about the Big Idea.**

_____

_____

_____

BIGIDEA
Scientists use mathematics in many ways.

Scientists rely on estimates when they cannot obtain exact data. Estimating is a quick way of determining how many birds are in this photo.

Which math skills have you used to study science? ✎ **Which math skills do you need to practice?**

_____

_____

_____

Big Question:

❓ How do scientists use measurement and mathematics? Chapter 2

✎ **After reading the chapter, write what you have learned about the Big Idea.**

_____

_____

_____

Atoms are the building blocks of matter.

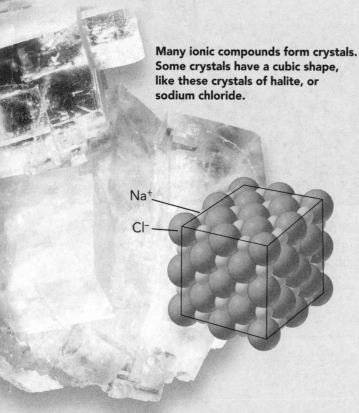

Many ionic compounds form crystals. Some crystals have a cubic shape, like these crystals of halite, or sodium chloride.

Na⁺

Cl⁻

If the building blocks of matter are the same, then what makes everything different?

✎ **What more would you like to know?**

_____

_____

_____

_____

Big Questions:

❓ How is the periodic table organized? Chapter 3

❓ How is matter conserved in a chemical reaction? Chapter 4

✎ **After reading the chapter, write what you have learned about the Big Idea.**

_____

_____

_____

Earth's land, water, air, and life form a system.

A severe storm, drought, or wildfire could cause changes in Yellowstone National Park that would affect these bison.

What do you already know about how changes in one part of Earth can affect another part?

✎ **What would you like to know?**

_____

_____

_____

Big Questions:

❓ How does water cycle on Earth? Chapter 5

❓ How does the sun's energy affect Earth's atmosphere? Chapter 6

❓ How do meteorologists predict the weather? Chapter 7

✎ **After reading the chapters, write what you have learned about the Big Idea.**

_____

_____

_____

Living things interact with their environment.

People depend on the ocean's living resources, such as codfish, for food.

What do you already know about how you get food, water, and shelter from your surroundings? ✏️ **What more would you like to know?**

_____

_____

_____

Big Questions:

❓ How do people use Earth's resources?
Chapter 8

❓ What are some of Earth's energy sources?
Chapter 9

✏️ **After reading the chapters, write what you have learned about the Big Idea.**

_____

_____

_____

_____

Living things are alike yet different.

Grasses and wildflowers look different, but they all grow in soil and need sunlight and water.

What do you already know about how all living things are alike yet different? ✏️ **What more would you like to know?**

_____

_____

_____

_____

Big Question:

❓ How are living things alike yet different?
Chapter 10

✏️ **After reading the chapter, write what you have learned about the Big Idea.**

_____

_____

_____

_____

_____

BIGIDEA
Living things change over time.

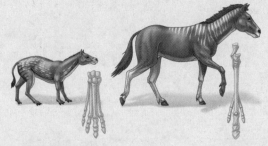

Modern horses are descended from much smaller animals with toes instead of hooves.

What do you already know about how life forms change? What more would you like to know?

_____

_____

Big Question:

❓ How do life forms change over time? Chapter 11

✏️ **After reading the chapter, write what you have learned about the Big Idea.**

_____

_____

BIGIDEA
Genetic information passes from parents to offspring.

Once in a while, a koala joey is born with white fur instead of the usual gray fur. Even with such a striking difference, you can tell the joey is related to its mother.

What do you already know about how offspring resemble their parents? What more would you like to know?

_____

_____

Big Question:

❓ Why don't offspring always look like their parents? Chapter 12

✏️ **After reading the chapter, write what you have learned about the Big Idea.**

_____

_____

HOW COULD POLLUTION FROM ASIA AFFECT PEOPLE IN THE ARCTIC?

How do science and society affect each other?

These children are sledding in Igloolik, Nunavut, in northern Canada. The sky is so blue and clear that you would think that the cold arctic air would be fresh and clean. However, pollution generated thousands of kilometers away affects the air, snow, water, wildlife, and people of the Arctic. Pollutants from burning fossil fuels migrate north. High concentrations of chemicals that evaporate from televisions, paints, and pesticides in countries worldwide, have been found in the people that live in small Arctic towns like Igloolik.

▲ **Develop Hypotheses** **How do you think pollution produced thousands of kilometers away ends up in the Arctic?**

_____

_____

_____

_____

> **UNTAMED SCIENCE** Watch the **Untamed Science** video to learn more about scientific inquiry.

Using Scientific Inquiry

Academic Standards for Science

8.NS.1–8.NS.11, 8.DP.1–8.DP.4, 8.DP.9

Getting Started

Check Your Understanding

1. **Background** Read the paragraph below and then answer the question.

Emi studied hard to prepare for her science lab investigation. She was concerned because her **research** was complex. However, it was also well **organized**. Emi wanted to use her lab report as a **sample** of her science work.

> **Research** is information collected from careful study of a subject.
>
> To be **organized** is to be arranged in an orderly way.
>
> A **sample** is a portion of something that is used to represent the whole thing.

• Why would being organized help Emi prepare for her lab investigation?

_____

_____

_____

> **MY READING WEB** If you have trouble completing the question above, visit **My Reading Web** and type in *Using Scientific Inquiry*.

Vocabulary Skill

Identify Multiple Meanings Words you use every day may have different meanings in science. Look at the different meanings of the words below.

Word	Everyday Meaning	Scientific Meaning
model	*n.* A person who poses for an artist Example: Julio worked as a *model* for a sculptor in Daytona Beach.	*n.* A representation of an object or process Example: A globe is a *model* of Earth.
cost	*n.* The price paid by someone for a certain object or service Example: The *cost* of the train ticket was $35.	*n.* An undesirable outcome of a decision Example: Dirty air might be one *cost* of not using "clean" energy.

2. **Quick Check** Circle the sentence below that uses the scientific meaning of the word *cost*.

• The cost of repairing the highway was $12 million.

• One cost of building a new highway might be more cars on the road.

science

subjective reasoning

controlled experiment

A B C

opinion

Chapter Preview

LESSON 1
- science • observing
- quantitative observation
- qualitative observation
- classifying • inferring
- predicting • analyzing
- Identify Supporting Evidence
- Observe

LESSON 2
- skepticism • data
- empirical evidence
- objective reasoning
- subjective reasoning
- pseudoscience
- Outline
- Interpret Data

LESSON 3
- scientific inquiry • hypothesis
- independent variable
- dependent variable
- controlled experiment • bias
- repeated trial • replication
- scientific explanation
- Summarize
- Develop Hypotheses

LESSON 4
- scientific literacy
- evidence • opinion
- Summarize
- Interpret Data

> VOCAB FLASH CARDS For extra help with vocabulary, visit **Vocab Flash Cards** and type in *Using Scientific Inquiry.*

1 How Scientists Work

 UNLOCK THE BIG

🔑 **How Do Scientists Explore the Natural World?**
8.NS.1, 8.NS.2, 8.NS.3, 8.NS.8

MY PLANET DIARY

The Road to Discovery
Today, paclitaxel is one of the most effective drugs against cancer. But it was not well known until Dr. Susan Horwitz's work drew attention to it. Horwitz went to college to study history, but after taking a biology class, she became fascinated with how scientists form and test their ideas. After graduating with a biology degree, she went on to a graduate program in biochemistry. At the time, there were very few women in graduate schools, but that didn't stop Dr. Horwitz. Armed with a doctorate degree, Horwitz eventually moved to her current position at Albert Einstein School of Medicine. It was there that she discovered how paclitaxel stopped the growth of cancer cells. Her work convinced pharmaceutical companies to turn paclitaxel into a medicine that now saves many lives.

BIOGRAPHY

Model of the paclitaxel molecule

Write your answers to each question below.

1. Why did Susan Horwitz decide to become a scientist?

_____
_____
_____
_____
_____

2. What do you think is the difference between the way historians and scientists think?

_____
_____
_____
_____

> PLANET DIARY Go to **Planet Diary** to learn more about how scientists work.

Lab® zone Do the Inquiry Warm-Up
How Does a Scientist Think?

Vocabulary

- science • observing • quantitative observation
- qualitative observation • classifying • inferring
- predicting • analyzing

Skills

- Reading: Identify Supporting Evidence
- Inquiry: Observe

How Do Scientists Explore the Natural World?

Paclitaxel is one of the many great success stories of science. **Science** is a way of learning about the natural world. Science is also the knowledge gained through this exploration. **Scientists explore the natural world by using skills such as observing, classifying, making models, inferring, and predicting. They form and test their ideas through scientific investigation.**

Observing Paclitaxel is a drug made from the bark of the Pacific yew tree, shown in **Figure 1.** The seeds and leaves of all yew trees are poisonous, but Native Americans found that they could make teas from the bark and needles. They observed that drinking the tea sometimes made people who were sick feel better. **Observing** means using one or more of your senses to gather information. Native Americans observed the effects of the tea on sick people and decided that the tea could help treat headaches and other health problems. Observing also means using tools, such as a microscope, to help your senses.

Observations can be quantitative or qualitative. A **quantitative observation** deals with numbers, or amounts. For example, seeing that a person has a fever of 101 degrees Fahrenheit is a quantitative observation. A **qualitative observation** deals with descriptions that cannot be expressed in numbers. Feeling that a person's head is warm is a qualitative observation.

Academic Standards for Science

8.NS.1 Make predictions and develop testable questions based on research and prior knowledge.

8.NS.2 Plan and carry out investigations as a class, in small groups or independently often over a period of several class lessons.

8.NS.3 Collect quantitative data with appropriate tools or technologies and use appropriate units to label numerical data.

8.NS.8 Analyze data, using appropriate mathematical manipulation as required, and use it to identify patterns and make inferences based on these patterns.

FIGURE 1 ·······················
What Do You Observe?
The photo shows the berries and bark of the slow-growing and ancient Pacific yew tree.

✎ **Observe Write one quantitative observation and one qualitative observation about the tree.**

_____

_____

8.NS.3

5

did you

know?......

The bark of the Florida yew tree also contains a compound that can treat cancer. Threats of harvesting this endangered tree worried many conservationists. Fortunately, in 1993, researchers found a way to make the compound synthetically in a laboratory.

Organizing Data

In 1962, plant biologists collected samples of different types of trees. They were searching for a cure to cancer. They sent the samples back to a laboratory that ran tests to see what effect these samples had on cancer cells. Then the samples were classified according to their results. **Classifying** is grouping together items that are alike in some way. Paclitaxel, from the yew tree sample, was classified as having anticancer effects. **Figure 2** shows a test that can be used to classify samples.

Making Models

Once people realized that paclitaxel had an effect on cancer cells, they needed to figure out what it was made of. They built a model that showed the arrangement of atoms in a molecule of paclitaxel. Making models involves creating representations of complex objects or processes. Some models can be made of actual objects, such as balls and sticks. Others are in the form of drawings or mathematical equations. Models help people study things that can't be observed directly. By using models, scientists were able to better understand the properties of paclitaxel.

Inferring

Susan Horwitz examined how paclitaxel affected cancer cells. The invention of the electron microscope allowed scientists to observe how cells divide. From her observations, Horwitz inferred that paclitaxel stopped cancer cells from dividing.

When you explain or interpret things that you observe, you are **inferring.** Making an inference is not guessing. Inferences are based on reasoning from your prior knowledge and from what you observe. By making inferences about how paclitaxel worked, Horwitz was able to show that paclitaxel could be an effective anticancer drug.

FIGURE 2 ·······

Classifying Cancer Colonies   8.NS.8

Scientists observed the effects of different tree samples on cancer cells. Each petri dish began with 10 colonies of cancer cells. The diagrams show the results after being treated with the tree samples.

✎ **Complete these tasks.**

1. **Observe** Count and record the number of cancer cell colonies below each petri dish.

2. **Infer** What can you infer about each of the samples from the petri dishes that were treated?

_____

_____

_____

3. **Classify** Which sample(s) should be classified as possible cancer treatment(s)? Explain.

_____

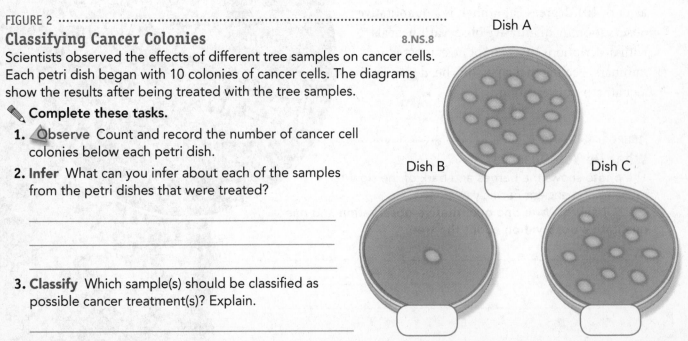

Predicting

Paclitaxel only kills some kinds of cancer cells. After running tests on mice, scientists made predictions about what types of human cancer paclitaxel might treat. **Predicting** means making a statement or a claim about what will happen in the future based on past experience or evidence.

Scientists planted human tumors onto mice. Then they gave the mice paclitaxel. The mice with breast tumors showed signs of recovery. From this observation, scientists predicted that paclitaxel could help treat breast cancer.

Predictions and inferences are related. While inferences are attempts to explain what has already happened, predictions are forecasts about what will happen. If you see a puddle of water on the floor, you might infer that a glass spilled. If, however, you see someone bump into a glass, you can predict that it's about to make a mess.

Identify Supporting Evidence Determine if the statement below is a prediction or an inference. Then underline the sentence in the text that supports your answer. "The alarm clock is blinking 12:00 because the electricity went out temporarily."

do the math!

Only a small amount of paclitaxel can be produced from the bark of a single Pacific yew. It requires 120 kilograms of paclitaxel to treat 60,000 patients with 2 grams each of the drug per year.

1 Calculate If 1 kilogram of bark can produce about 0.015 kilogram of paclitaxel, how much bark is needed to make 120 kilograms of paclitaxel?

2 CHALLENGE You need to cut down 3 trees to get about 5 kilograms of bark. About how many trees do you have to cut down each year to make enough paclitaxel for 60,000 patients?

3 Evaluate the Impact on Society Some people think that the destruction of so many trees and the habitat of forest animals was too high a price to pay for paclitaxel. Explain why you agree or disagree with this opinion.

8.NS.8

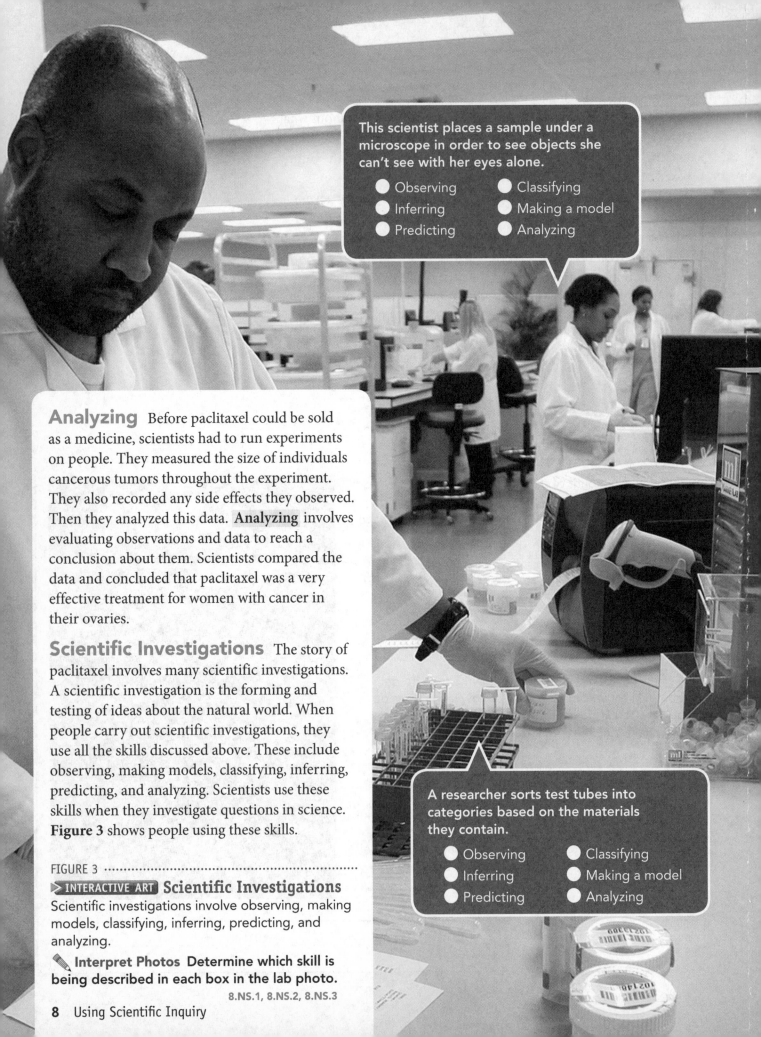

This scientist places a sample under a microscope in order to see objects she can't see with her eyes alone.

- ⬤ Observing
- ⬤ Inferring
- ⬤ Predicting
- ⬤ Classifying
- ⬤ Making a model
- ⬤ Analyzing

Analyzing Before paclitaxel could be sold as a medicine, scientists had to run experiments on people. They measured the size of individuals cancerous tumors throughout the experiment. They also recorded any side effects they observed. Then they analyzed this data. **Analyzing** involves evaluating observations and data to reach a conclusion about them. Scientists compared the data and concluded that paclitaxel was a very effective treatment for women with cancer in their ovaries.

Scientific Investigations The story of paclitaxel involves many scientific investigations. A scientific investigation is the forming and testing of ideas about the natural world. When people carry out scientific investigations, they use all the skills discussed above. These include observing, making models, classifying, inferring, predicting, and analyzing. Scientists use these skills when they investigate questions in science. **Figure 3** shows people using these skills.

FIGURE 3 ··
▶ INTERACTIVE ART **Scientific Investigations**
Scientific investigations involve observing, making models, classifying, inferring, predicting, and analyzing.

✎ **Interpret Photos** Determine which skill is being described in each box in the lab photo.

8.NS.1, 8.NS.2, 8.NS.3

A researcher sorts test tubes into categories based on the materials they contain.

- ⬤ Observing
- ⬤ Inferring
- ⬤ Predicting
- ⬤ Classifying
- ⬤ Making a model
- ⬤ Analyzing

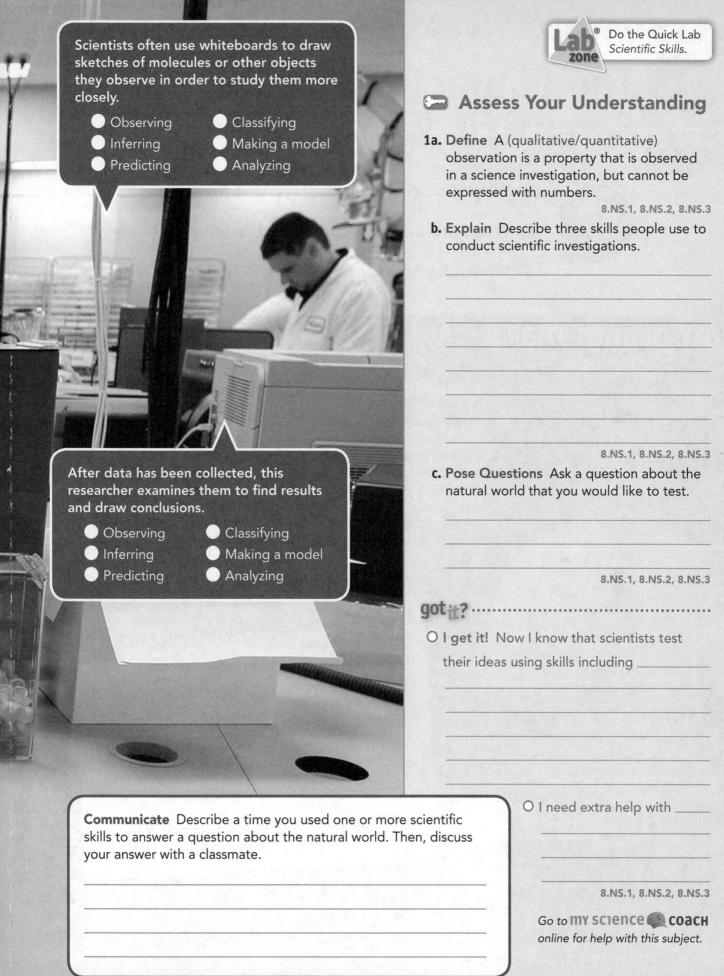

Scientists often use whiteboards to draw sketches of molecules or other objects they observe in order to study them more closely.

- ● Observing
- ● Inferring
- ● Predicting
- ● Classifying
- ● Making a model
- ● Analyzing

After data has been collected, this researcher examines them to find results and draw conclusions.

- ● Observing
- ● Inferring
- ● Predicting
- ● Classifying
- ● Making a model
- ● Analyzing

Communicate Describe a time you used one or more scientific skills to answer a question about the natural world. Then, discuss your answer with a classmate.

_____

_____

_____

_____

Lab zone® Do the Quick Lab *Scientific Skills.*

🗝 Assess Your Understanding

1a. Define A (qualitative/quantitative) observation is a property that is observed in a science investigation, but cannot be expressed with numbers.

8.NS.1, 8.NS.2, 8.NS.3

b. Explain Describe three skills people use to conduct scientific investigations.

_____

_____

_____

_____

_____

_____

_____

8.NS.1, 8.NS.2, 8.NS.3

c. Pose Questions Ask a question about the natural world that you would like to test.

_____

_____

_____

8.NS.1, 8.NS.2, 8.NS.3

got it? ....

○ **I get it!** Now I know that scientists test their ideas using skills including _____

_____

_____

_____

○ I need extra help with _____

_____

_____

8.NS.1, 8.NS.2, 8.NS.3

Go to **MY SCIENCE** Ⓢ **COACH** *online for help with this subject.*

The Characteristics of Scientific Knowledge

UNLOCK THE BIG

🔑 **What Do Scientific Investigations Involve?**
8.NS.1, 8.NS.2, 8.NS.3, 8.NS.7, 8.NS.8, 8.DP.9

🔑 **What Are Scientific and Pseudoscientific Thinking?**
8.NS.1, 8.NS.2, 8.NS.3, 8.NS.8

🔑 **What Characterizes Science and Its Methods?**
8.NS.1, 8.NS.2, 8.NS.3

MY PLANET DIARY for Indiana

BIOGRAPHY

A Scientific Success

Dr. Percy Lavon Julian (1899–1975) was a renowned research chemist who grew up and studied in Indiana. His first experiments isolated simple compounds found in plants. He used this knowledge to later develop drugs to treat glaucoma, slow down the effects of Alzheimer's disease, and prevent miscarriages. Julian also created aerofoam, a flame retardant that saved the lives of countless sailors during World War II.

Dr. Percy Julian became the first African-American chemist inducted into the National Academy of Sciences in 1973.

Communicate Discuss the question with a partner. Write your answer below.

Why do you think it's important for scientists like Dr. Julian to be curious?

_____

_____

_____

_____

Lab zone® Do the Inquiry Warm-Up
Developing a Theory.

▶ **PLANET DIARY** Go to **Planet Diary** to learn more about scientific investigations.

Vocabulary

- skepticism • data • empirical evidence
- objective reasoning • subjective reasoning
- pseudoscience

Skills

- ↻ Reading: Outline
- △ Inquiry: Interpret Data

What Do Scientific Investigations Involve?

As you just read, scientists use certain skills, such as observing and inferring, in scientific investigations. They also bring important attitudes to investigations. These attitudes include curiosity, honesty, creativity, and open-mindedness, or the willingness to accept new ideas. But scientists are also skeptical. Their **skepticism,** which is an attitude of having doubt, keeps scientists from accepting faulty ideas and may lead to new understandings.

🔑 **In addition to the skills and attitudes of scientists, scientific investigations involve collecting evidence in a scientific way and using that evidence to make inferences and to reach conclusions. Figure 1** shows an investigation that researchers performed with crows to find out if crows could recognize an individual human face. To test their idea, researchers wore caveman masks while they trapped, banded, and released several of the crows living in a group in a specific area. During this process, the captured crows cawed loudly. Later, researchers walked among the group of crows to observe how the banded crows reacted. On different walks, the researchers wore the caveman masks, different masks, or no masks.

FIGURE 1 ·······································

Cause and Effect

Researchers wanted to see if crows could recognize a specific human face.

✏️ **Complete these tasks.**

1. **Classify** Read the two statements below. Write *O* next the statement that is an observation. Write *I* next to the statement that is an inference.

   _____ The crow caws because it does not like to be handled.

   _____ The crow caws when it is banded.

2. **Observe** Use the evidence from the During Capture picture to circle the banded crows in the After Capture picture.

3. **Identify** Look at the After Capture picture. What are some other ways besides cawing that the crows reacted?

   _____

   _____

   _____

During Capture

After Capture

Collecting Empirical Evidence
In the crow investigation, the researchers walking among the crows recorded their observations in notebooks. The information they recorded is called data. **Data** (singular: *datum*) are facts, figures, and other evidence collected during a scientific investigation.

When data are collected in a precise, logical, and consistent manner, the data are called empirical evidence. **Empirical evidence** is data that are collected using scientific processes that describe particular observations. All scientific investigations involve the collection of relevant empirical evidence. **Figure 2** shows some of the data that the crow researchers collected on some of their walks.

FIGURE 2 ·····································

> REAL-WORLD INQUIRY **Conclusions and Empirical Evidence**

The table below uses tally marks to show the number of times that a banded crow had a specific type of reaction to two different researchers at a certain site.

✎ **Answer the questions on each notebook page.**

8.NS.7, 8.NS.8, 8.DP.9

1. **Make Generalizations** Why might a scientist choose to use a table to record this kind of data?

_____

_____

A Banded Crow's Reactions	Researcher Wearing Caveman Mask	Researcher Wearing Different Mask
No reaction	—	⦀⦀⦀⦀⦀ ⦀⦀⦀⦀⦀ ⎸
Looking at researcher	⫽	—
Looking at and cawing at researcher	⫼	—
Cawing and following researcher	⦀⦀⦀⦀⎸	—

2. **Interpret Data** Using the data from the table, make a bar graph in the space below, or on a computer or calculator. Label the *x*- and *y*-axes of your graph.

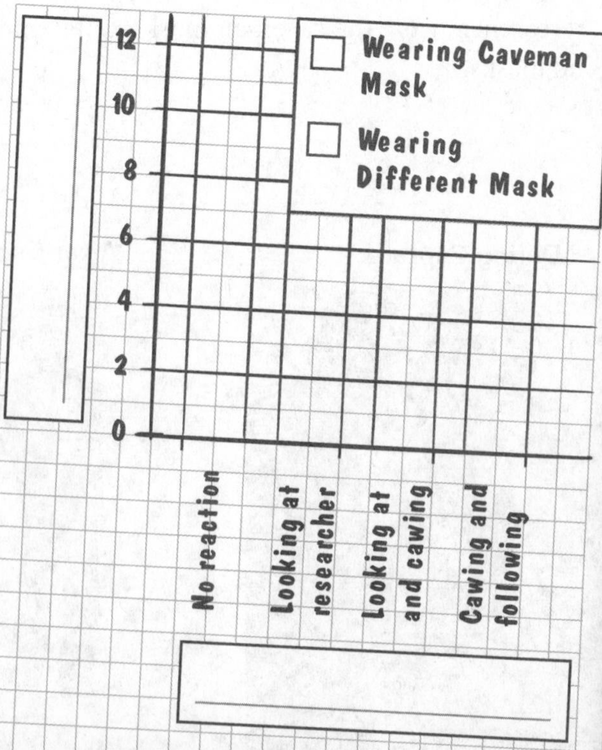

☐ Wearing Caveman Mask

☐ Wearing Different Mask

(bar graph grid with y-axis values 0, 2, 4, 6, 8, 10, 12 and x-axis labels: No reaction, Looking at researcher, Looking at and cawing, Cawing and following)

Analyzing Empirical Evidence

After scientists collect empirical evidence, they carefully look for patterns in it that allow them to make inferences and predict trends. Once they have collected a lot of data that show the same patterns, they use logic and reasoning to state a conclusion. In the crow investigation, the researchers studied all the data they collected. Each set of data showed a similar pattern. Crows banded by the researchers cawed at and followed researchers wearing caveman masks more often than other researchers without masks or with different masks. Therefore, the researchers concluded that crows can recognize an individual human face.

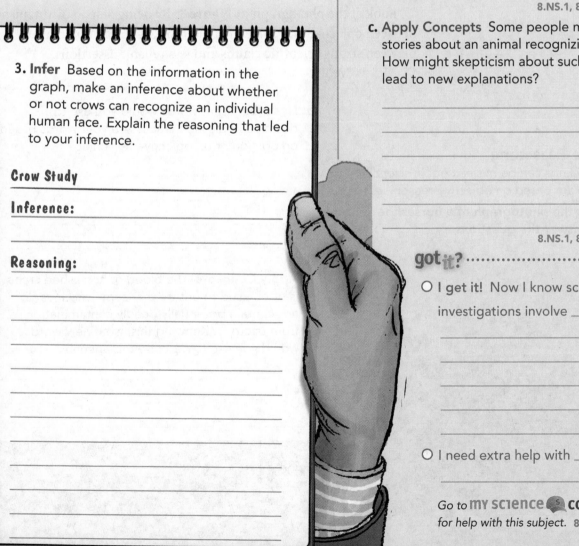

3. Infer Based on the information in the graph, make an inference about whether or not crows can recognize an individual human face. Explain the reasoning that led to your inference.

Crow Study

Inference:
_____
_____

Reasoning:
_____
_____
_____
_____
_____
_____
_____
_____
_____
_____
_____
_____

Do the Quick Lab Activities of Science.

Assess Your Understanding

1a. Review (Empirical evidence/Logical reasoning) is data collected using scientific processes that describe particular observations.

8.NS.1, 8.NS.2, 8.NS.3

b. Relate Evidence and Explanation What evidence allowed the crow researchers to conclude that crows can recognize an individual human face?

_____
_____
_____
_____
_____
_____

8.NS.1, 8.NS.2, 8.NS.3

c. Apply Concepts Some people might tell stories about an animal recognizing them. How might skepticism about such stories lead to new explanations?

_____
_____
_____
_____
_____
_____

8.NS.1, 8.NS.2, 8.NS.3

got it?

○ **I get it!** Now I know scientific investigations involve _____

_____
_____
_____

○ **I need extra help with** _____

_____

Go to **my science coach** *online for help with this subject.* 8.NS.1, 8.NS.2, 8.NS.3

13

Academic Standards for Science

8.NS.1 Make predictions and develop testable questions based on research and prior knowledge.

8.NS.2 Plan and carry out investigations as a class, in small groups or independently often over a period of several class lessons.

8.NS.3 Collect quantitative data with appropriate tools or technologies and use appropriate units to label numerical data.

8.NS.8 Analyze data.

Outline Read the text and complete the outline.

1. _____

   a. Based on evidence

   b. Example: _____

   _____

2. Subjective Reasoning

   a. _____

   _____

   b. Example: Crows are stupid.

FIGURE 3 ·······················

Subjective Reasoning

Personal feelings can be misleading. In science, conclusions are based on objective reasoning.

✎ **Look at the photograph of a horseshoe crab and answer the questions.**

What Are Scientific and Pseudoscientific Thinking?

Recall that the crow researchers used reasoning to review their data. Then the researchers drew a logical conclusion from their data. Scientific thinking requires a logical way of reasoning based on gathering and evaluating evidence. Look at **Figure 3.** Scientific thinking can be divided into two general types of reasoning: objective reasoning and subjective reasoning.

Objective and Subjective Reasoning

Objective reasoning is reasoning that is based on evidence. Because scientific reasoning relies on gathering and evaluating evidence, it is objective reasoning.

In contrast, **subjective reasoning** is reasoning that is based on personal feelings or personal values. For instance, you might think crows are stupid. As a result, you might conclude crows could not possibly recognize humans. If you based your conclusion on your personal feelings, you could reach the wrong conclusion.

Look at the photograph in **Figure 3.** By being able to distinguish between objective and subjective reasoning, you can distinguish between strong scientific claims and less reliable assertions.

1. **Describe** What words would you use to describe horseshoe crabs? Are your words based on opinion or on objective reasoning?

   _____

   _____

   _____

2. **Apply Concepts** The blood of horseshoe crabs is often used to ensure that some vaccines do not contain potentially deadly contamination from bacteria. Knowing this, what new words would you use to describe this animal?

   _____

   _____

   _____

Science Versus Pseudoscience

For thousands of years, people imagined that patterns in the stars looked like humans, animals, or objects. What does the star pattern in **Figure 4** look like to you? Perhaps you know that astronomy is the scientific study of stars. But do you know what astrology is? It is the use of stars to predict the course of human events. Unlike astronomy, astrology is not a science.

Astrologists claim that the course of human life in part depends on the stars. They make use of data regarding the positions of the stars. But they base their predictions on subjective reasoning rather than empirical evidence. So astrology can be classified as a pseudoscience. A **pseudoscience** is a set of beliefs that may make use of science. But the conclusions and predictions of a pseudoscience are not based on observation, objective reasoning, or scientific evidence.

🔑 **Science is based on empirical evidence and well-reasoned interpretation of data. Pseudoscience may make use of scientific data. But the conclusions of pseudoscience are based on subjective reasoning, faulty reasoning, or faulty beliefs, not on careful examination of evidence.**

Taurus

Aldebaran

FIGURE 4 ··
Starry-Eyed
Scientists make use of empirical evidence and relevant data to draw conclusions. People who practice pseudoscience do not.

✏️ **Identify Faulty Reasoning Look at the outline above of the star pattern called Taurus (also known as "the bull"). Identify whether each statement below is based on science (S) or on pseudoscience (P).**

_____ People whose zodiac sign is Taurus tend to be loyal.

_____ Aldebaran is the brightest star in the constellation Taurus.

_____ Each year, Taurus reaches its highest point in the sky in January.

_____ Taurus is a constellation, or pattern of stars.

_____ Scientists know that bulls are colorblind. So many people whose zodiac sign is Taurus cannot tell green and red apart. 8.NS.8

Nonscientific Ways of Knowing The study of science provides a logical, well-reasoned understanding of the natural world. But understanding other aspects of the world requires training outside of science. Look at **Figure 5.** Many artists apply their understanding of mathematics when they use points, lines, angles, shapes, and sizes to define spaces. But knowing mathematics would not provide you with a complete understanding of the meaning of an abstract painting. You would need training in the history and principles of art to fully understand the aesthetics, or beauty, of such a painting.

The study of science can also provide only a partial understanding of subjects such as philosophy and history. For example, scientists do not claim to be able to explain the meaning of life. Nor do scientists seek to explain the circumstances that led to major historic events.

FIGURE 5 ···

Eyes of the Beholder
Many artists create beauty in their art by using the science of defining spaces in a series of lines, angles, and shapes.

✏ CHALLENGE Find three simple shapes in the painting and outline them. How does your appreciation of this piece of art relate to the science of shapes? How does it relate to your personal sense of beauty?

_____

_____

_____

_____

"Untitled" (1920) by George Grosz.
© 2009 VAGA

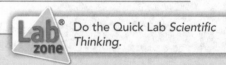
Do the Quick Lab *Scientific Thinking.*

🔑 **Assess Your Understanding**

2a. Summarize The conclusions of

(science/pseudoscience) are based on

subjective reasoning.

8.NS.1, 8.NS.2, 8.NS.3

b. Identify Faulty Reasoning Is palm-reading a science or a pseudoscience? Explain.

_____

_____

_____

_____

8.NS.1, 8.NS.2, 8.NS.3

got it?

○ **I get it!** Now I know that science is based on empirical evidence. Although pseudoscience makes use of scientific data, the conclusions of pseudoscience are based on _____

_____

○ **I need extra help with** _____

_____

Go to MY SCIENCE ⓢ COACH online for help with this subject. 8.NS.1, 8.NS.2, 8.NS.3

What Characterizes Science and Its Methods?

🔑 **Science is characterized by an ordered approach to learning about the world.** This approach relies on using skills to collect empirical data, analyzing the data to find patterns that lead to inferences and trends, and using objective reasoning to reach conclusions. Because scientific investigations are ordered, other scientists can repeat them.

> **Academic Standards for Science**
>
> **8.NS.1** Make predictions and develop testable questions based on research and prior knowledge.
>
> **8.NS.2** Plan and carry out investigations as a class, in small groups or independently often over a period of several class lessons.
>
> **8.NS.3** Collect quantitative data with appropriate tools or technologies and use appropriate units to label numerical data.

Scientists once thought that coral reefs thrive only in shallow water because sunlight can easily reach them. But in 1999, scientists discovered a reef off Florida's southwest coast that lies at depths between 60 and 80 meters. Scientists think that this reef thrives because the water around it is extremely clear so sunlight can reach it.

❶ Summarize How did scientists revise their original thinking to explain where coral reefs can thrive?

_____

_____

❷ Discuss How does the revised idea illustrate the nature of science?

_____

_____

_____

Coral at Florida's Pulley Ridge

Although science is based on empirical evidence and objective reasoning, its results are open to change. Sometimes, scientific investigations produce data that show new patterns. If the new patterns do not contradict existing ones, scientists keep their existing conclusions, or perhaps revise them slightly. However, sometimes, new patterns contradict existing patterns. Scientists must then throw out their old conclusions.

 Do the Quick Lab
Science and Its Methods.

🔑 **Assess Your Understanding**

got it?··

○ **I get it!** Now I know that science is

characterized by _____

_____

_____

○ **I need extra help with** _____

Go to MY SCIENCE ⑤ COACH *online for help with this subject.*   **8.NS.1, 8.NS.2, 8.NS.3**

Designing an Experiment

🔑 **What Is Scientific Inquiry?**
8.NS.1

🔑 **How Do You Design an Experiment?**
8.NS.1, 8.NS.2, 8.NS.3, 8.NS.4, 8.NS.5, 8.NS.6, 8.NS.7, 8.NS.8, 8.NS.9, 8.NS.10, 8.NS.11

🔑 **What Is a Scientific Explanation?**
8.NS.1, 8.NS.2, 8.NS.3

MY PLANET DIARY

DISCOVERY

A Galactic Garden

Orbiting Earth is an amazing experience. But eating dehydrated space food can be boring and unappetizing. So, scientists conducted an experiment to see whether they could grow vegetables in space. They picked an old Thanksgiving favorite: sweet potatoes. They grew some cuttings onboard a shuttle and some cuttings on Earth. The cuttings were placed under similar conditions in space and on Earth for five days. They discovered that the number of roots that sprouted were the same in both places. But the roots of those in space actually grew faster! The cuttings that grew in space had more sugar and starch than those on Earth. Astronauts, however, hope that space potatoes taste just as good!

Write your answers to each question below.

1. What was the purpose of the experiment?

_____

_____

_____

_____

2. Why do you think the scientists grew cuttings both in space and on Earth?

_____

_____

_____

_____

_____

_____

▶ PLANET DIARY Go to **Planet Diary** to learn more about designing experiments.

Lab zone® Do the Inquiry Warm-Up What's the Question?

Vocabulary
- scientific inquiry • hypothesis • independent variable
- dependent variable • controlled experiment • bias
- repeated trial • replication • scientific explanation

Skills
⟲ Reading: Summarize
△ Inquiry: Develop Hypotheses

What is Scientific Inquiry?

It's Monday morning. You drag yourself out of bed and go to the kitchen. You pour yourself a bowl of cereal with milk and eat a spoonful. Yuck! Something tastes awful. The milk has gone sour. What happened? Your questioning is the beginning of the **scientific inquiry** process. **Scientific inquiry is the process of gathering evidence about the natural world and proposing explanations based on this evidence.**

Posing Questions and Defining a Problem

Scientific inquiry often begins with a question that leads to an observation. Your observation about the sour milk may lead you to ask a question: What made the milk go bad so quickly? Questions come from your experiences, observations, and natural curiosity. Look at **Figure 1** to pose a question about the strawberries.

Once you've posed your question, you should define a problem that can be tested. It is possible that others have already investigated the same problem. You can do research to find what information is known about the topic before you try to answer your question.

Look for the milk icon to follow the steps of the scientific inquiry.

✎ **Identify** In the text, circle the question posed about the sour milk.

> **Academic Standards for Science**
>
> **8.NS.1** Make predictions and develop testable questions based on research and prior knowledge.

FIGURE 1 ···

Posing Questions
Scientific inquiry starts with a question.

✎ **Pose Questions** Observe the photo. Then pose a question you could test about the strawberries.

_____

_____

_____

8.NS.1

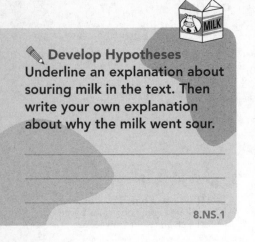

Develop Hypotheses
Underline an explanation about souring milk in the text. Then write your own explanation about why the milk went sour.

_____

_____

_____

8.NS.1

Developing a Hypothesis
How could you answer your question about the milk becoming sour? You start by developing a hypothesis. A **hypothesis** (plural: *hypotheses*) is a possible answer to a scientific question. It is also a possible explanation. For example, you know that you bought the milk five days ago. You also know that you left the milk out overnight. So, you may suspect that the temperature at which the milk is kept contributes to how quickly the milk goes sour. Your hypothesis might be that milk turns sour more quickly if it is left at room temperature for too long. Use **Figure 2** to practice developing a hypothesis.

Hypotheses are not facts. In science, a fact is an observation or description that has been confirmed repeatedly. For example, that milk has calcium is a fact that describes something found in milk. However, a hypothesis is one possible explanation to answer a question.

In science, you must be able to test a hypothesis. Researchers perform investigations and collect data that either support or fail to support a hypothesis.

FIGURE 2 ·······················

Developing a Hypothesis
Adam wonders why he has been sleeping less than usual.

Develop Hypotheses Write an explanation that might answer Adam's question.

_____

_____

_____

8.NS.1

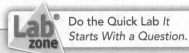
Do the Quick Lab *It Starts With a Question.*

🔑 Assess Your Understanding

1a. Pose Questions Write a testable question about what causes cavities.

_____

_____

8.NS.1

b. Develop Hypotheses Write another possible explanation for why milk sours.

_____

_____

_____

8.NS.1

got it?

○ **I get it!** Now I know that scientific inquiry is

_____

_____

_____

○ **I need extra help with** _____

Go to **my science ⓢ coach** *online for help with this subject.*   8.NS.1

How Do You Design an Experiment?

Once you have a hypothesis, you need to test it. **You can design an experiment that follows reliable scientific principles to test a hypothesis.** To test a hypothesis that milk will sour quicker if left out at room temperature than at colder temperatures, you could smell the milk periodically when it is left out at room temperature. But how do you know that the milk wouldn't turn sour in the refrigerator? You cannot know unless you smell the milk periodically when it is left in the refrigerator, as well.

Controlling Variables Suppose you want to test the temperature. You could observe how milk smells when it is kept at different temperatures over time. All other variables, or factors that can change in an experiment, must be the same. This includes variables such as the type of milk used and the container it's kept in. By keeping these variables the same, you will know that any differences in the odor of the milk are due to temperature alone.

The one factor that is purposely changed to test a hypothesis is the **independent variable.** In this experiment, the independent variable is air temperature. The factor that may change in response to the independent variable is the **dependent variable.** Here, the dependent variable is the time it takes the milk to sour. Look at **Figure 3**.

FIGURE 3 ··

Controlling Variables

A student wants to test whether shampoo cleans oily hair better than water alone. The student mixes oil with water in one test tube and oil with soapy water in another test tube. She watches to see when the mixture separates.

 Use the data table to complete the activities.

1. **Classify** What is the independent variable? What is the dependent variable?

   _____

   _____

2. **Identify** Name two other possible variables in this experiment.

   _____

   _____

3. **Draw Conclusions** Write a summary of what was observed in this experiment. What can you conclude?

   _____

   _____

Academic Standards for Science

8.NS.1 Make predictions and develop testable questions.

8.NS.2 Plan and carry out investigations.

8.NS.3 Collect quantitative data and use appropriate units to label numerical data.

8.NS.4 Incorporate variables that can be changed, measured, or controlled.

8.NS.5 Use the principles of accuracy and precision when making measurement.

8.NS.6 Test predictions with multiple trials.

8.NS.7 Keep accurate records in a notebook during investigations.

8.NS.8 Analyze data and use it to identify patterns and make inferences based on these patterns.

8.NS.9 Evaluate possible causes for differing results.

8.NS.10 Compare the results of an experiment with the prediction.

8.NS.11 Communicate findings using graphs, charts, maps and models through oral and written reports.

✎ **Name** In the text, circle the independent variable and underline the dependent variable for the milk experiment. 8.NS.4

Amount of Soap in Water (mL)	Time of Oil and Water Separation (seconds)
0	15
1.5	105

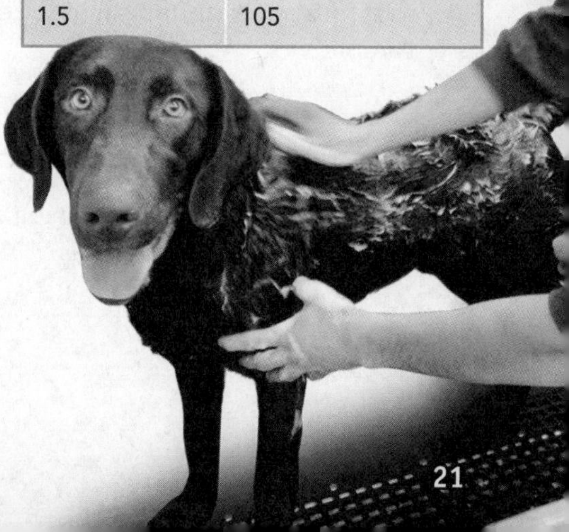

Designing a Controlled Experiment
A scientific experiment in which only one variable is changed at a time is called a **controlled experiment.** You decide to test the milk at three different temperatures, as shown in **Figure 4.** All other variables are kept the same. If your experiment were to have more than one independent variable, there would be no way to tell which variable influenced your results.

For example, in this experiment you are testing the effect of three temperatures on the time it takes milk to sour. You will keep all variables the same, except temperature. However, if you were to use different types of milk for each of your samples or kept each sample in a different kind of container, then you would not know which variable caused the milk to sour quickly. Was it temperature? Was it the type of milk? For this reason, you can only test one variable at a time in a controlled experiment.

Experimental Bias
In any experiment there is a risk of introducing experimental **bias,** an error in the design of the experiment. The error may make a particular result more likely. For example, without meaning to, you might use a carton of milk that is beyond its expiration date.

Summarize Explain how bias can affect an experiment.

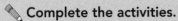

_____

_____

_____

_____

_____

FIGURE 4 ••••••••••••••••••••••
▶VIRTUAL LAB A Controlled Experiment
In this experiment, the temperatures must be different enough that your results can only be due to temperature.

✎ **Complete the activities.**

1. **Design Experiments** Label each milk sample with the temperature at which it could be tested. (*Hint:* Average room temperature is 22°C.)

2. **Apply Concepts** What is another variable that must be kept the same for each milk sample?

_____

3. **Analyze Sources of Error** How could testing milk that is past its expiration date introduce experimental bias?

_____

_____

8.NS.4, 8.NS.9

Collecting and Interpreting Data You are almost ready to begin your experiment. You decide to test the milk every 12 hours. Before starting your experiment, determine what observations you will make and what data you will gather. Recall that data are the facts, figures, and other information gathered through qualitative and quantitative observations. A helpful tool to use while collecting data is a data table. A data table is an organized way to collect and record your observations.

After your data have been collected, they need to be interpreted. Tools such as diagrams, graphs, and models can help you interpret data. They can reveal patterns or trends. For example, you might organize the data for the milk experiment in a graph. You could use the graph to compare the time it took for each sample to sour.

do the math!

Information organized in a data table can be made into a graph. This data table shows the percent of students who finished testing over a period of time.

❶ Graph Plot the data on the graph. Identify the independent and dependent data.

_____

_____

_____

_____

Students Finished (%)	Time (min)
0	30
2	45
50	60
98	75

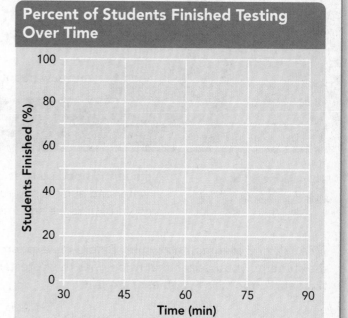

Percent of Students Finished Testing Over Time

❷ Read Graphs Describe the difference in the percent of students finished testing between 30 and 45 minutes and between 45 and 60 minutes.

_____

_____

_____

_____

_____

_____

❸ CHALLENGE After about how many minutes would you predict that all the students will finish their testing?

_____

8.NS.8

Drawing Conclusions Once you've collected your data, you can draw a conclusion. A conclusion is a summary of what you have learned from an experiment. When drawing a conclusion, examine the data objectively to see if the results support or fail to support your hypothesis. Also, consider whether the data allow you to draw a conclusion at all based on the results.

You may decide that the data support your hypothesis. The milk at room temperature smelled sour sooner than the milk kept refrigerated. Now, repeat your experiment to see if you get the same results. A conclusion is unreliable if it comes from the results of one experiment. Many trials are needed before a hypothesis can be accepted as true. A **repeated trial** is a repetition of an experiment.

Sometimes your data won't support your hypothesis. When this happens, check your experiment for errors, or bias, and for improvements. Maybe you could have tested the milk every 6 hours. Sometimes you cannot draw a firm conclusion from your data. For example, you might discover that milk left at room temperature, 22°C, soured sooner than milk left at 35°C.

Hypotheses are valuable even when they are not supported by the data. They can lead to further investigation. For example, you may decide to test whether milk's exposure to light has an effect on how quickly it sours. How would you design an experiment to test your new hypothesis?

apply it!

A student dipped squares of nylon, polyester, and cotton in water and hung them up to dry. He then measured the amount of time the squares took to dry.

1 **Analyze Experimental Results** Before the experiment, the student hypothesized that nylon dries the fastest. Do the data support his hypothesis? Explain.

_____

_____

Fabric	Trial 1	Trial 2	Trial 3	Trial 4
Nylon	28 min	25 min	27 min	33 min
Polyester	17 min	19 min	19 min	25 min
Cotton	44 min	45 min	45 min	51 min

2 **Identify Experimental Bias** Are the results from one trial different from the others? If so, how might the student have introduced bias that resulted in the different results?

3 **Apply Concepts** Based on these results, what kind of socks would you want to wear on a fishing trip?

_____

8.NS.1, 8.NS.9, 8.NS.10

_____

_____

_____

Communicating

Scientists communicate, or share their results with others through writing and speaking. They give talks at meetings, exchange information on the Internet, or publish articles in scientific journals.

When scientists share the results of their research, they describe their procedure and data so that others can repeat their experiments. A **replication** is an attempt by a different group of scientists to conduct the same experiment. Different groups of scientists must run replications and obtain similar results before these results can be used as evidence to support a hypothesis. Even after results are accepted, ongoing skepticism can lead to new understanding of a scientific replication.

Sometimes, scientists from around the world work together on scientific inquiries that are part of a larger project. For example, the International Space Station is one of the largest international scientific projects in history. Sixteen nations participate in it. The goal is to conduct experiments in unusual conditions, such as near-weightlessness. On such a large project, scientists must share their ideas and results regularly.

✏️ **Communicate**
You conclude that milk left at room temperature (22°C) sours quicker than refrigerated milk. Write a catchy newspaper headline that communicates this to other scientists.

VOLUME 22, NO. 03

INDIANA SCIENCE WEEKLY

MILK

Lab zone® Do the Lab Investigation
Become a Learning Detective.

🔑 Assess Your Understanding

2a. Identify At the beach, a student tests the effectiveness of three sunscreens, each with a different sun protection factor. What is the independent variable in her experiment?

_____

_____

8.NS.1, 8.NS.2, 8.NS.3, 8.NS.4, 8.NS.5, 8.NS.6, 8.NS.7, 8.NS.8, 8.NS.9, 8.NS.10, 8.NS.11

b. Design Experiments Controlling

_____ and eliminating

_____ are important parts

of designing an experiment.
8.NS.1, 8.NS.2, 8.NS.3, 8.NS.4, 8.NS.5, 8.NS.6, 8.NS.7, 8.NS.8, 8.NS.9, 8.NS.10, 8.NS.11

got it? ....

○ **I get it!** Now I know that you design an experiment _____

_____

○ **I need extra help with** _____

Go to **MY SCIENCE ⑤ COACH** *online for help with this subject.*
8.NS.1, 8.NS.2, 8.NS.3, 8.NS.4, 8.NS.5, 8.NS.6, 8.NS.7, 8.NS.8, 8.NS.9, 8.NS.10, 8.NS.11

8.NS.1 Make predictions and develop testable questions based on research and prior knowledge.

8.NS.2 Plan and carry out investigations as a class, in small groups or independently often over a period of several class lessons.

8.NS.3 Collect quantitative data with appropriate tools or technologies and use appropriate units to label numerical data.

What Is a Scientific Explanation?

If you are studying chemistry or physics, you can usually design and conduct controlled experiments, as shown in **Figure 5.** If you are studying astronomy or geology, however, it can be difficult or even impossible to carry out controlled experiments.

When you study astronomy or geology, you are often trying to understand how things happened in the past. You must make observations and then use what you already know to draw conclusions. Drawing a conclusion from observations is a way to develop a **scientific explanation.** 🔑 **A scientific explanation is a generalization that makes sense of observations by using logical reasoning.** For example, in 2000, workers digging a road in Tennessee discovered a layer of black soil filled with bones. Scientists examined the bones to find out what animals had lived at this site. Scientists knew these animals had lived in North America between 4 and 7 million years ago. Using this data, they reasoned that the site must be the same age! Things in the natural world that cannot be studied through a controlled experiment often rely on scientific explanation.

FIGURE 5 ··

Think Pink

Baby flamingos are born with white feathers, but over time they turn bright pink. Sometimes the feathers of adult flamingos fade back to white. Why does this happen?

✎ **Design Experiments** Plan an investigation to determine if something in their diet causes flamingos' feathers to turn pink.

---

❶ Question

Does a flamingo's diet of shrimp affect the color of its feathers?

---

❷ Hypothesis

_____

_____

8.NS.1

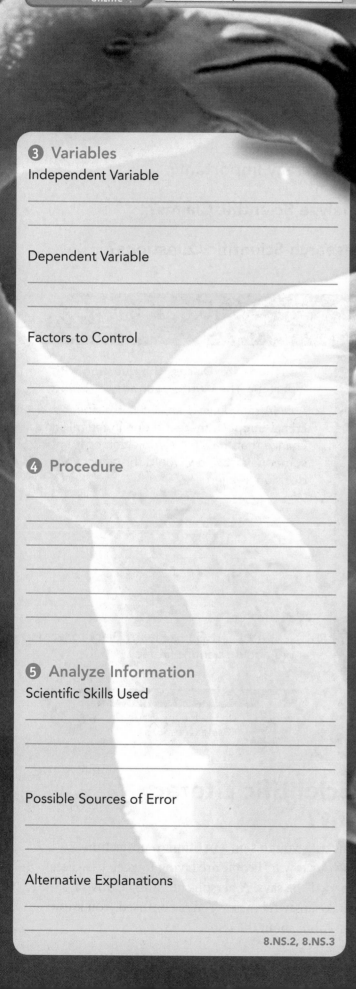

3 Variables

Independent Variable

_____

_____

Dependent Variable

_____

_____

Factors to Control

_____

_____

_____

_____

4 Procedure

_____

_____

_____

_____

_____

_____

_____

5 Analyze Information

Scientific Skills Used

_____

_____

_____

Possible Sources of Error

_____

_____

_____

Alternative Explanations

_____

8.NS.2, 8.NS.3

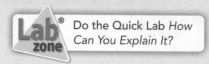

Do the Quick Lab *How Can You Explain It?*

🔑 Assess Your Understanding

3a. Review What is one problem that studying the past causes for a geologist?

_____

_____

_____

_____

8.NS.1, 8.NS.2, 8.NS.3

b. Summarize How does a scientist explain something when a controlled experiment cannot be carried out?

_____

_____

_____

_____

_____

8.NS.1, 8.NS.2, 8.NS.3

c. Make Generalizations What types of sources might a scientist use to investigate a question about flamingos before designing an experiment?

_____

_____

_____

_____

_____

8.NS.1, 8.NS.2, 8.NS.3

got it? ....

○ **I get it!** Now I know that a scientific

explanation is _____

_____

_____

○ **I need extra help with** _____

Go to **MY SCIENCE** ⑤ **COACH** *online for help with this subject.*   8.NS.1, 8.NS.2, 8.NS.3

27

Scientific Literacy

UNLOCK THE BIG ?

🔑 **Why Is Scientific Literacy Important?**
8.NS.8, 8.NS.9, 8.NS.10, 8.NS.11

🔑 **How Do You Analyze Scientific Claims?**
8.NS.8, 8.NS.9, 8.NS.10

🔑 **How Do You Research Scientific Questions?**
8.NS.1, 8.NS.2, 8.NS.8

my planet Diary

DNA Detective

If you watch TV crime programs, then you know that investigators often use DNA testing to solve a case. How does DNA testing help? Scientists can identify people by examining their DNA. A person's DNA is unique, like a person's fingerprint.

In the future, you may need more information about DNA evidence than what is given in TV programs. For example, if you are selected to sit on a jury in a trial that uses DNA evidence, you will want to know scientific details about DNA to make your decision.

FUN FACTS

Communicate **Discuss the question with a partner. Then write your answer below.**

A DNA sample links an accused suspect to a crime. Suppose there is a one in ten million chance that the DNA sample comes from someone else. How would this affect your decision as a juror?

_____

_____

_____

_____

_____

> PLANET DIARY Go to **Planet Diary** to learn more about scientific literacy.

Lab zone® Do the Inquiry Warm-Up *Posing Questions.*

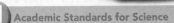
Academic Standards for Science

8.NS.8 Analyze data and use it to identify patterns and make inferences based on these patterns.

8.NS.9 Evaluate possible causes for differing results.

8.NS.10 Compare the results of an experiment with the prediction.

8.NS.11 Communicate findings using graphs, charts, maps and models through oral and written reports.

Why Is Scientific Literacy Important?

Suppose someone asks you to sign a petition to protect the Canada geese in your town. "People are trying to keep the geese away from our parks!" he says. A person standing nearby says, "But the geese make an awful mess." You're confused. You know you need to learn more about the issue.

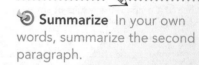

Vocabulary
- scientific literacy   • evidence
- opinion

Skills
- Reading: Summarize
- Inquiry: Interpret Data

Scientific Literacy
To understand the many issues you encounter, you need scientific literacy. **Scientific literacy** means understanding scientific terms and principles well enough to ask questions, evaluate information, and make decisions. **By having scientific literacy, you will be able to identify good sources of scientific information, evaluate them for accuracy, and apply the knowledge to questions or problems in your life.**

Evidence and Opinion
To evaluate scientific information, you must first distinguish between evidence and opinion. In science, **evidence** includes observations and conclusions that have been repeated. Evidence may or may not support a scientific claim. An **opinion** is an idea that may be formed from evidence but has not been confirmed by evidence. In **Figure 1,** try separating evidence from opinion.

Summarize In your own words, summarize the second paragraph.

_____

_____

_____

_____

_____

_____

_____

FIGURE 1 ·······························

Evidence and Opinion
Should your town try to keep Canada geese away from the parks?

✎ **Distinguish Evidence and Opinion** Under each statement in the boxes, label the statement as evidence or opinion.

Geese spend up to 12 hours a day eating grass and roots.

_____

Geese are too messy.

_____

 Lab zone® Do the Quick Lab *Scientific Literacy Survey.*

🔑 Assess Your Understanding

got it? ··

○ **I get it!** Now I know that by having scientific literacy _____

_____

○ **I need extra help with** _____

Go to **my science** ⓢ **coach** *online for help with this subject.*

How Do You Analyze Scientific Claims?

Scientific literacy gives you the tools to analyze scientific claims. Scientific reasoning gives you the process. **You can use scientific reasoning to analyze scientific claims by looking for bias and errors in the research, evaluating data, and identifying faulty reasoning.**

FIGURE 2 ·····································

Analyzing Scientific Claims

✏️ **Read about this research and think about the researcher's conclusion. Then answer the question in each box.**   8.NS.8, 8.NS.9

A researcher needs to find out if people in a town have good computer skills. The researcher advertises online for participants to take the test. He offers a free thumb drive as a payment.

Twenty people take the test. Everyone gets a perfect score.

The researcher concludes that the town's residents have excellent computer skills.

Identify Experimental Bias What is an important source of experimental bias in this research?

_____

_____

_____

Analyze Sources of Error What is an important source of error in this research?

_____

_____

_____

_____

apply it!

Read the sample advertisement. Then use scientific reasoning to analyze its claims.

1 Interpret Data How many subjects were in the study?

_____

2 Evaluate Scientific Claims Do the research results support the claim that using *KnowHow* helps people get better grades? Explain your answer.

_____
_____
_____

3 CHALLENGE Was Subject B's score actually 25% higher than Subject A's score? Calculate.

_____
_____

8.NS.8, 8.NS.9

Improve Your Test Scores!

A scientifically proven new way to get better grades!

Just look at our research results.

Subject A: Studied for 30 minutes in front of the TV and didn't use our product. Scored 72 points!

Subject B: Studied for 3 hours with a tutor and used KnowHow! Scored 90 points!

That means 25% HIGHER GRADES with *KnowHow!*

You CAN make the grade! ORDER *KnowHow* TODAY!

Lab zone® Do the Quick Lab Analyzing Claims.

🔑 Assess Your Understanding

1a. Identify What is one way to use scientific reasoning to analyze scientific claims?

_____
_____
_____

8.NS.8, 8.NS.9, 8.NS.10

b. Make Generalizations Would a scientific claim based on one test be a good claim? Why or why not?

_____
_____
_____
_____

8.NS.8, 8.NS.9, 8.NS.10

got it?

○ **I get it!** Now I know that I can analyze scientific claims by _____
_____
_____
_____

○ **I need extra help with** _____

Go to MY SCIENCE COACH online for help with this subject.　　8.NS.8, 8.NS.9, 8.NS.10

31

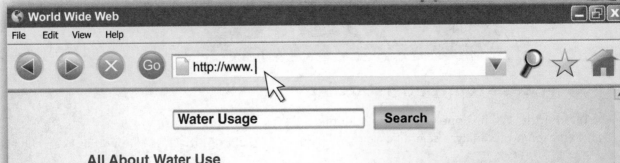

Academic Standards for Science

8.NS.1 Make predictions and develop testable questions based on research and prior knowledge.

8.NS.2 Plan and carry out investigations as a class, in small groups or independently often over a period of several class lessons.

8.NS.8 Analyze data.

Vocabulary Use Context to Determine Meaning
Underline the phrase in the text that helps you understand the word *relevant*.

How Do You Research Scientific Questions?

Chances are you will need to answer scientific questions to make decisions in your life. For example, suppose you injure your knee and the doctor gives you a choice of treatments. You need to do research before deciding. In science, you also need to do research to design an experiment.

To make decisions and design experiments, you need relevant and reliable background information. Relevant information is knowledge that relates to the question. Reliable, or consistent and truthful, information comes from a person or organization that is not biased. Generally, universities, museums, and government agencies are sources of reliable information. So are many nonfiction books, magazines, and educational Web sites. Look at the sources in **Figure 3**.

FIGURE 3 ·······································

Evaluating Sources of Information

✎ **Evaluate Data Reliability** Circle the most relevant and reliable source of information for your research about water use in your community. Explain your choice below.

_____

_____

_____

World Wide Web

File   Edit   View   Help

◀ ▶ ✕ Go   http://www. |

Water Usage   Search

All About Water Use

How much do you know about the water you use? Take this quiz. By Mr. Pickle's 6th-Grade Class

Effect of Water Rate Increases on Reducing Water Usage in Sydney

NSW Government, Australia

Water Usage by County

Your State Government Office of Water Resources and Conservation

EXPLORE THE BIG ? **All Bottled Up!**

How do science and society affect each other?

1 Clear plastics that could be used to make light, cheap bottles were invented.

2 Manufacturers made many plastic bottles for many beverages, which people buy.

3 Empty plastic bottles became litter. Bottle deposit laws encouraged recycling empty bottles.

4 Ways to recycle bottles into new, safe products were invented.

5 People bought products made from recycled bottles.

6 Bottles that use 30% less plastic were designed.

FIGURE 4 ···

> REAL-WORLD INQUIRY Science and society are interconnected.

✎ **Infer** Circle the boxes that show the work of science. Then explain below how the statements in boxes 3 and 4 show how science and other aspects of society affect each other.

_____

_____

_____

_____

8.NS.8

Lab zone® Do the Quick Lab *Sources of Information.*

🔑 **Assess Your Understanding**

2a. Review What is information that relates to a question called?

_____

8.NS.1, 8.NS.2

b. How do science and society affect each other?

_____

_____

_____

_____

8.NS.1, 8.NS.2

got it? ···

○ **I get it!** Now I know that to make informed decisions and design experiments, you

need _____

_____

○ **I need extra help with** _____

Go to my science ⑤ coach *online for help with this subject.* 8.NS.1, 8.NS.2

33

REVIEW THE BIG ?

Science affects society by allowing individuals, communities, and countries to analyze the
_____ and _____ of a decision.

LESSON 1 How Scientists Work
8.NS.1, 8.NS.2, 8.NS.3, 8.NS.8

🔑 Scientists explore the natural world by using skills such as observing, classifying, making models, inferring, and predicting. They form and test their ideas through scientific investigation.

Vocabulary
- science • observing
- quantitative observation
- qualitative observation
- classifying • inferring
- predicting • analyzing

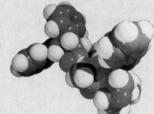

LESSON 2 The Characteristics of Scientific Knowledge
8.NS.1, 8.NS.2, 8.NS.3, 8.NS.7, 8.NS.8, 8.DP.9

🔑 Scientific investigations involve collecting and using evidence.

🔑 Science is based on empirical evidence and well-reasoned interpretation of data.

🔑 Science is characterized by an ordered approach to learning about the world.

Vocabulary • skepticism • data
- empirical evidence • objective reasoning
- subjective reasoning • pseudoscience

LESSON 3 Designing an Experiment
8.NS.1, 8.NS.2, 8.NS.3, 8.NS.4, 8.NS.5, 8.NS.6, 8.NS.7, 8.NS.8, 8.NS.9, 8.NS.10, 8.NS.11

🔑 Scientific inquiry is the process of gathering evidence and proposing explanations.

🔑 You can design an experiment that follows reliable scientific principles to test a hypothesis.

🔑 A scientific explanation is a generalization about observations by using logical reasoning.

Vocabulary • scientific inquiry • hypothesis
- independent variable • dependent variable
- controlled experiment • bias
- repeated trial • replication • scientific explanation

LESSON 4 Scientific Literacy
8.NS.1, 8.NS.2, 8.NS.8, 8.NS.9, 8.NS.10, 8.NS.11

🔑 By having scientific literacy, you will be able to identify good sources of scientific information, evaluate them for accuracy, and apply the knowledge to questions or problems in your life.

🔑 You can use scientific reasoning to analyze scientific claims by looking for bias and errors in the research, evaluating data, and identifying faulty reasoning.

🔑 To make decisions and design experiments, you need relevant and reliable background information.

Vocabulary
- scientific literacy • evidence • opinion

Review and Assessment

LESSON 1 **How Scientists Work**

1. When scientists group information into categories, they are

   a. analyzing.   **b.** making models.

   c. classifying.   **d.** observing.

                                   8.NS.2

2. Finding that the length of a caterpillar is 4.5 centimeters is a(n) _____ observation.

                                   8.NS.3

3. Infer What inference might a scientist make if she observed an increase in her energy after eating an afternoon snack?

_____

_____

_____

_____

                                   8.NS.1

LESSON 2 **The Characteristics of Scientific Knowledge**

4. Empirical evidence is data and observations that have been collected through

   a. the Internet.   **b.** inferring.

   c. scientific processes.   **d.** the imagination.

                                   8.NS.3

5. An attitude of doubt toward ideas is

   _____.

                                   8.NS.1

6. **Write About It** Neurology is, in part, the study of the brain's functions to determine how the brain controls the human nervous system. Phrenology is the study of the shape of a person's skull to determine that person's personality. Both neurology and phrenology are based on evidence that specific areas of the brain control specific functions. Which is a science? Which is a pseudoscience? Explain.

                              8.NS.1, 8.NS.2

LESSON 3 **Designing an Experiment**

7. What is often the first step in scientific inquiry?

   a. developing a hypothesis

   b. posing a question

   c. designing an experiment

   d. collecting data

                                     8.NS.1

8. The variable that is purposely changed in order to be tested is the _____

   _____

                                   8.NS.4

9. Compare and Contrast How are repetition and replication of an experiment different?

   _____

   _____

   _____

                                   8.NS.6

10. Why is it important to have only independent variable?

   _____

   _____

   _____

   _____

   _____

                                   8.NS.4

11. How do tools such as diagrams, graphs, and models help you understand the results of an experiment?

   _____

   _____

   _____

                          8.NS.8, 8.NS.11

12. A scientific explanation makes sense of observations using _____ reasoning.

                                   8.NS.8

LESSON 4 **Scientific Literacy**

13. Being able to understand basic scientific terms and principles well enough to apply them to your life is called

    a. evidence.   **b.** opinion.

    c. scientific literacy.   **d.** scientific questioning.

                                            8.NS.8

14. When you perform scientific research, you should look for information that is _____

                                            8.NS.9

15. Pose Questions A scientific study proves that frozen fruit is more nutritious than canned fruit. What questions would you want answered before you accept this claim?

_____

_____

_____

_____

_____

                            8.NS.9, 8.NS.10

16. Evaluate Data Reliability You are working on a science fair project and need to gather research on your topic. Where will you look for reliable information? Identify at least three different sources.

_____

_____

_____

_____

_____

_____

                              8.NS.1, 8.NS.2

How do science and society affect each other?

17. Scientists are studying the effects that melting ice might have on rising sea levels. Describe how the results of these studies might affect society.

_____

_____

_____

_____

_____

_____

_____

_____

_____

_____

_____

_____

_____

_____

_____

_____

_____

                            8.NS.1, 8.NS.2

Indiana ISTEP+ Practice

Multiple Choice

Mark only one answer for each question.

1. Lia tested the effect of temperature on plant growth. Before the experiment, she hypothesized that plants grow better in warm temperatures. The results of the experiment are shown below.

   How would you **best** describe the results of Lia's experiment?

   A. The results support the hypothesis.

   B. The results fail to support the hypothesis.

   C. No conclusion can be drawn from the results.

   D. The results are inaccurate.

   8.NS.8, 8.NS.10, 8.NS.11

2. Drew made observations while visiting the pet store. Which of the following is a quantitative observation he may have made?

   A. The store sells hamsters.

   B. The dogs are fed at 4:00 in the afternoon.

   C. The store's employees wear blue aprons.

   D. There are ten more cats than rabbits.

   8.NS.3

3. A controlled experiment

   A. introduces bias.

   B. tests several variables at once.

   C. tests only one variable and is free of bias.

   D. changes no variables.

   8.NS.4, 8.NS.9

4. Determining that the moon is the same age as Earth based on comparison of the age of moon rocks to the age of Earth rocks is an example of

   A. a scientific explanation.

   B. a qualitative observation.

   C. an estimate.

   D. anomalous data.

   8.NS.1, 8.NS.2, 8.NS.3

Constructed Reponse

Write your answer to Question 5 on the lines below.

5. Dowsing is the process of searching for underground water by walking over land while holding a stick. When the person holding the stick senses that the stick is shaking, the person might be standing near water. On what scientific principles, if any, is dowsing based? How might dowsing be based on faulty reasoning?

   _____

   _____

   _____

   _____

   _____

   _____

   _____

   8.NS.1, 8.NS.2, 8.NS.3

Extended Reponse

Use the graph below to answer Question 6. Write your answer on a separate sheet of paper.

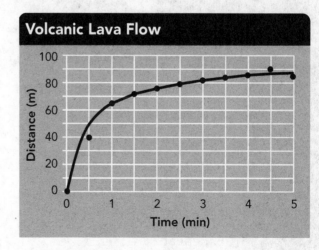

6. A scientist measured the distance that a stream of lava from a volcano flowed over 5 minutes. What logical conclusion you can draw from the graph of the scientist's data?

   8.NS.8, 8.NS.9, 8.NS.10, 8.NS.11

A RECIPE for Success

Before the 1800s, people thought that living things could appear from nonliving material. But Louis Pasteur did not think that this accepted theory was correct. He suspected that bacteria traveled on particles in the air and reproduced when they landed on biological material—like broth. Pasteur experimented to test his theory. His experiments were successful because they followed a good experimental design. Pasteur tested only one variable, included a control, and repeated his experiments.

Pasteur put broth into two flasks with curved necks. The necks would let in oxygen but keep out bacteria in air. Pasteur boiled the broth in one flask to kill any bacteria in the broth. He did not boil the broth in the other flask.

In a few days, the unboiled broth turned cloudy, showing that new bacteria were growing. The boiled broth remained clear. Pasteur then took the flask with clear broth and broke its curved neck. Bacteria from the air could enter the flask. In a few days, the broth became cloudy. Pasteur's results showed that bacteria were introduced into the broth through the air, and did not grow from the broth itself. He repeated the experiment, and showed that the results were not an accident.

Design It The Dutch scientist Jean-Baptiste van Helmont proposed a recipe for generating mice. He set up an experiment using dirty rags and a few grains of wheat in an open barrel. After about 21 days, mice appeared. The results, he concluded, supported his hypothesis that living things come from nonliving sources. What is wrong with van Helmont's experimental design? Using his hypothesis, design your own experimental procedure. What is your control? What is your variable?

Recipe for a Successful Experiment

1. Make a hypothesis.
2. Write a procedure.
3. Identify the control.
4. Identify the variable.
5. Observe and record data.
6. Repeat.
7. Make a conclusion.

BEWARE of Greenwashing!

Many businesses claim to produce environmentally friendly products. But how can you know the truth? *Greenwashing* is a term that combines the words *green* and *whitewashing*. It refers to the practice of making a product, service, or company appear to be more environmentally friendly than it really is.

Sometimes, identifying greenwashing is difficult because advertisements can be very persuasive. Fortunately, thinking like a scientist can help. As you evaluate a company's environmental claims, consider the following questions.

✓ **Is there proof?** Is there a scientific basis for the claims made by the company?

✓ **Is there a trade-off?** Does creating or delivering the product or service have negative environmental effects that are greater than the benefits of the product or service?

✓ **Are the claims meaningless?** Some labels, such as "100% natural," have no scientific or regulatory meaning.

✓ **Who says so?** Has a reliable source tested the company's claims?

Apply It Find advertisements for products that claim to have environmental benefits. Use the questions above to evaluate the claims. Then, create a brochure to educate the public about greenwashing.

 8.NS.8, 8.NS.11

Now Safe for the Environment!

CFC free

With **Eco-sensitive** ingredients

HOW CAN SCIENCE SPEED UP A JET?

How do scientists use measurement and mathematics?

This is a model of an F-16XL jet. The model represents just four percent of the jet's actual size. The model is being tested in a wind tunnel where fans blow air towards the jet. Smoke and lasers are then used to show how the air moves around the jet. The scientists are looking for smooth airflow around the jet to increase the jet's performance and reduce engine noise.

⚠️ **Infer** **Why do you think scientists would make a model of a jet and wind test it before building it?**

_____

_____

_____

_____

▶ **UNTAMED SCIENCE** Watch the **Untamed Science** video to learn more about how scientists use mathematics.

Mathematics and Models in Science

Academic Standards for Science

8.NS.1–8.NS.11, 8.DP.1–8.DP.11

2 Getting Started

Check Your Understanding

1. Background Read the paragraph below and then answer the question.

> Jane worked as a scientific **researcher** in the field of genetics. She designed experiments that provided **evidence** certain families can be at higher risk for specific diseases. Joan learned that genetics has had a great impact on how **society** treats diseases.

A **researcher** is anyone who studies a scientific problem.

Evidence is any object or result that indicates a certain theory is true.

Society is an organization of individuals, forming a larger unit such as a city or town.

• What is one activity a scientific researcher does?

_____

> **MY READING WEB** If you have trouble completing the question above, visit **My Reading Web** and type in *Mathematics and Models in Science.*

Vocabulary Skill

High-Use Academic Words High-use academic words are words that are used frequently in academic reading, writing, and discussions. These words are different from key terms because they appear in many subject areas.

Word	Definition	Example
trend	*n.* a general tendency or direction	An increase in song downloads shows a *trend* in the way people purchase music.
periodically	*adv.* at regular intervals	Scientists update their research *periodically* throughout their experiments.

2. Quick Check Complete each sentence with the correct high-use academic word.

• Melting glaciers show a _____ toward rising temperatures.

• Birds return to the nest _____ to tend to their chicks.

weight

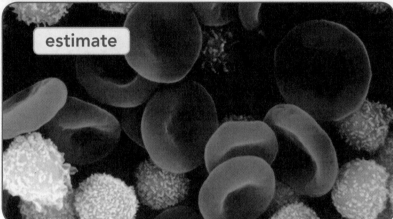

estimate

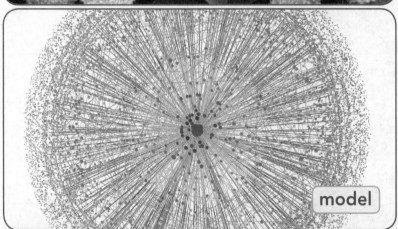

model

field

Chapter Preview

LESSON 1
- metric system
- International System of Units (SI)
- mass • weight • volume
- meniscus • density

🔄 Ask Questions
△ Measure

LESSON 2
- estimate • accuracy • precision
- significant figures • mean
- median • mode • range
- anomalous data • percent error

🔄 Identify the Main Idea
△ Interpret Data

LESSON 3
- graph • linear graph
- nonlinear graph • outlier

🔄 Relate Cause and Effect
△ Graph

LESSON 4
- model • system • input
- process • output • feedback

🔄 Identify the Main Idea
△ Make Models

LESSON 5
- field

🔄 Sequence
△ Observe

> VOCAB FLASH CARDS For extra help with vocabulary, visit **Vocab Flash Cards** and type in *Mathematics and Models in Science.*

Scientific Measurement

🔑 **Why Do Scientists Use a Standard Measurement System?**
8.NS.3, 8.NS.5, 8.NS.8

🔑 **What Are Some SI Units of Measure?**
8.NS.1, 8.NS.3, 8.NS.5, 8.NS.8, 8.NS.9

—— 610 meters

MY PLANET DIARY

Tallest or Deepest?

Misconception: The world's tallest structures must be built on land.

Until 2008, the world's tallest structure was the Petronius Compliant Tower, which was built on the ocean floor. This 610-meter-high tower is an oil platform in the Gulf of Mexico located 210 kilometers southeast of New Orleans. The pumps on the tower remove oil and natural gas from the Petronius oil field. Today, the 828-meter-high Burj Khalifa built on land in the city of Dubai, completed in 2010, is the tallest building in the world.

AR   MS
• Shreveport   AL   GA
TX   LA
Lafayette   ★ Baton Rouge
• New
Orleans   FL

Gulf of Mexico

MISCONCEPTION

Communicate **Discuss the questions with a partner. Then write your answers below.**

1. Name one measurement you think builders had to make when they were constructing the Petronius Compliant Tower.

_____

_____

_____

_____

_____

2. What is the tallest building where you live?

_____

_____

▶ **PLANET DIARY** Go to **Planet Diary** to learn more about scientific measurement.

 Lab zone® Do the Inquiry Warm-Up
What Is Scientific Measurement?

Drawing of the Petronius
Compliant Tower

—— 0 meters

Vocabulary
- metric system • International System of Units (SI)
- mass • weight • volume • meniscus • density

Skills
○ Reading: Ask Questions
△ Inquiry: Measure

Why Do Scientists Use a Standard Measurement System?

A standard measurement system enables scientists to share information or repeat experiments done by other scientists. Modern scientists use a version of the metric system called the International System of Units (SI)—from the French *Systéme International d'Unités*. Suppose you decided to measure length using your foot. Your friend decided to measure length using her hand. How would you be able to compare the length of a 5-foot object to a 7-hand one? Without a standard measurement system, it would be hard to share information about the world.

The **metric system** is a standard measurement system based on the number 10. Modern scientists use a version of the metric system called the **International System of Units (SI).** 🔑 **Using SI as the standard system of measurement allows scientists to compare data and communicate with each other about the results of scientific investigations.** Mass, length, and many other properties are measured using SI units. All SI units use the same set of prefixes. For example, a paper clip has a mass of about 1 gram. An object with ten times more mass than a paper clip has a mass of 10 grams, or 1 dekagram. A child could be 1 meter tall. A tree that is ten times taller than the child has a height of 10 meters, or 1 dekameter. **Figure 1** shows some common SI prefixes.

Academic Standards for Science

8.NS.3 Collect quantitative data and use appropriate units to label numerical data.

8.NS.5 Use the principles of accuracy and precision when making measurement.

8.NS.8 Analyze data, using appropriate mathematical manipulation as required.

○ **Ask Questions** Write a question you want to know about the SI system.

_____

_____

_____

FIGURE 1 ·····························

>VIRTUAL LAB **Prefixes of SI Units**
The man in this photo is one of the tallest men in the world at 2.46 meters, or 246 centimeters.

✎ **Name Complete the column in the table using the meter, which is the SI unit for length, as the base.**
8.NS.3

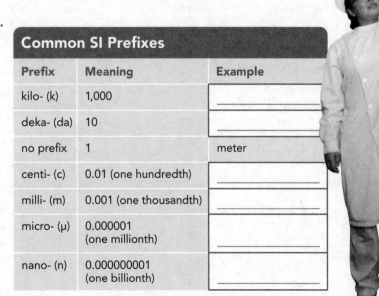

Common SI Prefixes		
Prefix	Meaning	Example
kilo- (k)	1,000	_____
deka- (da)	10	_____
no prefix	1	meter
centi- (c)	0.01 (one hundredth)	_____
milli- (m)	0.001 (one thousandth)	_____
micro- (μ)	0.000001 (one millionth)	_____
nano- (n)	0.000000001 (one billionth)	_____

do the math!

SI prefixes show how measurements increase or decrease by powers of 10. Use the table of SI prefixes in **Figure 1** to answer the questions.

1 **Calculate** A picnic blanket is 1 meter across. An ant is 1 centimeter in length. How many ants of the same length would fit end-to-end across the length of the picnic blanket?

_____

2 **Explain** The length of the grassy park where the ant lives is 1 kilometer. How many times longer than the ant is the park? Explain your answer.

_____

_____

_____

3 CHALLENGE How could you convert the length of the ant from centimeters to kilometers? How long is the ant in kilometers?

_____

_____

_____

_____

8.NS.3, 8.NS.5, 8.NS.8

 Do the Quick Lab
Measuring With SI.

🔑 Assess Your Understanding

1a. **Review** The International System of Units, or
_____ , is based on the _____ system.

8.NS.3, 8.NS.5

b. **Apply Concepts** A nickel coin weighs 5 grams. How many milligrams does it weigh?

_____

8.NS.3, 8.NS.5

c. **Calculate** Suppose the mass of a dog is 90 pounds. If 1 kilogram is equal to 2.2 pounds, what is the mass of the dog in kilograms?

_____

8.NS.3, 8.NS.5, 8.NS.8

d. **Make Generalizations** What might occur if the scientists in one country started to use a different system of measurement than the system used by scientists in the rest of the world?

_____

_____

_____

_____

_____

_____

8.NS.3, 8.NS.5

got it?

○ **I get it!** Now I know that scientists use SI to _____

_____

○ **I need extra help with** _____

Go to **MY SCIENCE COACH** online for help with this subject.

8.NS.3, 8.NS.5

What Are Some SI Units of Measure?

Scientists measure length, mass, volume, density, temperature, and time using SI units.

Length Length is the distance from one point to another. 🔑 **The basic SI unit for measuring length is the meter (m).** One meter is about the distance from the floor to a doorknob. Metric rulers are used to measure lengths smaller than a meter, such as a centimeter (cm), or millimeter (mm). A kilometer (km) is 1,000 times longer than a meter. **Figure 2** shows two organisms that can be measured with a ruler.

Academic Standards for Science

8.NS.1 Make predictions and develop testable questions based on research and prior knowledge.

8.NS.3 Collect quantitative data with appropriate tools or technologies and use appropriate units to label numerical data.

8.NS.5 Use the principles of accuracy and precision when making measurement.

8.NS.8 Analyze data, using appropriate mathematical manipulation as required, and use it to identify patterns and make inferences based on these patterns.

8.NS.9 Evaluate possible causes for differing results.

Conversions for Length

1 km	= 1,000 m
1 m	= 100 cm
1 m	= 1,000 mm
1 cm	= 10 mm

FIGURE 2 ·······················

Wing Length

You can use a metric ruler to measure the length of small objects. Line up one end of the object with the zero mark. Read the number at the other end of the object to find the length.

✏️ **Use the rulers to find the lengths of the bird and butterfly wings. Then complete the activities below.**

1. **Measure** What is the length of each wing?

_____

_____

_____

2. **Apply Concepts** Using the table in Figure 1, convert the length of each wing from centimeters to micrometers (μm).

_____

_____

8.NS.3, 8.NS.5

Mass

Mass Mass is the measure of the amount of matter in an object. 🔑 **The basic SI unit for measuring mass is the kilogram (kg).** The mass of dogs, people, cars, and other large objects is measured in kilograms. The mass of birds, cell phones, and other small objects is measured in grams (g) or milligrams (mg). The triple-beam balance shown in **Figure 3** is used to measure mass in grams.

When you step on a scale, you are measuring your weight. **Weight** is the measure of the force of gravity acting on an object. The basic SI unit for measuring weight is a measure of force called the newton (N). The pound is a non-SI unit commonly used in the United States to measure weight. When you stand on a scale, gravity pulls down on you and the springs in the scale compress. Gravity has a greater pull on objects with more mass, so these objects weigh more than objects with less mass. Weight changes as gravity changes, so you would weigh less on the moon because it has weaker gravity than Earth. However, an object's mass does not change with a change in gravity. **Figure 3** shows tools for measuring an object's mass and weight.

Conversions for Mass	
1 kg	= 1,000 g
1 g	= 1,000 mg

FIGURE 3 ···

Comparing Apples and Oranges

Triple-beam balances use weights to determine an object's mass. A spring scale is used to measure an object's weight.

1. **Measure** Find the mass of the apple by adding the masses of each weight on the balance.   8.NS.3, 8.NS.8

_____

2. **Define** The spring scale measures the weight of the

   oranges, which is a measure of the _____

   on the oranges.

3. **Infer** Suppose the oranges weigh 16.7 newtons on Earth. How would their weight change if they were on the moon?

_____

_____

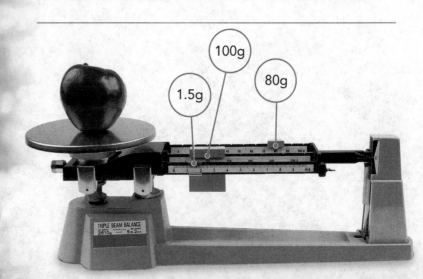

Volume

A microwave oven takes up space on a countertop. A jug of milk takes up space in the refrigerator. Air spreads out to take up space in a room. **Volume** is the amount of space taken up by an object or substance. 🔑 **The basic SI unit for measuring volume is the cubic meter (m³).** Other units include the liter (L) and cubic centimeter (cm³). Liters are used to measure liquids. Cubic meters or cubic centimeters are used to measure solid objects. Use this page to practice measuring volume.

Conversions for Volume	
1 L	= 1,000 mL
1 L	= 1,000 cm³
1 mL	= 1 cm³

Volume of Liquids

Use a graduated cylinder or beaker to measure the volume of liquids. Pour the liquid into one of these containers and read the level at the bottom of the **meniscus,** or curve of the liquid.

✏️ **Measure** What is the total volume of the liquid and berry in this photo?

_____

8.NS.3

Volume of Rectangular Solids

Use a ruler or meterstick to find the volume of rectangular solids. Measure the length, width, and height of the solid. Multiply these three values to get the volume.

✏️ **Calculate** What is the volume of the crate?

_____

8.NS.3, 8.NS.8

30 cm
42 cm
28 cm

Volume of Irregular Solids

You can use the displacement of water to measure the volume of an irregular solid, like a rock or a berry. Fill a graduated cylinder partially full with water. Measure the volume of the water. Now place the berry in the water. Measure the volume of the water again. To get the volume of the berry, subtract the original volume of the water from the volume of water that included the berry.

✏️ **Infer** Why would you get a more accurate measure of the volume of an irregular solid by using displacement instead of measuring with a ruler?

_____

_____

_____

8.NS.3

Density A foam brick and a clay brick can be the same size. If you pick them up, the clay brick feels heavy and the foam brick feels light. This is because the clay brick has a higher density than the foam brick. **Density** is the measure of how much mass is contained in a given volume. Units of mass are divided by units of volume to express the density of objects. 🔑 **The SI unit for density is kilograms per cubic meter (kg/m³), but scientists commonly use grams per milliliter (g/mL) or grams per cubic centimeter (g/cm³) to express density.** Look at **Figure 4** to compare the density of the balls in the picture.

FIGURE 4 ·······························

Predicting Density
Density determines if an object floats or sinks.

✎ **Predict** Circle the ball you think has the lower density. Explain your choice.

_____

_____

_____

_____

_____

_____

_____

8.NS.1

Table tennis ball

Golf ball

To find the actual value of an object's density, you can use a mathematical formula for calculating density. Once you have taken measurements to find both the mass and volume of an object, calculate its density using the following formula.

$$\text{Density} = \frac{\text{Mass}}{\text{Volume}}$$

apply it!

Once you find the volume and mass of an object, calculate its density using the formula.

❶ **Identify** Draw a line from the word *Meniscus* to the meniscus of each graduated cylinder.

❷ **Observe** What is the volume of water in each graduated cylinder? What is the volume of the bolt?

_____

_____

❸ **Calculate** The mass of the bolt is 101 grams. Find its density.

_____

_____

_____

8.NS.3, 8.NS.8

Meniscus

Meniscus

Using Density

The density of a pure substance is always the same, no matter how much of the substance you have. For example, the density of fresh water is always 1.0 g/cm^3, whether you have a drop of water or a whole lake. Figure 5 shows the density of some common substances.

When you know the density of an object, you also know whether it will sink or float in water. If an object's density is less than 1.0 g/cm^3, it will float. If its density is greater than 1.0 g/cm^3, the object will sink. If you have an object made out of an unknown substance, you can tell whether its density is greater than or less than 1.0 g/cm^3 by dropping the object in water!

FIGURE 5 ·············

Using Density

The planet Saturn could float in water because its density is less than 1.0 g/cm^3.

✎ **Infer** In the table, circle the liquids or solids that would float in water. Put a star next to those that would sink in water.

Densities of Common Substances

Substance	Density (g/cm³)
Gold	19.3
Gasoline	0.7
Milk	1.03
Water	1.0
Iron	7.8
Air	0.001
Ice	0.9
Aluminum	2.7

8.NS.8

✎ CHALLENGE Find the density of the surfboard and determine if the board should float. The surfboard's mass is 14 kg and its volume is 0.0875 m³. (*Hint:* The density of salt water is equal to about 1,025 kg/m³.)

_____

_____

8.NS.8

Time
How long would it take you to run 100 meters? Did you know that the fastest time recorded for running 100 meters is under 10 seconds? **The second (s) is the SI unit used to measure time.** Seconds can be divided into smaller units, such as milliseconds (ms). Sixty seconds make up a minute. Sixty minutes make up an hour. So there are 3,600 seconds in an hour (60 × 60 = 3,600).

Time is measured by clocks or stopwatches. A clock can measure time to the nearest second. Stopwatches like the one shown in **Figure 6** can measure time to the nearest hundredth of a second. The official timers used in the Olympics and other sports events can measure time to the nearest thousandth of a second!

FIGURE 6 ·····················
The Race Is On
The stopwatch shows the winning time in the last race at a school swim meet.

✎ **Answer the following questions about the race times.**

1. **Calculate** Jessica swims the last race in 22.56 seconds. By how much time did she lose the race?

_____

_____

8.NS.8

2. **Analyze Sources of Error** Why would machine-operated stopwatches be used at sports events instead of hand-operated stopwatches?

_____

_____

_____

_____

8.NS.9

Temperature

Temperature Did you need a jacket today, or could you wear shorts? You probably checked the temperature to find out. Temperature is a measure of the energy of motion of the particles in a substance. When molecules in air are moving fast and bouncing into each other, temperature is high and you feel hot. When these molecules slow down, temperature is lower and you feel cooler. Temperature affects the properties of some substances. For example, rising temperature can change a substance from a solid to a liquid to a gas.

Thermometers are instruments that measure temperature. Thermometers can have different temperature scales. Scientists commonly use thermometers with the Celsius temperature scale to measure temperature. On this scale, water freezes at 0°C and boils at 100°C. Scientists also use thermometers with the Kelvin scale to measure temperature. **Kelvin (K) is the official SI unit for temperature. The Kelvin scale starts at 0 K (absolute zero) and only goes up.** Units on the Kelvin scale are the same size as units on the Celsius scale. Use **Figure 7** to compare the Celsius and Kelvin scales.

FIGURE 7 ··

Kelvin and Celsius Scales

Liquid in a thermometer moves up or down as temperature changes.

✎ **Use the thermometer diagrams to complete the tasks.**

1. **Identify** Color in the Celsius thermometer to show how it would look when immersed in boiling water.

2. **Predict** Color in the Kelvin thermometer to show how it would look when immersed in ice water.

3. [CHALLENGE] Use the conversion chart to label the Kelvin thermometer with temperatures that correspond to the boiling point and freezing point of water.

8.NS.1, 8.NS.3

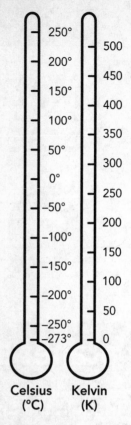

Celsius (°C)   Kelvin (K)

Conversions for Temperature

0°C	= 273 K
100°C	= 373 K

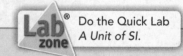
Do the Quick Lab
A Unit of SI.

🔑 Assess Your Understanding

2a. Identify A SI unit used to measure volume is the (cubic centimeter/millimeter).

8.NS.3

b. Sequence What steps would you take to determine the density of a rubber eraser?

_____

_____

_____

_____

_____

8.NS.2, 8.NS.3

got it?

○ **I get it!** Now I know that the SI units for length, mass, volume, density, time, and temperature are _____

_____

_____

○ **I need extra help with** _____

Go to **MY SCIENCE COACH** *online for help with this subject.*

8.NS.3

Mathematics and Scientific Thinking

UNLOCK THE BIG ?

🗝 **What Math Skills Do Scientists Use?**
8.NS.3, 8.NS.5, 8.NS.6, 8.NS.8, 8.NS.10, 8.NS.11

🗝 **What Math Tools Do Scientists Use?**
8.NS.3, 8.NS.5, 8.NS.6, 8.NS.8, 8.NS.9, 8.NS.10, 8.NS.11, 8.DP.9

My Planet Diary

Math in the Environment

For what job do you need to be able to solve for *x* and find the area of a polygon? You may be surprised to learn that people other than math teachers need to have these skills.

Rachel Sweeney is a coastal restoration project manager. Her job involves restoring barrier islands. She helps plan how to prevent erosion by building dikes. Dikes are long walls that help stop flooding.

Rachel uses math in her job every day. She uses estimation to determine the size of a grain of sand. Then she uses equations to calculate the volume of sand she needs to fill the dikes and what the mass of the sand will be. Without these math skills, Rachel's work in saving the environment would not be possible.

CAREER

Answer the questions below.

1. What are two math skills Rachel uses in her job?

_____

_____

2. Think about a job that interests you. How would that job use math?

_____

_____

_____

▷ **PLANET DIARY** Go to **Planet Diary** to learn more about mathematics and science.

Rachel Sweeney

With the help of people like Rachel Sweeney, barrier islands such as the ones shown may be saved from erosion.

Lab zone® Do the Inquiry Warm-Up *How Do Math and Science Work Together?*

Vocabulary
- estimate
- accuracy
- precision
- significant figures
- mean
- median
- mode
- range
- anomalous data
- percent error

Skills
↪ **Reading:** Identify the Main Idea
△ **Inquiry:** Interpret Data

What Math Skills Do Scientists Use?

The size of a grizzly bear, the number of bees in a hive, and the distance a kangaroo can jump are just a few of the interesting things that scientists investigate. Good math skills are essential as scientists collect and analyze data about their subject. 🗝 **When collecting data, scientists use math skills that include estimation, accuracy and precision, and significant figures.**

Estimation White blood cells help the human body fight disease. When a person's blood is tested, lab technicians count the number of white blood cells in a drop of the patient's blood. Doctors then use this count in their estimate of the total number of white blood cells in all of the patient's blood. An **estimate** is an approximation of a number based on reasonable assumptions. The estimated white blood cell count helps a doctor determine if the patient has an infection. Estimates are useful when it is impossible to count every individual or object. They are also useful when the thing being estimated, such as the distance of a star, cannot be measured directly. Use **Figure 1** to practice estimation.

Academic Standards for Science

8.NS.5 Use the principles of accuracy and precision when making measurement.

8.NS.6 Test predictions with multiple trials.

8.NS.8 Analyze data, using appropriate mathematical manipulation as required, and use it to identify patterns and make inferences based on these patterns.

8.NS.10 Compare the results of an experiment with the prediction.

8.NS.11 Communicate findings using graphs, charts, maps and models through oral and written reports.

FIGURE 1 ···

Estimating
This microscopic view shows red and white blood cells.

✎ **Use the photograph to complete these tasks.**

1. **Estimate** How many white blood cells (WBC) are in the microscopic field? _____

2. **Calculate** The sample is 500 times smaller than a microliter. A microliter is one millionth of a liter. Estimate the number of white blood cells in a microliter of the patient's blood.

   Number of WBC counted × 500 = _____ WBC per microliter

3. **Interpret Data** Patients with white blood cell counts greater than 10,500 WBC per microliter may have an infection. Could this patient have an infection? Explain.

_____

_____

8.NS.8

Accuracy and Precision

When scientists make measurements, they want to be both accurate and precise. **Accuracy** refers to how close the measurement is to the true or accepted value. **Precision** refers to how close a group of measurements are to each other.

Scientists try to use the highest quality tools to take measurements. They also measure the same object more than once. By repeating measurements with high-quality tools, scientists obtain the most accurate and precise results possible. Look at **Figure 2** to determine the accuracy and precision of the measurements.

Identify the Main Idea In the text, underline the main idea that describes how scientists are accurate and precise.

FIGURE 2 ·

Accuracy and Precision

Three teams measured the mass of the turtle below.

Interpret Diagrams Determine how accurate and precise each team's measurements are. Circle your answers in the boxes.   8.NS.3, 8.NS.5

Team One	Team Two	Team Three
Measurements	**Measurements**	**Measurements**
1. 172.5 g	1. 154.5 g	1. 153.7 g
2. 172.8 g	2. 121.7 g	2. 153.6 g
3. 172.6 g	3. 177.0 g	3. 153.9 g
This team was (accurate/not accurate).	This team was (accurate/not accurate).	This team was (accurate/not accurate).
This team was (precise/not precise).	This team was (precise/not precise).	This team was (precise/not precise).

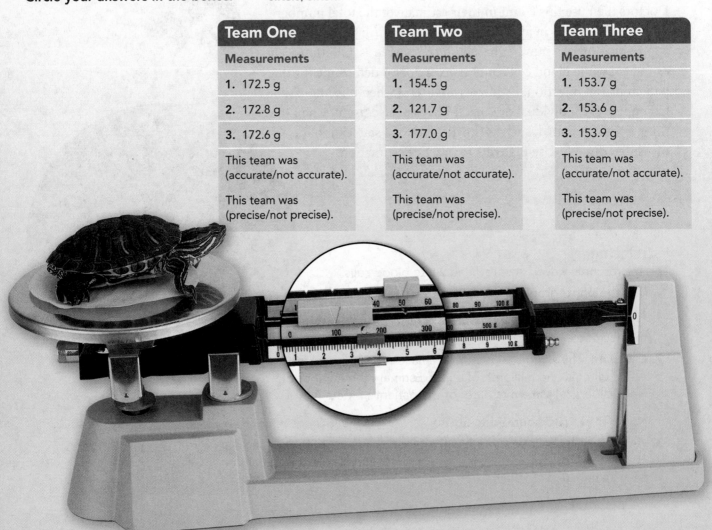

Significant Figures

Measurements are never completely precise. For example, a centimeter ruler allows you to measure centimeters precisely because these units are marked evenly with lines. If you want to measure a portion of a centimeter, you have to estimate that measurement between the lines. **Significant figures** communicate how precise measurements are. The significant figures in a measurement include all digits measured exactly, plus one estimated digit. If the measurement has only one digit, you can assume that it is estimated. Look at **Figure 3.**

FIGURE 3 ···

Significant Figures

An encyclopedia is 3.2 cm across its spine. The measurement *3.2 cm* has 2 significant figures, or sig figs. The *3* is a precise measurement. The *2* is an estimate.

✎ **Calculate** Read the boxes below and answer the questions.

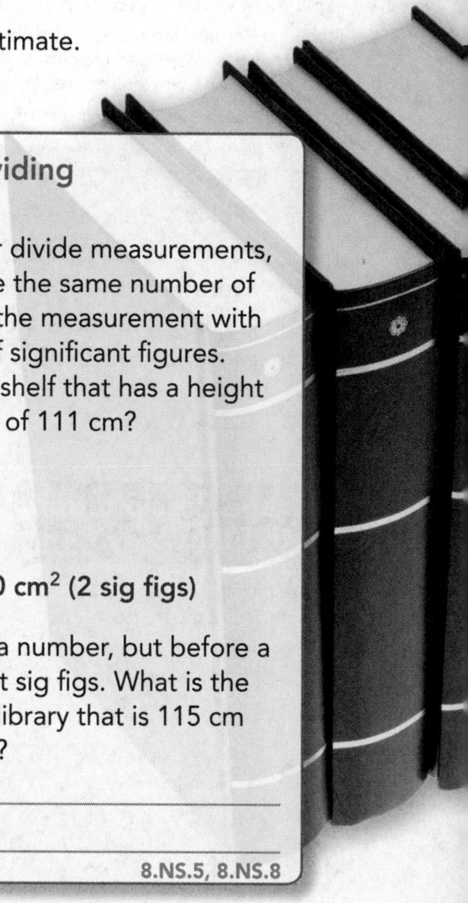

Adding or Subtracting Measurements

When you add or subtract measurements, the answer must have the same number of digits after the decimal point as the measurement with the fewest number of digits after the decimal point. If you add an encyclopedia to a row of books that is 42.12 cm, how long will the row be?

42.12 cm (2 places after the decimal)

+ 3.2 cm (1 place after the decimal)

45.32 cm ⟶ 45.3 cm (1 place after the decimal)

If you remove an encyclopedia from a row of books that is 42.12 cm, what will the new length of the row be?

_____

_____

Multiplying or Dividing Measurements

When you multiply or divide measurements, the answer must have the same number of significant figures as the measurement with the fewest number of significant figures. What is the area of a shelf that has a height of 33 cm and a width of 111 cm?

111 cm (3 sig figs)

× 33 cm (2 sig figs)

3,663 cm^2 ⟶ 3,700 cm^2 (2 sig figs)

Zeroes at the end of a number, but before a decimal point, are not sig figs. What is the area of a desk in the library that is 115 cm long and 45 cm wide?

_____

_____

8.NS.5, 8.NS.8

🔑 Assess Your Understanding

got it? ···

○ **I get it!** Now I know that scientists use math skills when they collect data that include_____

_____

○ **I need extra help with** _____

Go to **my science** 🔊 **coach** *online for help with this subject.*

8.NS.5, 8.NS.6, 8.NS.8, 8.NS.10, 8.NS.11

Lab® zone
Do the Quick Lab
Is It Accurate?

Academic Standards for Science

8.NS.3 Collect quantitative data and use appropriate units to label numerical data.

8.NS.5 Use the principles of accuracy and precision when making measurement.

8.NS.6 Test predictions with multiple trials.

8.NS.8 Analyze data, using appropriate mathematical manipulation as required, and use it to identify patterns and make inferences based on these patterns.

8.NS.9 Evaluate possible causes for differing results.

8.NS.10 Compare the results of an experiment with the prediction.

8.NS.11 Communicate findings using graphs, charts, maps and models through oral and written reports.

8.DP.9 Present evidence using mathematical representations.

What Math Tools Do Scientists Use?

Scientists use math to analyze data and draw conclusions about experimental results. **Scientists use many math tools to analyze data. Some of these tools include mean, median, mode, and range. Scientists also use percent error and other math tools to determine if the values of data points are reasonable.**

Mean, Median, Mode, and Range To understand a set of data, scientists use math tools. These tools help organize and summarize scientific data. Use **Figure 4** to learn more about mean, median, mode, and range.

FIGURE 4

Precipitation in South Bend The table below shows the average monthly precipitation in South Bend.

Use the table to calculate the mean, median, mode, and range of the rainfall data.

Average Precipitation, South Bend

Month	Average Precipitation (cm)
Jan	5.8
Feb	4.6
March	6.4
April	8.1
May	9.4
June	8.9
July	9.7
Aug	10.2
Sept	8.6
Oct	8.6
Nov	7.9
Dec	6.9

Mean The **mean** is the numerical average of a set of data. To find the mean, add all the numbers in the data set. Then divide by the total number of items that you added.

Mean of the rainfall data: ____________________

Median The **median** is the middle number in an ordered set of data. To find the median, list all the numbers in order from least to greatest. If the list has an odd number of entries, the median is the middle entry. If the list has an even number of entries, the median is the mean of the two middle entries.

Median of the rainfall data: ____________________

____

____

Mode The **mode** is the number that appears most often in a list of numbers.

Mode of the rainfall data: ____________________

Range The **range** of a data set is the difference between the greatest value in the set and the least value.

Range of the rainfall data: ____________________

8.NS.8

Reasonable and Anomalous Data Scientists must always ask themselves whether their data make sense and are reasonable. There is always an acceptable range of variation in collected data. However, some variation may not be acceptable. For example, suppose that a scientist is studying the wind speed of a hurricane that appears very strong. The scientist sees that the hurricane's wind speed has been measured at 56 km/hr, which is far lower than expected. The scientist is likely to check the equipment recording wind speed to see if it is functioning properly.

Human or equipment error can produce **anomalous data,** or data that do not fit with the data set. If a scientist sees a data point that is different from others, he or she will examine it for errors. If no errors were made, the anomalous data might be due to an unknown variable. Investigating the reason for anomalous data can lead scientists to new discoveries.

apply it!

Adult female black bears have masses from about 50 kilograms to 125 kilograms. Adult male black bears have masses from about 60 kilograms to 250 kilograms. Researchers measured the masses of five adult female black bears in their natural habitat. You can see their results in the table.

1 Identify Which mass is anomalous data?

_____

2 Solve Problems How could the researcher check the anomalous data?

_____

_____

3 CHALLENGE What might have produced the anomalous data?

_____

_____

_____

8.NS.8, 8.NS.9

Adult Female Black Bear Masses

Bear	Mass (in kg)
A	79
B	73
C	74
D	155
E	70

Adding It Up

How do scientists use measurement and mathematics?

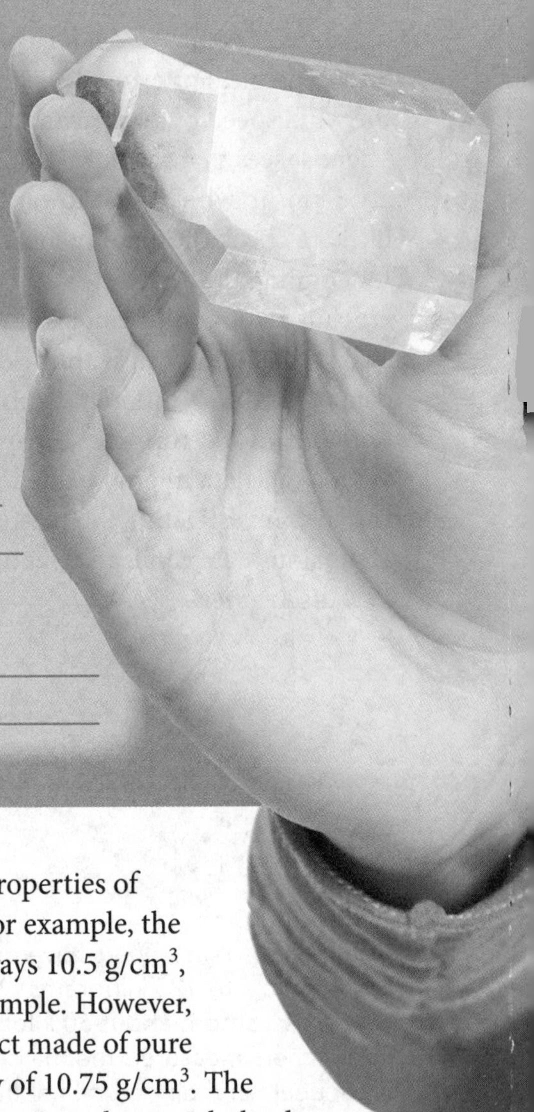

FIGURE 5 ···

>**INTERACTIVE ART** Two lab partners measured the mass and volume of a sample of quartz four times. They recorded their measurements in the table at the right.

✎ **Answer the questions.**

1. **Draw Conclusions** How do you think the partners measured the sample's mass and volume?

   _____

   _____

   _____

2. **Infer** Are the students' measurements precise? Explain.

   _____

   _____

FIGURE 6 ···············

Percent Error
A Nobel Prize medal is plated with gold. The density of gold is 19.3 g/cm³.

✎ **Calculate** A worker finds the density of the Nobel medal's plating to be 20.1 g/cm³. What is the percent error of his measurement?

_____

_____

_____

_____

Percent Error Some properties of substances never change. For example, the density of pure silver is always 10.5 g/cm³, no matter the size of the sample. However, when you measure an object made of pure silver, you may get a density of 10.75 g/cm³. The difference between the two density values might be due to an error you made when you measured the mass or volume of the silver. It could also be due to the accuracy of your measuring equipment. The percent difference between the known value of a substance and its measured value is called the **percent error.** A low percent error means that the experimental results were accurate. The formula below calculates percent error in the silver sample.

$$\text{Percent Error} = \frac{\text{experimental value} - \text{true value}}{\text{true value}} \times 100\%$$

$$\% E = \frac{10.75 \text{ g/cm}^3 - 10.5 \text{ g/cm}^3}{10.5 \text{ g/cm}^3} \times 100\%$$

$$\% E = \frac{0.25 \text{ g/cm}^3}{10.5 \text{ g/cm}^3} \times 100\% = 2.38$$

8.NS.8, 8.NS.9

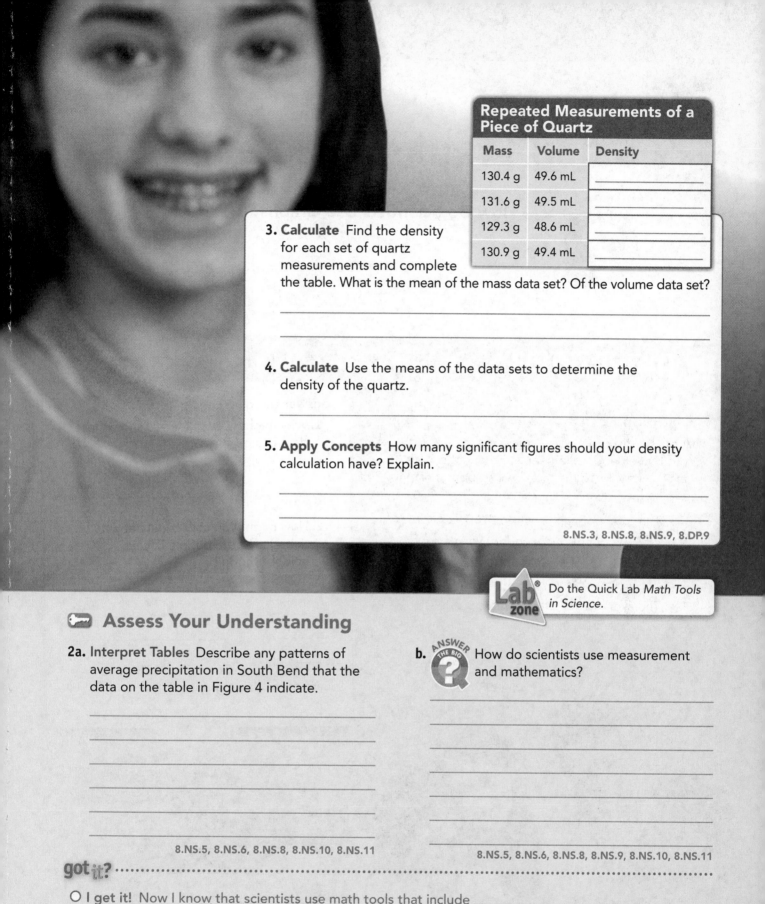

Repeated Measurements of a Piece of Quartz

Mass	Volume	Density
130.4 g	49.6 mL	_____
131.6 g	49.5 mL	_____
129.3 g	48.6 mL	_____
130.9 g	49.4 mL	_____

3. Calculate Find the density for each set of quartz measurements and complete the table. What is the mean of the mass data set? Of the volume data set?

_____

_____

4. Calculate Use the means of the data sets to determine the density of the quartz.

_____

5. Apply Concepts How many significant figures should your density calculation have? Explain.

_____

_____

8.NS.3, 8.NS.8, 8.NS.9, 8.DP.9

Lab zone Do the Quick Lab *Math Tools in Science.*

Assess Your Understanding

2a. Interpret Tables Describe any patterns of average precipitation in South Bend that the data on the table in Figure 4 indicate.

_____

_____

_____

_____

_____

8.NS.5, 8.NS.6, 8.NS.8, 8.NS.10, 8.NS.11

b. ANSWER THE BIG **?** How do scientists use measurement and mathematics?

_____

_____

_____

_____

_____

8.NS.5, 8.NS.6, 8.NS.8, 8.NS.9, 8.NS.10, 8.NS.11

got it? ....

○ **I get it!** Now I know that scientists use math tools that include _____

_____

○ **I need extra help with** _____

Go to **MY SCIENCE COACH** *online for help with this subject.*

8.NS.5, 8.NS.6, 8.NS.8, 8.NS.10, 8.NS.11

Using Graphs in Science

UNLOCK THE BIG ?

🔑 **How Do Scientists Use Graphs?**
8.NS.8, 8.NS.11, 8.DP.9

MY PLANET DIARY *for* Indiana

Indiana Population

A census is a survey that individuals take. It provides information about the people living in the state and country. Read the facts below about Indiana's population from a 2008 estimate.

- The total population was 6,376,792 people.
- 439,999 people were under five years old.
- 1,587,821 people were under the age of 18.
- 816,229 people were over the age of 65.
- The average age was 35 years old.

SCIENCE STATS

Answer the questions below.

1. Why might it be helpful to show these data in a graph?

_____

_____

2. How might you collect data about the ages of the people in your neighborhood?

_____

_____

_____

▶ PLANET DIARY Go to **Planet Diary** to learn more about graphs.

Lab zone ® Do the Inquiry Warm-Up *What's in a Graph?*

Vocabulary
• graph • linear graph
• nonlinear graph • outlier

Skills
↻ Reading: Relate Cause and Effect
△ Inquiry: Graph

How Do Scientists Use Graphs?

Have you ever been to an event that started off with a jet plane flyby? If so, you probably noticed that you could see the jets before you heard the roar of their engines. That is because sound travels slower than light. The speed of sound is also affected by the temperature of the medium it's traveling through, as shown by the data in **Figure 1.** To help understand what the data mean, you can use a graph. A **graph** is a "picture" of your data.

Kinds of Data Graphs can illustrate different types of data. 🔑 **Scientists use graphs to identify trends, make predictions, and recognize anomalous, or inconsistent, data.** Graphs display categorical and numerical data. Categorical data can be grouped into categories. For example, census information can be categorized by age group. Numerical data, such as temperature and the speed of sound, are continuous, ranging from small to large amounts. Different kinds of graphs are used to display these two kinds of data.

Kinds of Graphs Line graphs are used to display numerical data, such as the data in **Figure 1.** They may show how a dependent variable changes in response to an independent variable. Scientists control changes in the independent variable. Then they collect data about how the dependent variable responded to those changes. Bar graphs can be used to display both numerical and categorical data.

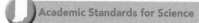

Academic Standards for Science

8.NS.8 Analyze data, using appropriate mathematical manipulation as required, and use it to identify patterns and make inferences based on these patterns.

8.NS.11 Communicate findings using graphs, charts, maps and models through oral and written reports.

8.DP.9 Present evidence using mathematical representations.

↻ **Relate Cause and Effect**
In the text, underline the cause and circle the effect of variables when scientists use them.

FIGURE 1 ···

Graphing the Speed of Sound

As temperatures rise, so does the speed at which sound travels through the air.

△ **Graph** Make a line graph by plotting the data from the table on the grid.
8.NS.8, 8.NS.11, 8.DP.9

Temp. (°C)	Speed of Sound (m/s)
−15	322
0	331
15	340
30	349
45	358

Speed of Sound as Temperature Changes

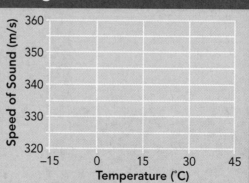

63

Linear and Nonlinear Graphs As you saw in the line graph in **Figure 1,** temperature and the speed of sound are related. Line graphs are powerful tools because they show how different sets of data are related. The line graph shows that as temperature increases, the speed of sound increases in a predictable way.

A line graph in which the data points yield a straight line is a **linear graph.** The relationship between temperature and the speed of sound can be shown by a linear graph. A graph in which the data points do not fall along a straight line is a **nonlinear graph.** Changes in population can be shown by a nonlinear graph.

If most points do not fall exactly along a line, a graph can still show a trend. A point that is not part of the trend is an anomalous data point called an **outlier.** When a graph does not have a clear trend, it usually means the variables are not related.

Vocabulary High-Use Academic Words When a graph shows a trend, you can make predictions about data beyond the axes of the graph. Which word below is a synonym for the word *trend*?

○ origin

○ course

○ point

Maximum Dive Depths of Sea Animals

Animal	Dive Depths (meters)
Leatherback sea turtle (LST)	1200
Emperor penguin (EP)	565
Elephant seal (ES)	1529
King penguin (KP)	343

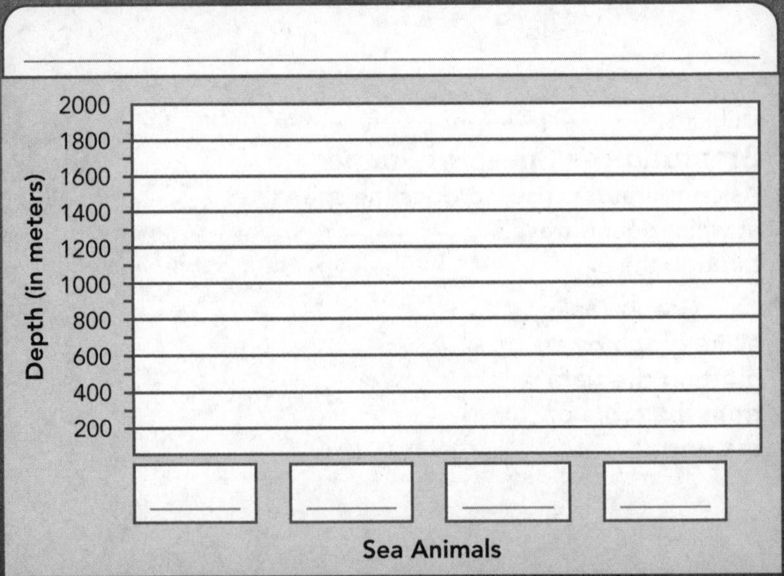

FIGURE 2 ·······················

▶ **INTERACTIVE ART** **Sea Life Diving Data**
The diving depths of several sea creatures were measured and recorded in the data table.

1. **Graph** Arrange the animals in order from shallowest to deepest divers in a bar graph. Label the x-axis with the animals' initials and title the graph.

2. **Draw Conclusions** What trend does the graph show?

_____

_____

_____

8.NS.8, 8.NS.11, 8.DP.9

Depth (in meters): 2000, 1800, 1600, 1400, 1200, 1000, 800, 600, 400, 200

Sea Animals

apply it!

The data table shows the number of tourists (in millions) visiting New Orleans between 2006 and 2009.

Year	Number of Visitors (in millions)
2006	3.7
2007	7.1
2008	7.6
2009	7.9

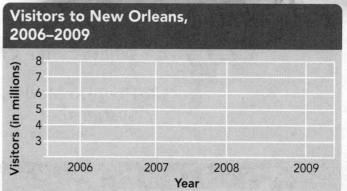

1 Graph Plot the data on the graph and connect the points.

2 **Read Graphs** The greatest increase in visitors was between _____

3 CHALLENGE Suppose the data for 2010 show that 4 million visitors visited New Orleans that year. How would you classify this data point? How would it be plotted on the graph?

_____

_____

_____

Visitors to New Orleans, 2006–2009

8.NS.8, 8.NS.11

® Do the Quick Lab *Recognizing Trends.*

🔑 Assess Your Understanding

1a. **Draw Conclusions** What does a graph with no trend indicate about the variables?

_____

8.NS.8, 8.NS.11

b. **Compare and Contrast** How are linear and nonlinear graphs alike? Different?

_____

_____

_____

_____

8.NS.8, 8.NS.11

got it? ....

○ **I get it!** Now I know that scientists use

graphs _____

_____

_____

○ **I need extra help with** _____

Go to MY SCIENCE COACH online for help with this subject. 8.NS.8, 8.NS.11

65

LESSON

4 Models and Systems

UNLOCK THE BIG Q?

🔑 **How Do Scientists Use Models?**
8.NS.8, 8.NS.11

🔑 **What Are the Characteristics of a System?**
8.NS.8, 8.NS.11

🔑 **How Do Models Help Scientists Understand Systems?**
8.NS.1, 8.NS.7, 8.NS.8, 8.NS.11

my planet Diary

SCIENCE AND TECHNOLOGY

Models Used in Films

As the lights in the movie theater dim, your excitement about the latest hit movie builds. For the next two hours, a different world flashes in front of you. Monsters snatch up people, or alien robots invade Earth.

These monsters and robots are not actual objects. Instead, filmmakers develop models that they incorporate into the scenes. These models are often made on the computer. Sometimes, the models they build are very small, even though they appear huge on the movie screen. The next time you watch a movie, can you tell which things are real and which are models?

Answer the questions below.

1. How do models help filmmakers?

_____

_____

_____

2. What might you need to make a model of if you were filming a movie at your school?

_____

_____

_____

> PLANET DIARY Go to **Planet Diary** to learn more about making models.

Lab zone ® Do the Inquiry Warm-Up *Models in Science.*

Vocabulary
- model • system • input
- process • output • feedback

Skills
↻ Reading: Identify the Main Idea
△ Inquiry: Make Models

How Do Scientists Use Models?

Many department stores use mannequins to show customers how certain outfits might look. A mannequin is a model. A **model** is any representation of an object or a process. You use models in your daily life without even realizing it. For example, you might use a globe to find a country. A globe is a model of Earth.

Scientists work with models for a specific purpose. **Scientists use models to test their ideas about things they cannot observe directly.** Scientists often build models to create a reasonable representation of things that are either very small or very large. These kinds of models are physical models—drawings (like the one in **Figure 1**) or three-dimensional objects. But many models are not physical objects. For example, many models are models of a process. A computer program might be used to model the movement of the stars as seen from Earth.

FIGURE 1 ·······················
Connecting the Dots
This model shows how networks (drawn as dots) connect to each other on the Internet. The bigger the dot, the more Internet traffic the network handles.

✏️ **Explain** Suppose all networks in the center of the model became unavailable for 24 hours. How can scientists use this model to predict how Internet traffic will be affected?

_____

_____

_____

8.NS.8, 8.NS.11

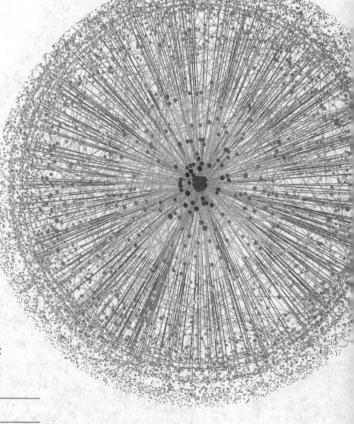

Do the Quick Lab
Working With Models

☞ Assess Your Understanding

got it? ···

○ I get it! Now I know that scientists use models to _____

_____

○ I need extra help with _____

Go to MY SCIENCE ⓢ COACH *online for help with this subject.*

8.NS.8

Analyze data, using
ate mathematical
ation as required, and use
ntify patterns and make
es based on these patterns.

Communicate findings using

What Are the Characteristics of a System?

Models are often used to represent systems. A **system** is a group of parts that work together to carry out a function. You may recall that Earth is a system that consists of air, life, water, ice, and rock. But look at **Figure 2.** Many things you use in your daily life are systems. A bicycle pump, a toaster, and a flashlight all contain parts that work together while performing a function.

Systems have common characteristics. **All systems have at least one input, at least one process, and at least one output.** An **input** is a material or the energy that goes into the system. A **process** is an action or series of actions that happen within the system. An **output** is the material or energy that comes out of a system. To understand input, process, and output, think of a toaster. The input is electricity. The process is heating the bread. The output is hot toast.

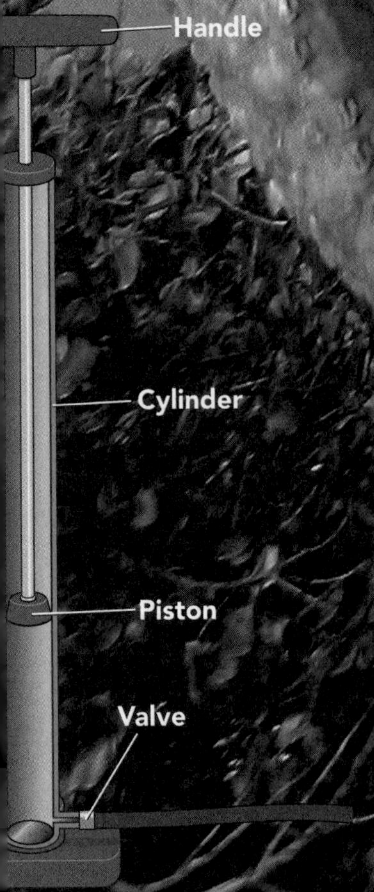

Handle

Cylinder

Piston

Valve

FIGURE 2······

▶ INTERACTIVE ART An Everyday System
In a bicycle pump, many parts work together as a system. ✎ Chart **Look at the pump and use what you know to fill in the chart.**

cle Pump as a System

	Inputs	Outputs

8.NS.8, 8.NS.11

Look at **Figure 3.** The harder you ride a bike, the more oxygen your muscles need. As a result, your circulatory system provides information to your heart indicating that you need more oxygen. So your heart starts beating faster. By beating faster, your heart provides more oxygen to your muscles. **Feedback** is output that changes a system in some way. When you exercise, your heart receives feedback that makes your heart pump faster.

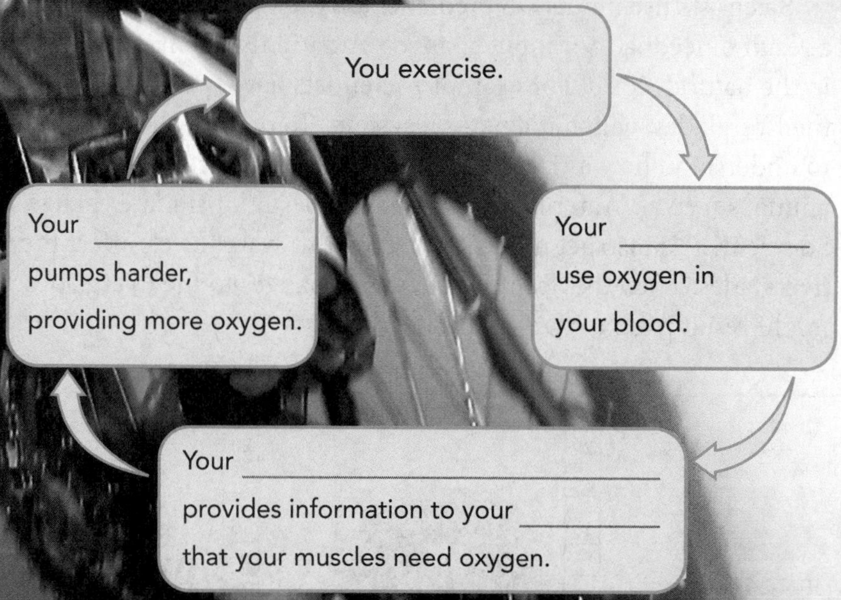

You exercise.

Your _____ pumps harder, providing more oxygen.

Your _____ use oxygen in your blood.

Your _____ provides information to your _____ that your muscles need oxygen.

FIGURE 3 ·····························

Feedback

When you exercise, your body's circulatory system feeds back information to your heart.

✎ **Fill in the blanks of the graphic organizer.**

Identify What is the input and output for this system?

_____

_____

_____

_____

_____

Lab zone® Do the Quick Lab *Characteristics of Systems.*

⚷ Assess Your Understanding

1a. Identify A (model/system) is a group of parts that work together to perform a function.

8.NS.8

b. Apply Concepts Is a handheld can opener a system? Explain.

_____

_____

_____

_____

8.NS.8

c. Infer What is the input when you use a can opener?

_____

_____

_____

_____

_____

_____

8.NS.8

got it? ··

○ **I get it!** Now I know that all systems have _____

and some systems have feedback.

○ **I need extra help with** _____

Go to **my science** ⓢ **coach** *online for help with this subject.*

8.NS.8

How Do Models Help Scientists Understand Systems?

It's easy to identify the materials and energy that make up the inputs and outputs of a system. But observing a system's process can be difficult. Models can help scientists understand a system's process. **Scientists build models to represent a process. They test whether the input and output from the model match the input and output of the system in the natural world.**

Scientists use models to predict changes in a natural system as a result of feedback or input changes. A natural system is a system in the natural world. For example, scientists have tried to restore the Everglades, which is a natural system. To do this, they need to understand how a rise in water levels might affect plant and animal survival. Water levels can rise as a result of climate change. So scientists construct models showing how water levels affect the Everglades. Then they can predict what changes to the Everglades might result from a change in water levels.

apply it!

The Cape Sable seaside sparrow nests in certain areas of the Everglades. In one model of the sparrow's nesting habits, the sparrows start to mate when water levels drop to 5 cm. After they mate, the sparrows need approximately 43 consecutive days during which the water level is lower than 16 cm. If water levels rise to 16 cm or higher during this time, the sparrows will abandon their nest.

Nest not drawn to scale

Nest not drawn to scale

2 **CHALLENGE** How might scientists use the information from your model to save the species?

_____

_____

8.NS.8, 8.NS.11

1 **Make Models** Shade in the water levels on each meterstick to show how Cape Sable seaside sparrow nests vary according to water levels.

Modeling Simple and Complex Systems

Some systems that scientists study are simple. There may be only a few parts in the system or a few steps in the process. A toaster is one example of a system that is made up of only a few parts. **Figure 4** shows another example of a simple system.

However, some systems are more complex. Many parts and many variables, or factors that can vary, interact in these systems. Often scientists may use a computer to keep track of the variables. For example, weather systems are very complex. Many factors affect weather, such as oceans, mountains and valleys, wind patterns, and the angle of the sun's rays. These factors can interact in many ways. As a result, scientists have a difficult time predicting when and where rain or snow will fall. Because such systems are difficult to model, scientists may model the specific part of the system that they wish to study. For instance, a hurricane is a complex natural system. To predict where a hurricane will make landfall, scientists might try to model winds that affect the hurricane's path.

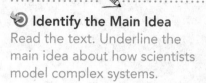

Identify the Main Idea
Read the text. Underline the main idea about how scientists model complex systems.

FIGURE 4 ·······································

The Mercury Cycle

Materials that contain the element mercury can be harmful to fish that eat them.

✎ **Look at the diagram and then complete the activities.**

1. Identify On the diagram, label the inputs, processes, and outputs of the system.

2. Predict Suppose you want less mercury to end up in fish. How might you change the inputs of the system?

_____

_____

_____

_____

8.NS.1

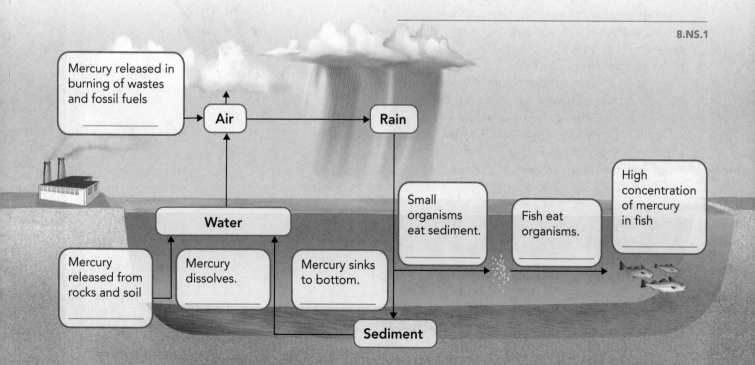

Mercury released in burning of wastes and fossil fuels
_____

Air

Rain

Water

Mercury released from rocks and soil
_____

Mercury dissolves.
_____

Mercury sinks to bottom.
_____

Small organisms eat sediment.

Fish eat organisms.

High concentration of mercury in fish
_____

Sediment

know?
....

The lion is nicknamed the "King of the Jungle." But in open savannas, female lions do most of the hunting.

Testing Assumptions
When scientists construct a model of a system, they begin with certain assumptions. For example, an astronomer might assume that in order for a planet to support life, the planet must have water.

Scientists check their assumptions. They compare the input and output of the model to the input and output in the natural world. If they match, then the assumptions are correct. If they do not match, scientists must change one or more assumptions. The revised model more accurately represents the natural world.

Sometimes scientists make assumptions to simplify the model. A scientist who wants to study how energy flows through a certain environment might use a model called a food chain. A food chain is a series of diagrams that shows what animals eat in a certain environment. For example, in a savanna, or grassy plain, a lion eats zebras and many other animals. Zebras eat grass. But the model may assume that lions eat only zebras. So the process that is shown in the model is somewhat simpler than the process that takes place in the natural world. Yet the model still accurately shows the relationship between the parts of the system. A food web, which you can draw in **Figure 5,** is a slightly more complex model of how energy flows through an environment.

8.NS.8, 8.NS.11

FIGURE 5 ·······················

Food Webs
Scientists use food webs to model how energy flows through a particular environment. In a food web, lines connect organisms that eat other organisms. For any two organisms, the organism that eats the other is always shown higher up on the food web. ✎ **Analyze Models and Systems** Construct a food web based on the images in the Picture Bank below. (*Hint:* Zebras and giraffes eat grass or leaves. Lions eat zebras and giraffes. Vultures eat lions, zebras, and giraffes.) Then answer the questions on the next page.

✏️ **Infer** What are the assumptions of this model?

_____
_____
_____
_____
_____

CHALLENGE How could you test this model to see if your assumptions are correct?

_____
_____
_____
_____
_____
_____

 Do the Lab Investigation
Selecting Models.

🔑 Assess Your Understanding

2a. Review Scientists check _____ by comparing the inputs and outputs of a model to inputs and outputs of a natural system.

8.NS.8

b. Explain A certain astronomer assumes that a planet must have water to support life. How does the astronomer's assumption help the astronomer search for life in the universe?

_____
_____
_____
_____
_____

8.NS.8

c. Predict What might make the astronomer change the assumption made in the previous question?

_____
_____
_____
_____
_____

8.NS.8

got it? ·····························

○ **I get it!** Now I know models help scientists understand natural systems by allowing scientists to test _____

_____
_____

and compare them to those of the natural world.

○ **I need extra help with** _____

Go to MY SCIENCE COACH *online for help with this subject.*

8.NS.8

73

Indiana

Safety in the Science Laboratory

UNLOCK THE BIG ?

🔑 **Why Prepare for a Scientific Investigation?**
8.NS.2, 8.NS.3

🔑 **What Should You Do if an Accident Occurs?**
8.NS.2, 8.NS.3

MY PLANET DIARY
for Indiana

Posted by: Rachel

Location: Monrovia, Indiana

Using laboratory safety is always key. My class was studying the formation of crystals, and my science teacher had us make our own! The crystals were poisonous and had to be made carefully. Our teacher said the ingredients of the crystals could be fatal. We wore goggles and aprons to protect ourselves from harmful chemicals. Listen to your teacher and follow rules.

Lab zone® Do the Inquiry Warm-Up *Can You Name the Safety Equipment?*

BLOG

Write your answer to the question on the lines below.
What are some steps you can take to create a safe lab environment?

_____

_____

_____

▶ **PLANET DIARY** Go to **Planet Diary** to learn more about lab safety.

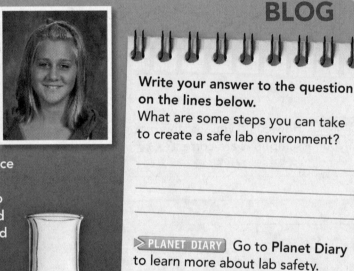

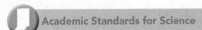
Academic Standards for Science

8.NS.2 Plan and carry out investigations as a class, in small groups, or independently often over a period of several class lessons.
8.NS.3 Collect quantitative data with appropriate tools or technologies and use appropriate units to label numerical data.

Why Prepare for a Scientific Investigation?

How do you prepare for a long trip? You probably find and reserve a place to stay weeks or months in advance. A few days before your trip, you begin to pack. You check the area's weather forecast and use the information to choose the appropriate clothes. After you make these preparations, you are ready to relax and enjoy your trip.

Vocabulary
- field

Skills
- Reading: Sequence
- Inquiry: Observe

Preparing for an Investigation Good preparation helps you have a safe, enjoyable trip. It can also help you perform a successful scientific investigation. 🔑 **Good preparation helps to keep you and your classmates safe when you perform a scientific investigation. It also keeps any living things you use safe.** To prepare for an investigation, read the procedures carefully. If you do not understand any part of the investigation, ask your teacher questions before you start. Make sure you know where all the safety equipment is located in the laboratory.

Working Safely in the Field Although you will do many of your investigations in the laboratory, you may do some investigations in the field. The **field** is any area outside a science laboratory. The field may be a nearby forest, park, or beach. Good preparation is important in the field because there are additional safety hazards, such as wild animals, poisonous plants, or severe weather, that you may encounter. Wear appropriate clothing, including hats and sunglasses, and bring appropriate equipment, such as gloves and safety goggles. Treat plants and animals with proper care and respect. Always work in the field with another person and an adult.

apply it!

These students are working in the field.

1 ⚠ **Observe** What clothing items protect these students?

_____

_____

_____

2 [CHALLENGE] Suppose the students are caught in a sudden rainstorm. How can they stay safe during the storm?

8.NS.2, 8.NS.3

Conducting the Investigation Safely

Whenever you perform a scientific investigation, your primary concern should be your safety and the safety of others. Keep in mind this rule: *Always follow your teacher's instructions and the directions exactly.* If you have an idea that you would like to try, ask your teacher before doing it.

There are certain safety measures you should take before, during, and after an investigation. Before you do any investigation, first make sure you know its safety symbols. Safety symbols alert you to possible sources of accidents in the investigation. Familiarize yourself with any equipment you will be using. Then, clean and organize your work area. Finally, label any containers you will be using. Look at **Figure 1** to see safety symbols and learn ways to be safe during and after a scientific investigation.

FIGURE 1 ⋯⋯⋯⋯⋯⋯⋯⋯⋯⋯⋯⋯⋯⋯⋯⋯⋯
Safety in the Laboratory
To be safe, there are a number of things you should do during and after a scientific investigation.

✎ **Relate Text and Visuals** For each scene shown, circle any safety equipment the students are using. Then, write in the boxes the names of four safety symbols that apply to that investigation.

During the investigation:

- Wear safety goggles to protect your eyes from chemical splashes, glass breakage, and sharp objects.
- Wear an apron to protect yourself and your clothes from chemicals.
- Wear heat-resistant gloves when handling hot objects.
- Wear plastic gloves to protect your skin when handling animals, plants, or chemicals.
- Handle live animals and plants with care.

After the investigation:
- Clean up your work area.
- Turn off and unplug any equipment, and return it to its proper place.
- Dispose of any wastes properly.
- Wash your hands thoroughly.

Safety Symbols

Animal safety	Disposal	Breakage	Heat-Resistant Gloves	Plastic Gloves	Corrosive chemical	Sharp Object	Safety Goggles	Plant safety	Lab Apron	Hand Washing	Flames

Caring for Plants and Animals Properly
When you are performing an investigation in the field, you are very likely to encounter plants and animals there. You may also work with plants and animals in the laboratory. Whether you are in the laboratory or in the field, you should treat living things with care and respect. Follow the animal care instructions listed in **Figure 2** when you are working with animals in the laboratory.

FIGURE 2 ·····························
Animal Care
You must treat the animals you use in an investigation properly and humanely.

✎ **Interpret Photos** **What information should you know about this turtle to care for it properly?**

_____

_____

_____

_____

_____

8.NS.2

Proper Animal Care
- Provide animals with enough space in their cage or terrarium.
- Provide proper food and clean drinking water.
- Clean the cages or terrariums regularly.
- Handle animals with care.

Lab zone® Do the Quick Lab
Be Prepared to Be Safe in the Field.

🔑 Assess Your Understanding

1a. Identify Give one safety practice you should always use at each stage of an investigation.

_____

_____

_____

8.NS.2, 8.NS.3

b. Infer What safety symbols would you expect to see in an investigation using animals?

_____

_____

8.NS.2, 8.NS.3

got it? ···

○ **I get it!** Now I know that I should prepare for a scientific investigation because _____

○ I need extra help with _____

Go to **MY SCIENCE ⬤ᔆ COACH** *online for help with this subject.*

8.NS.2, 8.NS.3

What Should You Do If an Accident Occurs?

Even with careful preparation, sometimes accidents occur during an investigation. In the event of an accident, what should you do? **Always alert your teacher first. Then follow your teacher's directions, and carry them out quickly.** If your teacher is not available, then find and alert the nearest adult. Familiarize yourself with the location and the proper use of all the emergency equipment in your laboratory. You can use some of the equipment shown in **Figure 3.** Knowing safety and first-aid procedures beforehand will prepare you to handle accidents properly.

Academic Standards for Science

8.NS.2 Plan, carry out investigations as a class, in small groups, or independently.

8.NS.3 Collect quantitative data and use appropriate units to label numerical data.

Sequence Underline the steps you should take when an accident occurs.

FIGURE 3 ·····

Emergency Equipment

8.NS.2

Use the emergency equipment shown in case of a fire or an injury.

Identify In each box, write how the equipment can help you in an emergency.

Lab zone® Do the Quick Lab *How Would You Respond to These Emergencies?*

Assess Your Understanding

got it? ·····

O **I get it!** Now I know that in case of an accident I should _____

_____

_____

_____

O **I need extra help with** _____

Go to MY SCIENCE COACH online for help with this subject.   8.NS.2, 8.NS.3

2 Study Guide

Scientists use _____ to communicate how precise their measurements are.

LESSON 1 Scientific Measurement

8.NS.1, 8.NS.3, 8.NS.5, 8.NS.8, 8.NS.9

🔑 The SI system allows scientists to compare data and communicate with each other about the results of scientific investigations.

🔑 SI units for length, mass, weight, volume, density, time, and temperature include meters, kilograms, newtons, cubic meters, kilograms per cubic meter, seconds, and kelvins.

Vocabulary
- metric system • International System of Units (SI)
- mass • weight • volume • meniscus • density

LESSON 2 Mathematics and Scientific Thinking

8.NS.3, 8.NS.5, 8.NS.6, 8.NS.8, 8.NS.9, 8.NS.10, 8.NS.11, 8.DP.9

🔑 Scientists use math skills that include estimation, accuracy and precision, and significant figures.

🔑 Scientists use math tools including mean, median, mode, range, and percent error.

Vocabulary
- estimate • accuracy • precision
- significant figures • mean • median • mode
- range • anomalous data • percent error

LESSON 3 Using Graphs in Science

8.NS.8, 8.NS.11, 8.DP.9

🔑 Scientists use graphs to identify trends, make predictions, and recognize anomalous data.

Vocabulary
- graph
- linear graph
- nonlinear graph
- outlier

LESSON 4 Models and Systems

8.NS.1, 8.NS.7, 8.NS.8, 8.NS.11

🔑 Scientists use models to test their ideas about things they cannot observe directly.

🔑 All systems have input, process, and output.

🔑 Scientists build models to represent a process. They test whether the input and output from the model match the input and output of the system in the natural world.

Vocabulary
- model • system • input • process • output
- feedback

LESSON 5 Safety in the Science Laboratory

8.NS.2, 8.NS.3

🔑 Good preparation helps to keep you and your classmates safe when you perform a scientific investigation. It also keeps any living things you use safe.

🔑 In the event of an accident, always alert your teacher first. Then follow your teacher's directions, and carry them out quickly.

Vocabulary
- field

Review and Assessment

LESSON 1 **Scientific Measurement**

1. A newton is the SI unit for

   a. mass.   **b.** density.

   c. volume.   **d.** weight.

8.NS.3

2. The SI system of measurement is based on the

_____

8.NS.3

3. Calculate Find the volume of the object at the right. Explain your method.

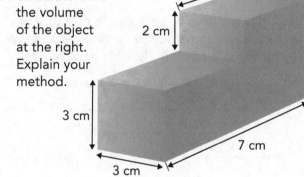

_____

_____

_____

_____

8.NS.3, 8.NS.5

4. Apply Concepts Will an object with a volume of 77 grams per cubic centimeter and a mass of 65 grams float or sink in water? Explain.

_____

_____

8.NS.3, 8.NS.5, 8.NS.8

5. ✏️ Write About It Your friend sends you an e-mail about an experiment that she read about. She mentions that the results from the experiment work best at −2 K. Write an e-mail back to your friend explaining why she must be mistaken about the temperature.

8.NS.3, 8.NS.5

LESSON 2 **Mathematics and Scientific Thinking**

6. How close a measurement is to its true or accepted value is

   a. accuracy.   **b.** estimation.

   c. precision.   **d.** range.

8.NS.5

7. Nineteen is the _____ for the data set 25, 19, 18, 31, 19, 22.

8.NS.8

8. Interpret Data How many significant figures are in the measurement 230 kg?

_____

8.NS.5

9. Calculate You measure the mass of a model car to be 230 grams. The actual mass is 218 grams. What is your percent error?

_____

_____

8.NS.8

Use the table below to answer Question 10.

Month and Year	Number of Ducks
Nov. 2009	356,000
Dec. 2009	656,000
Jan. 2010	976,000

10. Interpret Tables The table shows the estimated number of ducks counted in an area over several months. Why are the counts only estimates?

_____

_____

_____

_____

_____

_____

8.NS.5, 8.NS.8, 8.NS.9, 8.NS.11

LESSON 3 Using Graphs in Science

11. Anomalous data shows on a graph as a(n)

   a. nonlinear graph.   **b.** trend.

   c. linear graph.   **d.** outlier.

                           8.NS.8, 8.NS.9

12. In a linear graph, data points fall along a(n)

_____

                                 8.NS.8

13. **math!** Plot a line graph using this data table from a summer science camp. Determine if the graph is linear or nonlinear and label any outliers.

Year	Number of Campers
1	52
2	60
3	63
4	41
5	70

                             8.NS.8, 8.NS.11

LESSON 4 Models and Systems

14. A model is any representation of an object or

   a. an opinion.   **b.** a process.

   c. an investigation.   **d.** data.

                         8.NS.8, 8.NS.11

15. A system is a group of parts that work

together to _____.

                         8.NS.8, 8.NS.11

16. Explain Meteorologists use models to help them predict the weather, but their predictions are not always correct. Explain why this is so.

_____

_____

_____

_____

_____

                         8.NS.8, 8.NS.11

LESSON 5 Safety in the Science Laboratory

17. What safety equipment should you use when you handle live animals?

   a. sunglasses   **b.** heat-resistant gloves

   c. plastic container   **d.** plastic gloves

                         8.NS.2

18. You should always work in the _____ with another person or adult.

                         8.NS.2

19. Infer You have volunteered to take care of your classroom's mouse for the week. To care for the mouse properly, what must you do?

_____

_____

_____

_____

                         8.NS.2

APPLY THE BIG ? How do scientists use measurement and mathematics?

20. Suppose a scientist wants to measure the lengths of twenty queen bees from twenty different hives. How would the scientist find the mean of the data set? Why might the scientist choose to compare the queens' lengths in a bar graph?

_____

_____

_____

_____

_____

_____

           8.NS.2, 8.NS.3, 8.NS.8, 8.NS.11

Indiana ISTEP+ Practice

Multiple Choice

Mark only one answer for each question.

1. What might be one reason scientists would build a model of Earth like the one shown here?

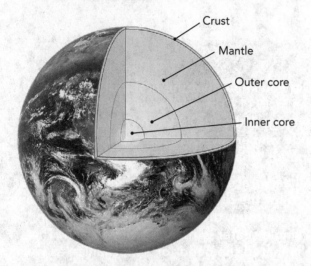

   Crust

   Mantle

   Outer core

   Inner core

   A. to show the color of the continents
   B. to show the depths of Earth's oceans
   C. to show the layers of Earth
   D. to show pressure inside Earth

   8.NS.8, 8.NS.11

2. Nicole measured the height of her locker as 39.8 cm, 42.3 cm, 42.0 cm, and 43.1 cm. The locker is actually 45.5 cm. Which **best** describes Nicole's measurements?

   A. They were accurate.
   B. They were precise.
   C. They were both accurate and precise.
   D. They were neither accurate nor precise.

   8.NS.5

3. Which SI unit would you use to measure the volume of a tomato?

   A. gram
   B. grams per cubic meter
   C. cubic centimeter
   D. newton

   8.NS.3

4. What is the median for the data set 32, 40, 38, 41, 36?

   A. 9
   B. 38
   C. 93.5
   D. 187

   8.NS.8

Constructed Response

Write your answer to Question 5 on the lines below.

5. Suppose you are cleaning up after a scientific investigation in the laboratory. As you are cleaning a glass container, it slips from your hands and breaks in the sink. What should you do?

   _____

   _____

   _____

   _____

   8.NS.2

Extended Response

Use the graph below to answer Question 6.

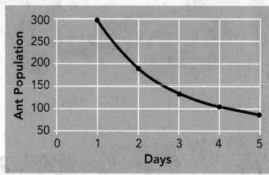

6. What kind of trend do the data show? Predict what the ant population will be at 6 days. Explain your prediction.

   8.NS.8, 8.NS.11

THE RACE TO BE FASTER

Did you know that the first Indianapolis 500 ran in 1911? The winner of the first race only averaged about 120 km/h (75 mph). Today Indy winners average more than twice that speed! What changed in all that time?

All early racecars were two-seaters. One seat was for the driver and one was for a mechanic. Ray Harroun, the winner in 1911, raced in a single-seater with a rear-view mirror. This eliminated the need for a mechanic—as well as the additional weight!

As technology progressed, the engines and exteriors of cars were manufactured from lightweight metal alloys and polymers. Engines became smaller, lighter, and more powerful. The cars became more aerodynamic. New designs decreased the resistance from air when traveling at high speeds, called drag. Race cars also switched fuels from gasoline to ethanol, allowing for smaller gas tanks. These modifications made the cars faster—and the races more exciting!

Design It Design a toy race car that is built for speed. Brainstorm potential design solutions. Document your ideas with labeled drawings and choose the best design. Build a prototype and measure how fast the car can travel on a set course without pushing it. Present your data using graphs or tables. Using this information, redesign your prototype to make the car faster. See Appendix A on page 508 for more information about the design process.

8.NS.1–8.NS.11, 8.DP.1–8.DP.11

AQUANAUTS

Science has sent people to the moon and robots to Mars. But vast amounts of Earth's surface—the parts that are deep underwater—remain unexplored.

Aquarius, the world's first underwater research station, is located more than 18 meters below the ocean's surface off the southern tip of Florida. The scientists and crew who work in *Aquarius* are called aquanauts.

Aquanauts are marine biologists and oceanographers. While on board *Aquarius*, the aquanauts may study nearby coral reefs or test new technology for marine exploration. *Aquarius* has allowed scientists to study and observe undersea life in ways that were previously impossible. Aquanaut missions are also helping the National Aeronautics and Space Administration (NASA). Because the undersea habitat is similar to a space station, NASA uses *Aquarius* to explore the challenges of living in space.

Design It Find out more about *Aquarius* and the missions it supports. Then write a news article to tell the public about the underwater research station, its missions, and the people who work on it. Remember to write an attention-grabbing headline and exciting lead paragraph.

8.NS.2, 8.NS.11

Warm and dry inside Aquarius, an aquanaut looks out at the ocean. ▼

HOW
WOULD
YOU
SORT OUT
THIS MESS?

How is the periodic table organized?

Maybe you know someone with a messy room like this one. Imagine how difficult it would be to find things that you need. For example, what if you had misplaced your homework in this room? Where would you look for it? You might have to search for a long, long time! **Classify** **If this were your room, how would you organize the things inside it?**

_____

_____

_____

_____

_____

_____

> **UNTAMED SCIENCE** Watch the **Untamed Science** video to learn more about organizing matter.

Elements and the Periodic Table

Academic Standards for Science

8.1.1, 8.1.2, 8.1.3, 8.1.4, 8.1.6, 8.4.1, 8.4.3,
8.NS.1, 8.NS.2, 8.NS.8, 8.NS.10, 8.NS.11

3 Getting Started

Check Your Understanding

1. Background Read the paragraph below and then answer the question.

Katherine and her family are having a barbecue. They are burning charcoal in the grill to provide heat to cook their food. Charcoal is one form of the element carbon. As the charcoal burns, it reacts with oxygen molecules in the air. Each oxygen molecule contains two atoms.

An **element** is a pure substance that cannot be broken down into any other substances by chemical or physical means.

A **molecule** is a group of two or more atoms held together by chemical bonds.

An **atom** is the basic particle from which all elements are made.

• How can oxygen be both an element and a molecule?

_____

_____

> MY READING WEB If you had trouble completing the question above, visit **My Reading Web** and type in *Elements and the Periodic Table.*

Vocabulary Skill

Greek Word Origins Many science words in English come from Greek. For example, the word *autograph* comes from the Greek words *auto,* meaning "self," and *graph,* meaning "written." An *autograph* is one's name written in one's own handwriting. Look at the Greek origins and their meanings below.

Greek Origin	Meaning	Key Words
atomos	Cannot be cut, indivisible	Atom, atomic number, atomic mass
di	Two, double	Diatomic molecule

2. Quick Check Predict the meaning of *diatomic molecule.*

_____

_____

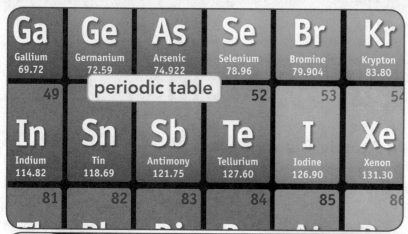

periodic table

Ga	Ge	As	Se	Br	Kr
Gallium 69.72	Germanium 72.59	Arsenic 74.922	Selenium 78.96	Bromine 79.904	Krypton 83.80
49		52	53		54
In	Sn	Sb	Te	I	Xe
Indium 114.82	Tin 118.69	Antimony 121.75	Tellurium 127.60	Iodine 126.90	Xenon 131.30
81	82	83	84	85	86

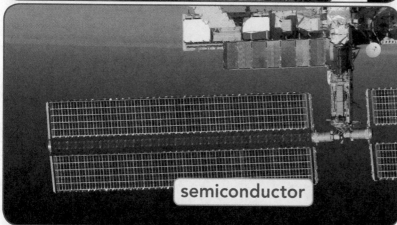

corrosion

semiconductor

noble gas

Chapter Preview

LESSON 1

- atom • electron • nucleus
- proton • energy level
- neutron • atomic number
- isotope • mass number

↻ **Compare and Contrast**

△ **Make Models**

LESSON 2

- atomic mass • periodic table
- chemical symbol • period
- group

↻ **Relate Text and Visuals**

△ **Predict**

LESSON 3

- metal • luster • malleable
- ductile • thermal conductivity
- electrical conductivity • reactivity
- corrosion • alkali metal
- alkaline earth metal
- transition metal

↻ **Ask Questions**

△ **Infer**

LESSON 4

- nonmetal • diatomic molecule
- halogen • noble gas • metalloid
- semiconductor

↻ **Summarize**

△ **Classify**

▸ **VOCAB FLASH CARDS** For extra help with vocabulary, visit **Vocab Flash Cards** and type in *Elements and the Periodic Table.*

Introduction to Atoms

UNLOCK THE BIG ?

🔑 **How Did Atomic Theory Develop?**
8.1.4, 8.NS.1, 8.NS.8, 8.NS.10

🔑 **What Is the Modern Model of the Atom?**
8.1.4, 8.4.1

MY PLANET DIARY

DISCOVERY

Nanowhiskers

What's more than 16,000 times thinner than a human hair, and, when added to fabric, able to repel spills, stains, and the smell of the sweatiest of socks? It's a nanowhisker!

Nanowhiskers are tiny threads that measure about 10 nanometers (nm) in length and 1.5 nanometers in diameter (1 nm equals 0.000000001 m). They are often made of carbon or silver atoms. Scientists have found a way to bond nanowhiskers to individual threads of cloth. The nanowhiskers are so small and so close together that they form a barrier that prevents substances from ever touching the fabric. Nanowhiskers made from silver can even kill bacteria on your feet and stop socks from smelling!

Communicate Write your answer to each question below. Then discuss your answers with a partner.

1. Why are nanowhiskers used to repel stains on fabrics?

_____
_____
_____
_____
_____
_____

2. What uses for nanowhiskers can you imagine?

_____
_____

> PLANET DIARY Go to **Planet Diary** to learn more about atomic structure.

Lab zone® Do the Inquiry Warm-Up *What's in the Box?*

Vocabulary

- atom • electron • nucleus • proton • energy level
- neutron • atomic number • isotope • mass number

Skills

↻ Reading: Compare and Contrast
△ Inquiry: Make Models

How Did Atomic Theory Develop?

If you could see a single atom, what would it look like? Studying atoms is difficult because atoms are so small. The smallest visible speck of dust may contain 10 million billion atoms! Scientists have created models to describe atoms because they are so small. Models of the atom have changed many times.

Around 430 B.C., the Greek philosopher Democritus proposed that matter was formed of small pieces that could not be cut into smaller parts. He used the word *atomos,* meaning "uncuttable," for these smallest possible pieces. In modern terms, an **atom** is the smallest particle that still can be considered an element.

The idea of atoms began to develop again in the 1600s. As people did experiments, atomic theory began to take shape. **⚷ Atomic theory grew as a series of models that developed from experimental evidence. As more evidence was collected, the theory and models were revised.**

Dalton's Atomic Theory Using evidence from many experiments, John Dalton, an English chemist, inferred that atoms had certain characteristics. Dalton thought that atoms were like smooth, hard balls that could not be broken into smaller pieces. The main ideas of Dalton's theory are summarized in **Figure 1.**

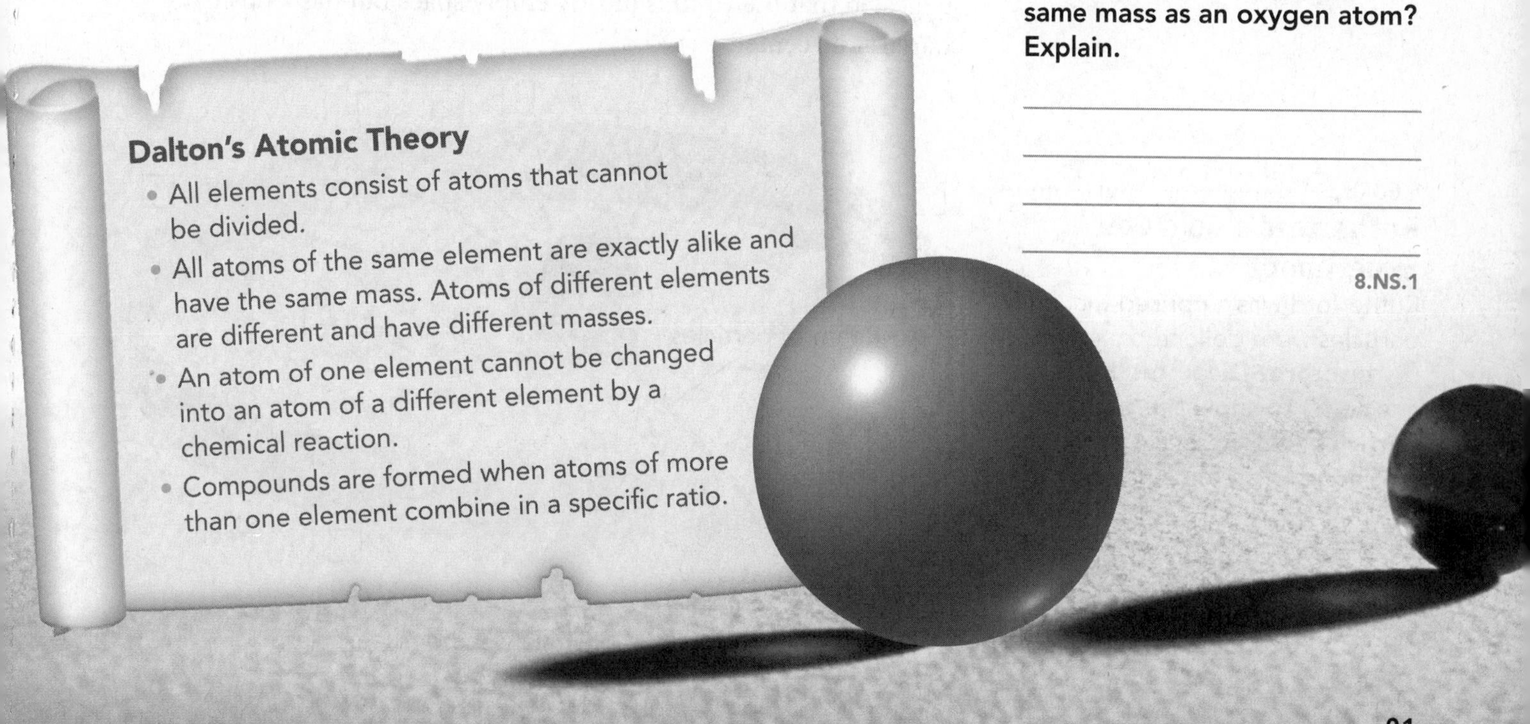

Dalton's Atomic Theory

- All elements consist of atoms that cannot be divided.
- All atoms of the same element are exactly alike and have the same mass. Atoms of different elements are different and have different masses.
- An atom of one element cannot be changed into an atom of a different element by a chemical reaction.
- Compounds are formed when atoms of more than one element combine in a specific ratio.

ⓘ Academic Standards for Science

8.1.4 Describe the structure of an atom and relate the arrangement of electrons to how that atom interacts with other atoms.

8.NS.1 Make predictions and develop testable questions based on research and prior knowledge.

8.NS.8 Analyze data.

8.NS.10 Compare the results of an experiment with the prediction.

FIGURE 1 ·····························

Dalton's Model

Dalton thought that atoms were smooth, hard balls.

✎ **Predict** Read the summary of Dalton's theory. Based on this theory, would you expect a carbon atom to have the same mass as an oxygen atom? Explain.

_____

_____

_____

_____

8.NS.1

Thomson's Model

Dalton's atomic theory has some similarities to today's models, but there are many differences. One important change is that atoms are now known to be made of even smaller parts. In 1897, J.J. Thomson discovered that atoms contain negatively charged particles called **electrons.** Yet scientists knew that atoms themselves had no electrical charge. So Thomson reasoned that atoms must also contain some sort of positive charge. This positive charge must balance the negative charge of the electrons.

Thomson proposed a model like the one shown in **Figure 2.** He described an atom that had electrons scattered throughout a ball of positive charge—something like seeds in a watermelon.

Rutherford's Model

In 1911, one of Thomson's former students, Ernest Rutherford, found evidence that challenged Thomson's model. Rutherford's research team aimed a beam of positively charged particles at a thin sheet of gold foil. A diagram of the experiment is shown in **Figure 3.** Rutherford and his team predicted that, if Thomson's model were correct, the charged particles would pass straight through the foil. They also predicted that the paths of some particles would bend, or deflect, slightly. The particles would be only slightly deflected because the positive charge was thought to be spread out in the gold atoms.

Rutherford observed that most of the particles passed straight through the foil with little or no deflection. But to everyone's surprise, a few particles were deflected by the gold foil at very large angles. Based on the results of his experiment, Rutherford suggested that the atom is mostly empty space but has a positive charge at its center.

FIGURE 2 ·····························
Thomson's Model
Thomson suggested that atoms had negatively charged electrons set in a positive sphere. Each electron is represented above by the symbol e⁻.

FIGURE 3 ·····························
Rutherford's Gold Foil Experiment
Rutherford was surprised that a few particles were deflected strongly.
✎ **Interpret Diagrams Place a check (✔) to show the paths of the particles that were not predicted by Thomson's atomic model.** 8.NS.8

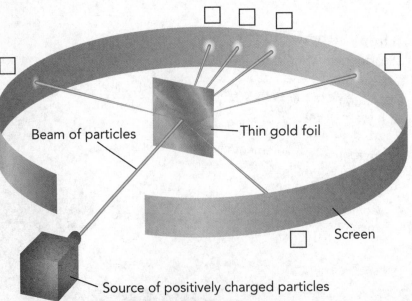

Beam of particles

Thin gold foil

Screen

Source of positively charged particles

Like charges repel each other. So Rutherford inferred that an atom's positive charge must be packed within a small region in its center, called the **nucleus** (NOO klee us). (The plural of *nucleus* is *nuclei*.) Any particle that was deflected strongly had been repelled by a gold atom's nucleus. Rutherford's new model of the atom, which is shown in **Figure 4,** is like a cherry. The pit models the nucleus of the atom. The rest of the fruit is the space taken up by the electrons. Later research suggested that the nucleus was made up of one or more positively charged particles. Rutherford called the positively charged particles in an atom's nucleus **protons.**

FIGURE 4 ....
Rutherford's Model
According to Rutherford's model, an atom was mostly open space. The "6+" in the model means that there are six protons in the nucleus.

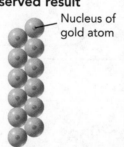

apply it!

Use the diagrams below to compare the expected and observed results of Rutherford's gold foil experiment. Part **a** shows the expected paths of the charged particles through the atoms of the gold foil. In part **b**, draw the observed paths of the charged particles. Show at least one particle that is deflected strongly. **8.NS.10**

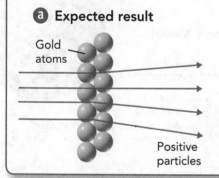

a Expected result

Gold atoms

Positive particles

b Observed result

Nucleus of gold atom

Bohr's Model One of Rutherford's students was Niels Bohr, a Danish scientist. In 1913, Bohr revised the atomic model again. Bohr suggested that electrons are found only in specific orbits around the nucleus. The orbits in Bohr's model look like planets orbiting the sun or the rings of a tree, as shown in **Figure 5.** Each possible electron orbit in Bohr's model has a fixed energy.

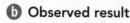

FIGURE 5 ....
Bohr's Model
Niels Bohr suggested that electrons move in specific orbits around the nucleus of an atom.

6+

6e⁻

Cloud Model In the 1920s, the atomic model changed again. Scientists determined that electrons do not orbit the nucleus like planets, as Bohr suggested. Instead, electrons move rapidly within a cloudlike region around the nucleus. Look at **Figure 6.** The orange "cloud" is a visual model. It represents where electrons are likely to be found. An electron's movement is related to its **energy level,** or the specific amount of energy it has. Electrons at different energy levels are likely to be found in different places.

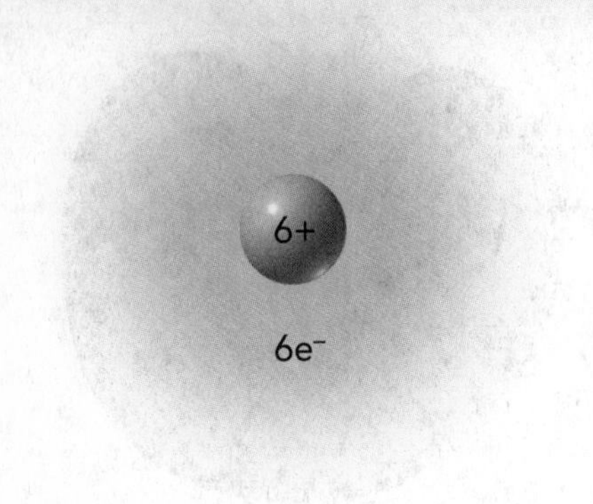

FIGURE 6 ·····························
Cloud Model
Electrons move rapidly in different directions around the nucleus.

apply it!

Scientists have used models to help them understand atoms. You can too!

❶ **Make Models** Match each object with the atomic model the object most closely represents.

❷ **CHALLENGE** An object is missing for one of the atomic models listed. In the space provided, draw an object that represents this model.   **8.NS.8**

Dalton's Model

Thomson's Model

Bohr's Model

Cloud Model

Lab zone ® Do the Quick Lab *Visualizing an Electron Cloud.*

🔑 Assess Your Understanding

1a. Define An atom is _____
_____.
    8.1.4

b. Describe Bohr's model of the atom consisted
of a central _____ surrounded by
electrons moving in specific _____.
    8.1.4

c. 🔄 **Compare and Contrast** How is the cloud model of the atom different from Bohr's model?

_____
_____
_____
_____
_____
    8.1.4

got it? ·······························

○ **I get it!** Now I know that atomic theory changed with time because _____
_____

○ **I need extra help with** _____

    Go to **MY SCIENCE** ⑤ **COACH** *online for help with this subject.*   8.1.4

What Is the Modern Model of the Atom?

In 1932, English scientist James Chadwick showed that another particle exists in the nucleus of atoms. This particle, called a **neutron,** was hard to find because it has no electric charge.

Scientists have learned more about the atom since then. One modern model of the atom is shown in **Figure 7.** 🔑 **At the center of the atom is a tiny, dense nucleus containing protons and neutrons. Surrounding the nucleus is a cloudlike region of moving electrons.**

Most of an atom's volume is the space in which the electrons move. This space is huge compared to the space taken up by the nucleus. Imagine holding a pencil while standing in the middle of a stadium. If the nucleus were the size of the pencil's eraser, the electrons would reach as far away as the top row of seats!

New research supports the modern model of the atom. However, scientists still don't know the details of the smallest scales of matter. Who will develop the next model of the atom? Maybe it will be you!

Academic Standards for Science

8.1.4 Describe the structure of an atom and relate the arrangement of electrons to how that atom interacts with other atoms.

8.4.1 Understand how the strength of attractive forces between particles helps to explain many physical properties of the material.

FIGURE 7 ·······························

Modern Model of an Atom

A carbon atom has a nucleus made up of positively charged protons and neutral neutrons. The nucleus is surrounded by a cloud of negatively charged electrons.

✎ **Identify** How many protons are in the carbon atom?

_____

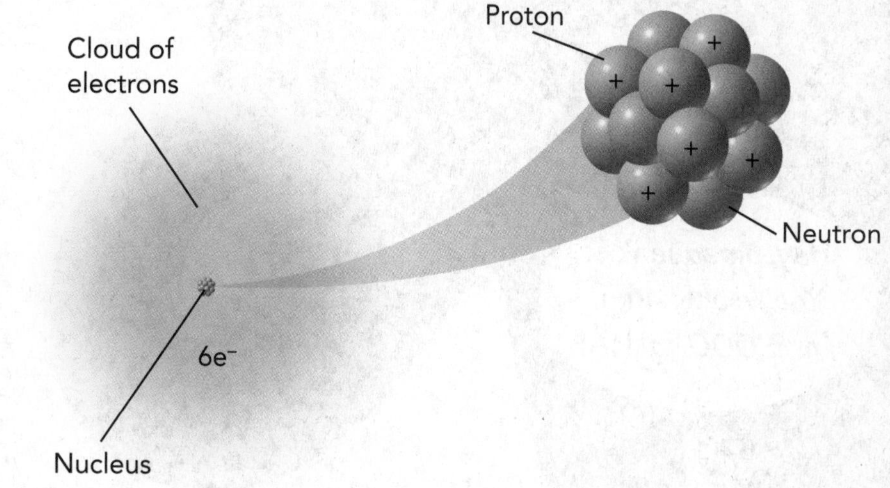

Cloud of electrons

Proton

Neutron

$6e^-$

Nucleus

Particle Charges

In **Figure 7,** protons are shown by a plus sign (+). Electrons are shown by the symbol e^-. According to the scale used for measuring charge in atoms, protons have a charge of +1. Electrons have exactly the opposite charge. So electrons have a charge of −1. If you count the number of protons in **Figure 7,** you'll see there are six. The number of protons equals the number of electrons. As a result, the positive charge from the protons equals the negative charge from the electrons. The charges balance, making the atom neutral. Neutrons don't affect the charge of an atom because they have a charge of zero.

·············· ✎ ··············

🔄 **Compare and Contrast**

A proton has a charge of _____.

An electron has a charge

of _____.

A neutron has a charge

of _____.

Comparing Particle Masses Although electrons may balance protons charge for charge, they can't compare when it comes to mass. It takes almost 1,840 electrons to equal the mass of one proton. A proton and a neutron are about equal in mass. Together, the protons and neutrons make up almost all the mass of an atom.

Figure 8 compares the charges and masses of the three atomic particles. Atoms are too small to be described by everyday units of mass, such as grams or kilograms. Sometimes scientists use units known as atomic mass units (amu). A proton or a neutron has a mass equal to about one amu.

Atomic Number Every atom of an element has the same number of protons. For example, every carbon atom has 6 protons and every iron atom has 26 protons. The number of protons in the nucleus of an atom is the **atomic number** of that atom's element. The definition of an element is based on its atomic number. Carbon's atomic number is 6 and iron's is 26.

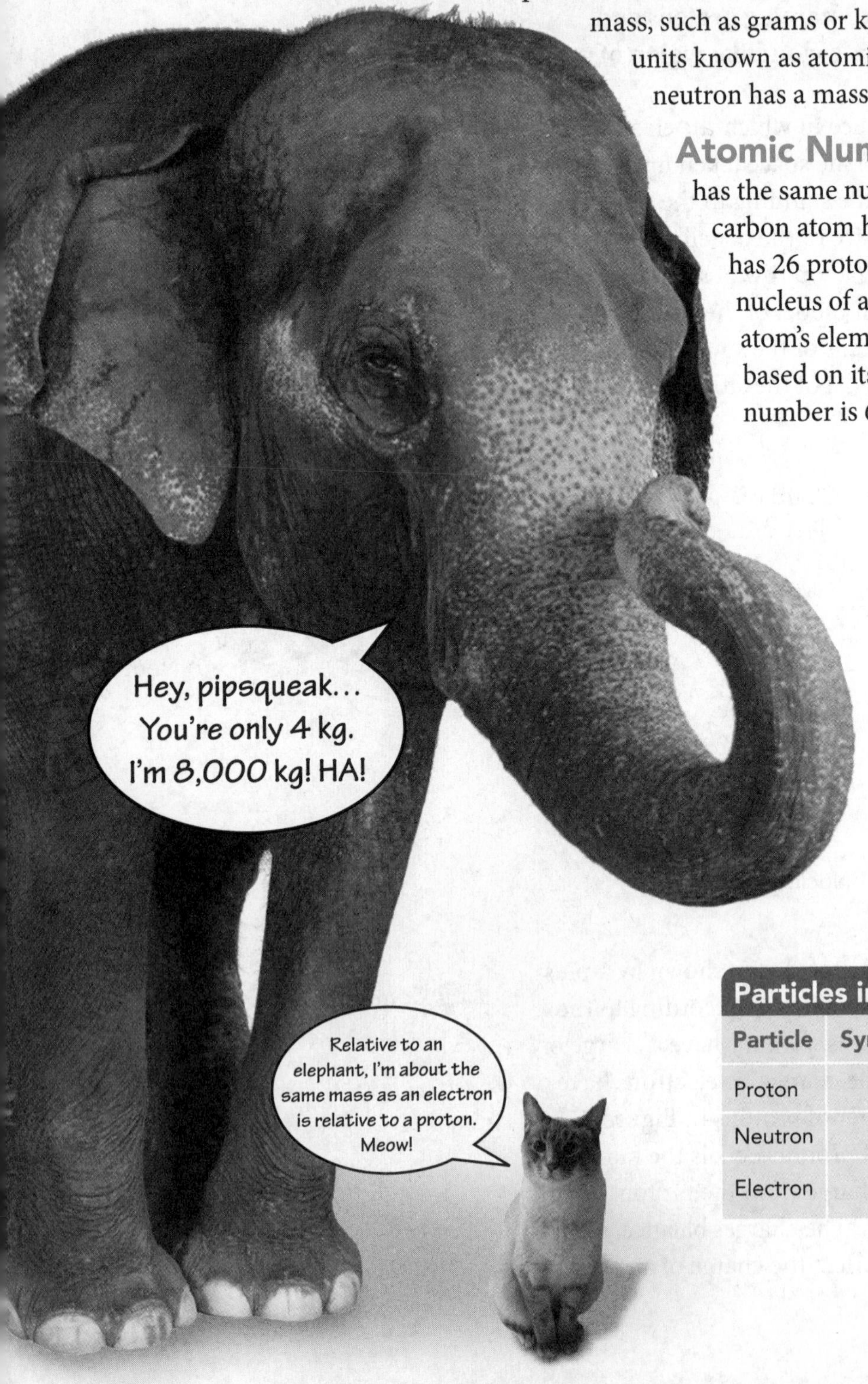

Hey, pipsqueak...
You're only 4 kg.
I'm 8,000 kg! HA!

Relative to an elephant, I'm about the same mass as an electron is relative to a proton. Meow!

FIGURE 8 ·······················

⊳ INTERACTIVE ART **Particles in an Atom**
An atom is made up of protons, neutrons, and electrons.

✎ **Review** Complete the table by filling in the correct charge for each atomic particle.

Particles in an Atom				
Particle	Symbol	Charge	Mass (amu)	Model
Proton	p^+	_____	1	●
Neutron	n	_____	1	●
Electron	e^-	_____	$\frac{1}{1,840}$	●

Isotopes

All atoms of an element have the same number of protons. The number of neutrons can vary. Atoms with the same number of protons and different numbers of neutrons are called **isotopes** (EYE suh tohps). **Figure 9** shows three isotopes of carbon.

An isotope is identified by its **mass number,** which is the sum of the protons and neutrons in the atom. The most common isotope of carbon has a mass number of 12 (6 protons + 6 neutrons) and may be written as "carbon-12." About 99 percent of naturally occurring carbon is carbon-12. Two other isotopes are carbon-13 and carbon-14. Despite their different mass numbers, all three carbon isotopes react the same way chemically.

FIGURE 9 ·······················
Isotopes of Carbon
All isotopes of carbon contain 6 protons. They differ in the number of neutrons.

✎ **Relate Text and Visuals** Fill in the missing information for each isotope below.

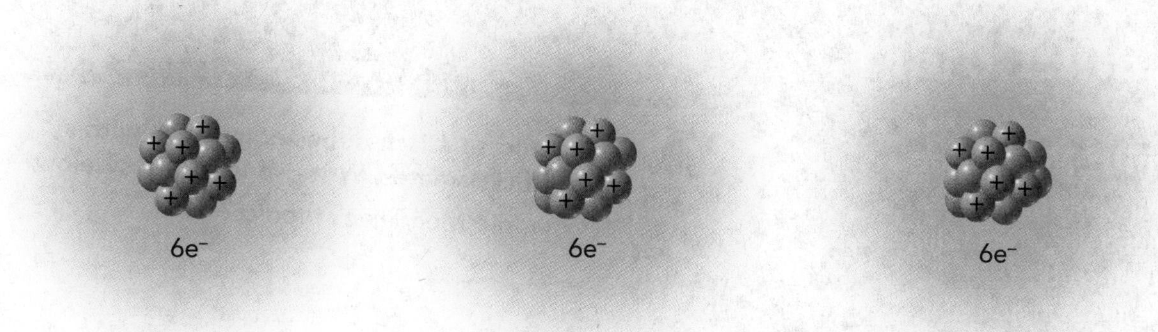

Carbon-12

☐ Protons

6 Neutrons

Carbon-13

6 Protons

☐ Neutrons

Carbon-☐

6 Protons

8 Neutrons

6e⁻ 6e⁻ 6e⁻

Lab zone® Do the Quick Lab
How Far Away Is the Electron?

🔑 Assess Your Understanding

2a. Explain What is atomic number? How is atomic number used to distinguish one element from another?

_____

_____

_____

_____

8.1.4

b. Apply Concepts The atomic number of nitrogen is 7. How many protons, neutrons, and electrons make up an atom of nitrogen-15?

_____

_____

_____

_____

8.1.4

got it? ···

○ **I get it!** Now I know that the modern model of the atom can be described as_____

_____

○ **I need extra help with** _____

Go to MY SCIENCE ⓢ COACH *online for help with this subject.*

8.1.4

Organizing the Elements

🔑 **What Did Mendeleev Discover?**
8.1.2, 8.NS.1, 8.NS.8

🔑 **What Information Does the Periodic Table Contain?**
8.1.2, 8.NS.1, 8.NS.8

🔑 **How Is the Periodic Table Useful?**
8.1.2, 8.1.3, 8.NS.1, 8.NS.8

my PLANET DiARY   VOICES FROM HISTORY

Dmitri Mendeleev

The Russian chemist Dmitri Mendeleev (men duh LAY ef) is given credit for creating the first version of the periodic table in 1869. By arranging the elements according to their atomic masses, he predicted that new elements would be discovered:

> We must expect the discovery of many yet unknown elements—for example, elements analogous [similar] to aluminum and silicon—whose atomic weight [mass] would be between 65 and 75.

Within 17 years, chemists had discovered these missing elements.

Communicate Discuss these questions with a group of classmates. Write your answers below.

1. What did Mendeleev predict?

_____

_____

_____

_____

2. Make a prediction based on an observation or a pattern you recognize.

_____

_____

_____

_____

> PLANET DIARY Go to **Planet Diary** to learn more about the periodic table.

 Lab zone Do the Inquiry Warm-Up *Which Is Easier?*

Academic Standards for Science

8.1.2 Understand that elements are organized on the periodic table based on atomic number.

8.NS.1 Make predictions based on research and prior knowledge.

8.NS.8 Analyze data.

What Did Mendeleev Discover?

By 1869, a total of 63 elements had been discovered. A few were gases. Two were liquids. Most were solid metals. Some reacted explosively as they formed compounds. Others reacted slowly. Scientists wondered if the properties of elements followed a pattern. Dmitri Mendeleev discovered a set of patterns that applied to all the elements.

Vocabulary

- atomic mass • periodic table
- chemical symbol • period
- group

Skills

- ⟳ Reading: Relate Text and Visuals
- △ Inquiry: Predict

Mendeleev's Work Mendeleev knew that some elements had similar chemical and physical properties. For example, silver and copper are both shiny metals. Mendeleev thought these similarities were important clues to a hidden pattern.

To find that pattern, Mendeleev wrote each element's melting point, density, and color on an individual card. He also included the element's atomic mass. The **atomic mass** of an element is the average mass of all the isotopes of that element. Mendeleev tried arranging the cards in different ways.

 Mendeleev noticed that a pattern of properties appeared when he arranged the elements in order of increasing atomic mass. He found that the properties repeated regularly. For example, lithium, sodium, and potassium showed several common properties. As you can see from **Figure 1,** these elements react with water in a similar way. (The letters *amu* mean "atomic mass units.") Mendeleev lined up the cards for these elements to form their own group. He did the same with other elements that shared similar properties.

FIGURE 1 ······························

Metals That React With Water

Lithium, sodium, and potassium all react with water.

✎ **Observe** Write down your observations of each reaction.

8.NS.8

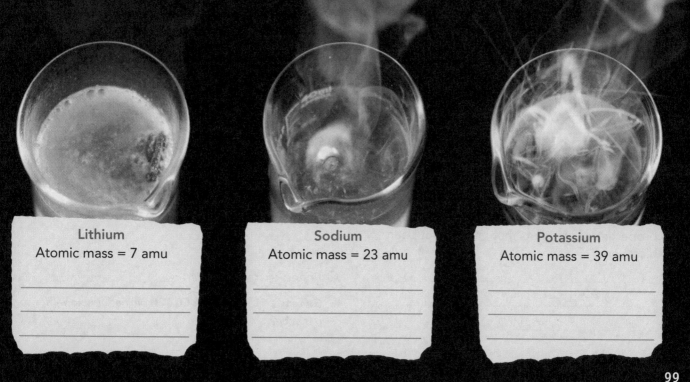

Lithium
Atomic mass = 7 amu

Sodium
Atomic mass = 23 amu

Potassium
Atomic mass = 39 amu

The Periodic Table

Mendeleev created the first periodic table in 1869. A **periodic table** is an arrangement of elements showing the repeating pattern of their properties. (The word *periodic* means "in a regular, repeated pattern.") The periodic table shown in **Figure 2** was an improved version published in 1871.

As scientists discovered new elements and learned more about atomic structure, the periodic table changed. It is now known that the number of protons in the nucleus, given by the atomic number, determines the chemical properties of an element. Modern periodic tables are arranged in order of increasing atomic number.

Group I	Group II	Group III	Group IV	Group V	Group VI	Group VII	Group VIII
H = 1							
Li = 7	Be = 9.4	B = 11	C = 12	N = 14	O = 16	F = 19	
Na = 23, K = 39	Mg = 24, Ca = 40	Al = 27.3, — = 44	Si = 28, Ti = 48	P = 31, V = 51	S = 32, Cr = 52	Cl = 35.5, Mn = 55	Fe = 56, Co = 59, Ni = 59, Cu = 63.
(Cu = 63), Rb = 85	Zn = 65, Sr = 87	— = 68, Yt = 88	— = 72, Zr = 90	As = 75, Nb = 94	Se = 78, Mo = 96	Br = 80, — = 100	Ru = 104, Rh = 104, Pd = 106, Ag = 108.
(Ag = 108), Cs = 133	Cd = 112, Ba = 137	In = 113, Di = 138	Sn = 118, Ce = 140	Sb = 122, —	Te = 125, —	I = 127, —	— — — —
(—), —	—, —	—, Er = 178	—, La = 180	—, Ta = 182	—, W = 184	—, —	Os = 195, Ir = 197, Pt = 198, Au = 199.
(Au = 199), —	Hg = 200	Tl = 204	Pb = 207, Th = 231	Bi = 208, —	U = 240		

FIGURE 2 ·················
Mendeleev's Periodic Table
In his periodic table, Mendeleev left blank spaces. He predicted that the blank spaces would be filled by elements that had not yet been discovered. He even correctly predicted the properties of those new elements.

Lab zone® Do the Quick Lab *Classifying.*

🔑 Assess Your Understanding

1a. Review In what order did Mendeleev arrange the elements in his periodic table?

_____

_____

8.1.2

b. Predict How could Mendeleev predict the properties of elements that had not yet been discovered?

_____

_____

_____

8.1.2

got it? ·····················

○ **I get it!** Now I know that when Mendeleev arranged the elements in order of increasing atomic mass, _____

_____

_____

○ **I need extra help with** _____

Go to **my science ⓢ coach** *online for help with this subject.*
8.1.2

What Information Does the Periodic Table Contain?

The periodic table contains information about each of the known elements. 🗝 **In this book, the periodic table includes the atomic number, chemical symbol, name, and atomic mass for each element.** The information that the periodic table lists about potassium is shown below in **Figure 3**.

❶ Atomic Number The first piece of information is the number 19, the atomic number of potassium. Every potassium atom has 19 protons in its nucleus.

❷ Chemical Symbol Just below the atomic number is the letter K—the **chemical symbol** for potassium. Chemical symbols contain either one or two letters. Often, an element's symbol is an abbreviation of the element's name in English. Other elements have symbols that are abbreviations of their Latin names.

❸ Atomic Mass The last piece of information is the average atomic mass. For potassium, this value is 39.098 amu (atomic mass units). The atomic mass is an average because most elements consist of a mixture of isotopes.

The modern periodic table is shown in **Figure 4** on the next two pages. Can you find potassium?

FIGURE 3 ·······························

Potassium

Potassium has an atomic number of 19 and an atomic mass of 39.098 amu. Bananas are rich in potassium.

Academic Standards for Science

8.1.2 Understand that elements are organized on the periodic table based on atomic mass.

8.NS.1 Make predictions based on research and prior knowledge.

8.NS.8 Analyze data.

apply it!

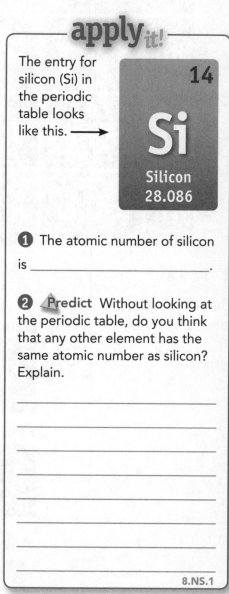

The entry for silicon (Si) in the periodic table looks like this. →

14

Si

Silicon

28.086

❶ The atomic number of silicon is _____.

❷ 🖊 **Predict** Without looking at the periodic table, do you think that any other element has the same atomic number as silicon? Explain.

_____

_____

_____

_____

_____

_____

_____

8.NS.1

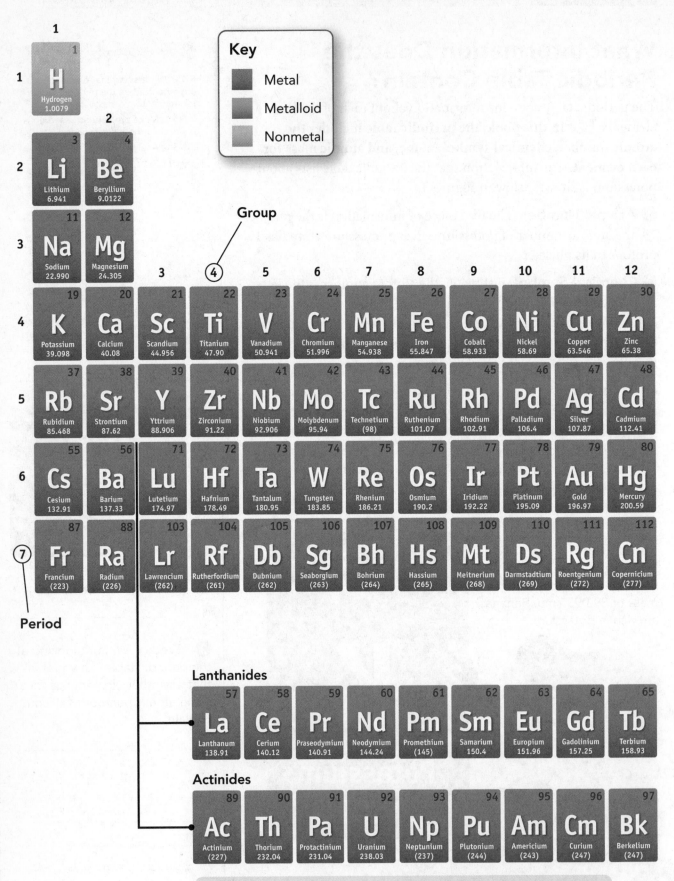

The lanthanides and the actinides are placed off the table to save space and to make the rest of the table easier to read. Follow the line to see how they fit in the table.

Many periodic tables include a zigzag line that separates the metals from the nonmetals. Metalloids, found on either side of the line, share properties of both metals and nonmetals.

18
2 He Helium 4.0026

13	14	15	16	17
5 B Boron 10.81	**6** C Carbon 12.011	**7** N Nitrogen 14.007	**8** O Oxygen 15.999	**9** F Fluorine 18.998	**10** Ne Neon 20.179
13 Al Aluminum 26.982	**14** Si Silicon 28.086	**15** P Phosphorus 30.974	**16** S Sulfur 32.06	**17** Cl Chlorine 35.453	**18** Ar Argon 39.948
31 Ga Gallium 69.72	**32** Ge Germanium 72.59	**33** As Arsenic 74.922	**34** Se Selenium 78.96	**35** Br Bromine 79.904	**36** Kr Krypton 83.80
49 In Indium 114.82	**50** Sn Tin 118.69	**51** Sb Antimony 121.75	**52** Te Tellurium 127.60	**53** I Iodine 126.90	**54** Xe Xenon 131.30
81 Tl Thallium 204.37	**82** Pb Lead 207.2	**83** Bi Bismuth 208.98	**84** Po Polonium (209)	**85** At Astatine (210)	**86** Rn Radon (222)
113 (284)	**114** (289)	**115** (288)	**116** (292)		**118** (294)

The discoveries of elements 113 and above have not yet been officially confirmed. Atomic masses in parentheses are those of the most stable isotopes.

66 Dy Dysprosium 162.50	**67** Ho Holmium 164.93	**68** Er Erbium 167.26	**69** Tm Thulium 168.93	**70** Yb Ytterbium 173.04

98 Cf Californium (251)	**99** Es Einsteinium (252)	**100** Fm Fermium (257)	**101** Md Mendelevium (258)	**102** No Nobelium (259)

FIGURE 4 ···

> **INTERACTIVE ART** The Periodic Table

The periodic table is one of the most valuable tools to a chemist. ✎ **Interpret Tables** Find the element identified by the atomic number 25 on the periodic table. Use the information to fill in the blanks below.   8.NS.8

Name of element: _____

Chemical symbol: _____

Atomic mass: _____

Lab Do the Quick Lab
zone *Using the Periodic Table.*

🔑 **Assess Your Understanding**

2a. Compare and Contrast Describe two differences between Mendeleev's periodic table and the modern periodic table.

_____

_____

_____

_____

_____
                                          8.1.2

b. Interpret Tables An atom of which element has 47 protons in its nucleus?

_____
                                          8.1.2

got it? ···

○ **I get it!** Now I know that information found in the periodic table for each element includes _____

_____

_____

○ **I need extra help with** _____

Go to **MY SCIENCE COACH** *online for help with this subject.*   8.1.2

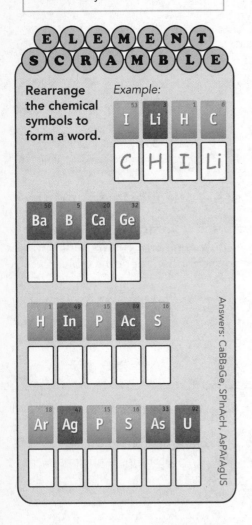
ELEMENT SCRAMBLE

Rearrange the chemical symbols to form a word.

Example:

I	Li	H	C

| C | H | I | Li |

Ba	B	Ca	Ge

H	In	P	Ac	S

Ar	Ag	P	S	As	U

Answers: CaBBaGe, SPInAcH, AsPArAgUS

How Is the Periodic Table Useful?

Look at the periodic table on the previous two pages. Notice that the atomic numbers increase from left to right. Also notice that each color-coded region corresponds to a different class of elements—metals, nonmetals, and metalloids.

As you look across a row, the elements' properties change in a predictable way. 🔑 **An element's properties can be predicted from its location in the periodic table.** This predictability is the reason that the periodic table is so useful to chemists.

Periods The periodic table is arranged in rows called **periods.** A period contains a series of different elements. From left to right, the properties of the elements change in a pattern. Metals are shown on the left of the table and nonmetals are located on the right. Metalloids are found between the metals and nonmetals. This pattern is repeated in each period. **Figure 5** shows the elements of Period 3.

FIGURE 5 ....

Elements of Period 3

The properties of the Period 3 elements change as you move across the period.

✏️ **Classify** Use three different colors to fill in the key below. Then color in each element in Period 3 according to your key.

8.NS.8

11	12	13	14	15	16	17	18
Na	**Mg**	**Al**	**Si**	**P**	**S**	**Cl**	**Ar**
Sodium	Magnesium	Aluminum	Silicon	Phosphorus	Sulfur	Chlorine	Argon
22.990	24.305	26.982	28.086	30.974	32.06	35.453	39.948

Key

☐ Metal

☐ Metalloid

☐ Nonmetal

Groups

Groups The modern periodic table has 7 periods, which form 18 columns. The elements in a column form a **group.** Groups are also known as families. The groups are numbered from Group 1 on the left of the table to Group 18 on the right.

The pattern of properties repeats in each period, so the elements in each group have similar characteristics. For example, except for hydrogen, the elements in Group 1 are all metals that react violently with water. Group 17 elements are very reactive, but Group 18 elements are generally nonreactive. The elements of Group 10 are shown in **Figure 6.**

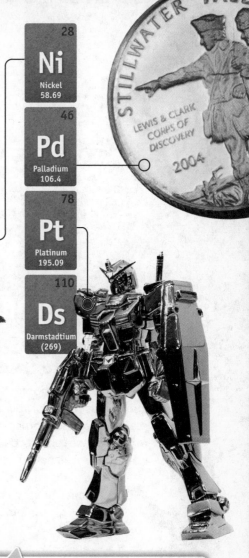

| 28 |
| Ni |
| Nickel |
| 58.69 |

| 46 |
| Pd |
| Palladium |
| 106.4 |

| 78 |
| Pt |
| Platinum |
| 195.09 |

| 110 |
| Ds |
| Darmstadtium |
| (269) |

FIGURE 6 ···························

Elements of Group 10
The elements of Group 10 include nickel (Ni), palladium (Pd), platinum (Pt), and darmstadtium (Ds). Darmstadtium is not found in nature, but scientists believe it exhibits properties similar to the other Group 10 metals.

✏️ CHALLENGE Look at the photos of nickel, palladium, and platinum. What properties would you predict for darmstadtium?

8.NS.1

_____

_____

Lab zone® Do the Quick Lab
Expanding the Periodic Table.

🗝 Assess Your Understanding

3a. Name The rows in the periodic table are

· called _____. The columns in the

periodic table are called _____.

8.1.2

b. Describe What do elements in the same group in the periodic table have in common?

_____

_____

8.1.2, 8.1.3

c. Predict Use the periodic table to name two elements that you would expect to have properties very much like those of calcium (Ca).

_____

_____

_____

_____

8.1.2, 8.1.3

got it? ···

○ **I get it!** Now I know that the periodic table is useful because _____

_____

○ **I need extra help with** _____

Go to MY SCIENCE ⑤ COACH *online for help with this subject.*

8.1.2, 8.1.3

105

Metals

UNLOCK THE BIG

🔑 **What Are the Properties of Metals?**
8.1.1, 8.1.3, 8.1.6, 8.4.3, 8.NS.8

🔑 **How Are Metals Classified?**
8.1.3, 8.1.6, 8.NS.8

my planet Diary
for Indiana

TECHNOLOGY

From Iron to Steel

Gary, Indiana, is home to one of the world's oldest and largest steel production facilities. Steel is mostly made up of the element iron (Fe). Before steel can be produced, several steps are necessary to extract the iron from rocks called iron ore. Iron is extracted in a process known as smelting. Smelting happens in a large stove called a blast furnace. All that remains after the smelting process is molten iron—ready to be refined into steel.

Communicate **Discuss the question with a partner. Write your answer below.**

Do you think producing steel is an expensive process? Explain.

_____

_____

_____

▷ **PLANET DIARY** Go to Planet Diary to learn more about metals.

Lab® zone Do the Inquiry Warm-Up *Why Use Aluminum?*

Vocabulary

- metal • luster • malleable • ductile • thermal conductivity
- electrical conductivity • reactivity • corrosion • alkali metal
- alkaline earth metal • transition metal

Skills

- ↻ Reading: Ask Questions
- △ Inquiry: Infer

What Are the Properties of Metals?

It's hard to imagine modern life without metals. The cars and buses you ride in are made of steel, which is mostly iron (Fe). Airplanes are covered in aluminum (Al). Can you identify the objects that contain metals in **Figure 1** below?

Elements can be classified by their characteristic properties, which are physical or chemical attributes that are unique to a particular substance. These properties include density, boiling and melting points, hardness, and thermal and electrical conductivity. **Metals** are elements that are good conductors of electric current and heat. They also tend to be shiny and bendable—like copper wire, for instance. The majority of elements in the periodic table are metals.

> **Academic Standards for Science**
>
> **8.1.1** Explain that all matter is composed of particular arrangements of atoms.
>
> **8.1.3** Explain how the arrangement of atoms and molecules determines chemical properties.
>
> **8.1.6** Explain that elements have characteristic properties.
>
> **8.4.3** Investigate the properties of natural materials.
>
> **8.NS.8** Analyze data.

FIGURE 1 ···

Metals

Many of the objects around you contain metals.

✎ **Communicate** Circle the objects that will set off the metal detector. Then, with a partner, look around your classroom and make a list of the objects you see that contain metals.

_____

_____

_____

This stone, called magnetite, is made out of a compound of iron.

_____

_____

Gold can be pounded into coins.

_____

_____

Copper is often used for electrical wires.

_____

_____

FIGURE 2 ···

Physical Properties of Metals

Metals have certain physical properties.

✏ **Interpret Photos** After reading about the physical properties of metals below, identify the property or properties of metals exhibited by each of the objects above.

8.NS.8

Physical Properties **Figure 2** shows some common metal objects. 🔑 **The physical properties of metals include luster, malleability, ductility, and conductivity.** A material that has a high **luster** is shiny and reflective. A **malleable** (MAL ee uh bul) material is one that can be hammered or rolled into flat sheets or other shapes. A **ductile** material is one that can be pulled out, or drawn, into long wires. Copper is both malleable and ductile. It can be made into thin sheets or drawn into wires.

Thermal conductivity is the ability of an object to transfer heat. The ability of an object to carry electric current is called **electrical conductivity.** Most metals are good thermal conductors and electrical conductors. Metals also generally have low specific heats. Recall that specific heat is the amount of energy required to raise the temperature of 1 gram of a material by 1 kelvin. This means that only a small amount of thermal energy is required to raise the temperature of a metal.

Some metals are magnetic. Iron, cobalt (Co), and nickel (Ni) are attracted to magnets and can be made into magnets. Most metals are solids at room temperature. Only mercury (Hg) is a liquid at room temperature.

Chemical Properties The ease and speed with which an element combines, or reacts, with other substances is called its **reactivity.** Metals usually react by losing electrons to other atoms. Some metals are very reactive. For example, sodium (Na) reacts strongly with water. By comparison, gold (Au) and platinum (Pt) do not react easily with other substances.

The reactivities of other metals fall somewhere between those of sodium and gold. Iron, for example, reacts slowly with oxygen in the air, forming iron oxide, or rust. The iron chain in **Figure 3** is coated with reddish brown rust. The deterioration of a metal due to a chemical reaction in the environment is called **corrosion.**

FIGURE 3 ·······················
Reactivity of Metals
This iron chain is coated with rust after being exposed to air and water.

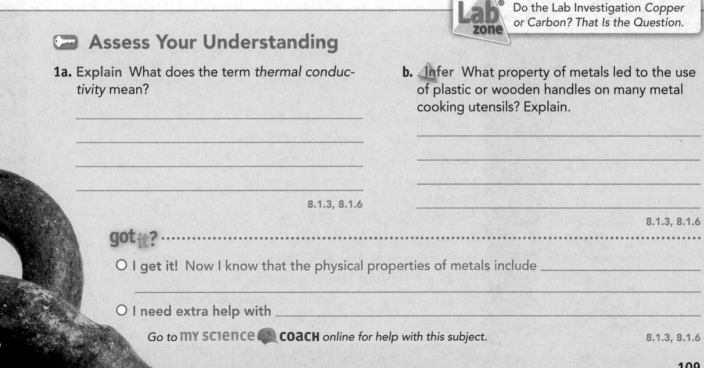

apply it!

The forks shown are made of silver (Ag).

1 Some of the silver forks shown have lost their luster—they have become tarnished. This is an example of _____.

2 ⚠Infer What properties of gold and platinum make these metals desirable for jewelry?   8.NS.8

_____

_____

_____

Lab zone Do the Lab Investigation *Copper or Carbon? That Is the Question.*

🔑 Assess Your Understanding

1a. Explain What does the term *thermal conductivity* mean?

_____

_____

_____

_____

8.1.3, 8.1.6

b. ⚠Infer What property of metals led to the use of plastic or wooden handles on many metal cooking utensils? Explain.

_____

_____

_____

_____

8.1.3, 8.1.6

got it? ···

○ I get it! Now I know that the physical properties of metals include _____

○ I need extra help with _____

Go to MY SCIENCE Ⓢ COACH *online for help with this subject.*   8.1.3, 8.1.6

19
K
Potassium
39.098

Academic Standards for Science

8.1.3 Explain how the arrangement of atoms and molecules determines chemical properties of substances.

8.1.6 Explain that elements have characteristic properties.

8.NS.8 Analyze data and use it to identify patterns and make inferences.

FIGURE 4 ·······························
Fireworks
Compounds containing potassium are used in fireworks.

FIGURE 5 ·······························
X-Ray of Healthy Bones
Calcium compounds are an essential part of teeth and bones.

20
Ca
Calcium
40.08

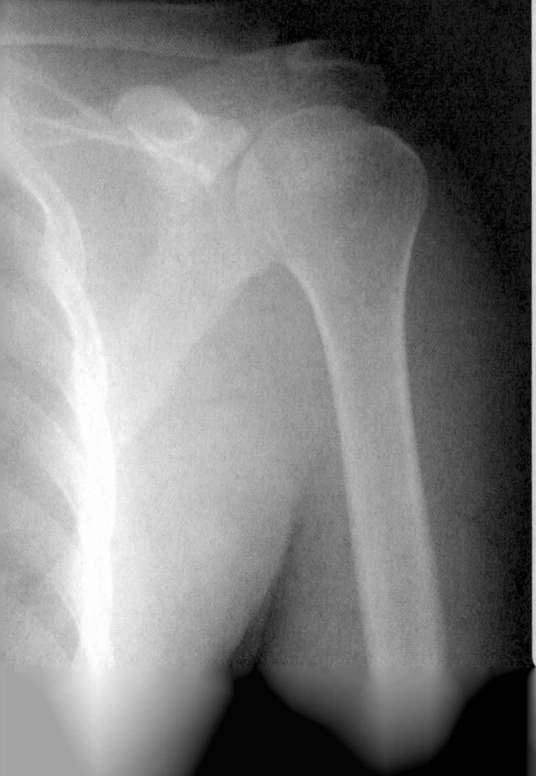

How Are Metals Classified?

The metals in a group have similar properties. Properties within a group change gradually as you look across the periodic table. For example, the reactivity of metals tends to decrease from left to right across the table. **In the periodic table, metals are classified as alkali metals, alkaline earth metals, transition metals, metals in mixed groups, lanthanides, and actinides.**

Alkali Metals The metals of Group 1, from lithium (Li) to francium (Fr), are called the **alkali metals.** These metals are the most reactive metals in the periodic table. Alkali metals are so reactive that they are never found as uncombined elements in nature. They are found only in compounds. Compounds that contain potassium (K) are used in fireworks, such as those shown in **Figure 4.**

Shade in the alkali metals on the periodic table.

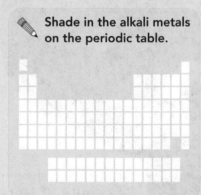

In the laboratory, chemists can isolate alkali metals from their compounds. As pure, uncombined elements, some of the alkali metals are shiny and so soft you can cut them with a plastic knife. These elements have low densities and melting points. For example, sodium melts at 98°C and has a density of 0.97 g/cm^3—less than water.

Alkaline Earth Metals
The metals of Group 2 are called the **alkaline earth metals.** These metals are harder and denser, and melt at higher temperatures than the alkali metals. For example, magnesium (Mg) is a hard metal that melts at 648.8°C.

Shade in the alkaline earth metals on the periodic table.

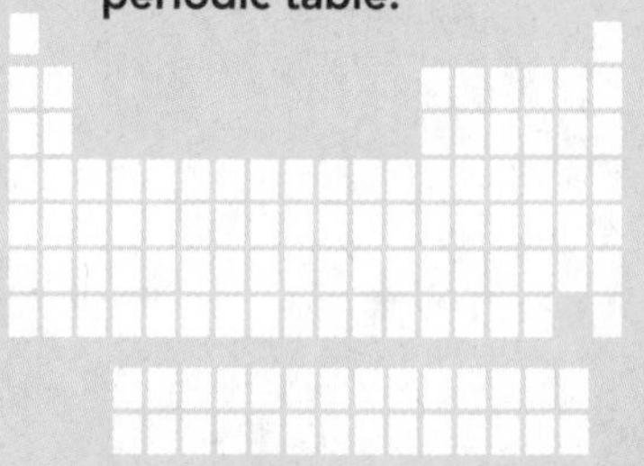

Alkaline earth metals are very reactive, though not as reactive as the alkali metals. These metals are also never found uncombined in nature. Calcium (Ca) is one of the most common alkaline earth metals. Calcium compounds are essential for bone health. **Figure 5** shows an X-ray of healthy bones.

do the math! Analyzing Data

Melting Points in a Group of Elements

Properties of elements in a single group in the periodic table often change according to a certain pattern. The graph shows the melting points of the Group 1 elements, or the alkali metals.

1 **Read Graphs** The melting points of the alkali metals (increase/decrease) from lithium to francium.

2 **Interpret Data** Which of the alkali metals are liquids at 50°C?

3 CHALLENGE If element 119 were discovered, it would fall below francium in Group 1. Predict the approximate melting point of element 119.

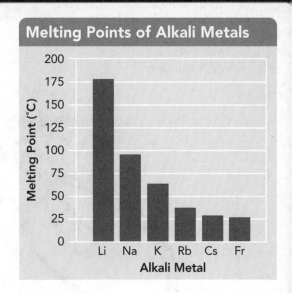

Melting Points of Alkali Metals

8.NS.8

Transition Metals

The elements in Groups 3 through 12 are called the **transition metals.** The transition metals include iron, copper, nickel, gold, and silver. Most of these metals are hard and shiny solids. However, mercury is a liquid at room temperature. Except for mercury, the transition metals often have high melting points and high densities. They are also good conductors of heat and electric current, and are very malleable. As shown in **Figure 6,** gold is sometimes used to coat an astronaut's visor.

The transition metals are less reactive than the metals in Groups 1 and 2. When iron reacts with air, forming rust, it sometimes takes many years to react completely.

Shade in the transition metals on the periodic table.

79
Au
Gold
196.97

FIGURE 6
Astronaut Visor
The gold film in an astronaut's visor protects the eyes and face from the sun without interfering with vision.

FIGURE 7 ·····················

Aluminum Bicycle Frame
Bicycle frames and wheel rims
often contain aluminum.

🖊 **Shade in the metals in mixed groups on the periodic table.**

Metals in Mixed Groups

Bicycle frames, such as the one in
Figure 7, often contain aluminum
because it is durable but light. Aluminum is in Group 13 of the periodic
table. Only some of the elements in
Groups 13 through 16 are metals. Other metals in these groups that
you may be familiar with are tin (Sn) and lead (Pb). A thin coating of tin protects steel from corrosion in some cans of food. Lead
was once used in paints and water pipes. Lead is no longer used for
these purposes because it was found to be poisonous. Now its most
common use is in automobile batteries.

🖊 **Shade in the lanthanides and actinides on the periodic table.**

Lanthanides and Actinides

Two rows of elements are
placed below the main part of the periodic table. The elements in
the top row are the lanthanides (LAN thuh nydz). Compounds
containing neodymium (Nd), a lanthanide, are used to make laser
light. These lasers are used for surgery, for cutting metals, and in
laser range finders, such as the one shown in **Figure 8.**

The elements below the lanthanides are
called actinides (AK tuh nydz). Many of
these elements are not found in nature but
are made artificially in laboratories.

FIGURE 8 ·····················

Laser Range Finder

A compound containing neodymium is used
to produce the laser light in a range finder.
The range finder uses a laser beam to determine the distance to an object.

Transuranium Elements Elements that follow uranium (U) in the periodic table are transuranium elements. These elements are made, or synthesized, when nuclear particles are forced to crash into one another. They are sometimes called synthetic elements. For example, plutonium (Pu) is synthesized by bombarding nuclei of uranium-238 with neutrons in a nuclear reactor.

To make elements with atomic numbers above 95, scientists use devices called particle accelerators that move atomic nuclei at extremely high speeds. If these nuclei crash into the nuclei of other elements with enough energy, the particles can combine into a single nucleus. An example of a particle accelerator is shown in **Figure 9.**

In general, the difficulty of synthesizing new elements increases with atomic number. So new elements have been synthesized only as more powerful particle accelerators have been built. Elements in the periodic table with atomic numbers greater than 111 do not yet have permanent names or symbols. In the future, scientists around the world will agree on permanent names and symbols for these elements.

FIGURE 9 ·····················
Particle Accelerator
The heaviest synthetic elements are synthesized using particle accelerators.

✎ **Ask Questions** Before reading about transuranium elements, ask a *What* or *How* question. As you read, write the answer to your question.

_____

_____

_____

_____

_____

_____

_____

Lab zone® Do the Quick Lab *Finding Metals.*

🔑 Assess Your Understanding

2a. Identify Which family of elements in the periodic table contains the most reactive metals?

_____

8.1.3, 8.1.6, 8.4.3

b. Infer Period 4 of the periodic table contains the elements potassium, calcium, and copper. Which is the least reactive?

_____

8.1.3, 8.1.6, 8.4.3

c. Apply Concepts How is plutonium made?

_____

_____

_____

8.1.3, 8.1.6

got it? ··

○ **I get it!** Now I know that metals are classified in the periodic table as _____

_____

_____

_____

○ **I need extra help with** _____

_____

Go to **my science COACH** *online for help with this subject.* 8.1.3, 8.1.6

Nonmetals and Metalloids

UNLOCK THE BIG ?

🔑 **What Are the Properties of Nonmetals?**
8.1.1, 8.1.3, 8.1.6, 8.4.3, 8.NS.8

🔑 **What Are the Families Containing Nonmetals?**
8.1.3, 8.1.6, 8.NS.8

my planet Diary

MISCONCEPTION

Something in the Air

A common misconception is that the air in the atmosphere is mostly oxygen.

Fact: At sea level, air is actually only about 21 percent oxygen by volume. Nitrogen makes up about 78 percent of the atmosphere. The remaining one percent is made up of several gases, including argon and carbon dioxide.

Evidence: Oxygen is actually toxic at high concentrations. If you breathed in pure oxygen, you would eventually get very sick.

Communicate Write your answer to each question below. Then discuss your answers with a partner.

1. Why don't scuba divers fill their tanks with pure oxygen?

_____

_____

_____

_____

2. Can you think of anything else that is good for you in small amounts but bad for you in large amounts?

_____

_____

_____

_____

> PLANET DIARY Go to **Planet Diary** to learn more about nonmetals.

Lab zone Do the Inquiry Warm-Up *What Are the Properties of Charcoal?*

Vocabulary

- nonmetal • diatomic molecule • halogen
- noble gas • metalloid • semiconductor

Skills

Reading: Summarize

Inquiry: Classify

What Are the Properties of Nonmetals?

Life on Earth depends on many nonmetals. For example, carbon (C), nitrogen (N), phosphorus (P), hydrogen (H), and oxygen (O) are all nonmetal elements found in your body's DNA. A model of DNA is shown in **Figure 1.** While many compounds made with nonmetals are essential to life, some nonmetals are poisonous and highly reactive. Still others are nonreactive. Compared to metals, nonmetals have a much wider variety of properties. However, nonmetals do have several properties in common.

Physical Properties A **nonmetal** is an element that lacks most of the properties of a metal. Except for hydrogen, the nonmetals are found on the right side of the periodic table. 🔑 **In general, most nonmetals are poor conductors of electric current and heat. Solid nonmetals tend to be dull and brittle.** If you were to hit most solid nonmetals with a hammer, they would break or crumble into a powder. Also, nonmetals usually have lower densities than metals.

Many nonmetals are gases at room temperature. The air you breathe contains mostly nitrogen and oxygen. Some nonmetal elements, such as carbon, sulfur (S), and iodine (I), are solids at room temperature. Bromine (Br) is the only nonmetal that is a liquid at room temperature.

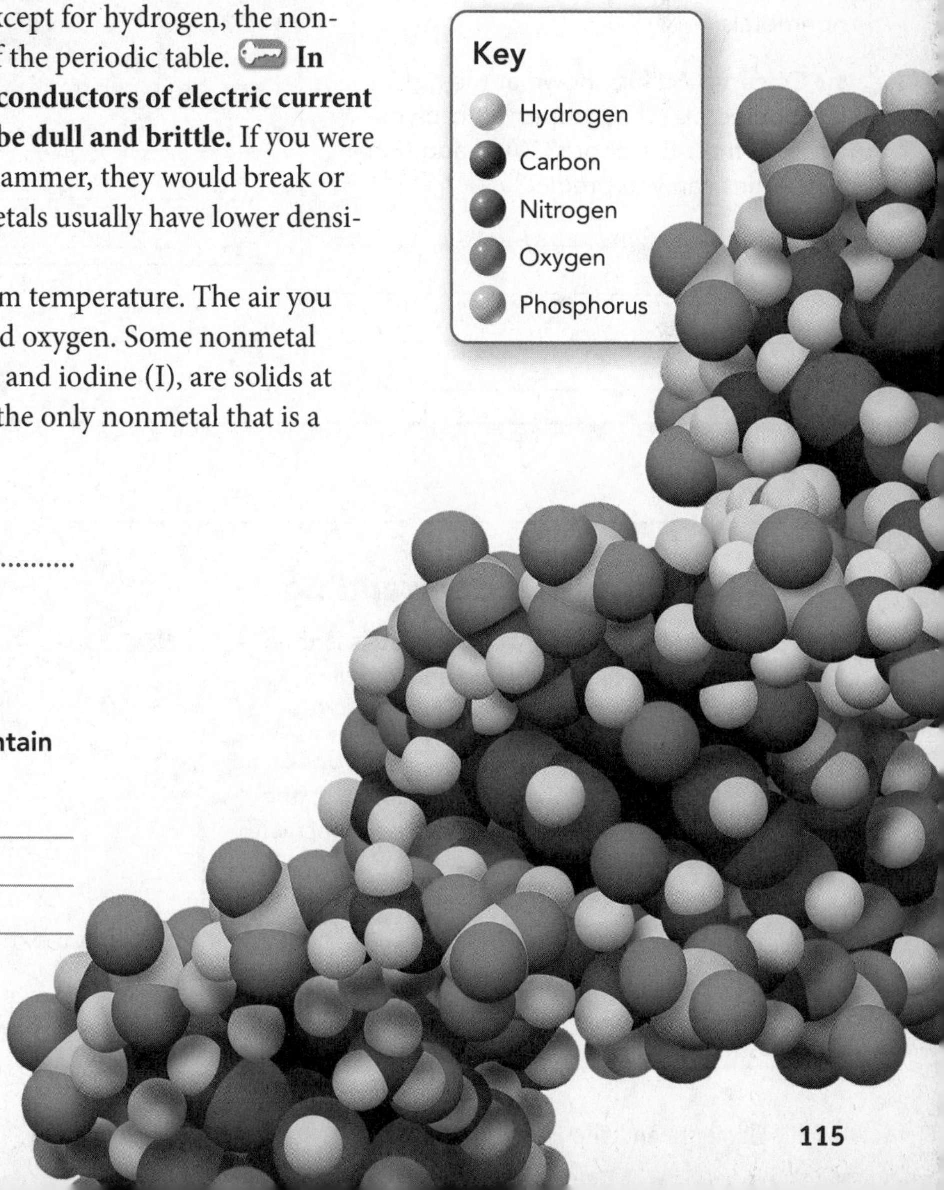

FIGURE 1 ·······························

DNA

DNA, which is made up of atoms of nonmetals, is essential to life.

✏️ Identify **Can you think of other substances essential to life that contain nonmetals?**

_____

_____

_____

Academic Standards for Science

8.1.1 Explain that all matter is composed of particular arrangements of atoms.

8.1.3 Explain how the arrangement of atoms and molecules determines chemical properties of substances.

8.1.6 Explain that elements have characteristic properties.

8.4.3 Investigate the properties of natural materials.

8.NS.8 Analyze data.

Key

- Hydrogen
- Carbon
- Nitrogen
- Oxygen
- Phosphorus

115

Chemical Properties Atoms of nonmetals usually gain or share electrons when they react with other atoms. When nonmetals and metals react, electrons move from the metal atoms to the nonmetal atoms. For example, when sodium and chlorine react to form table salt (NaCl), an electron moves from the sodium atom to the chlorine atom.

Many nonmetals can form compounds with other nonmetals. In these types of compounds, the atoms share their electrons to form bonds. When two or more atoms bond this way, they form a molecule. A water (H_2O) molecule consists of two hydrogen atoms and one oxygen atom.

apply it!

Most properties of nonmetals are the opposite of the properties of metals.

❶ **Compare and Contrast** Complete the table about the properties of metals and nonmetals.

❷ **Observe** Sulfur, shown at the right, is a nonmetal. What properties can you observe from the photo? What additional properties can you predict?

_____

_____

_____

_____

Properties of Metals	Properties of Nonmetals
Shiny	Dull
Malleable	_____
Good conductors of electric current	_____ _____ _____
_____ _____ _____	Poor conductors of heat

8.NS.8

Lab zone® Do the Quick Lab *Carbon—A Nonmetal.*

🗝 Assess Your Understanding

1a. Identify What property of nonmetals is the opposite of being *malleable* and *ductile*?

_____

8.1.3, 8.1.6

b. Make Generalizations What happens to the atoms of most nonmetals when they react with other elements?

_____

_____

_____

_____

8.1.3, 8.1.6

got it? ....

○ **I get it!** Now I know that the physical properties of nonmetals are that_____

_____

_____

_____

○ **I need extra help with** _____

_____

Go to MY SCIENCE COACH *online for help with this subject.* 8.1.3, 8.1.6

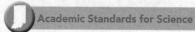

What Are the Families Containing Nonmetals?

Look back at the periodic table. There are nonmetals in Group 1 and in Groups 14–18. 🔑 **The families containing nonmetals include the carbon family, the nitrogen family, the oxygen family, the halogen family, the noble gases, and hydrogen.**

Academic Standards for Science

8.1.3 Explain how the arrangement of atoms and molecules determines chemical properties of substances.

8.1.6 Explain that elements have characteristic properties.

8.NS.8 Analyze data.

Before you read about the families containing nonmetals, refer to the periodic table to complete the table below.

Family	Group	Nonmetals in Family
Carbon family	14	
Nitrogen family	15	
Oxygen family	16	
Halogen family	17	
Noble gases	18	
Hydrogen	1	

The Carbon Family In Group 14, only carbon is a nonmetal. Carbon is especially important in its role in the chemistry of life. Proteins, DNA, and fats all contain carbon.

Most of the fuels that are burned to yield energy contain carbon. Coal contains large amounts of carbon. Gasoline is made from crude oil, a mixture of carbon compounds with one carbon atom to chains of several hundred carbon atoms. A diamond, which is shown in **Figure 2**, is made of pure carbon.

6
C
Carbon
12.011

✏️ Shade in the nonmetal in Group 14 on the periodic table.

FIGURE 2 ⋯⋯⋯⋯⋯⋯⋯

Diamond
Diamonds are made of pure carbon.

The Nitrogen Family

Group 15, the nitrogen family, contains two nonmetals, nitrogen and phosphorus. Nitrogen makes up about 78 percent of Earth's atmosphere by volume. In nature, nitrogen exists as two nitrogen atoms bonded together to form a diatomic molecule, N_2. A **diatomic molecule** is made up of two atoms. In this form, nitrogen is not very reactive.

Although living things need nitrogen, most of them are unable to use nitrogen from the air. However, certain kinds of bacteria can use the nitrogen from the air to form compounds. This process is called nitrogen fixation. Plants can then take in these nitrogen compounds formed by the bacteria in the soil. Farmers also add nitrogen compounds to the soil in the form of fertilizers. Lightning, shown in **Figure 3,** also converts nitrogen in the atmosphere into a form that can be used by plants.

Phosphorus is the other nonmetal in the nitrogen family. Much more reactive than nitrogen, phosphorus in nature is always found in compounds.

✎ Shade in the nonmetals in Group 15 on the periodic table.

FIGURE 3 ···

Lightning

The energy released in the atmosphere in the form of lightning is able to break the bonds between nitrogen atoms, causing them to react with oxygen. Plants are able to use the nitrogen in this form.

✎ CHALLENGE **How do you get the nitrogen you need?**

_____

_____

7
N
Nitrogen
14.007

The Oxygen Family

Group 16, the oxygen family, contains three nonmetals—oxygen, sulfur, and selenium (Se). Oxygen is a gas at room temperature, whereas sulfur and selenium are both solids.

You are using oxygen right now. With every breath, oxygen travels into your lungs. There, it is absorbed into your bloodstream, which distributes it all over your body. Like nitrogen, oxygen (O_2) is a diatomic molecule. Oxygen is relatively reactive, so it can combine with almost every other element.

If you have ever smelled the odor of a rotten egg, then you are already familiar with the smell of some sulfur compounds. Sulfur is used in the manufacturing of rubber for rubber bands and automobile tires, like the one shown in **Figure 4.**

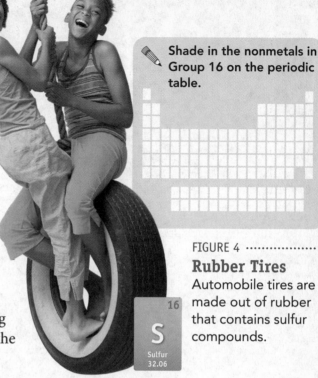

✏️ Shade in the nonmetals in Group 16 on the periodic table.

FIGURE 4 ·····················
Rubber Tires
Automobile tires are made out of rubber that contains sulfur compounds.

| 16 |
| S |
| Sulfur |
| 32.06 |

The Halogen Family

Group 17 contains the nonmetals fluorine (F), chlorine (Cl), bromine, and iodine. These elements are also known as the **halogens,** which means "salt forming." The properties of astatine (At) are unknown because it is extremely rare.

✏️ Shade in the nonmetals in Group 17 on the periodic table.

All of the halogens are very reactive. Fluorine is the most reactive of all the elements. It is so reactive that it reacts with almost every known substance, including water. Chlorine gas is extremely dangerous, but it is used in small amounts to kill bacteria in water supplies.

Though the halogen elements are dangerous, many of the compounds that halogens form are quite useful. Compounds of fluorine make up the nonstick coating on cookware. Fluorine compounds are also found in toothpaste, which is shown in **Figure 5,** because they help prevent tooth decay.

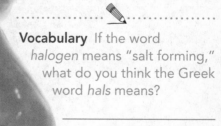

| 9 |
| F |
| Fluorine |
| 18.998 |

FIGURE 5 ·····························
Toothpaste
Toothpastes often contain fluorine compounds.

✏️ **Vocabulary** If the word *halogen* means "salt forming," what do you think the Greek word *hals* means?

_____

_____

_____

He Ne Ar Kr Xe

FIGURE 6 ·····················

Neon Lights

Glowing electric lights are often called "neon lights" even though they are usually filled with other noble gases or mixtures of them. The lights above show the symbols for helium (He), neon (Ne), argon (Ar), krypton (Kr), and xenon (Xe).

The Noble Gases The elements in Group 18 are known as the noble gases. They do not ordinarily form compounds because atoms of noble gases do not usually gain, lose, or share electrons. As a result, the noble gases are usually nonreactive. Even so, scientists have been able to synthesize some noble gas compounds in the laboratory.

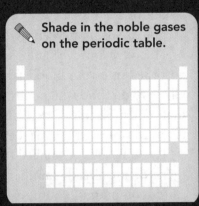

Shade in the noble gases on the periodic table.

You have probably seen a floating balloon filled with helium (He). Noble gases are also used in glowing electric lights, such as the ones shown in **Figure 6**.

Hydrogen Alone in the upper left corner of the periodic table is hydrogen—the element with the simplest atoms. The chemical properties of hydrogen are very different from those of the other elements, so it cannot be grouped in with a family.

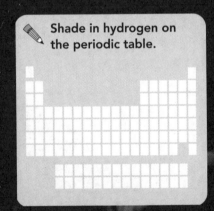

Shade in hydrogen on the periodic table.

Hydrogen makes up more than 90 percent of the atoms in the universe. Stars—like the sun, shown in **Figure 7**—contain massive amounts of hydrogen. But, hydrogen makes up only 1 percent of the mass of Earth's crust, oceans, and atmosphere. Hydrogen is rarely found on Earth as a pure element. Most hydrogen is combined with oxygen in water.

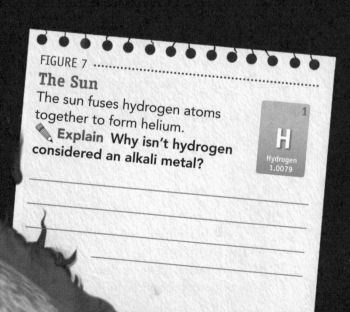

FIGURE 7 ·······················

The Sun

The sun fuses hydrogen atoms together to form helium.

Explain Why isn't hydrogen considered an alkali metal?

_____

_____

_____

_____

1
H
Hydrogen
1.0079

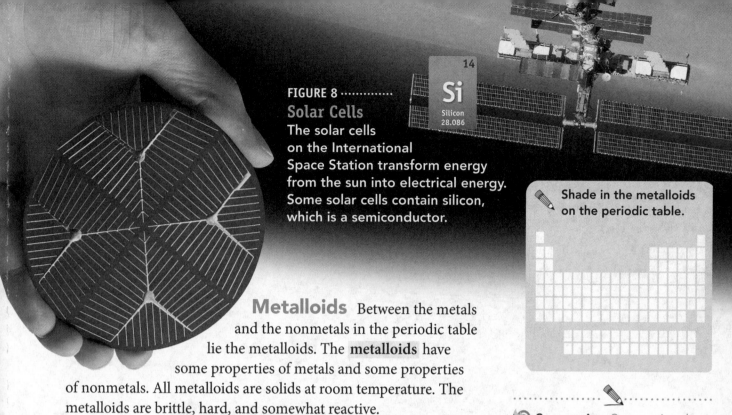

FIGURE 8
Solar Cells
The solar cells on the International Space Station transform energy from the sun into electrical energy. Some solar cells contain silicon, which is a semiconductor.

14
Si
Silicon
28.086

Metalloids Between the metals and the nonmetals in the periodic table lie the metalloids. The **metalloids** have some properties of metals and some properties of nonmetals. All metalloids are solids at room temperature. The metalloids are brittle, hard, and somewhat reactive.

The most common metalloid is silicon (Si). Ordinary sand, which is mostly silicon dioxide, (SiO_2) is the main component of glass. A compound of boron (B) and oxygen is added during the process of glassmaking to make heat-resistant glass.

A metalloid's most useful property is the ability to conduct electric current. The conductivity of a metalloid can depend on temperature, exposure to light, or the presence of impurities. For this reason, metalloids such as silicon and germanium (Ge) are used to make semiconductors. **Semiconductors** are substances that can conduct electric current under some conditions but not under other conditions. Semiconductors are used to make computer chips, transistors, and lasers. Semiconductors are also used in solar cells, such as the ones shown in **Figure 8**.

Shade in the metalloids on the periodic table.

Summarize Summarize the properties of the metalloids.

_____
_____
_____
_____
_____
_____
_____

apply it!

Use this portion of the periodic table to answer the questions.

❶ **Classify** List the chemical symbols of the nonmetals: _____. The remaining elements are classified as _____

❷ Selenium has properties similar to (sulfur/bromine) because they are in the same (period/group).

8.NS.8

14	15	16	17
Si	**P**	**S**	**Cl**
Silicon	Phosphorus	Sulfur	Chlorine
28.086	30.974	32.06	35.453
32	33	34	35
Ge	**As**	**Se**	**Br**
Germanium	Arsenic	Selenium	Bromine
72.59	74.922	78.96	79.904

Alien Periodic Table

How is the periodic table organized?
FIGURE 9 ·····················

> **VIRTUAL LAB** Imagine that inhabitants of another planet send a message to Earth that contains information about 30 elements. However, the message contains different names and symbols for these elements than those used on Earth. ✎ Infer Using the clues provided, fill in the periodic table with these "alien" names. 8.NS.8

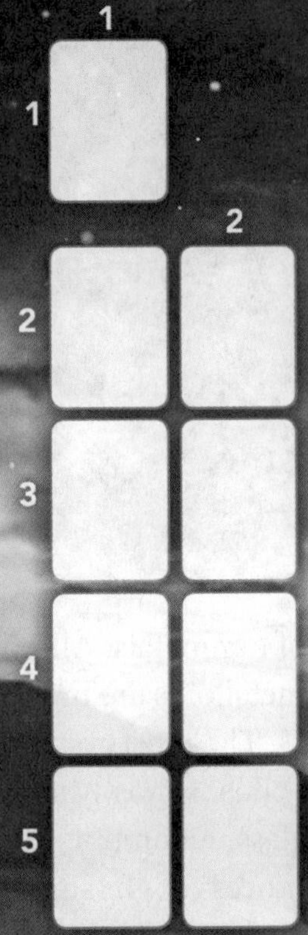

Alien Elements

The noble gases are **bombal** (Bo), **wobble** (Wo), **jeptum** (J), and **logon** (L). Among these gases, wobble has the greatest atomic mass and bombal the least. Logon is lighter than jeptum.

The most reactive group of metals are **xtalt** (X), **byyou** (By), **chow** (Ch), and **quackzil** (Q). Of these metals, chow has the lowest atomic mass. Quackzil is in the same period as wobble.

Apstrom (A), **vulcania** (Vc), and **kratt** (Kt) are nonmetals in Group 17. Vulcania is in the same period as quackzil and wobble.

The metalloids are **ernst** (E), **highho** (Hi), **terriblum** (T), and **sississ** (Ss). Sississ is the metalloid with the greatest atomic mass. Ernst is the metalloid with the lowest atomic mass. Highho and terriblum are in Group 14. Terriblum has more protons than highho. **Yazzer** (Yz) touches the zigzag line, but it's a metal, not a metalloid.

The lightest element of all is called **pfsst** (Pf). The heaviest element in the group of 30 elements is **eldorado** (El). The most chemically active nonmetal is apstrom. Kratt reacts with byyou to form table salt.

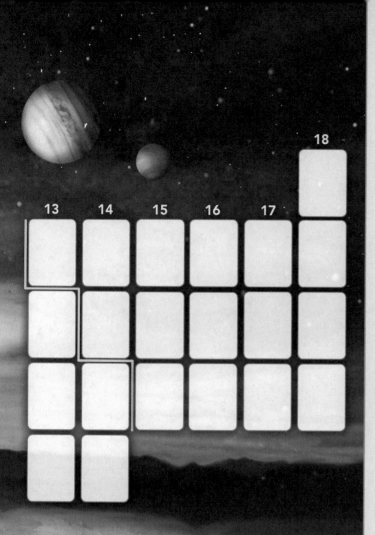

The element **doggone** (D) has only 4 protons in its atoms.

Floxxit (Fx) is important in the chemistry of life. It forms compounds made of long chains of atoms. **Rhaatrap** (R) and **doadeer** (Do) are metals in the fourth period, but rhaatrap is less reactive than doadeer.

Magnificon (M), **goldy** (G), and sississ are all members of Group 15. Goldy has fewer electrons than magnificon.

Urrp (Up), **oz** (Oz), and **nuutye** (Nu) are in Group 16. Nuutye is found as a diatomic molecule and has the same properties as a gas found in Earth's atmosphere. Oz has a lower atomic number than urrp.

The element **anatom** (An) has atoms with a total of 49 electrons. **Zapper** (Z) and **pie** (Pi) are both members of Group 2. Zapper has fewer protons than pie.

Do the Quick Lab *Finding Nonmetals.*

🔑 Assess Your Understanding

2a. **List** What are the nonmetals in Group 16 of the periodic table?

_____

_____

_____

8.1.3, 8.1.6

b. **Compare and Contrast** How do the chemical properties of the halogens compare to those of the noble gases?

_____

_____

_____

8.1.3, 8.1.6, 8.4.3

c. ANSWER THE BIG ? How is the periodic table organized?

_____

_____

_____

_____

_____

_____

_____

_____

8.1.2, 8.1.3, 8.1.6

got it? ••••••••••••••••••••••••••••••••

○ **I get it!** Now I know that the families containing nonmetals include _____

_____

_____

○ **I need extra help with** _____

Go to MY SCIENCE ⓢ COACH online for help with this subject.   8.1.3, 8.1.6

In the periodic table, the elements are organized in order of _____ atomic number.

The properties of the elements repeat in each _____.

LESSON 1 Introduction to Atoms
8.1.4, 8.4.1, 8.NS.1, 8.NS.8, 8.NS.10

🔑 Atomic theory grew as a series of models that developed from experimental evidence.

🔑 At the center of the atom is a tiny, dense nucleus containing protons and neutrons. Surrounding the nucleus is a cloudlike region of moving electrons.

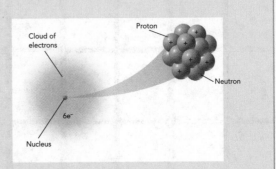

Vocabulary
- atom • electron • nucleus • proton
- energy level • neutron • atomic number
- isotope • mass number

LESSON 2 Organizing the Elements
8.1.2, 8.1.3, 8.NS.1, 8.NS.8

🔑 Mendeleev noticed a pattern of properties in elements arranged by increasing atomic mass.

🔑 The periodic table includes each element's atomic number, symbol, name, and atomic mass.

🔑 The properties of an element can be predicted from its location in the periodic table.

Vocabulary
- atomic mass • periodic table
- chemical symbol • period • group

LESSON 3 Metals
8.1.1, 8.1.3, 8.1.6, 8.4.3, 8.NS.8

🔑 The physical properties of metals include luster, malleability, ductility, and conductivity.

🔑 Metals are classified as alkali metals, alkaline earth metals, transition metals, metals in mixed groups, lanthanides, and actinides.

Vocabulary
- metal • luster • malleable • ductile
- thermal conductivity • electrical conductivity
- reactivity • corrosion • alkali metal
- alkaline earth metal • transition metal

LESSON 4 Nonmetals and Metalloids
8.1.1, 8.1.3, 8.1.6, 8.4.3, 8.NS.8

🔑 In general, most nonmetals are poor conductors. Solid nonmetals tend to be dull and brittle.

🔑 The families containing nonmetals include the carbon family, the nitrogen family, the oxygen family, the halogen family, the noble gases, and hydrogen.

Vocabulary
- nonmetal • diatomic molecule • halogen
- noble gas • metalloid • semiconductor

Review and Assessment

LESSON 1 Introduction to Atoms

1. The atomic number of an element is determined by the number of

  a. protons.   **b.** electrons.

  c. neutrons.   **d.** isotopes.

                                       8.1.4

2. Two isotopes of an element have the same number of _____ but different numbers of _____.

                                       8.1.4

3. Relate Cause and Effect How can an atom be electrically neutral when it contains particles that are charged?

_____

_____

_____

_____

                                       8.1.4

4. Relate Evidence and Explanation How did Rutherford's experimental evidence lead to the development of a new atomic model?

_____

_____

_____

_____

_____

_____

_____

                                       8.1.4

5. **Write About It** Write a letter that Thomson might have sent to another scientist explaining why an atom must contain positive charges as well as negative charges. The letter should also explain why Thomson proposed the atomic model that he did.

                                       8.1.4

LESSON 2 Organizing the Elements

6. The rows in the periodic table are called

  a. groups.   **b.** periods.

  c. nonmetals.   **d.** metals.

                                       8.1.2

7. Dmitri Mendeleev constructed the first periodic table, which is _____

_____

_____

                                       8.1.2

8. Apply Concepts Below is an entry taken from the periodic table. Identify the type of information given by each labeled item.

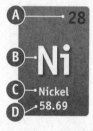

_____

_____

_____

_____

                                       8.1.2

9. Make Generalizations Why aren't the atomic masses of most elements whole numbers?

_____

_____

_____

                                       8.1.2

10. **Write About It** Write an advertisement that you could use to sell copies of Mendeleev's periodic table to chemists in 1869. Be sure to emphasize the benefits of the table to the chemical profession. Remember, the chemists have never seen such a table.

                                   8.1.2, 8.NS.11

125

CHAPTER
3

LESSON 3 Metals

11. Of the following, the group that contains elements that are the most reactive is the

  a. alkali metals.   **b.** alkaline earth metals.

  c. carbon family.   **d.** noble gases.

             8.1.3, 8.1.6, 8.4.3

12. A property of metals is high thermal conductivity, which is _____

_____.

             8.1.3, 8.1.6, 8.4.3

13. Predict Using the periodic table, predict which element—potassium, aluminum, or iron—is most reactive. Explain your answer.

_____

_____

_____

_____

             8.1.3, 8.1.6, 8.NS.1

LESSON 4 Nonmetals and Metalloids

14. Unlike metals, solid nonmetals are

  a. good conductors of heat and electric current.

  b. malleable.

  c. dull and brittle.

  d. ductile.

             8.1.3, 8.1.6, 8.4.3

15. Two elements that have properties similar to those of chlorine are _____

_____.

             8.1.3, 8.1.6

16. Infer What property of the materials used in computer chips makes them useful as switches that turn electricity on and off?

_____

_____

_____

_____

             8.1.3, 8.1.6, 8.4.3

APPLY THE BIG ? How is the periodic table organized?

17. A portion of the periodic table is shown above. Which element on the periodic table has properties that are most similar to those of nitrogen (N)? Why do Aluminum, Silicon, and Phosphorus appear in the order shown? Explain.

_____

_____

_____

_____

_____

_____

_____

_____

_____

_____

_____

_____

_____

_____

_____

_____

_____

_____

_____

_____

             8.1.3, 8.1.6, 8.4.3

Indiana ISTEP+ Practice

Multiple Choice

Circle the letter of the best answer.

1. A portion of the periodic table is shown below.

Which elements are noble gases?

A. oxygen, fluorine, and neon

B. sulfur, chlorine, and argon

C. fluorine and chlorine

D. neon and argon

8.1.6

2. What information about each element is NOT provided by the periodic table?

A. number of electrons in each atom

B. atomic number

C. atomic mass

D. chemical symbol

8.1.2

3. Elements that are gases at room temperature are likely to be classified as which of the following?

A. metals

B. nonmetals

C. metalloids

D. semiconductors

8.1.2, 8.1.6

4. Which property of aluminum makes it a suitable metal for soft-drink cans?

A. It has good electrical conductivity.

B. It can be hammered into a thin sheet (malleability).

C. It can be drawn into long wires (ductility).

D. It can reflect light (luster).

8.1.3, 8.1.6, 8.4.3

Constructed Response

Write your answer to Question 5 on the lines below.

5. Why is the mass of a carbon atom greater than the total mass of its protons and electrons?

_____

_____

_____

8.1.4

Extended Response

Use the table below to help you answer Question 6. Write your answer on a separate sheet of paper.

Element	Appearance	Reactivity	Conducts Electricity
A	Greenish-yellow gas	High	No
B	Shiny red solid	Moderate	Yes
C	Colorless gas	None	No
D	Silver-white solid	High	Yes

6. Identify each element as an alkali metal, transition metal, halogen, or noble gas. Explain your answers.

8.1.2, 8.1.6

Discovery of the Elements

More than 100 chemical elements have been discovered or created on Earth. The following stories describe some of the spectacular ways in which elements have been discovered:

1669 Phosphorus

In 1669, alchemist Hennig Brand was searching for a way to turn lead into gold. He hypothesized that animal urine might contain a substance that could cause the transformation. In the process of heating the urine to obtain a pure substance, he discovered a material that glowed in the dark. That material is phosphorus, which is important in maintaining a healthy body.

1811 Iodine

As French chemist Barnard Courtois isolated sodium and potassium compounds from seaweed ashes, he accidentally added too much sulfuric acid. The mess he created sent out a cloud of violet-colored gas that condensed on metal surfaces in the room. That gas was iodine. Even today, some iodine is isolated from seaweed. Having enough iodine in your diet can prevent illness and allow for healthy development.

1936 Technetium

Italian chemists Emilio Segrè and Carlo Perrier made technetium in a cyclotron in 1936. This was the first element to be produced artificially. Technetium is similar in appearance to platinum, but is very radioactive. Because it breaks down quickly, technetium is not found in nature.

Flame tests historically helped chemists to identify elements. ▶

Research It Find out more about the discovery of the following elements: helium, copper, Americium, aluminum, and silicon. Then, create a timeline that shows when each element was discovered and how that discovery affected human life.

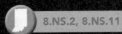
8.NS.2, 8.NS.11

Elements
of the Human Body

It's elemental! Atoms of only five different elements make up 98 percent of the mass of the human body.

Oxygen and Hydrogen About two thirds of the body consists of water. So, in terms of mass, more than half of the body is oxygen atoms, and another 10 percent is hydrogen atoms. Both oxygen and hydrogen are also present in other body parts.

Carbon The key element in organic molecules is carbon. Organic molecules make up all body tissues, including muscles.

Calcium and Phosphorus The hard, strong parts of bones are built mostly of calcium phosphate crystals, which contain calcium, phosphorus, and oxygen.

Trace Elements Some elements exist in the body in small amounts, but play important roles. For example, chemical reactions inside body organs require enzymes that contain magnesium. The thyroid gland needs iodine to control growth. The element iron makes up less than one twentieth of 1 percent of the body, yet is an extremely important part of the hemoglobin molecule. Red blood cells use hemoglobin to carry oxygen throughout the body.

Graph It Research how the human body acquires these elements. Then use the data from the table of Elements in the Human Body to create a circle graph that shows the relative percentages of each element in the body.

 8.NS.2, 8.NS.8, 8.NS.11

Elements in the Human Body

Element	Approximate mass (%)
Oxygen	65
Carbon	18
Hydrogen	10
Nitrogen	3
Calcium	1
Phosphorus	1
Potassium, Sulfur, Sodium, Chlorine	0.1–0.3 percent each
Copper, Magnesium, Zinc, Iron, Selenium, Molybdenum, Fluorine, Iodine, Manganese, Cobalt	less than 0.1 percent each

HOW DO BEES MAKE HONEY?

How is matter conserved in a chemical reaction?

Honeybees drink nectar from flowers. They store the nectar in a honey sac found inside their bodies. Nectar begins changing into honey in the honey sac. Nectar is mostly water, which evaporates during the honey-making process.

> UNTAMED SCIENCE Watch the **Untamed Science** video to learn more about chemical reactions.

After collecting nectar, the honeybees return to the hive where they spit the nectar into the mouths of house bees. Chemicals in the mouths of the house bees continue changing the nectar into honey until it is ready to be stored in the honeycomb.

Draw Conclusions Explain why bees must collect more nectar than actual honey that is produced.

_____

_____

_____

Chemical Reactions

Academic Standards for Science

8.1.1, 8.1.3, 8.1.4, 8.1.5, 8.1.6, 8.1.7, 8.1.8, 8.4.1,
8.4.2, 8.4.3, 8.NS.1–8.NS.11, 8.DP.1

4 Getting Started

Check Your Understanding

1. **Background** Read the paragraph below and then answer the question.

Alex is doing an experiment to see how vinegar reacts with **ionic compounds.** He measures the **mass** of a sample of baking soda. Alex records the measurement in his lab book next to the **chemical formula** for baking soda, $NaHCO_3$.

An **ionic compound** consists of positive and negative ions.

Mass is the amount of material in an object.

A **chemical formula** shows the ratio of elements in a compound.

- Which substance is an ionic compound in the experiment that Alex is conducting?

_____

> **MY READING WEB** If you had trouble completing the question above, visit **My Reading Web** and type in *Chemical Reactions*.

Vocabulary Skill

Identify Multiple Meanings Some familiar words have more than one meaning. Words you use every day may have different meanings in science.

Word	Everyday Meaning	Scientific Meaning
matter	*n.* a subject of discussion, concern, or action **Example:** We had an important *matter* to discuss in the meeting.	*n.* anything that has mass and takes up space **Example:** Solids, liquids, and gases are states of *matter.*
product	*n.* anything that is made or created **Example:** Milk and cheese are dairy *products.*	*n.* a substance formed as a result of a chemical reaction **Example:** In a chemical reaction, substances can combine to form *products.*

2. **Quick Check** Circle the sentence below that uses the scientific meaning of the word *product*.

- She brought napkins and other paper **products** to the picnic.
- Table salt is the **product** of the reaction of sodium and chlorine.

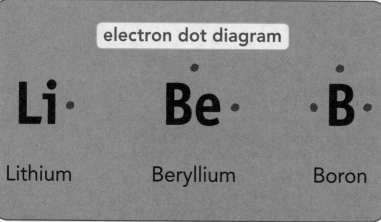

electron dot diagram

Li·   Be·   ·B·

Lithium   Beryllium   Boron

ionic compound

$CaCO_3$

crystal

I want it!

I want it more!

polar bond

Chapter Preview

LESSON 1
- valence electron
- electron dot diagram
- chemical bond

🔄 **Relate Cause and Effect**
△ **Predict**

LESSON 2
- ion • polyatomic ion
- ionic bond • ionic compound
- chemical formula • subscript
- crystal

🔄 **Relate Text and Visuals**
△ **Interpret Data**

LESSON 3
- covalent bond • molecule
- double bond • triple bond
- molecular compound
- nonpolar bond • polar bond

🔄 **Compare and Contrast**
△ **Graph**

LESSON 4
- physical change
- chemical change
- reactant • product
- precipitate • exothermic reaction
- endothermic reaction

🔄 **Relate Cause and Effect**
△ **Graph**

LESSON 5
- chemical equation
- law of conservation of mass
- open system • closed system
- coefficient • synthesis
- decomposition • replacement

🔄 **Summarize**
△ **Make Models**

▶ VOCAB FLASH CARDS For extra help with vocabulary, visit **Vocab Flash Cards** and type in *Chemical Reactions*.

Atoms, Bonding, and the Periodic Table

What Determines an Element's Chemistry?
8.1.1, 8.1.3, 8.1.4, 8.1.5, 8.1.6, 8.4.1, 8.4.3, 8.NS.1, 8.NS.8

my planet diary

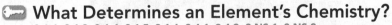

FUN FACTS

Elemental Effects

Many people enjoy fireworks displays. Did you know that chemistry plays a big part in the beauty and the noise? The different colors and effects produced depend on the properties of the elements in the chemical compounds used in each firework rocket. These compounds produce smoke, color bursts, loud noises, or a combination of these effects when they are detonated.

The table below lists some elements found in the compounds used in rockets. It shows the effects these elements produce.

Using what you know about the periodic table, answer the questions below. After you finish the lesson, check your answers.

What elements do you think were used to produce the fireworks display in the photo? What groups of the periodic table do these elements belong to?

_____

_____

_____

Element	Effect
Strontium	Red color
Barium	Green color
Copper	Blue color
Sodium	Yellow color
Magnesium or aluminum	White color
Potassium or sodium	Whistling sound
Potassium and sulfur	White smoke

> PLANET DIARY Go to **Planet Diary** to learn more about elements.

Lab zone Do the Inquiry Warm-Up *What Are the Trends in the Periodic Table?*

Vocabulary
- valence electron
- electron dot diagram
- chemical bond

Skills
- Reading: Relate Cause and Effect
- Inquiry: Predict

What Determines an Element's Chemistry?

How do atoms combine to form compounds? The answer has to do with electrons and their energy levels.

Valence Electrons The number of protons in a neutral atom equals the number of electrons. The electrons of an atom are found in different energy levels. Electrons at higher energy levels have higher amounts of energy. The **valence electrons** (VAY luns) of an atom are those electrons that have the highest energy. Valence electrons are involved in chemical bonding. 🔑 **The number of valence electrons in each atom helps determine the chemical properties of that element.**

Electron Dot Diagrams Each atom of an element has a certain number of valence electrons. The number of valence electrons is specific to that element. Different elements can have from 1 to 8 valence electrons. **Figure 1** demonstrates one way to show the number of valence electrons in an element. An **electron dot diagram** includes the symbol for the element surrounded by dots. Each dot stands for one valence electron.

Bonding Atoms tend to be more stable if they have 8 valence electrons. Atoms of neon (Ne), argon (Ar), krypton (Kr), and xenon (Xe) have 8 valence electrons. These elements are nonreactive, or stable. Helium (He) is stable with 2 electrons.

Atoms tend to form bonds so that they have 8 valence electrons and become more stable. Hydrogen needs only to 2 to be stable. When atoms bond, valence electrons may be transferred from one atom to another. Or they may be shared between the atoms. A **chemical bond** is the force of attraction that holds atoms together as a result of the rearrangement of electrons between them.

H ·   · C̈ ·   · Ö :

Hydrogen   Carbon   Oxygen

Neon

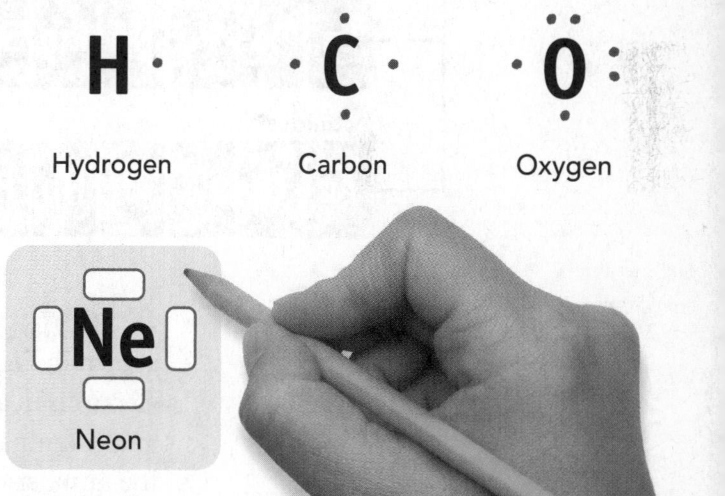

FIGURE 1 ....

Electron Dot Diagrams

The valence electrons of an atom are shown as dots around the symbol of the element.

✏️ **Interpret Diagrams Complete the electron dot diagram for neon by drawing the correct number of dots.**

8.NS.8

135

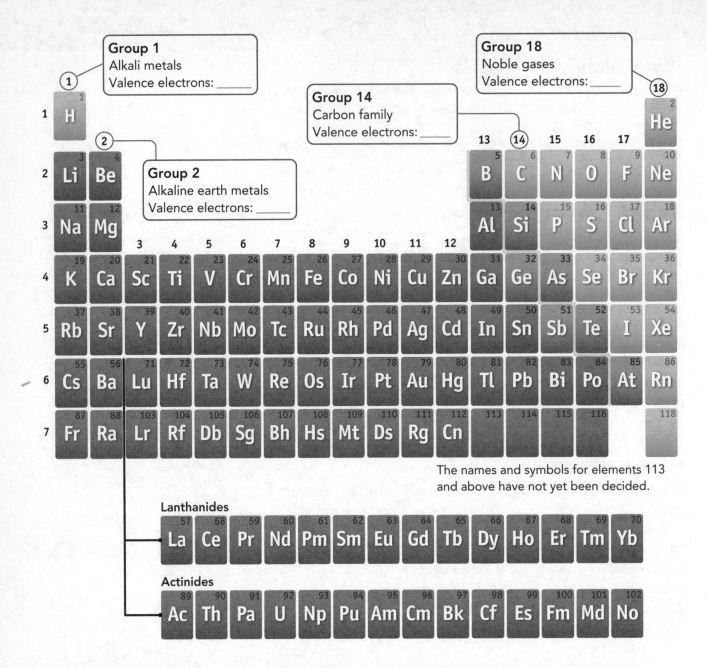

Group 1
Alkali metals
Valence electrons: _____

Group 2
Alkaline earth metals
Valence electrons: _____

Group 14
Carbon family
Valence electrons: _____

Group 18
Noble gases
Valence electrons: _____

The names and symbols for elements 113 and above have not yet been decided.

Lanthanides

Actinides

FIGURE 2 ·······························
> INTERACTIVE ART **Periodic Table of the Elements**
The periodic table is arranged in order of increasing atomic number. The number of valence electrons also increases from left to right across a period.

✎ **Interpret Tables** As you read the lesson, fill in the number of valence electrons for each group circled above.
8.NS.8

Applying the Periodic Table The periodic table is shown in **Figure 2.** It gives you information about the valence electrons in atoms. The table is organized into rows, called periods, and columns, called groups. The atomic number of an element is the number of protons in each atom of that element.

The elements in the periodic table are in order by increasing atomic number. The number of valence electrons increases from left to right across each period. Each period begins with an element that has 1 valence electron. Except for Period 1, a given period ends with an element that has 8 valence electrons. This repeating pattern means that the elements within a group (except for Period 1) always have the same number of valence electrons. As a result, the elements in each group have similar properties.

Each element in Periods 2 and 3 has one more valence electron than the element to its left. Group 1 elements have 1. Group 2 elements have 2. Group 13 elements have 3 valence electrons. Group 14 elements have 4, and so on. (Elements in Groups 3 to 12 follow a slightly different pattern.)

apply it!

The symbols for the elements in Periods 2 and 3 are shown below. The correct electron dot diagrams are shown for only half of the elements.

① Complete the electron dot diagrams for nitrogen, oxygen, fluorine, sodium, magnesium, aluminum, silicon, and argon.

② Fluorine (F) and Chlorine (Cl) are in Group ____.
A fluorine atom has _____ valence electrons.
A chlorine atom has _____ valence electrons.

③ Predict How many valence electrons does a bromine (Br) atom have? _____

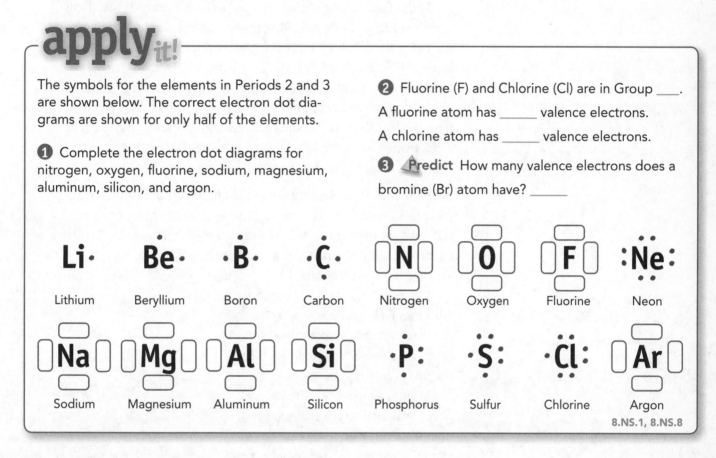

8.NS.1, 8.NS.8

Noble Gases The Group 18 elements are the noble gases. Atoms of the noble gases have 8 valence electrons, except for helium, which has 2. Atoms with 8 valence electrons (or 2, in the case of helium) are stable. They are unlikely to gain or lose electrons or to share electrons with other atoms. Noble gases do not react easily with other elements. Some don't react at all. But, chemists have been able to make some noble gases form compounds with a few other elements.

FIGURE 3 ·····················
Camera Flashes
Argon, a noble gas, is used to produce camera flashes.

Metals The metals are the elements in the blue section of the periodic table in **Figure 2.** Metal atoms react by losing their valence electrons. In general, the reactivity of a metal depends on how easily its atoms lose valence electrons. The reactivity of metals decreases from left to right across the periodic table.

At the far left side of the periodic table is Group 1, the alkali metals. Each alkali metal is the most reactive element in its period. Atoms of the alkali metals have 1 valence electron. Except for lithium (Li), when a Group 1 atom loses an electron, it is left with a stable arrangement of 8 electrons in the highest energy level. These electrons are in a lower energy level than the 1 valence electron that was lost. (Lithium atoms are left with a stable arrangement of 2 electrons.) The alkali metals are so reactive that they can cause an explosion when added to water!

Nonmetals The elements in the orange section of the periodic table in **Figure 2** are the nonmetals. Nonmetal atoms become stable when they gain or share enough electrons to have 8 valence electrons. (Hydrogen atoms are left with a stable arrangement of 2 electrons.)

The nonmetals usually combine with metals by gaining electrons. Nonmetals can also combine with other nonmetals and metalloids by sharing electrons.

Atoms of Group 17, the halogens, have 7 valence electrons. A gain of one more electron gives these atoms a stable 8 electrons. The halogens react easily with other elements. **Figure 4** shows the reaction of bromine (Br), a halogen, with aluminum (Al).

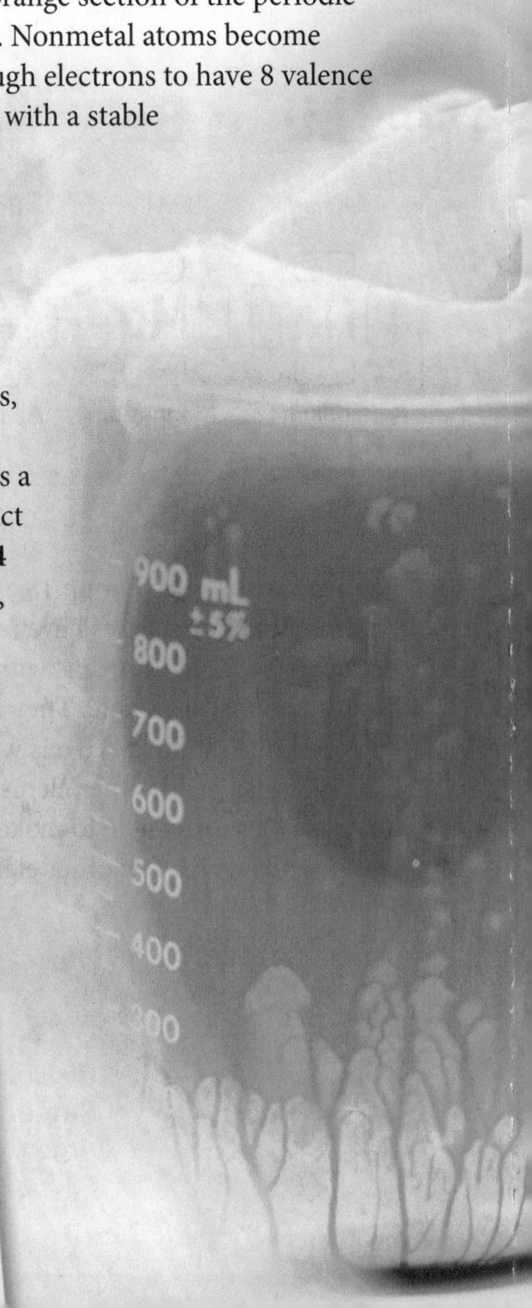

900 mL
±5%
800

700

600

500

400

300

FIGURE 4 ···········
Reactivity of Bromine
Aluminum reacts violently with bromine to produce aluminum bromide.

✎ CHALLENGE What would happen if an alkali metal was combined with a halogen? Explain.

_____

_____

_____

_____

Complete the table about groups of elements in the periodic table.

Group Number	Group Name	Number of Valence Electrons	Reactivity (High/Low)
1	Alkali metals	_____	_____
17	Halogens	_____	_____
18	Noble gases	_____	_____

Metalloids The metalloids lie along the zigzag line in the periodic table, between the metals and the nonmetals. Atoms of the metalloids can either lose or share electrons when they combine with other elements. Each metalloid has some of the properties of metals and some of the properties of nonmetals.

Hydrogen Hydrogen (H) is placed in Group 1 in the periodic table because it has 1 valence electron, but hydrogen is considered to be a nonmetal. The properties of hydrogen are very different from the properties of the alkali metals. Hydrogen shares its electron when forming compounds with other nonmetals to obtain a stable arrangement of 2 electrons.

FIGURE 5 ······························

Computer Chip
Silicon, a metalloid, is one of the most abundant elements on Earth. It is used to make computer processor chips.

Lab zone® Do the Quick Lab
Element Chemistry.

Assess Your Understanding

1a. Define What are valence electrons?

_____

_____

8.1.4

b. Explain Why do the properties of elements change in a regular way across a period?

_____

_____

_____

8.1.2, 8.1.4, 8.1.6, 8.4.3

c. ⟳ **Relate Cause and Effect** Explain the reactivity of the noble gases in terms of valence electrons.

_____

_____

_____

_____

_____

8.1.4, 8.1.6, 8.4.3

got it? ···

○ **I get it!** Now I know that the chemical properties of an element are determined by _____

○ I need extra help with _____

Go to MY SCIENCE COACH online for help with this subject.

8.1.4, 8.1.6, 8.4.3

Ionic Bonds

UNLOCK THE BIG ?

🔑 **How Do Ions Form?**
8.1.4, 8.1.5, 8.NS.8

🔑 **How Are the Formulas and Names of Ionic Compounds Written?**
8.1.4, 8.1.5, 8.NS.8

🔑 **What Are Properties of Ionic Compounds?**
8.1.4, 8.1.5, 8.1.6, 8.4.1, 8.4.2, 8.4.3, 8.NS.8

my PLANET DiARY

The Periodic Palette

Imagine calling the colors of the rainbow cadmium, chromium, cobalt, and manganese. These may not sound like the typical colors of the rainbow to you, but they do to many artists and painters!

The "colors" listed above are transition metal elements. These metals can form compounds known as ionic compounds. Many transition metal compounds are brightly colored. They can be used to make the pigments found in oil, acrylic, and watercolor paints. For example, cadmium and chromium compounds are used for red, orange, yellow, or green paints. Cobalt and manganese compounds are used for blue and violet paints.

FUN FACTS

Communicate Write your answer to each question below. Then discuss your answers with a partner.

1. Why are transition metal compounds often used in paint pigments?

_____

_____

_____

2. Some of the compounds used in paint pigments may cause serious health problems. Do you think that using these types of paints is worth the possible health risks? Why or why not?

_____

_____

_____

▶ PLANET DIARY Go to **Planet Diary** to learn more about ionic compounds.

Lab zone® Do the Inquiry Warm-Up *How Do Ions Form?*

Vocabulary
- ion • polyatomic ion • ionic bond • ionic compound
- chemical formula • subscript • crystal

Skills
🔄 Reading: Relate Text and Visuals
🔺 Inquiry: Interpret Data

How Do Ions Form?

You and a friend walk past a market that sells apples for 40 cents each and pears for 50 cents each. You have 45 cents and want an apple. Your friend also has 45 cents but wants a pear. If you give your friend a nickel, she will have 50 cents and can buy a pear. You will have 40 cents left to buy an apple. Transferring the nickel gets both of you what you want. In a simple way, your actions model what can happen between atoms.

Two Atoms Talking Together

I'm about to lose an electron!
Are you sure?
I'm positive!
K F K⁺ F⁻

FIGURE 1

How Ions Form
An atom that loses one of its electrons becomes a positively charged ion. The atom that gains the electron becomes a negatively charged ion.

✏️ **Interpret Diagrams**
Complete the electron dot diagrams for potassium (K) and fluorine (F) before and after the electron is transferred.

8.NS.8

Ions An **ion** (EYE ahn) is an atom or group of atoms that has an electric charge. 🔑 **When a neutral atom loses a valence electron, it loses a negative charge. It becomes a positive ion. When a neutral atom gains an electron, it gains a negative charge. It becomes a negative ion.** This is shown in **Figure 1**.

Metal atoms are likely to lose electrons. These atoms lose enough electrons to have a stable arrangement of 8 valence electrons at a lower energy level. A potassium (K) atom easily loses its 1 valence electron to become more stable. Nonmetal atoms are likely to gain electrons. These atoms gain enough electrons so that they have 8 valence electrons. A fluorine (F) atom gains 1 electron to have a stable arrangement of 8 valence electrons.

🔄 **Relate Text and Visuals**
Using the cartoon in **Figure 1**, explain why the potassium atom becomes positively charged and the fluorine atom becomes negatively charged.

_____
_____
_____
_____
_____
_____
_____

141

FIGURE 2 ·····················

> **INTERACTIVE ART** Ions

Ions have electric charges.

Common Ions and Their Charges		
Name	Charge	Symbol or Formula
Lithium	1+	Li^+
Sodium	1+	Na^+
Potassium	1+	K^+
Ammonium	1+	NH_4^+
Calcium	2+	Ca^{2+}
Magnesium	2+	Mg^{2+}
Aluminum	3+	Al^{3+}
Fluoride	1–	F^-
Chloride	1–	Cl^-
Iodide	1–	I^-
Bicarbonate	1–	HCO_3^-
Nitrate	1–	NO_3^-
Oxide	2–	O^{2-}
Sulfide	2–	S^{2-}
Carbonate	2–	CO_3^{2-}
Sulfate	2–	SO_4^{2-}

Common Ions **Figure 2** lists the names of some common ions. Notice that some ions are made of several atoms. The ammonium ion is made of 1 nitrogen atom and 4 hydrogen atoms. Ions that are made of more than 1 atom are called **polyatomic ions** (pahl ee uh TAHM ik). The prefix *poly-* means "many," so *polyatomic* means "many atoms." Like other ions, polyatomic ions have an overall positive or negative charge.

Ionic Bonds When atoms that easily lose electrons react with atoms that easily gain electrons, valence electrons are transferred from one type of atom to another. The transfer gives each type of atom a more stable arrangement of electrons. Look at **Figure 3** to see how sodium atoms and chlorine atoms react to form sodium chloride (table salt).

❶ The sodium atom has 1 valence electron. The chlorine atom has 7 valence electrons.

❷ The valence electron of the sodium atom is transferred to the chlorine atom. Both atoms become ions. The sodium atom becomes a positive ion (Na^+). The chlorine atom becomes a negative ion (Cl^-).

❸ Oppositely charged particles attract, so the positive Na^+ ion and the negative Cl^- ion attract. An **ionic bond** is the attraction between two oppositely charged ions. The resulting compound is called an **ionic compound.** It is made up of positive and negative ions. In an ionic compound, the total positive charge of all the positive ions equals the total negative charge of all the negative ions.

FIGURE 3 ···

Formation of an Ionic Bond

Follow the steps to see how an ionic bond forms between a sodium atom and a chlorine atom.

✎ **Infer** **Complete the electron dot diagrams for the sodium and chlorine atoms and their ions.**

8.NS.8

▲ Sodium metal

▲ Chlorine gas

Na
Transfer of an electron
❷

Cl
❶

❸ **Na⁺** **Cl⁻**
Sodium ion   Chloride ion

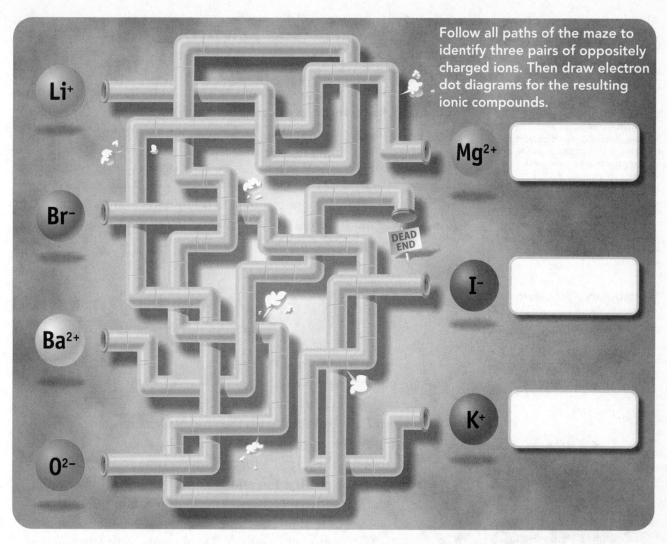

Follow all paths of the maze to identify three pairs of oppositely charged ions. Then draw electron dot diagrams for the resulting ionic compounds.

Li⁺

Br⁻

Ba²⁺

O²⁻

Mg²⁺

DEAD END

I⁻

K⁺

Lab zone® Do the Quick Lab *Ion Formation.*

🔑 Assess Your Understanding

1a. Review An atom that loses a valence electron becomes a (positive/negative) ion. An atom that gains a valence electron becomes a (positive/negative) ion.

8.1.4

b. Apply Concepts Write the symbols for the ions that form when potassium and iodine react to form the ionic compound potassium iodide.

_____

8.1.5

c. Relate Cause and Effect Why is potassium iodide electrically neutral?

_____
_____
_____
_____
_____

8.1.4, 8.1.5

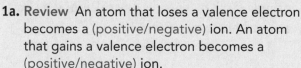

O **I get it!** Now I know ions form when _____
_____

O I need extra help with _____

Go to **MY SCIENCE** 💬 **COACH** *online for help with this subject.*

8.1.4, 8.1.5

143

Academic Standards for Science

8.1.4 Describe the structure of an atom and relate the arrangement of electrons to how that atom interacts with other atoms.

8.1.5 Explain that atoms join together to form molecules and compounds and illustrate with diagrams the relationship between atoms and compounds and/or molecules.

8.NS.8 Analyze data.

Vocabulary Choose the word that best completes the following sentence.

Mg is the _____ for magnesium.

How Are the Formulas and Names of Ionic Compounds Written?

You will often see a compound represented by its chemical formula. A **chemical formula** is a group of symbols that shows the ratio of elements in a compound. The formula for magnesium chloride is $MgCl_2$. What does this formula tell you?

Formulas of Ionic Compounds When ionic compounds form, the ions combine to balance the charges on the ions. The chemical formula for the compound reflects this balance. Look at the formula for magnesium chloride.

Chemical symbols → $MgCl_2$ ← Subscript

Figure 2 shows that the charge on the magnesium ion is 2+. The charge on each chloride ion is 1−. Two chloride ions balance the charge on the magnesium ion. The number "2" in the formula is a subscript. **Subscripts** tell the ratio of elements in a compound. The ratio of magnesium ions to chloride ions in $MgCl_2$ is 1 to 2.

🔑 **To write the formula for an ionic compound, write the symbol of the positive ion and then the symbol of the negative ion. Add the subscripts that are needed to balance the charges.**

If no subscript is written, it is understood that the subscript is 1. The formula NaCl tells you that there is a 1-to-1 ratio of sodium ions to chloride ions. Formulas for compounds of polyatomic ions are written in a similar way. Calcium carbonate has the formula $CaCO_3$. There is one calcium ion (Ca^{2+}) for each carbonate ion (CO_3^{2-}).

FIGURE 4 ·······································

Coral Reefs

Corals make calcium carbonate, which helps protect them. When coral dies, its calcium carbonate shell remains and adds structure to the reef.

✏️ **Identify** Circle the part of the formula representing the carbonate ion. Then identify the charge of each ion in the compound.

$CaCO_3$

8.NS.8

Naming Ionic Compounds

Magnesium chloride, sodium bicarbonate, sodium oxide—where do these names come from? 🔑 **For an ionic compound, the name of the positive ion comes first, followed by the name of the negative ion.** The name of the positive ion is usually the name of a metal. But, a few positive polyatomic ions exist, such as the ammonium ion (NH_4^+). If the negative ion is a single element, the end of its name changes to *-ide*. For example, MgO is named magnesium oxide. If the negative ion is polyatomic, its name usually ends in *-ate* or *-ite*. Ammonium nitrate (NH_4NO_3) is a common fertilizer for plants.

did you know?......

Calcium oxide (CaO), also known as lime, gives off a white light when heated. Theaters once used special lamps to focus this bright light on a single actor. So, the expression *in the limelight* describes a person who receives favorable attention.

apply *it!*

Chemists refer to compounds by either their names or their chemical formulas.

⚠ **Interpret Data** Use the periodic table and **Figure 2** to fill in the table.

Name	Positive Ion	Negative Ion	Formula
Magnesium chloride	Mg^{2+}	Cl^-	$MgCl_2$
Sodium bromide	_____	_____	_____
_____	_____	_____	Li_2O
_____	Mg^{2+}	S^{2-}	_____
Aluminum fluoride	_____	_____	_____
_____	_____	_____	KNO_3
_____	NH_4^+	Cl^-	_____

8.NS.8

Lab zone® Do the Quick Lab *How Do You Write Ionic Names and Formulas?*

🔑 Assess Your Understanding

2a. Explain The formula for sodium sulfide is Na_2S. Explain what this formula means.

_____

_____

_____

8.1.4, 8.1.5

b. Apply Concepts Write the formula for calcium chloride. Explain how you determined this formula.

_____

_____

_____

8.1.4, 8.1.5

got *it?* ......

○ **I get it!** Now I know that to write the formula for an ionic compound, _____

_____

_____

○ **I need extra help with** _____

Go to MY SCIENCE Ⓢ COACH *online for help with this subject.*

8.1.4, 8.1.5

Academic Standards for Science

8.1.4 Describe the structure of an atom and relate the arrangement of electrons to how that atom interacts with other atoms.

8.1.5 Explain that atoms join together to form molecules and compounds and illustrate with diagrams the relationship between atoms and compounds and/or molecules.

8.1.6 Explain that elements and compounds have characteristic properties.

8.4.1 Understand how the strength of attractive forces between particles in a material helps to explain many physical properties of the material.

8.4.2 Rank the strength of attractions between particles.

8.4.3 Investigate the properties of natural materials.

8.NS.8 Analyze data.

FIGURE 5 ·····················
Halite
The ions in ionic compounds are arranged in specific three-dimensional shapes called crystals. Some crystals have a cubic shape, like these crystals of halite, or sodium chloride.

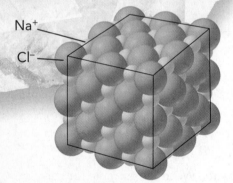

Na⁺

Cl⁻

What Are Properties of Ionic Compounds?

Compounds have properties that are different from their component elements. You have already read about the properties of metals and nonmetals, but what are the properties of the ionic compounds that form when metals and nonmetals react? **In general, ionic compounds form hard, brittle crystals that have high melting points. They conduct electric current when dissolved in water or melted.**

Ionic Crystals Ionic compounds form solids by building up repeating patterns of ions. **Figure 5** shows a chunk of halite, which is how sodium chloride occurs naturally. Pieces of halite have a cubic shape. Equal numbers of Na^+ and Cl^- ions in halite are attracted in an alternating pattern, as shown in the diagram. The ions form an orderly, three-dimensional arrangement called a **crystal.**

Every ion in an ionic compound is attracted to ions of an opposite charge that surround it. The pattern formed by the ions is the same no matter what the size of the crystal. In a single grain of salt, the crystal pattern extends for millions of ions in every direction. Many crystals of ionic compounds are hard and brittle. This is due to the strength of their ionic bonds and the attractions among all the ions.

High Melting Points
The ions in the crystal have to break apart for an ionic compound to melt. It takes a huge amount of energy to separate the ions in a crystal, because the attraction between the positive and negative ions is so great. As a result, ionic compounds have very high melting points. The melting point of sodium chloride is 801°C.

apply it!

Galena, or lead sulfide (PbS), has a structure similar to that of table salt.

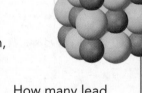

S²⁻

Pb²⁺

❶ Infer The chemical formula of lead sulfide tells you that it contains _____ S^{2-} ion(s) for every Pb^{2+} ion.

❷ What holds the ions together in galena?

_____

_____

❸ CHALLENGE If the pattern of ions shown here for galena is expanded in every direction, how many sulfide ions would surround each lead ion? _____ How many lead ions would surround each sulfide ion? _____

8.NS.8

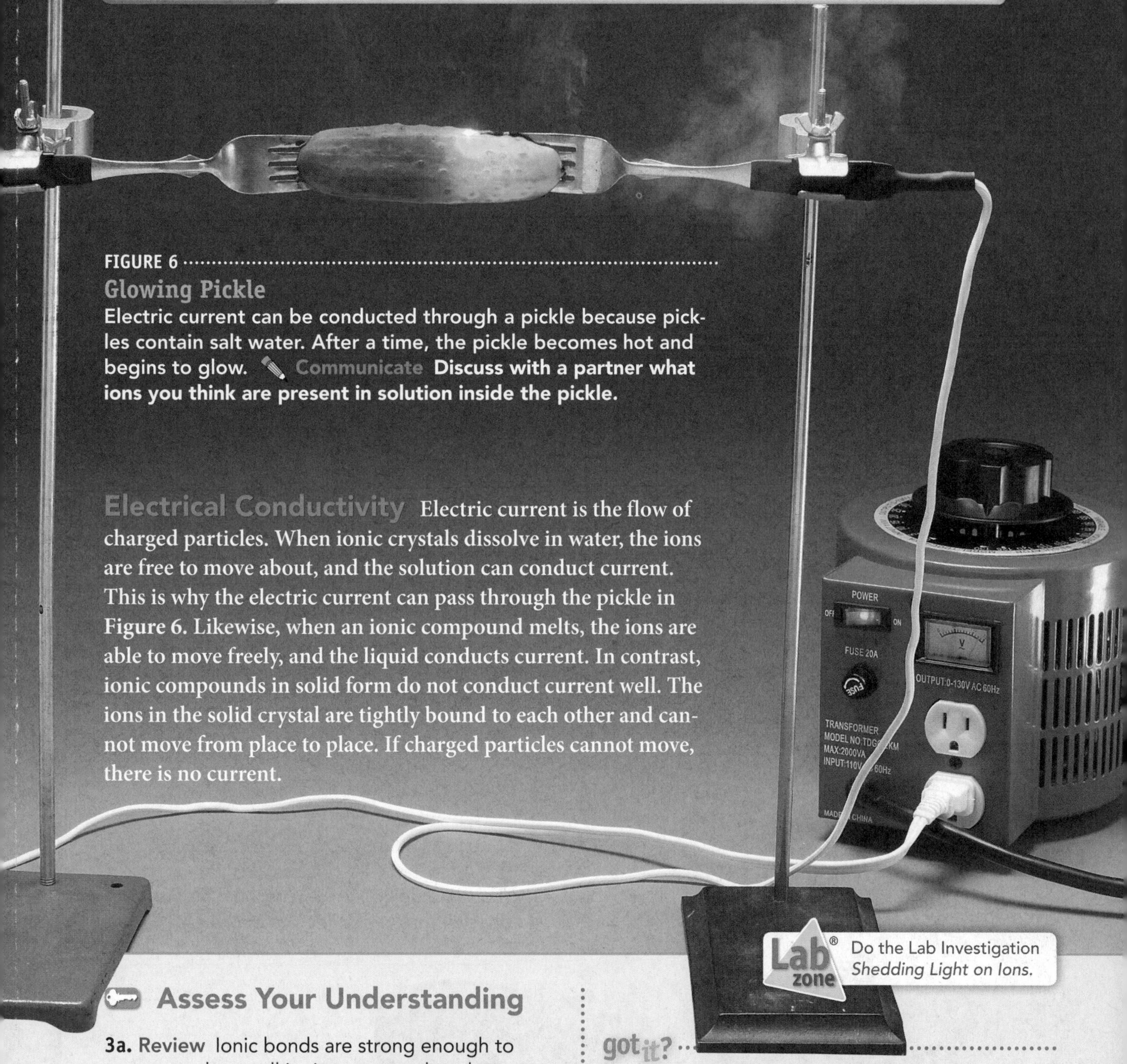

FIGURE 6
Glowing Pickle
Electric current can be conducted through a pickle because pickles contain salt water. After a time, the pickle becomes hot and begins to glow. ✎ Communicate **Discuss with a partner what ions you think are present in solution inside the pickle.**

Electrical Conductivity
Electric current is the flow of charged particles. When ionic crystals dissolve in water, the ions are free to move about, and the solution can conduct current. This is why the electric current can pass through the pickle in **Figure 6.** Likewise, when an ionic compound melts, the ions are able to move freely, and the liquid conducts current. In contrast, ionic compounds in solid form do not conduct current well. The ions in the solid crystal are tightly bound to each other and cannot move from place to place. If charged particles cannot move, there is no current.

🔑 **Assess Your Understanding**

3a. Review Ionic bonds are strong enough to cause almost all ionic compounds to be

_____ at room temperature.

8.1.4, 8.1.5

b. Relate Cause and Effect Solid table salt does not conduct electric current. How does dissolving salt in water allow electric current to flow?

_____

_____

_____

8.1.4, 8.1.5, 8.1.6

Do the Lab Investigation
Shedding Light on Ions.

got it?

○ **I get it!** Now I know that properties of ionic compounds include _____

_____

_____

○ **I need extra help with** _____

_____

Go to **my science** COACH *online for help with this subject.*

8.1.4, 8.1.5, 8.1.6

Covalent Bonds

🔑 **How Are Atoms Held Together in a Covalent Bond?**
8.1.4, 8.1.5, 8.NS.8

🔑 **What Are Properties of Molecular Compounds?**
8.1.4, 8.1.5, 8.1.6, 8.4.1, 8.4.2, 8.4.3, 8.NS.1, 8.NS.8

🔑 **How Do Bonded Atoms Become Partially Charged?**
8.1.4, 8.1.5, 8.1.6, 8.4.1, 8.4.2, 8.NS.8, 8.NS.11

MY PLANET DIARY

Sticky Feet

Have you ever seen a gecko climbing up a wall or running across a ceiling? Geckos seem to defy gravity. They have tiny hairs that cover the pads of their feet. These hairs branch out into hundreds of smaller structures, called *spatulae*. When a gecko climbs a wall, billions of spatulae on its feet come into contact with the surface. Scientists believe that geckos can stick to surfaces because of the billions of small attractive forces, called van der Waals forces, between the molecules of the spatulae and the molecules on the surface. Now, scientists are developing adhesives that can copy the characteristics of the spatulae.

DISCOVERY

Communicate Answer the following questions. Then discuss your answers with a partner.

1. Why is it important that billions of spatulae come into contact with the surface the gecko is climbing?

_____

_____

_____

_____

_____

_____

2. What uses do you think you could find for an adhesive that works like the gecko's foot?

_____

_____

_____

_____

_____

> PLANET DIARY Go to **Planet Diary** to learn more about attractions between molecules.

Lab zone® Do the Inquiry Warm-Up *Covalent Bonds.*

Vocabulary
- covalent bond
- molecule
- double bond
- triple bond
- molecular compound
- nonpolar bond
- polar bond

Skills
- Reading: Compare and Contrast
- Inquiry: Graph

How Are Atoms Held Together in a Covalent Bond?

You and a friend walk past a bakery that sells giant chocolate chip cookies for one dollar each. But each of you has only 50 cents. If you combine your money, you can buy a cookie and split it. So, you can afford a cookie by sharing your money. Similarly, 2 atoms can form a bond by sharing electrons. The chemical bond formed when 2 atoms share electrons is called a **covalent bond.** Covalent bonds usually form between nonmetal atoms. Ionic bonds usually form when a metal combines with a nonmetal.

Electron Sharing Nonmetals can bond to other nonmetals by sharing electrons. Atoms of some nonmetals can bond with each other. **Figure 1** shows how 2 fluorine atoms can react by sharing a pair of electrons. By sharing electrons, each fluorine atom is surrounded by 8 valence electrons. **The attractions between the shared electrons and the protons in the nucleus of each atom hold the atoms together in a covalent bond.** The 2 bonded fluorine atoms form a **molecule.** A molecule is a neutral group of atoms joined by covalent bonds.

Academic Standards for Science

8.1.4 Describe the structure of an atom and relate the arrangement of electrons to how that atom interacts with other atoms.

8.1.5 Explain that atoms join together to form molecules and compounds and illustrate with diagrams the relationship between atoms and compounds and/or molecules.

8.NS.8 Analyze data.

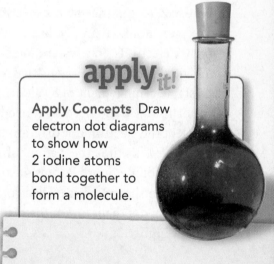

apply it!

Apply Concepts Draw electron dot diagrams to show how 2 iodine atoms bond together to form a molecule.

FIGURE 1 ·······························

Sharing Electrons
By sharing 2 electrons in a covalent bond, each fluorine atom gains a stable set of 8 valence electrons.

✎ **Interpret Diagrams** Circle the shared electrons that form a covalent bond between the 2 fluorine atoms.

8.NS.8

F F

Fluorine atom   Fluorine atom

F F

Fluorine molecule

8.1.5, 8.NS.8

149

Single Bonds	Double Bond	Triple Bond

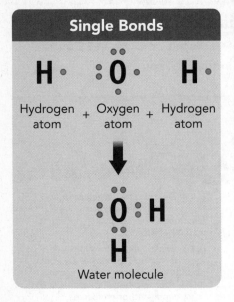

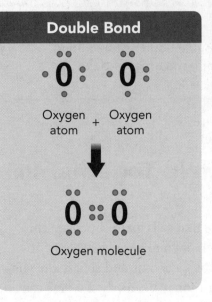

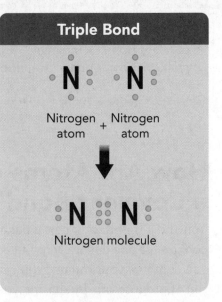

FIGURE 2 ······················

Covalent Bonds

Atoms can form single, double, and triple covalent bonds by sharing one or more pairs of electrons.

How Many Bonds?

Look at the electron dot diagrams in **Figure 2.** Count the valence electrons around each hydrogen and oxygen atom. Hydrogen has 1 valence electron. Oxygen has 6 valence electrons. In a water molecule, oxygen forms one covalent bond with each of 2 hydrogen atoms. As a result, the oxygen atom has a stable arrangement of 8 valence electrons. Each hydrogen atom forms one bond because it needs only 2 electrons to be stable.

Look at the electron dot diagram of the oxygen molecule (O_2) in **Figure 2.** This time the 2 atoms share 2 pairs of electrons, forming a **double bond.** Atoms of some elements, such as nitrogen, can share 3 pairs of electrons, forming a **triple bond.** The electron dot diagram for the nitrogen molecule (N_2) is also shown in **Figure 2.**

CHALLENGE In a carbon dioxide (CO_2) molecule, the carbon atom forms a double bond with each of the 2 oxygen atoms. Draw the electron dot diagram for carbon dioxide below.

8.1.5, 8.NS.8

 Do the Quick Lab *Sharing Electrons.*

Assess Your Understanding

O **I get it!** Now I know that the atoms in a covalent bond are held together by _____

_____

O **I need extra help with** _____

Go to MY SCIENCE ⑤ COACH *online for help with this subject.*   8.1.4, 8.1.5

What Are Properties of Molecular Compounds?

Academic Standards for Science

8.1.4 Describe the structure of an atom and relate the arrangement of electrons to how that atom interacts with other atoms.

8.1.5 Explain that atoms join together to form molecules and compounds and illustrate with diagrams the relationship between atoms and compounds and/or molecules.

8.1.6 Explain that elements and compounds have characteristic properties.

8.4.1 Understand how the strength of attractive forces between particles in a material helps to explain many physical properties of the material.

8.4.2 Rank the strength of attractions between particles.

8.4.3 Investigate the properties of natural materials.

8.NS.1 Make predictions based on research and prior knowledge.

8.NS.8 Analyze data.

Water, oxygen, and sucrose (table sugar, $C_{12}H_{22}O_{11}$) are all examples of molecular compounds. A **molecular compound** is a compound that is made up of molecules. The molecules of a molecular compound contain atoms that are covalently bonded. Ionic compounds are made up of ions and do not form molecules. **Unlike ionic compounds, molecular compounds usually do not conduct electric current when melted or dissolved in water. Also, compared to ionic compounds, molecular compounds generally have lower melting points and boiling points.**

Poor Conductivity

Most molecular compounds do not conduct electric current. Molecular compounds do not contain charged particles that are available to move, so there is no current. Have you ever noticed that some wires are insulated with plastic or rubber? These materials are made up of molecular compounds. Even as liquids, molecular compounds are poor conductors. Pure water does not conduct electric current. Neither does table sugar when it is melted or dissolved in pure water.

Low Melting Points and Boiling Points

Forces hold the molecules close to one another in a molecular solid. But the forces between molecules are much weaker than the forces between ions. Compared with an ionic solid, less heat must be added to a molecular solid to separate the molecules and change it from a solid to a liquid. For example, table salt melts at 801°C, but table sugar melts at about 190°C.

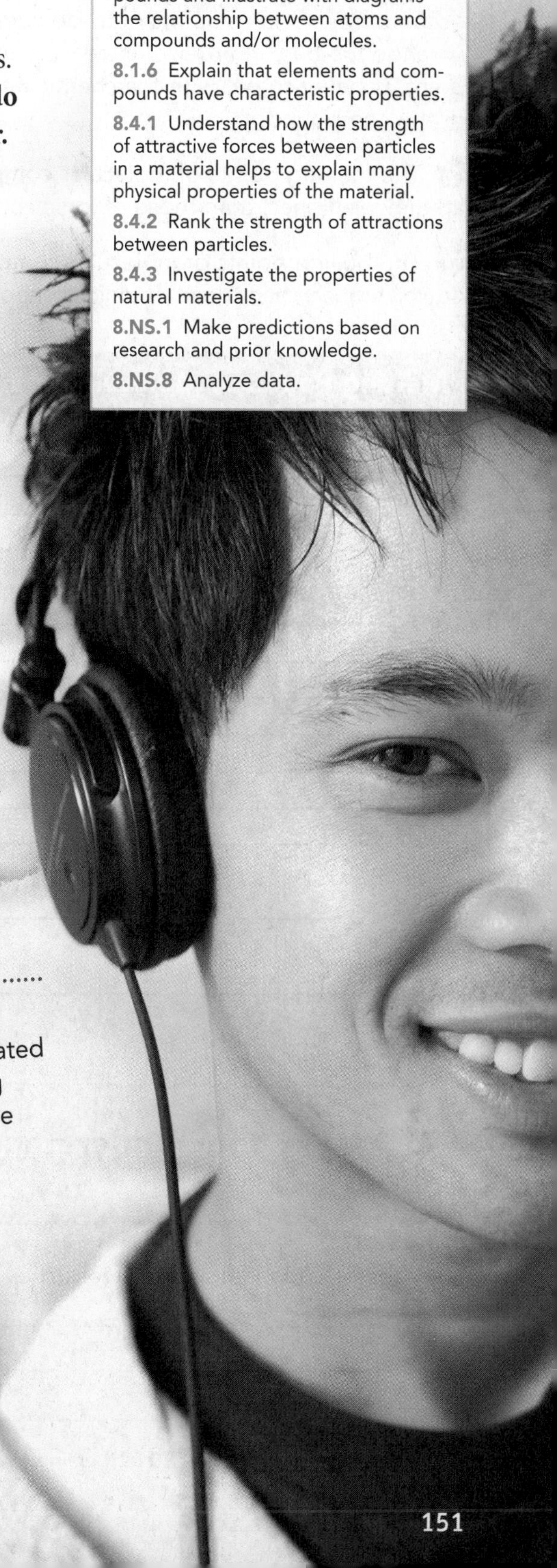

FIGURE 3
Headphones
Wires, such as the ones found on your headphones, are insulated with plastic or rubber to prevent electric current from flowing between the wires. The insulation also allows you to touch the wires without being shocked or electrocuted.

Observe What are some other objects that have insulated wires?

____

____

____

____

____

do the math! Analyzing Data

Molecular and Ionic Compounds

The table shows the melting points and boiling points of a few molecular compounds and ionic compounds.

1 Graph In the space below, draw a bar graph of the melting points of these compounds. Arrange the bars in order of increasing melting point. Label each bar with the chemical formula of the compound.

2 The melting points of molecular compounds are (lower/higher) than those of ionic compounds.

3 The boiling points of molecular compounds are (lower/higher) than those of ionic compounds.

Substance	Formula	Melting Point (°C)	Boiling Point (°C)
Calcium chloride	$CaCl_2$	775	1,935
Isopropyl alcohol	C_3H_8O	–87.9	82.3
Octane	C_8H_{18}	–56.8	125.6
Sodium chloride	NaCl	800.7	1,465
Water	H_2O	0	100

▇ Molecular compound   ▢ Ionic compound

4 Predict Ammonia (NH_3) has a melting point of –78°C and a boiling point of –34°C. These data suggest that ammonia is a(n) (molecular/ionic) compound.

8.NS.1, 8.NS.8

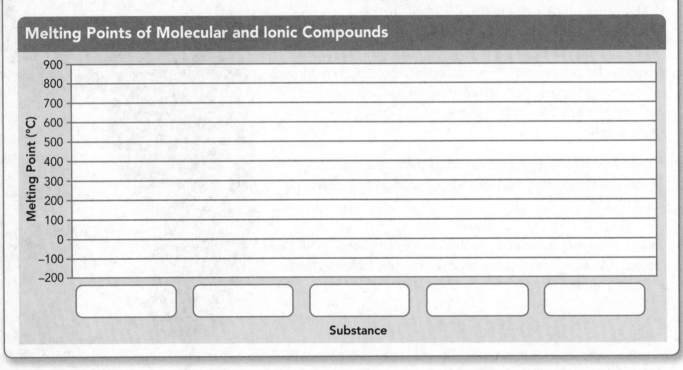

Melting Points of Molecular and Ionic Compounds

Melting Point (°C): 900, 800, 700, 600, 500, 400, 300, 200, 100, 0, –100, –200

Substance

Lab zone®   Do the Quick Lab *Properties of Molecular Compounds.*

🔑 Assess Your Understanding

got it? ....

○ I get it! Now I know that properties of molecular compounds include _____

_____

○ I need extra help with _____

Go to MY SCIENCE 🄢 COACH online for help with this subject.

8.1.4, 8.1.5, 8.1.6

How Do Bonded Atoms Become Partially Charged?

Have you ever played tug-of-war? If you have, you know that when one team pulls the rope with more force than the other team, the rope moves toward the side of the stronger team. The same is true of electrons in a covalent bond. Atoms of some elements pull more strongly on the shared electrons of a covalent bond than do atoms of other elements. As a result, the electrons are shared unequally. **Unequal sharing of electrons causes covalently bonded atoms to have slight electric charges.**

Nonpolar Bonds and Polar Bonds If 2 atoms pull equally on the electrons, neither atom becomes charged. This happens when identical atoms are bonded. A covalent bond in which electrons are shared equally is a **nonpolar bond.** The hydrogen molecule (H_2) shown in **Figure 4** has a nonpolar bond.

When electrons in a covalent bond are shared unequally, the atom with the stronger pull gains a slightly negative charge. The atom with the weaker pull gains a slightly positive charge. A covalent bond in which electrons are shared unequally is a **polar bond.** Hydrogen fluoride (HF), also shown in **Figure 4,** has a polar bond.

Academic Standards for Science

8.1.4 Describe the structure of an atom and relate the arrangement of electrons to how that atom interacts with other atoms.

8.1.5 Explain that atoms join together to form molecules and compounds and illustrate with diagrams the relationship between atoms and compounds and/or molecules.

8.1.6 Explain that elements and compounds have characteristic properties.

8.4.1 Understand how the strength of attractive forces between particles in a material helps to explain many physical properties of the material.

8.4.2 Rank the strength of attractions between particles.

8.NS.8 Analyze data.

8.NS.11 Communicate findings.

Compare and Contrast
In a nonpolar bond electrons are shared (equally/unequally).
In a polar bond electrons are shared (equally/unequally).

FIGURE 4 ·······················
ART IN MOTION **Nonpolar and Polar Bonds**
Hydrogen forms a nonpolar bond with another hydrogen atom. In hydrogen fluoride, fluorine attracts electrons more strongly than hydrogen does. The bond formed is polar.

Round 1: H₂

Round 2: HF

I want it!

I want it more!

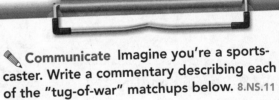

Communicate Imagine you're a sportscaster. Write a commentary describing each of the "tug-of-war" matchups below. **8.NS.11**

Round 1: Hydrogen (H_2)

_____

_____

_____

_____

Round 2: Hydrogen Fluoride (HF)

_____

_____

_____

_____

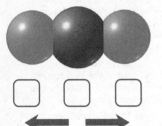

Nonpolar Molecule
Carbon dioxide

Opposite pulling cancels.

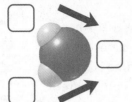

Polar Molecule
Water

Electrons pulled
toward oxygen

FIGURE 5 ···

Nonpolar and Polar Molecules

Both carbon dioxide and water molecules contain polar bonds. However, only water is a polar molecule.

✎ **Interpret Diagrams** Draw a positive (+) sign next to the atoms that gain a slight positive charge. Draw a negative (–) sign next to the atoms that gain a slight negative charge.

8.NS.8

Polar Bonds in Molecules

A molecule is polar if it has a positively charged end and a negatively charged end. However, not all molecules containing polar bonds are polar overall. In a carbon dioxide molecule, the oxygen atoms attract electrons more strongly than the carbon atom does. The bonds between the oxygen and carbon atoms are polar. But, as you can see in **Figure 5,** a carbon dioxide molecule has a straight-line shape. The two oxygen atoms pull with equal strength in opposite directions. The attractions cancel out, so the molecule is nonpolar.

A water molecule, with its two polar bonds, is itself polar. As you can see in **Figure 5,** a water molecule has a bent shape. The two hydrogen atoms are at one end of the molecule. The oxygen atom is at the other end of the molecule. The oxygen atom attracts electrons more strongly than do the hydrogen atoms. As a result, the end of the molecule with the oxygen atom has a slight negative charge. The end of the molecule with the hydrogen atoms has a slight positive charge.

FIGURE 6 ··

▶ **INTERACTIVE ART** **Bonding and Properties**

The Dead Sea is a saltwater lake in the Middle East. It is so salty that neither fish nor plants can survive in it. The water contains many dissolved compounds, including sodium chloride, magnesium chloride, and potassium chloride.

✎ **Review** Answer the questions about water and sodium chloride.

Water (H_2O)

Water is an example of a(n) _____ (ionic/molecular) compound.

This type of bond forms when _____
_____
_____

Properties of these compounds include _____
_____
_____
_____

Close-up of salt

Attractions Between Molecules

Opposite charges attract. Polar molecules are connected to each other by weak attractions between their slight negative and positive charges. These attractions are called van der Waals forces. The negatively charged oxygen ends of the polar water molecules attract the positively charged hydrogen ends of nearby water molecules. Van der Waals forces pull water molecules toward each other. They are also the reason a gecko's feet can grip onto smooth surfaces, such as glass.

The properties of polar and nonpolar compounds are different because of differences in attractions between their molecules. The melting point and boiling point of water are much higher than the melting point and boiling point of oxygen. The attractions between the polar water molecules require more energy to overcome than the attractions between the nonpolar oxygen molecules.

Sodium Chloride (NaCl)

Sodium chloride is an example of a(n) (ionic/molecular) compound.

This type of bond forms when _____
_____
_____

Properties of these compounds include _____
_____
_____
_____

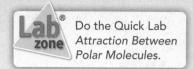
Do the Quick Lab
Attraction Between
Polar Molecules.

🔑 Assess Your Understanding

1a. Review What type of bonds are formed when atoms share electrons unequally?

_____

8.1.5

b. Predict Would carbon dioxide or water have a higher boiling point? Explain.

_____
_____
_____
_____
_____

8.1.6, 8.NS.1

c. How can bonding determine the properties of a substance?

_____
_____
_____
_____
_____
_____
_____
_____

8.1.4, 8.1.5

got it? ....

○ **I get it!** Now I know that some atoms in covalent bonds become slightly negative or slightly positive when _____
_____

○ **I need extra help with** _____
_____

Go to MY SCIENCE ⓢ COACH online for help with this subject. 8.1.4, 8.1.5

Observing Chemical Change

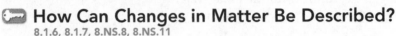

UNLOCK THE BIG ?

🔑 **How Can Changes in Matter Be Described?**
8.1.6, 8.1.7, 8.NS.8, 8.NS.11

🔑 **How Do You Identify a Chemical Reaction?**
8.1.7, 8.NS.1, 8.NS.8

MY PLANET DIARY

PROFILE

Chemistry in the Kitchen

Teen chef Fatoumata Dembele knows that chemical reactions are an important part of cooking great food. In fact, Fatoumata is so skilled at using chemistry in the kitchen that she won an award for her recipes.

Fatoumata knows that to prepare some foods, such as eggs, adding heat is required. Other foods, such as gelatin, need to have heat removed to taste best. Fatoumata says you have to keep a close eye on food while it's cooking. A good chef always pays attention to signs of change. For example, when you cook meat, the color is what tells you when it's ready. A raw steak is red, but a medium steak should be dark brown on the outside and pink in the center. Fatoumata prefers her steak well done. She knows it's ready when the meat is brown all the way through. For chefs like Fatoumata, there is one particular property that matters the most. It's the taste!

Write your answers to the questions below.

1. Energy is required for chemical reactions to take place. What form of energy is used in cooking?

_____

2. Think of something you've cooked before. What changes did you observe in the food?

_____
_____
_____

▶ PLANET DIARY Go to **Planet Diary** to learn more about chemical changes.

 Do the Inquiry Warm-Up *What Happens When Chemicals React?*

Vocabulary

- physical change • chemical change
- reactant • product • precipitate
- exothermic reaction • endothermic reaction

Skills

- Reading: Relate Cause and Effect
- Inquiry: Graph

How Can Changes in Matter Be Described?

Picture yourself frying an egg. You crack open the shell, and the yolk and egg white spill into the pan. As the egg heats up, the white changes from a clear liquid to a white solid. The egg, the pan, and the stove are all examples of matter. Recall that matter is anything that has mass and takes up space. An important part of chemistry is describing matter.

Properties of Matter Matter is often described by its characteristic properties, which are physical or chemical attributes that are unique to a particular substance.

How would you describe the penny in **Figure 1A**? It is solid, shiny, and hard. A physical property is a characteristic of a substance that can be observed without changing the substance into another substance. The temperature at which a solid melts is a physical property. Color, texture, density, and conductivity are other physical properties of matter.

A chemical property is a characteristic of a substance that describes its ability to change into other substances. To observe the chemical properties of a substance, you must try to change it into another substance. For example, **Figure 1B** shows a penny that has turned green. This color change demonstrates a chemical property of the penny's copper coating. When copper is exposed to air, it reacts over time to form a dull, crusty solid. Another chemical property is a material's ability to burn in the presence of oxygen. This property is called flammability.

FIGURE 1 ·············

Properties of Copper

Pennies are coated with copper.

✎ **Complete the following tasks.**

1. **Classify** Check off which properties of copper are physical properties and which are chemical properties.

2. **Communicate** Add two properties to the list and ask a classmate to classify them as physical or chemical.

Copper

Property	Physical	Chemical
• Reddish color	☐	☐
• Reacts with oxygen	☐	☐
• Smooth texture	☐	☐
• Conducts heat	☐	☐
• Not flammable	☐	☐
• _____	☐	☐
• _____	☐	☐

8.NS.8

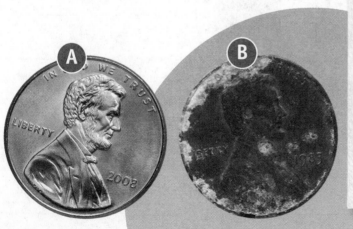

157

A

_____

FIGURE 2 ·················
> INTERACTIVE ART **Changes in Matter**
Matter can undergo both physical and chemical changes.

✎ **Identify** Label each apple with the type of change it has undergone.

B

_____

Changes in Matter Like properties of matter, there are two types of changes in matter. 🗝 **Changes in matter can be described in terms of physical changes and chemical changes.** A **physical change** is any change that alters the form or appearance of a substance but does not change it into another substance. When you cut an apple in half, as shown in **Figure 2A,** you cause a physical change. In a physical change, some of the physical properties of the material may be altered, but the chemical composition remains the same. Bending, crushing, and cutting are all physical changes. Changes in the state of matter, such as melting, freezing, and boiling, are also physical changes.

Sometimes when matter changes, its chemical composition is changed. For example, when a cut apple is left out in the air, it turns brown, as shown in **Figure 2B.** Compounds in the apple react with the oxygen in the air to form new compounds. A change in matter that produces one or more new substances is a **chemical change,** or chemical reaction. In a chemical change, the atoms rearrange to form new substances. When a substance undergoes a chemical change, it results in different physical properties as well. Burning and rusting are both chemical changes. Substances that undergo the chemical changes are called **reactants.** The new substances that form are the **products.**

apply it!

Changes in matter occur everywhere in your daily life.

❶ **Apply Concepts** Paper that has been (torn/burned) has undergone a chemical change.

❷ **Interpret Photos** Label the change in each set of pictures as a physical or chemical change.

❸ CHALLENGE In the correct box, draw or explain how the leaf will look if it undergoes a physical change and if it undergoes a chemical change.

_____

_____

Physical	Chemical

8.NS.8

Bonding and Chemical Change Chemical changes occur when existing bonds break and new bonds form. As a result, new substances are produced. Atoms form bonds when they share or transfer electrons. The reaction pictured in **Figure 3** involves both the breaking of shared bonds and the transfer of electrons.

Oxygen gas (O_2) in the air consists of molecules made up of two oxygen atoms bonded together. These bonds break when oxygen reacts with magnesium (Mg) and a new ionic bond forms. The compound magnesium oxide (MgO) is produced. Magnesium oxide, a white powder, has properties that differ from those of either shiny magnesium or invisible oxygen gas. For example, while magnesium melts at 650°C, magnesium oxide melts at 2,800°C.

↪ **Relate Cause and Effect**
Find and underline the effect caused by breaking and forming bonds.

FIGURE 3 ·······················

Breaking and Making Bonds

✎ **Summarize** On the lines below the diagrams, describe what happens to the bonds in each of the steps as oxygen reacts with magnesium.

①

_____

_____

②

_____

_____

8.NS.11

Lab zone Do the Quick Lab
Observing Change.

🗝 **Assess Your Understanding**

1a. Review The freezing point of water is a (physical/chemical) property. The ability of oxygen to react with iron to cause rust is a (physical/chemical) property.   8.1.6, 8.1.7

b. Pose Questions When silver coins are found in ancient shipwrecks, they are coated with a black crust. Ask a question that could help you determine whether the silver underwent a chemical change or physical change. Explain.

_____

_____

_____

_____

8.1.7

got it?

○ **I get it!** Now I know that two ways changes in matter can be described are _____

_____

_____

_____

_____

○ **I need extra help with** _____

Go to **MY SCIENCE COACH** *online for help with this subject.*   8.1.6, 8.1.7

Academic Standards for Science

8.1.7 Explain that chemical changes occur when substances react and form one or more different products, whose physical and chemical properties are different from those of the reactants.

8.NS.1 Make predictions.

8.NS.8 Analyze data and use it to identify patterns and make inferences.

Vocabulary Identify Multiple Meanings Precipitation can mean rain, snow, or hail. In chemistry, precipitation is the formation of a solid from

_____

_____

_____

Design Experiments Describe how you would test the best method for separating the precipitate from the liquid in curdled milk.

_____

_____

_____

_____

_____

_____

_____

How Do You Identify a Chemical Reaction?

Look at the images in **Figure 4**. Even without reading the caption, you probably can tell that each image shows a chemical reaction. How can you tell when a chemical reaction occurs? **Chemical reactions involve changes in properties and changes in energy that you can often observe.**

Changes in Properties One way to detect chemical reactions is to observe changes in the physical properties of the materials. Changes in properties result when new substances form. For instance, formation of a precipitate, gas production, and a color change are all possible evidence that a chemical reaction has taken place. Many times, physical properties such as texture and hardness may also change in a chemical reaction.

Changes in physical properties can be easy to recognize in a chemical reaction, but what about the chemical properties? During a chemical reaction, reactants interact to form products with different chemical properties. For example, sodium (Na) and chlorine (Cl_2) react to form an ionic compound, sodium chloride (NaCl). Both reactants are very reactive elements. However, the product, sodium chloride, is a very stable compound.

❶ Formation of a Precipitate

The mixing of two liquids may form a precipitate. A **precipitate** (pree SIP uh tayt) is a solid that forms from liquids during a chemical reaction. For example, the precipitate seen in this curdled milk has formed from the liquids milk and lemon juice.

FIGURE 4 ·······

Evidence of Chemical Reactions

Many kinds of change provide evidence that a chemical reaction has occurred.

8.NS.1

Bonding and Chemical Change

Chemical changes occur when existing bonds break and new bonds form. As a result, new substances are produced. Atoms form bonds when they share or transfer electrons. The reaction pictured in **Figure 3** involves both the breaking of shared bonds and the transfer of electrons.

Oxygen gas (O_2) in the air consists of molecules made up of two oxygen atoms bonded together. These bonds break when oxygen reacts with magnesium (Mg) and a new ionic bond forms. The compound magnesium oxide (MgO) is produced. Magnesium oxide, a white powder, has properties that differ from those of either shiny magnesium or invisible oxygen gas. For example, while magnesium melts at 650°C, magnesium oxide melts at 2,800°C.

↻ **Relate Cause and Effect**
Find and underline the effect caused by breaking and forming bonds.

FIGURE 3

Breaking and Making Bonds

✎ **Summarize** On the lines below the diagrams, describe what happens to the bonds in each of the steps as oxygen reacts with magnesium.

1 $O : O \rightarrow O + O$

_____

_____

2 $Mg + O \rightarrow Mg^{2+} O^{2-}$

_____

_____

8.NS.11

Lab zone Do the Quick Lab *Observing Change.*

🔑 Assess Your Understanding

1a. Review The freezing point of water is a (physical/chemical) property. The ability of oxygen to react with iron to cause rust is a (physical/chemical) property.   8.1.6, 8.1.7

b. Pose Questions When silver coins are found in ancient shipwrecks, they are coated with a black crust. Ask a question that could help you determine whether the silver underwent a chemical change or physical change. Explain.

_____

_____

_____

8.1.7

got it?

○ **I get it!** Now I know that two ways changes in matter can be described are _____

_____

_____

_____

_____

○ **I need extra help with** _____

Go to **MY SCIENCE** 💬 **COACH** *online for help with this subject.*   8.1.6, 8.1.7

Vocabulary Identify Multiple Meanings Precipitation can mean rain, snow, or hail. In chemistry, precipitation is the formation of a solid from

_____

_____

How Do You Identify a Chemical Reaction?

Look at the images in **Figure 4**. Even without reading the caption, you probably can tell that each image shows a chemical reaction. How can you tell when a chemical reaction occurs? 🗝 **Chemical reactions involve changes in properties and changes in energy that you can often observe.**

Changes in Properties One way to detect chemical reactions is to observe changes in the physical properties of the materials. Changes in properties result when new substances form. For instance, formation of a precipitate, gas production, and a color change are all possible evidence that a chemical reaction has taken place. Many times, physical properties such as texture and hardness may also change in a chemical reaction.

Changes in physical properties can be easy to recognize in a chemical reaction, but what about the chemical properties? During a chemical reaction, reactants interact to form products with different chemical properties. For example, sodium (Na) and chlorine (Cl_2) react to form an ionic compound, sodium chloride (NaCl). Both reactants are very reactive elements. However, the product, sodium chloride, is a very stable compound.

❶ Formation of a Precipitate

The mixing of two liquids may form a precipitate. A **precipitate** (pree SIP uh tayt) is a solid that forms from liquids during a chemical reaction. For example, the precipitate seen in this curdled milk has formed from the liquids milk and lemon juice.

Design Experiments Describe how you would test the best method for separating the precipitate from the liquid in curdled milk.

_____

_____

_____

_____

_____

_____

_____

FIGURE 4 ·································

Evidence of Chemical Reactions
Many kinds of change provide evidence that a chemical reaction has occurred.

8.NS.1

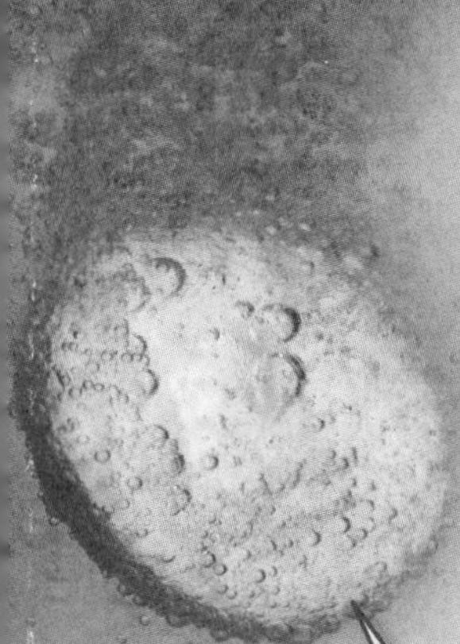

Although you may observe a change in matter, the change does not always indicate that a chemical reaction has taken place. Sometimes physical changes give similar results. For example, when water boils, the gas bubbles you see are made of molecules of water, just as the liquid was. Boiling is a physical change. The only sure evidence of a chemical reaction is that one or more new substances are produced.

2 Gas Production

Another observable change is the formation of a gas from solid or liquid reactants. Often, the gas formed can be seen as bubbles.

✎ **Observe** Bread dough rises from gas bubbles produced when yeast reacts with sugar. What evidence in a slice of bread shows the presence of gas?

_____
_____
_____
_____
_____
_____

3 Color Change

A color change can signal that a new substance has formed. For example, avocados turn brown when they react with oxygen in the air.

✎ **Apply Concepts** Draw or describe evidence of a chemical reaction you have observed in food or in other types of matter. Label the evidence as a color change, formation of a precipitate, or gas production.

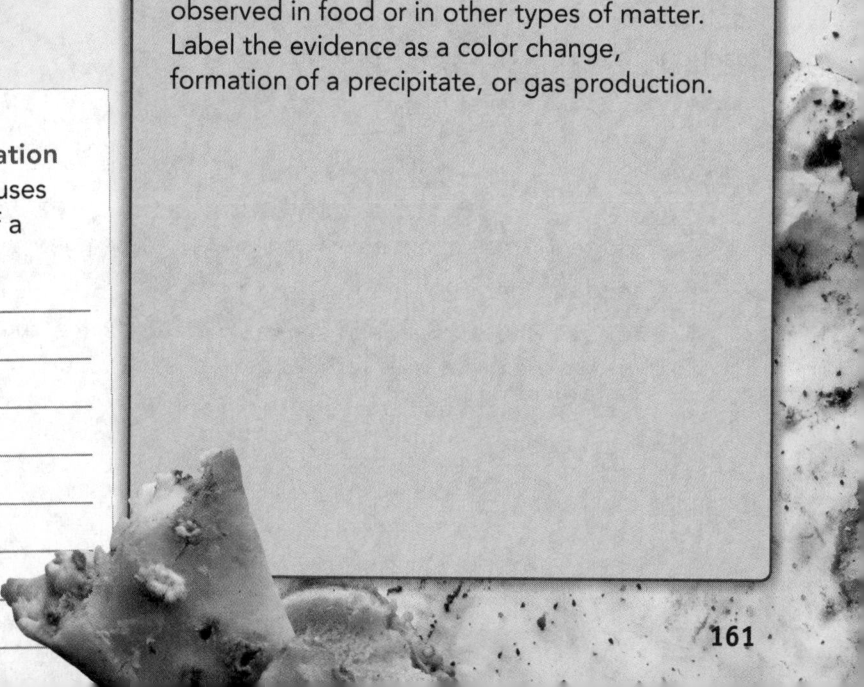

✎ **Relate Evidence and Explanation** Adding food coloring to water causes a color change. Is this evidence of a chemical reaction? Explain.

_____
_____
_____
_____
_____
_____
_____
_____

161

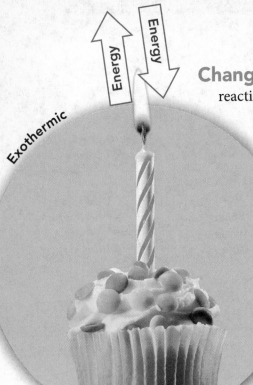

Changes in Energy Recall that a chemical reaction occurs when bonds break and new bonds form. Breaking bonds between atoms or ions requires energy, while forming bonds releases energy.

In an **exothermic reaction** (ek soh THUR mik), the energy released as the products form is greater than the energy required to break the bonds of the reactants. The energy is usually released as heat. For example, some stoves use natural gas. When natural gas burns, it releases heat. This heat is used to cook your food. Similarly, the reaction between oxygen and other fuels that produce fire, such as wood, coal, oil, or the wax of the candle shown in **Figure 5,** release energy in the form of light and heat.

In an **endothermic reaction** (en doh THUR mik), more energy is required to break the bonds of the reactants than is released by the formation of the products. The energy can be absorbed from nearby matter. When energy is absorbed, it causes the surroundings to become cooler. In **Figure 5,** baking soda undergoes an endothermic reaction when it is mixed with vinegar. The reaction absorbs heat from its surroundings, so the reaction feels cold. Not all endothermic reactions result in a temperature decrease. Many endothermic reactions occur only when heat is constantly added, as when you fry an egg. Heat must be applied throughout the entire process in order for the reactions that cook the egg to continue.

FIGURE 5 ···
▶VIRTUAL LAB **Exothermic and Endothermic Reactions**
Chemical reactions either absorb energy or release energy.

✎ **Complete the following tasks.**

1. **Interpret Photos** Shade in the arrow that indicates the direction the net energy is moving for each reaction.

2. **Infer** How might each reaction feel if you were to put your hands near it?

_____

_____

do the math! Analyzing Data

A student adds magnesium oxide to hydrochloric acid. She measures the temperature of the reaction every minute. Her data are recorded in the table.

1 Graph Plot the data from the table onto the graph. Then name the graph.

2 Interpret Data Is the reaction endothermic or exothermic? Explain.

_____

_____

_____

_____

_____

_____

Time (min)	Temperature (°C)
0	20
1	24
2	27
3	29
4	29

8.NS.8

3 Read Graphs In which time interval did the temperature increase the most?

_____

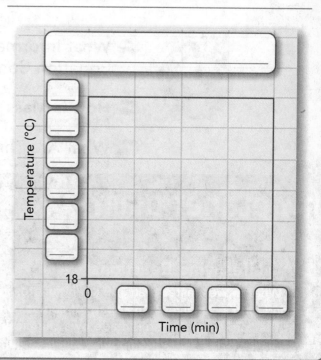

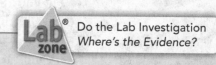

Lab zone® Do the Lab Investigation
Where's the Evidence?

🗝 Assess Your Understanding

2a. List What changes in physical properties can be used as evidence that a chemical reaction has occurred?

_____

_____

_____

8.1.7

b. Apply Concepts What evidence of a chemical change is observed when rust forms on iron?

_____

_____

8.1.7

c. Compare and Contrast How are endothermic and exothermic reactions the same? How are they different?

_____

_____

_____

_____

_____

_____

8.1.7

got it? ....

○ **I get it!** Now I know that two kinds of changes you can observe when chemical reactions occur are

_____

○ I need extra help with _____

Go to MY SCIENCE ⬤ₛ COACH *online for help with this subject.*

8.1.7

163

LESSON 5
Describing Chemical Reactions

UNLOCK THE BIG

🔑 **What Information Does a Chemical Equation Contain?**
8.1.8, 8.NS.8, 8.NS.11

🔑 **How Is Mass Conserved During a Chemical Reaction?**
8.1.8, 8.NS.8

🔑 **What Are Three Types of Chemical Reactions?**
8.1.8, 8.NS.1, 8.NS.8

MY PLANET DiARY

Lifesaving Reactions

What moves faster than 300 km/h, inflates in less than a second, and saves lives? An airbag, of course! Did you know that the "air" in an airbag is made by a chemical reaction? A compound called sodium azide (NaN_3) breaks down into sodium metal (Na) and nitrogen gas (N_2). The nitrogen gas fills the airbag and cushions the passengers in an accident.

It's important that the correct amount of sodium azide is used. The mass of sodium azide in the airbag before the collision will equal the mass of sodium and nitrogen that is made by the reaction. If too little or too much nitrogen gas is made, the airbag will not inflate properly.

FUN FACTS

Write your answer to the question below.

What might happen if an airbag doesn't contain the correct amount of sodium azide?

_____

_____

_____

_____

_____

> PLANET DIARY Go to **Planet Diary** to learn more about the law of conservation of mass.

 Lab zone® Do the Inquiry Warm-Up *Did You Lose Anything?*

Academic Standards for Science

8.1.8 Demonstrate that in a chemical change, the total numbers of each kind of atom in the product are the same as in the reactants and that the total mass of the reacting system is conserved.

8.NS.8 Analyze data.

8.NS.11 Communicate findings using models.

What Information Does a Chemical Equation Contain?

Cell phone text messages, like the one shown in **Figure 1,** use symbols and abbreviations to express ideas in shorter form. A type of shorthand is used in chemistry, too. A **chemical equation** is a way to show a chemical reaction, using symbols instead of words. Chemical equations are shorter than sentences, but they contain plenty of information. In chemical equations, chemical formulas and other symbols are used to summarize a reaction.

Vocabulary
- chemical equation
- law of conservation of mass
- open system
- closed system
- coefficient
- synthesis
- decomposition
- replacement

Skills
- Reading: Summarize
- Inquiry: Make Models

FIGURE 1 ·······································

Symbols and Abbreviations
Text messages, like chemical equations, let you express ideas in shorter form.

✎ **Interpret Photos Translate the text message using complete words and sentences.**

R u doin chem hw? Idk the chem rxn 4 makin H2O. Itl b ez 1s we stdy this chpt! Txt me l8r w/ the ans, k? Thx.

Formulas in an Equation
You may recall that a chemical formula is a combination of symbols that represents the elements in a compound. For example, CO_2 is the formula for carbon dioxide. The formula tells you that the ratio of carbon atoms to oxygen atoms in this compound is 1 to 2. Carbon dioxide is a molecular compound. Each carbon dioxide molecule has 1 carbon atom and 2 oxygen atoms. **Figure 2** lists the formulas of other familiar compounds.

Formulas of Familiar Compounds

Compound	Formula
Propane	C_3H_8
Sugar (sucrose)	$C_{12}H_{22}O_{11}$
Rubbing alcohol	C_3H_8O
Ammonia	NH_3
Baking soda	$NaHCO_3$
Water	
Carbon dioxide	
Sodium chloride	

FIGURE 2 ·······································

Chemical Formulas
The formula of a compound identifies the elements in the compound and the ratio in which their atoms or ions are present.

✎ **Interpret Tables Complete the table by filling in the missing chemical formulas.**

8.NS.8

FIGURE 3 ⋯⋯⋯⋯⋯⋯⋯⋯⋯⋯⋯⋯⋯⋯⋯⋯⋯⋯⋯⋯⋯⋯

Modeling a Chemical Equation

Like a skateboard, a chemical equation has a basic structure.

⚠ **Make Models Complete the equation by filling in the number of the skateboard parts shown. Determine the number of complete skateboards that can be made and draw them as the product.**

8.NS.11

_____ wheels + _____ trucks + _____ decks ➡ _____ skateboards

Structure of an Equation

Suppose you are building a skateboard. What parts do you need? How many of each part are necessary to build a complete skateboard? **Figure 3** summarizes everything you need to build several skateboards. Similarly, a chemical equation summarizes everything needed to carry out a chemical reaction.

All chemical equations have a basic structure that is followed. 🔑 **A chemical equation tells you the substances you start with in a reaction and the substances that are formed at the end.** The substances you have at the beginning are the reactants. When the reaction is complete, you have new substances, called the products.

The formulas for the reactants are written on the left, followed by an arrow. You read the arrow as "yields," or "reacts to form." The formulas for the products are written to the right of the arrow. When there are two or more reactants, they are separated by plus signs. In a similar way, plus signs are used to separate two or more products. Below is the general structure of a chemical equation.

Reactant + Reactant → Product + Product

The number of reactants and products can vary. Some reactions have only one reactant or product. Other reactions have two, three, or more reactants or products. For example, the reaction that occurs when limestone, or calcium carbonate ($CaCO_3$), is heated has one reactant and two products (CaO and CO_2).

$$CaCO_3 \rightarrow CaO + CO_2$$

apply it!

Molecules of nitrogen (N_2) and hydrogen (H_2) react to form ammonia (NH_3).

① **Identify** Indicate the number of H_2 and N_2 molecules needed to yield two molecules of NH_3.

② **Make Models** Draw the correct number of reactant molecules in the boxes on the left side of the equation.

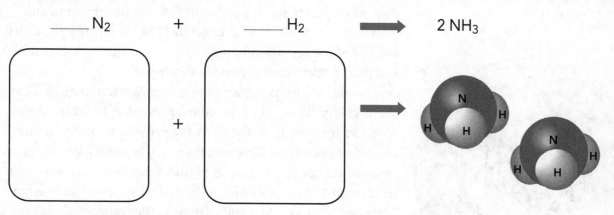

_____ N_2 +   _____ H_2 ➡   2 NH_3

③ **Describe** What bonds of the reactants are broken in this reaction? What bonds are formed in the product?

_____

_____

_____

_____

8.NS.11

 Do the Quick Lab *Information in a Chemical Equation.*

🗝 Assess Your Understanding

1a. **Explain** What do the formulas, arrows, and plus signs tell you in a chemical equation?

_____

_____

_____

_____

_____

8.1.8

b. **Interpret Data** Write the chemical equation for the following reaction: The elements carbon and oxygen combine to yield the compound carbon dioxide.

_____

8.1.8

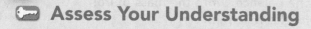

got it? ⋯⋯⋯⋯⋯⋯⋯⋯⋯⋯⋯⋯⋯⋯⋯⋯⋯⋯⋯⋯⋯⋯⋯⋯⋯

○ **I get it!** Now I know that a chemical equation tells you _____

_____

○ **I need extra help with** _____

Go to **MY SCIENCE** **COACH** online for help with this subject.

8.1.8

Academic Standards for Science

8.1.8 Demonstrate that in a chemical change, the total numbers of each kind of atom in the product are the same as in the reactants and that the total mass of the reacting system is conserved.

8.NS.8 Analyze data, using appropriate mathematical manipulation.

did you know?

Antoine Lavoisier is known as the father of modern chemistry, but he was also a lawyer and a tax collector. Despite his support for reform, his connection to tax collection led to his unfortunate beheading in 1794 during the French Revolution.

How Is Mass Conserved During a Chemical Reaction?

Look at the reaction below in **Figure 4**. Iron and sulfur can react to form iron sulfide (FeS). Can you predict the mass of iron sulfide, knowing the mass of the reactants? It might help you to know about a principle first demonstrated by the French chemist Antoine Lavoisier in 1774. This principle, called the **law of conservation of mass**, states that during a chemical reaction, matter is not created or destroyed.

The idea of atoms explains the conservation of mass. 🔑 **In a chemical reaction, all of the atoms present at the start of the reaction are present at the end of the reaction.** Atoms are not created or destroyed. However, they may be rearranged to form new substances. Look again at **Figure 4**. Suppose 1 atom of iron reacts with 1 atom of sulfur. At the end of the reaction, you have 1 iron atom bonded to 1 sulfur atom in the compound iron sulfide (FeS). All the atoms in the reactants are present in the products. The amount of matter does not change. According to the law of conservation of mass, the total mass stays the same before and after the reaction.

FIGURE 4 ···

> **INTERACTIVE ART** **Conservation of Mass**

In a chemical reaction, matter is not created or destroyed.

✎ **Calculate** On the balance, write the mass of iron sulfide produced by this reaction.

8.NS.8

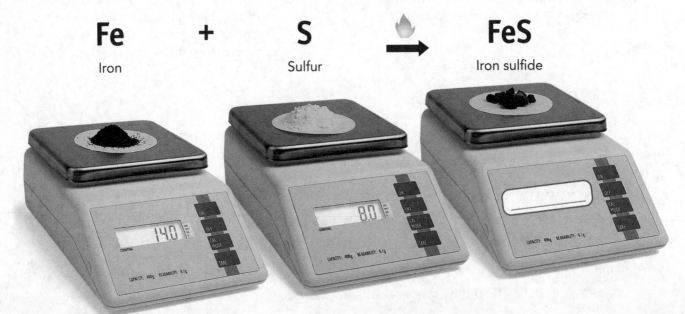

Fe + S 🔥→ FeS

Iron   Sulfur   Iron sulfide

Open and Closed Systems At first glance, some reactions may seem to violate the principle of conservation of mass. It's not always easy to measure all the matter involved in a reaction. For example, if you burn a match, oxygen comes into the reaction from the surrounding air, but how much? Likewise, the products escape into the air. Again, how much?

A fish bowl is an example of an open system. It contains different types of matter that are interacting with each other. In an **open system,** matter can enter from or escape to the surroundings. If you want to measure all the matter before and after a reaction, you have to be able to contain it. In a **closed system,** matter does not enter or leave. A chemical reaction that occurs inside a sealed, airtight container is a closed system. The enclosed ecosphere shown in **Figure 5** doesn't allow any mass to enter or escape.

FIGURE 5 ·······················

Open and Closed Systems
Matter cannot enter or leave a closed system, as it can in an open system.

✎ **Complete the following tasks.**

1. **Identify** Label each system as open or closed.

2. **Design Experiments** Which system would you use to demonstrate conservation of mass? Why?

_____

_____

_____

_____

3. CHALLENGE Why do you think the fish bowl above is considered a system, but an empty fish bowl is not?

_____

_____

Balancing Chemical Equations The principle of conservation of mass means that the total number of atoms of each element in the reactants must equal the total number of atoms of each element in the products. To be accurate, a chemical equation must show the same number of atoms of each element on both sides of the equation. Chemists say an equation is balanced when conservation of mass is correctly shown. How can you write a balanced chemical equation?

STEP 1 Write the Equation Suppose you want to write a balanced chemical equation for the reaction between hydrogen and oxygen that forms water. To begin, write the correct chemical formulas for both reactants and the product. Place the reactants, H_2 and O_2, on the left side of the arrow, separated by a plus sign. Then write the product, H_2O, on the right side of the arrow.

Hydrogen   Oxygen   Water

STEP 2 Count the Atoms Count the number of atoms of each element on each side of the equation. Recall that a subscript tells you the ratio of elements in a compound.

Hydrogen + Oxygen ⟶ Hydrogen atom(s)
atom(s)   atom(s)   Oxygen atom(s)

After counting, you find 2 atoms of oxygen in the reactants but only 1 atom of oxygen in the product. How can the number of oxygen atoms on both sides of the equation be made equal? You cannot change the formula for water to H_2O_2 because H_2O_2 is the formula for hydrogen peroxide, a completely different compound. So how can you show that mass is conserved?

STEP 3 **Use Coefficients to Balance Atoms** To balance the equation, use coefficients. A **coefficient** (koh uh FISH unt) is a number placed in front of a chemical formula in an equation. It tells you the amount of a reactant or a product that takes part in a reaction. The coefficient applies to every atom of the formula it is in front of. If the coefficient is 1, you don't need to write it.

Balance the number of oxygen atoms by changing the coefficient of H_2O to 2. Again, count the number of atoms on each side of the equation.

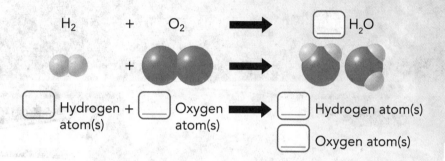

Balancing the oxygen atoms "unbalances" the number of hydrogen atoms. There are now 2 hydrogen atoms in the reactants and 4 in the product. How can you balance the hydrogen? Try changing the coefficient of H_2 to 2. Then, count the atoms again.

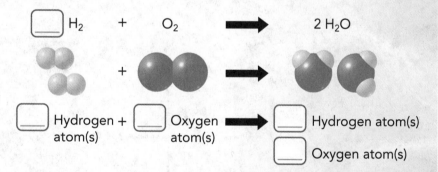

STEP 4 **Look Back and Check** Is the number of atoms of each element in the reactants equal to the number of atoms of each element in the products? If so, mass is conserved and the equation is balanced. The balanced equation tells you 2 hydrogen molecules react with 1 oxygen molecule to yield 2 water molecules.

do the
math! **Sample Problem**

Apply Concepts Balance the equations.

❶ $KClO_3 \rightarrow KCl + O_2$

_____

❷ $NaBr + Cl_2 \rightarrow NaCl + Br_2$

_____

_____

❸ $Na + Cl_2 \rightarrow NaCl$

_____

_____

8.NS.8

❶ Write the equation.
$Mg + O_2 \rightarrow MgO$

❷ Count the atoms.
$Mg + O_2 \rightarrow MgO$
$\quad 1 \quad\quad 2 \quad\quad 1\ 1$

❸ Use coefficients to balance.
$2\ Mg + O_2 \rightarrow 2\ MgO$
$\quad\ 2 \quad\quad 2 \quad\quad\ 2\ 2$

❹ Look back and check.

171

How Can Chemical Reactions Generate *SPEED*?

How is matter conserved in a chemical reaction?

FIGURE 6 ···

> **INTERACTIVE ART** One day, you might be able to drink the exhaust from your car! Sounds gross, right? Well, it could be possible with hydrogen fuel cells. Hydrogen fuel cells use a chemical reaction between hydrogen and oxygen to generate energy for running a car. In the process, water is produced.

✎ **Review** Use what you've learned about chemical reactions to answer questions about fuel cells.

1 **Endothermic or Exothermic?**

The reaction in a fuel cell is used to power cars and other devices. Is it an endothermic or exothermic reaction? Explain.

_____

_____

_____

_____

_____

2 **Conservation of Mass**

Inside a fuel cell, hydrogen is converted into H^+ ions. These ions combine with oxygen to produce energy for the car and water as exhaust. Describe how the fuel cell obeys the law of conservation of mass.

_____

_____

_____

_____

_____

_____

_____

Fuel Cell

An astronaut gathers packets for drinking.

3 Properties of Matter

Hydrogen fuel cells power missions in space. Describe why the product of fuel cells would be more beneficial to space missions than that of other fuels.

_____

_____

_____

_____

_____

_____

Do the Quick Lab
Is Matter Conserved?

🔑 Assess Your Understanding

2a. Infer If the total mass of the products in a reaction is 90 grams, what was the total mass of the reactants?

_____

8.1.8

b. Apply Concepts Balance the equations.

- $Al + CuO \rightarrow Al_2O_3 + Cu$
- $Fe_2O_3 + C \rightarrow Fe + CO_2$
- $SO_2 + O_2 \rightarrow SO_3$

_____

_____

_____

8.1.8, 8.NS.8

c. **ANSWER THE BIG ?** How is matter conserved in a chemical reaction?

_____

_____

_____

_____

_____

_____

_____

_____

8.1.8

got it? ....

○ **I get it!** Now I know that the masses of reactants and products must be _____ _____

○ **I need extra help with** _____

Go to **MY SCIENCE** ⓢ **COACH** *online for help with this subject.* 8.1.8

4 Balance the Chemical Equation

Hydrogen must be obtained from decomposing fuels like methane (CH_4). Balance the equation for generating hydrogen for fuel cells.

$$CH_4 + H_2O \rightarrow CO + H_2$$

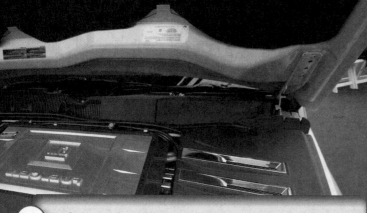

Aluminum (Al) reacts with silver tarnish (Ag_2S) to yield pure silver (Ag) in a baking soda solution.

$$3 Ag_2S + 2 Al \rightarrow 6 Ag + Al_2S_3$$

1 Classify What type of reaction is this?

_____

_____

2 Interpret Data Which element replaces another in the reaction?

_____

_____

_____

3 CHALLENGE Use information from the reaction to design an experiment that could be used to remove the tarnish (Ag_2S) from a silver fork.

_____

_____

_____

_____

_____

_____

_____

_____

8.NS.1, 8.NS.8

What Are Three Types of Chemical Reactions?

In a chemical reaction, substances may combine to make a more complex substance. They may break apart to make simpler substances. They may even exchange parts. In each case, new substances are formed. ⟐ **Three types of chemical reactions are synthesis, decomposition, and replacement.**

Synthesis Some musicians use a machine called a synthesizer. A synthesizer combines different electronic sounds to make music. To synthesize is to put things together. In chemistry, when two or more elements or compounds combine to make a more complex substance, the reaction is classified as **synthesis** (SIN thuh sis). The reaction of phosphorus with oxygen is a synthesis reaction.

$$P_4 + 3 O_2 \rightarrow P_4O_6$$

Decomposition In contrast to a synthesis reaction, a **decomposition** reaction occurs when compounds break down into simpler products. You probably have a bottle of hydrogen peroxide (H_2O_2) in your house to clean cuts. If you keep such a bottle for a very long time, you'll have water instead. Hydrogen peroxide decomposes into water and oxygen gas.

$$2 H_2O_2 \rightarrow 2 H_2O + O_2$$

Replacement When one element replaces another element in a compound, or if two elements in different compounds trade places, the reaction is called a **replacement.** Look at this example.

$$2 Cu_2O + C \rightarrow 4 Cu + CO_2$$

Copper metal is obtained by heating copper oxide with carbon. The carbon replaces the copper in the compound with oxygen.

The reaction between copper oxide and carbon is called a *single* replacement reaction because one element, carbon, replaces another element, copper, in the compound. In a *double* replacement reaction, elements in a compound appear to trade places with the elements in another compound. The following reaction is an example of a double replacement.

$$FeS + 2 HCl \rightarrow FeCl_2 + H_2S$$

FIGURE 7 ···

Types of Reactions

✎ **Complete the following tasks.** 8.NS.8

1. Interpret Diagrams Label each type of reaction represented.

2. Explain How are synthesis and decomposition reactions related to each other?

_____

_____

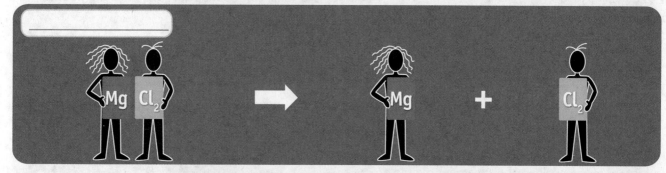

🔑 **Assess Your Understanding**

3a. Classify What type of chemical reaction is shown in the chemical equation below?

$$Zn + 2\ HCl \rightarrow H_2 + ZnCl_2$$

_____

8.1.8

b. Draw Conclusions The elements iron and oxygen can react to form the compound iron oxide. What type of reaction is this? Explain.

_____

_____

_____

8.1.8

Lab zone Do the Quick Lab *Categories of Chemical Reactions.*

got it? ··

○ **I get it!** Now I know that three types of chemical reactions are _____

○ **I need extra help with** _____

Go to **my science** 💬 **coach** *online for help with this subject.*

8.1.8

175

4 Study Guide

REVIEW THE BIG ?

The total mass before a chemical reaction equals _____

_____ .

LESSON 1 **Atoms, Bonding, and the Periodic Table**

8.1.1, 8.1.3, 8.1.4, 8.1.5, 8.1.6, 8.4.1, 8.4.3, 8.NS.1, 8.NS.8

🔑 The number of valence electrons in each atom of an element determines the chemical properties of that element.

Carbon

Vocabulary
• valence electron
• electron dot diagram
• chemical bond

LESSON 2 **Ionic Bonds**

8.1.4, 8.1.5, 8.1.6, 8.4.1, 8.4.2, 8.4.3, 8.NS.8

🔑 When a neutral atom loses or gains a valence electron, it becomes an ion.

🔑 For an ionic compound, the name of the negative ion follows the name of the positive ion.

🔑 Ionic compounds have high melting points.

Vocabulary
• ion   • polyatomic ion   • ionic bond
• ionic compound   • chemical formula
• subscript   • crystal

LESSON 3 **Covalent Bonds**

8.1.4, 8.1.5, 8.1.6, 8.4.1, 8.4.2, 8.4.3, 8.NS.1, 8.NS.8, 8.NS.11

🔑 Attractions between the shared electrons and the protons in the nucleus of each atom hold the atoms together in a covalent bond.

🔑 Molecular compounds have low melting points and do not conduct electric current.

🔑 Unequal sharing of electrons causes bonded atoms to have slight electric charges.

Vocabulary
• covalent bond   • molecule   • double bond   • triple bond
• molecular compound   • nonpolar bond   • polar bond

LESSON 4 **Observing Chemical Change**

8.1.6, 8.1.7, 8.NS.1, 8.NS.8, 8.NS.11

🔑 Changes in matter can be described in terms of physical changes and chemical changes.

🔑 Chemical reactions involve changes in properties and changes in energy that you can often observe.

Vocabulary
• physical change   • chemical change
• reactant   • product   • precipitate
• exothermic reaction   • endothermic reaction

LESSON 5 **Describing Chemical Reactions**

8.1.8, 8.NS.1, 8.NS.8, 8.NS.11

🔑 A chemical equation tells you the substances you start with in a reaction and the substances that are formed at the end.

🔑 In a chemical reaction, all of the atoms present at the start of the reaction are present at the end of the reaction.

🔑 Three types of chemical reactions are synthesis, decomposition, and replacement.

Vocabulary
• chemical equation   • law of conservation of mass
• open system   • closed system   • coefficient
• synthesis   • decomposition   • replacement

Review and Assessment

LESSON 1 Atoms, Bonding, and the Periodic Table

1. An electron dot diagram shows an atom's number of

  a. protons.   **b.** electrons.

  c. valence electrons. **d.** chemical bonds.

8.1.6

2. When atoms react, they form a chemical bond, which is defined as _____

_____

_____

8.1.4

Use the diagrams to answer Questions 3 and 4.

Ca   Ar   Na

Calcium   Argon   Sodium

N   O   Cl

Nitrogen   Oxygen   Chlorine

3. Infer Which of these elements can become stable by losing 1 electron? Explain.

_____

_____

_____

8.1.4, 8.1.5, 8.NS.8

4. Draw Conclusions Which of these elements is least likely to react with other elements? Explain.

_____

_____

8.1.4, 8.1.6

5. Write About It Go to your local grocery store and observe how the products on the shelves are organized. Write a paragraph comparing how food products are organized in a grocery store and how elements are organized in the periodic table.

8.1.2, 8.NS.11

LESSON 2 Ionic Bonds

6. When an atom loses or gains electrons, it becomes a(n)

  a. ion.   **b.** formula.

  c. crystal.   **d.** subscript.

8.1.4, 8.1.5

7. Magnesium chloride is an example of an ionic compound, which is a compound composed of

_____

8.1.4, 8.1.5, 8.1.6

8. Classify Based on their chemical formulas, which of these compounds is not likely to be an ionic compound: KBr, SO_2, or $AlCl_3$? Explain your answer.

_____

_____

_____

8.1.4, 8.1.5, 8.1.6

9. Write About It Pretend that you are the size of an atom and you are observing a reaction between a potassium ion and a fluorine atom. Describe how an ionic bond forms as the atoms react. Tell what happens to the valence electrons in each atom and how each atom is changed by losing or gaining electrons.

8.1.4, 8.1.5, 8.1.6, 8.NS.11

LESSON 3 Covalent Bonds

10. A covalent bond in which electrons are shared equally is called a

  a. double bond.   **b.** triple bond.

  c. polar bond.   **d.** nonpolar bond.

8.1.4, 8.1.5

11. The formulas N_2, H_2O, and CO_2 all represent molecules, which are defined as _____

_____

_____

8.1.4, 8.1.5, 8.1.6

12. Infer A carbon atom can form four covalent bonds. How many valence electrons does a carbon atom have?

_____

8.1.4, 8.1.5

LESSON 4 Observing Chemical Change

13. Which of the following results in a chemical change in matter?

   a. bending a straw   **b.** boiling water

   c. braiding hair   **d.** burning wood

                                    8.1.7

14. A solid that forms from liquids in a chemical reaction is called a(n) _____

                                      8.1.7

15. Interpret Photos What evidence in the photo below tells you that a chemical reaction may have occurred?

_____

_____

                                    8.1.7

16. Solve Problems Steel that is exposed to water and salt rusts quickly. If you were a shipbuilder, how would you protect a new ship? Explain.

_____

_____

_____

_____

                                    8.1.7

17. **Write About It** Suppose you have an Internet friend who is studying chemistry just like you are. Your friend claims the change from liquid water to water vapor is a chemical change. Write a brief e-mail that might convince your friend otherwise.

                                    8.1.7

LESSON 5 Describing Chemical Reactions

18. How can you balance a chemical equation?

   a. Change the coefficients.

   b. Change the products.

   c. Change the reactants.

   d. Change the subscripts.

                                    8.1.8

19. In an open system, such as a campfire, matter can _____

_____

                                      8.1.8

APPLY THE BIG ? How is matter conserved in a chemical reaction?

20. Rust forms when iron metal (Fe) reacts with oxygen (O_2) to produce iron oxide (Fe_2O_3). Write a balanced equation for this reaction. Suppose you find the mass of an iron object, let it rust, and measure the mass again. Predict whether the mass will increase, decrease, or stay the same. Explain your answer in terms of the law of conservation of mass.

_____

_____

_____

_____

_____

_____

_____

_____

_____

_____

                            8.1.8, 8.NS.1

Indiana ISTEP+ Practice

Multiple Choice

Circle the letter of the best answer.

1. The table below lists some ions and their charges.

Ions and Their Charges

Name	Charge	Symbol/Formula
Sodium	1+	Na^+
Calcium	2+	Ca^{2+}
Chloride	1–	Cl^-
Phosphate	3–	PO_4^{3-}

How many sodium ions are needed to balance the charge of one phosphate ion?

A. 1
B. 2
C. 3
D. 4

8.1.4, 8.1.5

2. Which of the following is the **best** evidence for a chemical reaction?

A. change in temperature
B. change of state
C. formation of a new substance
D. gas bubbles

8.1.7

3. Elements that have the same number of valence electrons are

A. within the same group of the periodic table.
B. within the same period of the periodic table.
C. called noble gases.
D. called metalloids.

8.1.2, 8.1.4

4. Which equation describes a synthesis reaction?

A. $2\ Na + Cl_2 \rightarrow 2\ NaCl$
B. $Mg + CuSO_4 \rightarrow MgSO_4 + Cu$
C. $2\ KI \rightarrow 2\ K + I_2$
D. $CH_4 + 2\ O_2 \rightarrow CO_2 + 2\ H_2O$

8.1.8

Constructed Response

Write your answer to Question 5 on the lines below.

5. The chemical formula for a glucose molecule is $C_6H_{12}O_6$. The subscripts represent the

_____

_____

_____

8.1.4, 8.1.5

Extended Response

Use the electron dot diagrams to help you answer Question 6. Write your answer on a separate sheet of paper.

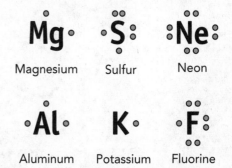

Magnesium   Sulfur   Neon

Aluminum   Potassium   Fluorine

6. Predict the formula for the compounds, if any, that would form from each of the following combinations of elements: magnesium and fluorine, aluminum and sulfur, and potassium and neon. If a compound is unlikely to form, explain the reason why.

8.1.4, 8.1.5, 8.1.6, 8.NS.11

LOOK, MA, WARM HANDS

Winter to many means braving shorter days and blasts of frosty air. Along with heavy clothes, gloves and thick socks, reusable hand warmers can help battle the chill.

Sodium acetate is a salt used in many things, including salt and vinegar chips. The solution in a sodium acetate heat pad is supersaturated. Flexing a metal disk within the heat pad causes a few sodium acetate molecules to come out of solution and form crystals. This causes an exothermic change, which brings the temperature of the solution up to 54°C. (Room temperature is about 22°C.) Placing the heat pad in boiling water causes the crystals to dissolve and become a solution again, so that you can reuse the heat pad. You add heat to dissolve the crystals. When they come out of solution, into their solid state, they release that heat.

So the next time your hands are cold on a chilly day, use a portable warmer and take advantage of the exothermic change!

Design It Design an experiment to determine whether rock salt produces an exothermic or endothermic change when it is placed on icy roads and driveways.

 8.NS.2, 8.DP.1

Safe Moist Heating Pad

To Activate — place pad on flat surface and flex metal disc in corner

To Recharge — place pad on top of cloth in boiling water for 15 minutes or until all crystals are dissolved

note: if crystals form while pad is cooling, recharge

Reusable sodium acetate heat pads use a change of state to generate heat.

Museum of Science

CAN YOU BE CLEAN AND GREEN?

It seems that everything is labeled with something "green" these days. Cleaning products are no exception, but can you make sure that you are both clean and "green"?

The best way to buy green is to read the ingredients list. In order to understand the ingredients and the claims, it helps to know how a product works and what the ingredients do. Detergents and soap work because they contain chemicals called surfactants. Surfactants are long, chain-like molecules. One end of the chain has a strong attraction to oil and dirt, and binds with them. The other end has a strong attraction to water, and binds with water molecules to wash the oil and dirt away. Today, many detergents use petroleum as a basis for surfactants. Petroleum is a nonrenewable resource that can pollute water sources. Some detergents use vegetable oils instead. These oils are renewable resources. Products that use them are more environmentally friendly than those that use petroleum-based surfactants.

Design It Some consumers fight going "green" because they think these products won't work as well. Design a test to compare how well a biodegradable detergent works with one that uses petroleum.

 8.NS.1–8.NS.10, 8.DP.1

WHERE IS THIS WATER GOING?

How does water cycle on Earth?

Watch out below! This river is carrying the kayaker straight down. But where did the water come from in the first place? Where is it going? And why is water important?

Develop Hypotheses Explain where you think the water in the river came from and where it will go next.

_____

_____

_____

_____

_____

_____

> UNTAMED SCIENCE Watch the **Untamed Science** video to learn more about water on Earth.

The Water Planet

Academic Standards for Science

8.2.1, 8.2.2, 8.2.6, 8.2.8, 8.NS.1–8.NS.11,
8.DP.1–8.DP.11

Check Your Understanding

1. Background Read the paragraph below and then answer the question.

> Have you ever sat at a window on a misty day? You might see **condensation** as drops of water form on the glass. These drops form when **water vapor** in the air cools and turns into a liquid. **Gravity** pulls the drops down the windowpane toward Earth's surface.

> **Condensation** occurs when a substance changes from a gas to a liquid.
>
> **Water vapor** is water in the gaseous state.
>
> **Gravity** is a force that attracts all objects toward each other.

- How do water drops form on the window?

_____

_____

▶ MY READING WEB If you had trouble completing the question above, visit **My Reading Web** and type in **The Water Planet.**

Vocabulary Skill

Latin Word Origins Many science words come to English from Latin. In this chapter you will learn the term *permeable*. *Permeable* comes from the Latin word parts *per-*, meaning "through"; *meare*, meaning "to go" or "to pass"; and *-bilis*, meaning "capable of."

| *per-* through | + | *meare* go or pass | + | *-bilis* capable of | = | *permeable* capable of going through |

Learn these Latin word parts to help you remember the vocabulary terms.

Latin Origin	Meaning	Example
trans-	across	transpiration, *n.*
spirare	to breathe	transpiration, *n.*
vapor	steam	evaporation, *n.*
videre	to separate	divide, *v.*

2. Quick Check Use the table to answer the question.
- Based on the table, predict the meaning of *transpiration*.

_____

groundwater

water cycle

divide

tributary

Chapter Preview

LESSON 1
- habitat
- groundwater
- water cycle
- evaporation
- transpiration
- precipitation

↻ **Identify the Main Idea**
△ **Observe**

LESSON 2
- tributary
- watershed
- divide
- reservoir
- eutrophication

↻ **Sequence**
△ **Form Operational Definitions**

LESSON 3
- salinity
- sonar
- seamount
- trench
- continental slope
- continental shelf
- abyssal plain
- mid-ocean ridge

↻ **Identify the Main Idea**
△ **Interpret Data**

LESSON 4
- current
- Coriolis effect
- climate
- El Niño
- La Niña

↻ **Compare and Contrast**
△ **Infer**

> **VOCAB FLASH CARDS** For extra help with vocabulary, visit **Vocab Flash Cards** and type in *The Water Planet.*

185

Water on Earth

UNLOCK
THE BIG
?

🔑 **Why Is Water Important?**
8.2.2, 8.2.7, 8.NS.1

🔑 **Where Is Water Found?**
8.2.2, 8.NS.8

🔑 **What Is the Water Cycle?**
8.2.1, 8.2.2, 8.NS.8

my planet diary

SCIENCE STATS

How Much Water Do You Use?

You take a shower. You brush your teeth. You take a big drink after soccer practice. All day long, you need water! How much water do you use in a day? How much do you think your whole state uses? The graph shows the water used per person in the ten states of the United States with the largest populations. The data include the water used for all purposes, including farming, industry, and electric power.

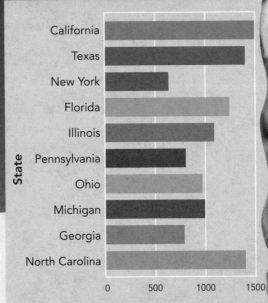

Water Use per Person per Day

Study the graph. Then answer the questions below.

1. In which state is the water use per person greatest? In which state is it least?

_____

_____

2. What do you think might explain the difference in water use between states?

_____

_____

> PLANET DIARY Go to **Planet Diary** to learn more about fresh water on Earth.

Do the Inquiry Warm-Up *Where Does the Water Come From?*

Vocabulary
- habitat • groundwater • water cycle • evaporation
- transpiration • precipitation

Skills
↻ Reading: Identify the Main Idea
△ Inquiry: Observe

Why Is Water Important?

What do you and an apple have in common? You both consist mostly of water! Water makes up nearly two thirds of your body's mass. That water is necessary to keep your body functioning. ⌗ **All living things need water in order to carry out their body processes. In addition, many living things live in water.**

Body Processes Without water, neither you nor an apple could survive. Water allows organisms to break down food, grow, reproduce, and get and use materials they need from their environments. Animals obtain water by drinking it or by eating foods that contain water. Most animals cannot survive more than a few days without water.

Plants and other organisms that make their own food also need water. Algae and plants use water, along with carbon dioxide and energy from the sun, to make their own food in a process called photosynthesis (foh toh SIN thuh sis). Other organisms get food by eating the plants, or by eating organisms that eat the plants.

Habitats Water provides habitats for many living things. An organism's **habitat** is the place where it lives and obtains all the things it needs to survive. Some organisms cannot live out of water. You are probably familiar with large water-dwelling organisms such as sharks. But most such organisms are microscopic. In fact, aquatic, or water, habitats contain more types of organisms than land habitats do.

Academic Standards for Science

8.2.2 Describe and model how water moves through the earth's crust, atmosphere, and oceans in a cyclic way.

8.2.7 Recognize that some of Earth's resources are finite and describe how recycling, reducing consumption and the development of alternatives can reduce the rate of their depletion.

8.NS.1 Make predictions based on research and prior knowledge.

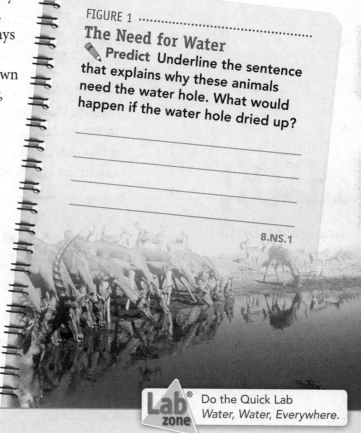

FIGURE 1 ·······························

The Need for Water
✎ **Predict** Underline the sentence that explains why these animals need the water hole. What would happen if the water hole dried up?

_____

_____

_____

_____

8.NS.1

Lab zone® Do the Quick Lab
Water, Water, Everywhere.

⌗ Assess Your Understanding

got it? ···

○ **I get it!** Now I know that living things use water _____

_____

○ **I need extra help with** _____

Go to **MY SCIENCE COACH** online for help with this subject.

8.2.2, 8.2.7

Academic Standards for Science

8.2.2 Describe and model how water moves through the earth's crust, atmosphere, and oceans in a cyclic way.

8.NS.8 Analyze data, using appropriate mathematical manipulation as required, and use it to identify patterns and make inferences based on these patterns.

🔄 **Identify the Main Idea**
Underline the main idea in each paragraph on this page.

Where Is Water Found?

When you turn on the tap, it might seem that an endless supply of fresh water comes out! But Earth's freshwater supply is very limited. 🔑 **Most of Earth's surface water—roughly 97 percent—is salt water found in oceans. Only 3 percent is fresh water.**

Of that 3 percent, about two thirds is frozen in huge masses of ice near the North and South poles. About a third of the fresh water is underground. A tiny fraction of fresh water occurs in lakes and rivers. An even tinier fraction is found in the atmosphere, most of it in the form of invisible water vapor, the gaseous form of water.

Oceans Find the oceans on the map in **Figure 2.** Pacific, Atlantic, Indian, and Arctic are the names used for the different parts of the ocean. (Some scientists call the area around Antarctica the Southern Ocean.) But the waters are really all interconnected, making up one big ocean. The Pacific Ocean is the largest, covering an area greater than all the land on Earth. The Atlantic Ocean is next largest, though the Indian Ocean is deeper. The Arctic Ocean surrounds the North Pole. Smaller saltwater bodies are called seas.

Ice Much of Earth's fresh water is frozen into sheets of ice. Massive ice sheets cover most of Greenland and Antarctica. Icebergs are floating chunks of ice made of fresh water that break off from ice sheets. You could also find icebergs in the Arctic Ocean and in the North Atlantic.

do the math!

Analyzing Data

These graphs show how much of Earth's water is found in different forms.

❶ **Read Graphs** Where is most water on Earth found? _____

❷ **Read Graphs** About what fraction of Earth's fresh water is in the form of ice?

_____

❸ **Interpret Data** How does the total amount of groundwater compare to the total amount of ice?

_____

_____

_____

8.NS.8

Salt water in oceans and salt lakes **97%**

Fresh water **3%**

Water vapor **0.04%**

Ice **69%**

Groundwater **30%**

Lakes and rivers **0.26%**

Rivers and Lakes

Look at **Figure 2.** All the rivers and lakes marked on the map contain fresh water, as do many other smaller rivers and lakes. North America's five Great Lakes contain about 20 percent of all the water in the world's freshwater lakes.

Groundwater

To find some of the fresh water on Earth, you have to look underground. When it rains or snows, most water that doesn't evaporate soaks into the ground. This water trickles through spaces between particles of soil and rock. Water that fills the cracks and spaces in underground soil and rock layers is called **groundwater.** Far more fresh water is located underground than in all of Earth's rivers and lakes.

FIGURE 2 ·······························

Earth's Major Waterways

The map shows Earth's oceans and some major freshwater sources.

✎ **Classify** Circle the names of three saltwater sources. Underline the names of three freshwater sources.

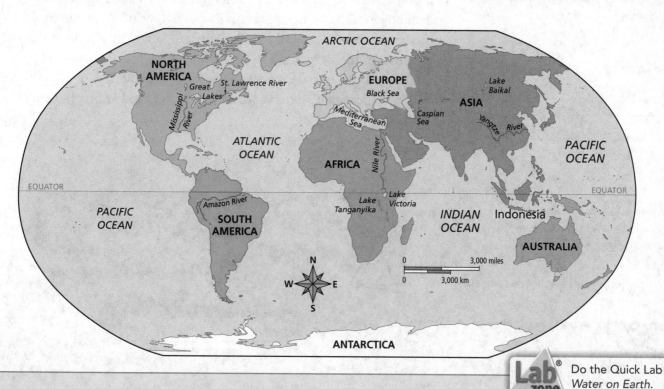

Lab zone® Do the Quick Lab *Water on Earth.*

Assess Your Understanding

1a. List What are the four main sources of fresh water on Earth?

_____

_____
8.2.2

b. Make Judgments Which freshwater source do you think is most important to people? Why?

_____

_____

_____
8.2.2

got it? ···

○ **I get it!** Now I know that Earth's water is found in _____

○ **I need extra help with** _____

Go to MY SCIENCE ⬤ COACH online for help with this subject.
8.2.2

Academic Standards for Science

8.2.1 Recognize and demonstrate how the sun's energy drives convection in the atmosphere and in bodies of water.

8.2.2 Describe and model how water moves through the earth's crust, atmosphere, and oceans in a cyclic way.

8.NS.8 Analyze data.

Vocabulary Latin Word Origins
The letter *e* in *evaporation* comes from the Latin word *ex*, meaning "away." *Vapor* is Latin for "water vapor." What do you predict that *evaporation* means?

_____

_____

What Is the Water Cycle?

Earth has its own built-in water recycling system: the water cycle. The **water cycle** is the continuous process by which water moves from Earth's surface to the atmosphere and back, driven by energy from the sun and gravity. 🔑 **In the water cycle, water moves between land, living things, bodies of water on Earth's surface, and the atmosphere.**

Water Evaporates Where does the water in a puddle go when it disappears? It evaporates, becoming water vapor. **Evaporation** is the process by which molecules at the surface of a liquid absorb enough energy to change to a gaseous state. Water constantly evaporates from the surfaces of bodies of water such as oceans and lakes, as well as from soil and your skin. Plants play a role, too, in this step of the water cycle. Plants draw in water from the soil through their roots. Eventually the water is given off through the leaves as water vapor in a process called **transpiration.**

FIGURE 3 ·······························

> **INTERACTIVE ART** The Water Cycle
The diagram below shows the processes of the water cycle.

✎ **Apply Concepts** As you read these two pages, label each process shown in the diagram.

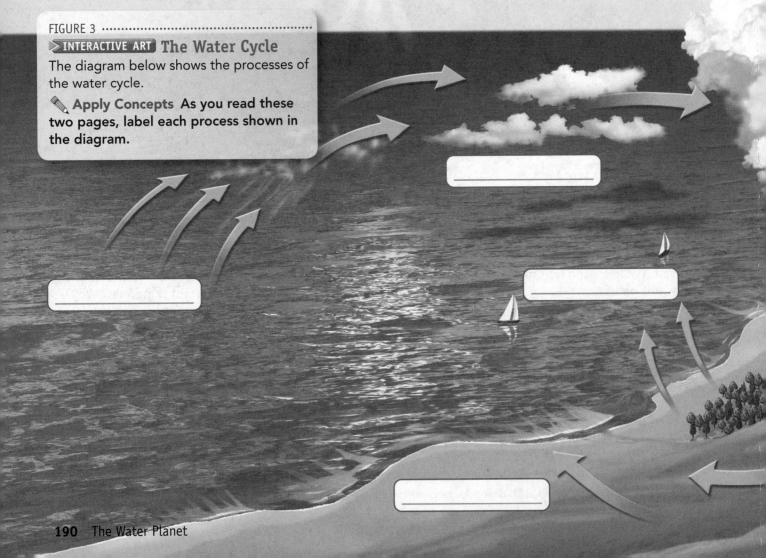

Condensation Forms Clouds

After a water molecule evaporates, warm air can carry the water molecule upward. Air tends to become colder as it rises. Water vapor condenses more easily at lower temperatures, so some water vapor cools and condenses into liquid water. Droplets of liquid water clump around solid particles in the air, forming clouds.

Water Falls as Precipitation

As more water vapor condenses, the water droplets grow larger. Eventually, they become so heavy that they fall back to Earth. Water that falls to Earth as rain, snow, hail, or sleet is called **precipitation.**

Most precipitation falls directly into the ocean. Of the precipitation that falls on land, most evaporates. A small amount of the remaining water runs off the surface into streams and lakes in a process called runoff, but most of it seeps into groundwater. After a long time, this groundwater may flow down to the ocean and evaporate again.

Precipitation is the source of almost all fresh water on and below Earth's surface. For millions of years, the total amount of water cycling through the Earth system has remained fairly constant—the rates of evaporation and precipitation are balanced.

_____

apply it!

❶ **Observe** What water cycle process can you observe here?

_____

❷ [CHALLENGE] What other process or processes can you infer are also taking place?

_____

❸ Give an example of a water cycle process you have seen.

_____

_____

8.NS.8

Lab zone Do the Lab Investigation *Water From Trees.*

🔑 Assess Your Understanding

2a. Identify What are the three major steps in the water cycle?

_____

_____

8.2.1, 8.2.2

b. Sequence Start with a puddle on a sunny day. How might water move through the water cycle and eventually fall as rain?

_____

_____

_____

_____

_____

8.2.1, 8.2.2

got it? ....

○ **I get it!** Now I know that the water cycle is _____

_____

_____

○ **I need extra help with** _____

Go to **my science coach** *online for help with this subject.* 8.2.1, 8.2.2

191

Surface Water

UNLOCK THE BIG ?

🔑 **What Is a River System?**
8.2.2, 8.NS.8

🔑 **What Are Ponds and Lakes?**
8.2.2, 8.NS.8

🔑 **How Can Lakes Change?**
8.2.2, 8.NS.11

MY PLANET DIARY

So Near, So Far

In Colorado's mountains, some rain seeps into the Fryingpan River. That river flows into the Colorado River and, more than 2,000 kilometers later, into the Gulf of California. Less than 15 kilometers away, rain seeps into the Arkansas River, which flows 2,350 kilometers until it joins the Mississippi River. Eventually, the Mississippi flows into the Gulf of Mexico. Water that fell less than 15 kilometers apart ends up almost 3,000 kilometers apart, in different oceans!

FUN FACT

Use the map and your knowledge of science to answer the following question.

Why do you think the two rivers that start so close together flow to such different locations?

_____

_____

_____

▶ PLANET DIARY Go to **Planet Diary** to learn more about water on Earth's surface.

Royal Gorge

Pueblo

KANSAS

PACIFIC OCEAN

GULF OF MEXICO

John Martin Reservoir

Great Bend

Wichita

COLORADO

 Do the Inquiry Warm-Up
Mapping Surface Waters.

Vocabulary
- tributary • watershed • divide • reservoir
- eutrophication

Skills
↻ Reading: Sequence

△ Inquiry: Form Operational Definitions

What Is a River System?

If you were hiking near the beginning of the Fryingpan and Arkansas rivers, you could observe tiny streams of water from melted snow. Gravity causes these tiny streams to flow downhill. As you follow one small stream, you would notice that the stream reaches another stream and joins it, forming a larger stream. That larger stream joins other streams until a small river forms.

Tributaries As you continue following the small river downhill, you might notice more streams joining the river. Eventually, the small river itself flows into a larger river. This river grows as more small rivers flow into it, before finally spilling into the ocean. The streams and smaller rivers that feed into a main river are called **tributaries.** Tributaries flow downward toward the main river, pulled by the force of gravity. ⚷ **A river and all the streams and smaller rivers that flow into it together make up a river system.**

> **Academic Standards for Science**
>
> **8.2.2** Describe and model how water moves through the earth's crust, atmosphere, and oceans in a cyclic way as liquid, vapor, and solid.
> **8.NS.8** Analyze data.

Why is the Arkansas River considered a tributary of the Mississippi River?

_____

_____

_____

FIGURE 1 ·······································

The Arkansas River

✎ **Make Judgments** Put a *K* on the map where you might go kayaking. Put an *F* where you might get water for farming. Put an *M* where you might build a manufacturing plant. Explain why you chose the locations you did. **8.NS.8**

_____

_____

_____

_____

ARKANSAS

Lake Dardanelle

Little Rock

Mississippi River

Kaw Lake

Tulsa

OKLAHOMA

Watersheds Just as all the water in a bathtub flows toward the drain, all the water in a river system drains into a main river. The land area that supplies water to a river system is called a **watershed.** Watersheds are sometimes known as drainage basins.

As you can see in **Figure 2,** the Missouri and Ohio rivers are quite long. Yet they flow into the Mississippi River. When rivers join another river system, the areas they drain become part of the largest river's watershed. The watershed of the Mississippi River covers nearly one third of the United States!

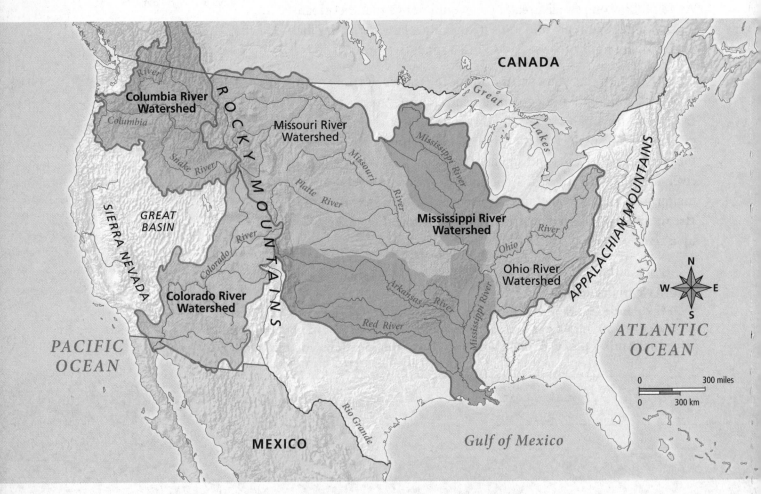

FIGURE 2 ··

Major Watersheds of the United States

This map shows watersheds of several large rivers in the United States. ✏ **Interpret Maps** Draw the path that water would take from the Platte River's source to the ocean. Which watersheds would the water pass through? 8.NS.8

_____

_____

_____

Divides What keeps watersheds separate? One watershed is separated from another by a ridge of land called a **divide**. Streams on each side of the divide flow in different directions. The Great Divide (also called the Continental Divide) is the longest divide in North America. It follows the line of the Rocky Mountains. West of this divide, water flows toward the Pacific Ocean. Some water is trapped between the Rockies and the Sierra Nevadas, in the Great Basin. Between the Rocky and Appalachian mountains, water flows toward the Mississippi River and into the Gulf of Mexico.

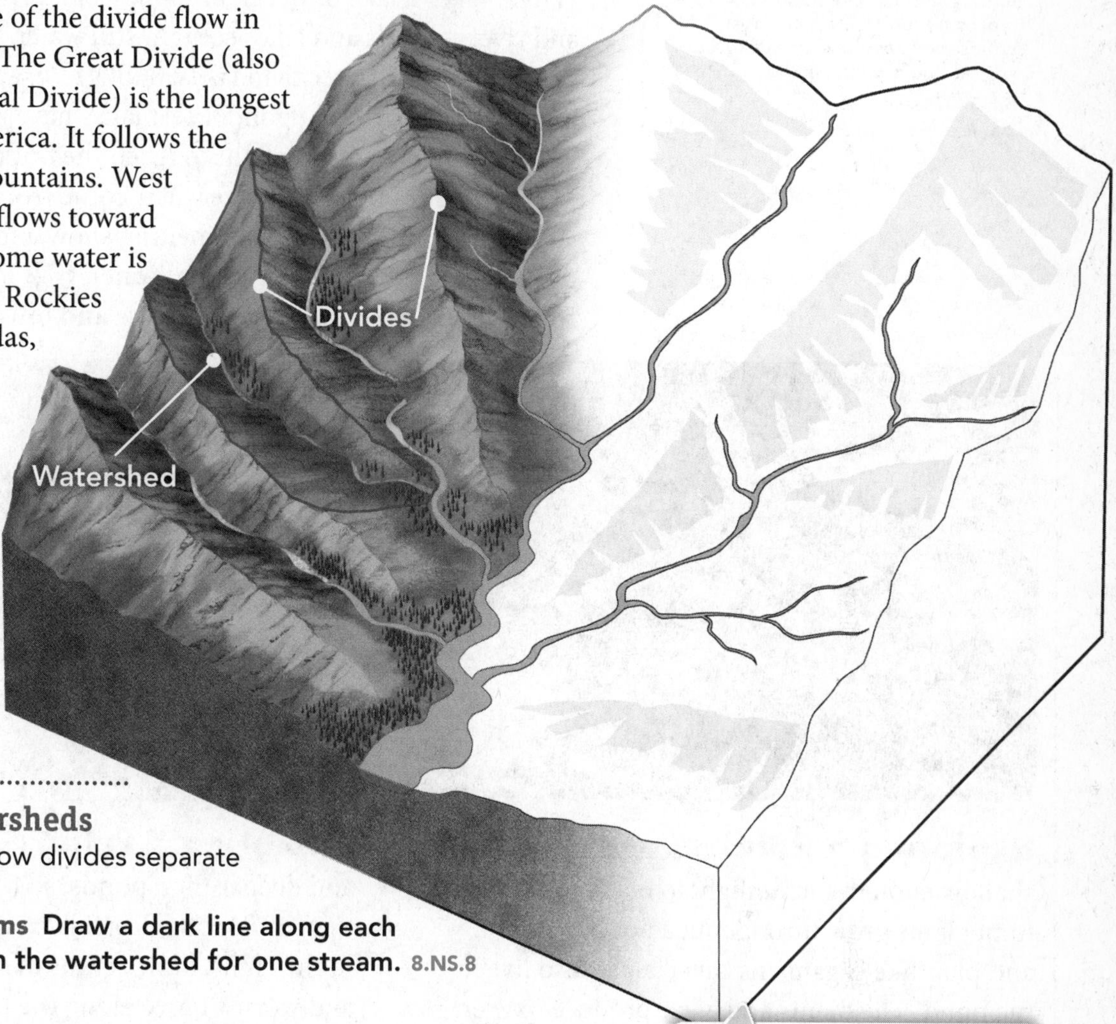

Divides

Watershed

FIGURE 3 ·······································

Divides and Watersheds

The diagram shows how divides separate land into watersheds.

🖉 **Interpret Diagrams** Draw a dark line along each divide. Then shade in the watershed for one stream. 8.NS.8

Lab zone® Do the Quick Lab *What Is a Watershed?*

🔑 Assess Your Understanding

1a. Identify A (divide/tributary) separates two watersheds. 8.2.2

b. Summarize How is a watershed related to a river system? _____

_____

_____ 8.2.2

c. Make Generalizations How can a stream be part of more than one watershed?

_____

_____

_____

_____

_____

_____ 8.2.2

got it? ·····································

○ **I get it!** Now I know that a river system is _____

_____

○ **I need extra help with** _____

_____

Go to **MY SCIENCE** ⬤⁵ **COACH** *online for help with this subject.* 8.2.2

Academic Standards for Science

8.2.2 Describe and model how water moves through the earth's crust, atmosphere, and oceans in a cyclic way, as liquid, vapor, and solid.

8.NS.8 Analyze data.

What Are Ponds and Lakes?

What makes a lake or pond different from a river? Unlike streams and rivers, ponds and lakes contain still water. In general, ponds are smaller and shallower than lakes. Sunlight usually reaches to the bottom of all parts of a pond. Most lakes have areas where the water is too deep for much sunlight to reach the bottom.

Where does pond and lake water come from? Some ponds and lakes are supplied by rainfall, melting snow and ice, and runoff. Others are fed by rivers or groundwater. **Ponds and lakes form when water collects in hollows and low-lying areas of land.**

Exploring a Pond Because the water is shallow enough for sunlight to reach the bottom, plants grow throughout a pond. Bacteria and plantlike organisms called algae also live in the pond. The plants and algae produce oxygen as they use sunlight to make food. Fish and other animals in the pond use the oxygen and food provided by plants and algae. Some animals also use these plants for shelter.

Exploring a Lake Lakes are usually larger and deeper than ponds, so little sunlight reaches the bottom of a deep lake. Fewer plants can live in in the chilly, dark depths of such a lake. Mollusks and worms move along the lake's sandy or rocky bottom. They eat food particles that drift down from the surface. Young bony fishes such as pike and sturgeon eat the tiny bottom-dwellers, while the adult fish eat other fish.

apply it!

① Complete the Venn diagram to compare and contrast characteristics of lakes and ponds.

② **Form Operational Definitions** Based on your answers, write an operational definition for *lake*.

_____

_____

_____

8.NS.8

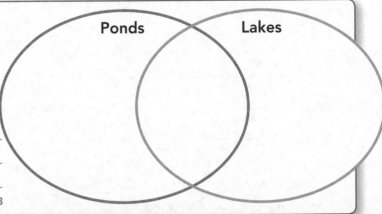

Ponds   Lakes

Lake Formation

Lakes can form through several natural processes. A river, for example, may bend and loop as it encounters obstacles in its path. Eventually, a new channel might form, cutting off a loop. The cutoff loop may become an oxbow lake.

Some lakes, such as the Great Lakes, formed in depressions created by ice sheets that melted at the end of the Ice Age. Other lakes were created by movements of Earth's crust that formed long, deep valleys called rift valleys. In Africa, Lake Tanganyika lies in a rift valley. Volcanoes can also form lakes. Lava or mud from a volcano can block a river, forming a lake. Lakes can also form in the empty craters of volcanoes.

People can create a lake by building a dam. A lake that stores water for human use is called a **reservoir.**

FIGURE 4 ....

Types of Lakes
The photos show examples of glacial, volcanic, and rift valley lakes. ✎ **Classify Write G on the glacial lake, V on the volcanic lake, and R on the rift valley lake.**

Lab zone | Do the Quick Lab Modeling How a Lake Forms.

🔑 Assess Your Understanding

2a. Explain What is one major difference between a lake and a pond?

_____

_____

8.2.2

b. Compare and Contrast How is a reservoir different from other kinds of lakes?

_____

_____

_____

8.2.2

got it?

○ **I get it!** Now I know that lakes and ponds are _

_____

_____

_____

_____

○ **I need extra help with** _____

Go to my science ⓢ COACH *online for help with this subject.*

8.2.2

197

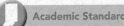
8.2.2 Describe and model how water moves through the earth's crust, atmosphere, and oceans in a cyclic way, as liquid, vapor, and solid.

8.NS.11 Communicate findings.

Sequence Which of the following processes occurs first during eutrophication?

○ Nutrients build up in a lake.

○ A lake is replaced by a meadow.

○ Plants stop carrying out photosynthesis.

How Can Lakes Change?

If you watch a lake or pond over many years, you will see it change. In time, the lake may shrink and become shallower. 🗝 **Natural processes and human activities can cause lakes to disappear.**

Eutrophication As lake organisms die, bacteria break down the bodies and release nutrients into the water. These nutrients, such as nitrogen and phosphorus, are chemicals that other organisms need. Over time, nutrients can build up in the lake in a process called **eutrophication** (yoo troh fih KAY shun). Algae use these nutrients and spread, forming a layer on the lake's surface.

Figure 5 shows how eutrophication can change a lake. When the algae layer becomes so thick that it blocks sunlight, plants cannot carry out photosynthesis, and they die. Without food and oxygen from the plants, animals die. Decaying material from dead organisms piles up on the bottom, making the lake shallower. As the area fills in, land plants grow in the mud. Eventually, the area fills with plants, and a meadow replaces the former lake.

The Human Role Though eutrophication occurs naturally, human activities can also cause or increase it. For example, fertilizer from farms runs off into ponds and lakes, providing extra nutrients to the algae. The extra nutrients speed up the growth of algae, leading to faster eutrophication.

FIGURE 5
Eutrophication
Summarize Write a caption for each diagram explaining the changes that occur during eutrophication. 8.NS.11

THE BIG ? An Endless Cycle

How does water cycle on Earth?

FIGURE 6 ....

REAL-WORLD INQUIRY Make a cycle diagram to show how water cycles. Include the processes listed below.

Processes

Evaporation

Condensation

Transpiration

Precipitation

Runoff

Include examples of:
a river system
a lake or pond
an ocean
groundwater

 Lab zone Do the Quick Lab *How Can Algal Growth Affect Pond Life?*

Assess Your Understanding

3a. Explain Eutrophication occurs when algae block sunlight in a lake or pond and plants cannot _____

8.2.2

b. ANSWER THE BIG ? How does water cycle on Earth?

_____
_____
_____
_____
_____

8.2.2

got it?

○ **I get it!** Now I know that lakes can change due to _____
_____
_____
_____
_____

○ **I need extra help with** _____
_____

Go to my science °COACH *online for help with this subject.*

8.2.2

Indiana

LESSON

3 Exploring the Ocean

UNLOCK THE BIG ?

🔑 **How Do Conditions Vary in Earth's Oceans?**
8.2.2, 8.NS.3, 8.NS.8

🔑 **What Are Some Features of the Ocean Floor?**
8.2.2, 8.NS.1

---

my planet Diary   SCIENCE AND TECHNOLOGY

Deep-Sea Escape

You've heard of how parachutes are used for escapes. But have you heard of a special suit that allows people to escape from a submarine 183 meters under water? The suit is designed to help sailors survive very cold temperatures and very high pressure. In an emergency, sailors put on this suit and enter a water-filled rescue chamber. Then the sailors shoot out, rising at two to three meters per second. If the suit tears, they have to exhale all the way to the surface so their lungs don't explode. At the surface, part of the suit inflates to become a life raft.

Discuss these questions with a classmate and write your answers below.

1. What technology was developed to help sailors escape a submarine accident?

_____

_____

_____

2. What would it feel like to escape from a submarine deep under water? How would you help your body adjust to the changing pressure?

_____

_____

▶ **PLANET DIARY** Go to **Planet Diary** to learn more about characteristics of the ocean.

 Lab zone® Do the Inquiry Warm-Up
What Can You Learn Without Seeing?

 Academic Standards for Science

8.2.2 Describe and model how water moves through the earth's crust, atmosphere, and oceans in a cyclic way, as liquid, vapor, and solid.

8.NS.3 Collect quantitative data.

8.NS.8 Analyze data.

How Do Conditions Vary in Earth's Oceans?

People have explored the ocean since ancient times. For centuries, the ocean has provided food and served as a route for trade and travel. Modern scientists have studied the characteristics of the ocean's waters and the ocean floor. 🔑 **The water in Earth's oceans varies in salinity, temperature, and depth.**

Vocabulary

- salinity
- sonar
- seamount
- trench
- continental slope
- continental shelf
- abyssal plain
- mid-ocean ridge

Skills

🔄 Reading: Identify the Main Idea

🔺 Inquiry: Interpret Data

Salinity

If you've ever swallowed a mouthful of water while you were swimming in the ocean, you know it's pretty salty. But just how salty? If you boiled a kilogram of ocean water in a pot until the water was gone, there would be about 35 grams of salt left in the pot. That's about two tablespoons of salt. **Salinity** is the total amount of dissolved salts in a sample of water. In most parts of the ocean, the salinity is between 34 and 37 parts per thousand.

The substance you know as table salt is sodium chloride. This salt is present in the greatest amount in ocean water. When sodium chloride dissolves in water, it separates into sodium and chloride particles called ions. Ocean water also contains smaller amounts of more than a dozen ions, including magnesium and calcium.

Near the ocean's surface, rain, snow, and melting ice add fresh water, lowering the salinity. Evaporation, on the other hand, increases salinity. Salt is left behind as the water evaporates. Salinity can also be higher near the poles. As the surface water freezes into ice, the salt is left behind in the remaining water.

Effects of Salinity

Salinity affects ocean water in different ways. For instance, fresh water freezes at 0°C. But ocean water doesn't freeze until the temperature drops to about −1.9°C. The salt acts as a kind of antifreeze by interfering with the formation of ice. Salt water also has a higher density than fresh water. That means that the mass of one liter of salt water is greater than the mass of one liter of fresh water. Because its density is greater, seawater lifts, or buoys up, less dense objects floating in it.

> **Vocabulary** **Suffixes** Circle the correct word to complete the sentence below.
>
> Ocean water has a higher (salinity/saline) than fresh water.

Composition of Ocean Water

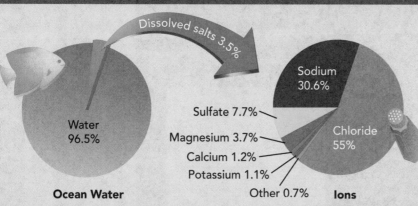

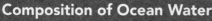

Dissolved salts 3.5%

Water 96.5%

Ocean Water

Sodium 30.6%

Sulfate 7.7%

Magnesium 3.7%

Calcium 1.2%

Potassium 1.1%

Other 0.7%

Chloride 55%

Ions

FIGURE 1

> **VIRTUAL LAB** **Composition of Ocean Water**

When salts dissolve, they separate into particles called ions.

✏️ **Read Graphs** In ocean water, which ion is most common? Which salt?

_____

_____

_____

8.NS.8

....✎..
⟲ **Identify the Main Idea**
Underline the two changes that
happen with depth.

Depth

Temperature The broad surface of the ocean absorbs energy from the sun. ⟞⟝ **Like temperatures on land, temperatures at the surface of the ocean vary with location and the seasons.** Near the equator, surface ocean temperatures often reach 25°C, about room temperature. The temperatures drop as you travel away from the equator. Warm water is less dense than cold water, so it doesn't sink. Warm water forms only a thin layer on the ocean surface.

Depth If you could swim from the surface of the ocean to the ocean floor, you would pass through a vertical section of the ocean. This section, shown in **Figure 2,** is referred to as the water column. ⟞⟝ **As you descend through the ocean, the water temperature decreases.** There are three temperature zones in the water column. The surface zone is the warmest. It typically extends from the surface to between 100 and 500 meters. The average temperature worldwide for this zone is 16.1°C. Next is the transition zone, which extends from the bottom of the surface zone to about 1 kilometer. Temperatures in the transition zone drop very quickly to about 4°C. Below the transition zone is the deep zone. Average temperatures there are 3.5°C in most of the ocean.

Water pressure, the force exerted by the weight of water, also changes with depth. ⟞⟝ **In the ocean, pressure increases by 1 bar, the air pressure at sea level, with each 10 meters of depth.** Due to the high pressure in the deep ocean, divers can descend safely only to about 40 meters without specialized equipment. To observe the deep ocean, scientists can use a submersible, an underwater vehicle built of materials that resist pressure.

FIGURE 2 ···
Changes With Depth
✎ Relate Text and Visuals The conditions in Earth's oceans change with depth.
1. Shade in each temperature zone in the depth bar and make a key.
2. Fill in the blank in the pressure bar to identify what happens to pressure with depth. 8.NS.3

Key

☐ _____

☐ _____

☐ _____

Pressure _____ with depth.

0.5 km

1.0 km

1.5 km

2.0 km

2.5 km

3.0 km

3.5 km

4.0 km

apply it!

Each panel of dials provides information about conditions at various depths in the ocean. 8.NS.3, 8.NS.8

1 ◢ **Interpret Data** Find the incorrect dial in each panel and correct its reading.

2 Label where in the ocean you might find each set of readings: surface zone, transition zone, or deep zone.

Depth (m)
Temperature
Pressure

3 **CHALLENGE** Based on the information in the panels, where is the most dense water in the ocean?

_____

_____

_____

_____

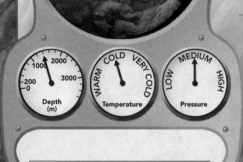

Depth (m)
Temperature
Pressure

Depth (m)
Temperature
Pressure

did you know?

The Deep Flight Super Falcon is the first winged submersible available to the public. It can "fly" quickly and easily to depths of more than 100 meters.

Lab zone Do the Quick Lab *Ocean Conditions.*

🔑 **Assess Your Understanding**

got it? ....

○ **I get it!** Now I know that the water in Earth's oceans varies in _____

_____

○ **I need extra help with** _____

Go to **MY SCIENCE COACH** *online for help with this subject.*

8.2.2

Academic Standards for Science

8.2.2 Describe and model how water moves through the earth's crust, atmosphere, and oceans in a cyclic way, as liquid, vapor, and solid.

8.NS.1 Make predictions based on research and prior knowledge.

What Are Some Features of the Ocean Floor?

The ocean is very deep—3.8 kilometers deep on average. That's more than twice as deep as the Grand Canyon. Humans can't survive the darkness, cold temperatures, and extreme pressure of the deep ocean. So scientists have developed technology to study the ocean floor. A major advance in ocean-floor mapping was **sonar**, SOund NAvigation and Ranging. This system uses sound waves to calculate the distance to an object. A ship's sonar system sends out pulses of sound that bounce off the ocean floor. The equipment then measures how quickly the sound waves return to the ship.

Once scientists mapped the ocean floor, they discovered that the deep waters hid mountain ranges bigger than any on land, as well as deep canyons. 🔑 **Major ocean floor features include trenches, the continental shelf, the continental slope, the abyssal plain, and the mid-ocean ridge. These features have all been formed by the interaction of Earth's plates.** You can see these feaures in **Figure 3**.

FIGURE 3 ·······························

Ocean Floor

✎ **Relate Text and Visuals**
Match the descriptions below with the ocean floor features in the image. Write the number for each description in the corresponding circles.
(Image not to scale. To show major ocean floor features, thousands of kilometers have been squeezed into one illustration.)

Ocean floor

Ocean floor

Molten _____ material

1 **Seamounts**
A **seamount** is a volcanic mountain rising from the ocean floor that doesn't reach the surface. Seamounts often form near mid-ocean ridges. Some seamounts were once volcanic islands. But they slowly sank because of the movement of the ocean floor toward a trench.

2 **Trenches**
A **trench** is a long, deep valley on the ocean floor through which old ocean floor sinks back toward the mantle. The Marianas Trench in the Pacific Ocean is 11 kilometers deep.

3 **Continental Slope**
At 130 meters down, the slope of the ocean floor gets steeper. The steep edge of the continental shelf is called the **continental slope.**

4 **Continental Shelf**
The **continental shelf** is a gently sloping, shallow area that extends outward from the edge of each continent. Its width varies from a few kilometers to as much as 1,300 kilometers.

FIGURE 4 ··

> INTERACTIVE ART **What are some characteristics of Earth's oceans?**

✏ **Predict** Your ship has been radioed by a submarine that has lost the use of its navigation instruments. Based on the information in their last transmission, where might the vessel be? What might the conditions of the water be at this depth? Discuss your prediction with a partner.

Last transmission from sub: "Depth reading 3,000 meters; passed over a flat plain...sonar returned waves quickly; possibly approaching mountains."

_____

_____

_____

_____

_____

_____

_____

_____

Lab zone ® Do the Quick Lab *The Shape of the Ocean Floor.*

🔑 **Assess Your Understanding**

1a. List What are four features of the ocean floor?

_____

_____

8.2.2

b. Explain Why has investigation of the ocean been difficult?

_____

8.2.2

c. What are some characteristics of Earth's oceans?

_____

_____

8.2.2

got it? ···

○ **I get it!** Now I know that the ocean floor has many different features formed by _____

_____

_____

○ **I need extra help with** _____

Go to **MY SCIENCE** ⑤ **COACH** *online for help with this subject.* 8.2.2

6 **Mid-Ocean Ridges**
Mid-ocean ridges are long chains of mountains on the ocean floors. Along the ridges, lava erupts and forms new ocean floor. Because of convection currents inside Earth, the ocean floor slowly moves toward a trench and sinks into the mantle.

5 **Abyssal Plain**
The **abyssal plain** (uh BIHS ul) is a broad area covered with thick layers of mud and silt. It's a smooth, nearly flat region of the ocean.

Currents and Climate

🔑 **What Causes Surface Currents?**
8.2.1, 8.2.3, 8.NS.8

🔑 **What Causes Deep Currents?**
8.2.1, 8.2.3, 8.NS.1, 8.NS.8

mY PLaneT DiaRY

EVERYDAY SCIENCE

Ducky Overboard

What happens when a ship loses its cargo at sea? Is it gone forever? You might think so. One ship traveling from Hong Kong to Tacoma, Washington, lost 29,000 plastic toys. They fell overboard in a storm and were considered lost at sea. But when hundreds of the toys began washing up on distant shores, scientists got excited.

One way scientists study ocean currents is by releasing empty bottles into the ocean. But of 500 to 1,000 bottles released, scientists might only recover 10. That doesn't give them much data. The large number of floating toys could give scientists better data from more data points.

The first toys were spotted off the coast of Alaska. Then beachcombers began finding them in Canada, in Washington, and even as far away as Scotland.

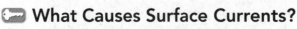

Discuss these questions with a classmate and write your answers below.

1. Why was the plastic toy spill so helpful to scientists studying ocean currents?

_____

_____

2. Have you ever found objects on the beach? What data would scientists need from you for their research?

_____

_____

Lab zone Do the Inquiry Warm-Up *Bottom to Top.*

▶ PLANET DIARY Go to **Planet Diary** to learn more about ocean currents.

Vocabulary
- current • Coriolis effect
- climate • El Niño • La Niña

Skills
- Reading: Compare and Contrast
- Inquiry: Infer

What Causes Surface Currents?

A **current** is a large stream of moving water that flows through the oceans. Unlike waves, currents carry water from one place to another. Some currents move water at the surface of the ocean. Other currents move water deep in the ocean.

🔑 **Surface currents affect water to a depth of several hundred meters. They are driven mainly by winds.** Surface currents follow Earth's major wind patterns. They move in circular patterns in the five major oceans. Most of the currents flow east or west, then double back to complete the circle, as shown in **Figure 1**.

Coriolis Effect Why do the currents move in these circular patterns? If Earth were standing still, winds and currents would flow in more direct paths between the poles and the equator. But as Earth rotates, the paths of the winds and currents curve. This effect of Earth's rotation on the direction of winds and currents is called the **Coriolis effect** (kawr ee OH lis). In the Northern Hemisphere, the Coriolis effect causes the currents to curve clockwise. In the Southern Hemisphere, the Coriolis effect causes the currents to curve counterclockwise.

Academic Standards for Science

8.2.1 Recognize and demonstrate how the sun's energy drive convection in the atmosphere and in bodies of water, which result in ocean currents and weather patterns.

8.2.3 Describe the characteristics of ocean currents and identify their effects on weather patterns.

8.NS.8 Analyze data.

FIGURE 1 ·····················

Surface Currents

✏️ **Infer** The toys that fell overboard washed up in many places. Two of the locations are marked with ducks below. Circle the currents that you think moved the toys to these spots. Discuss your answer with a classmate. 8.NS.8

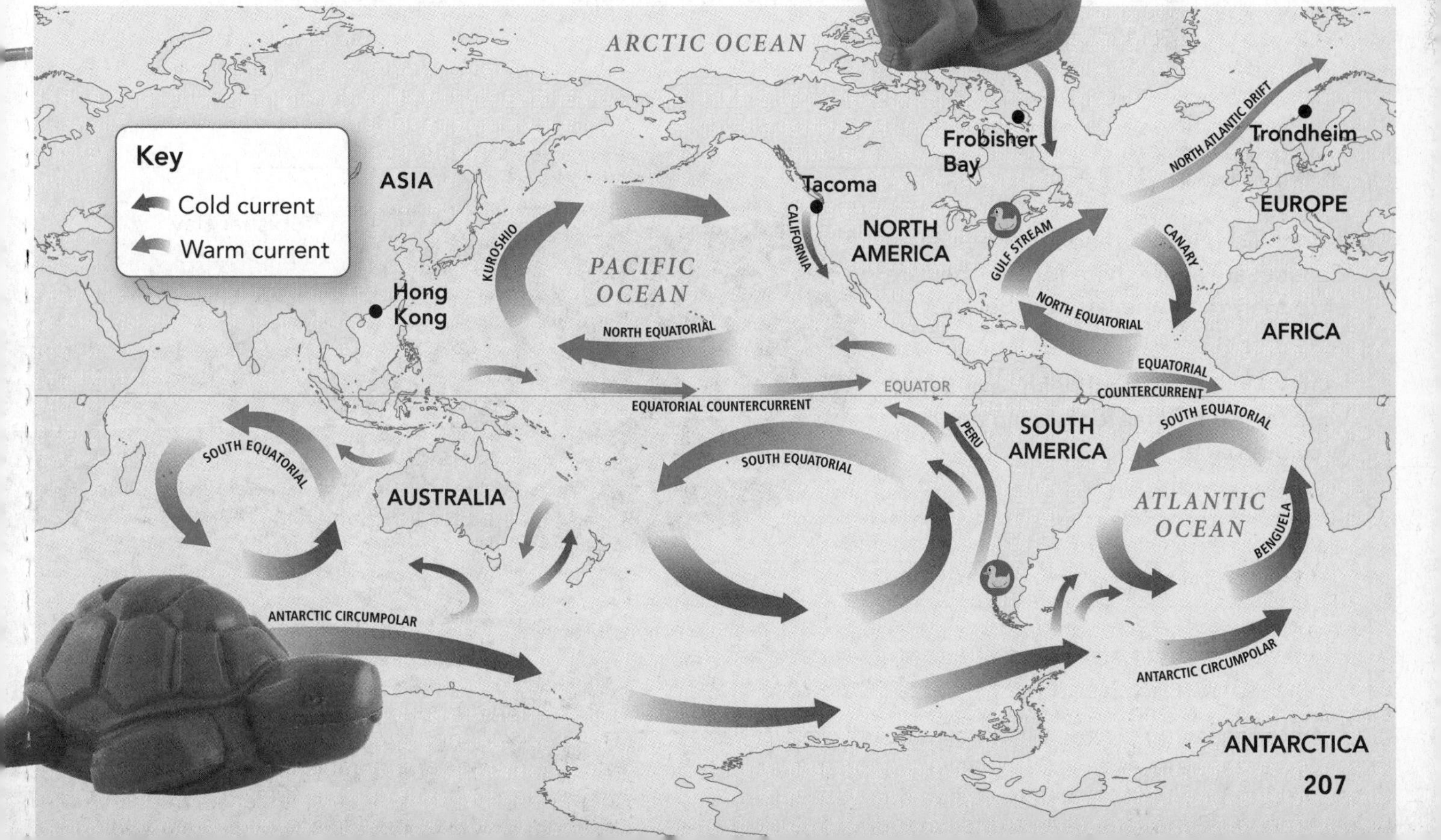

Key
- Cold current
- Warm current

ASIA

KUROSHIO

Hong Kong

PACIFIC OCEAN

NORTH EQUATORIAL

EQUATORIAL COUNTERCURRENT

SOUTH EQUATORIAL

AUSTRALIA

SOUTH EQUATORIAL

ANTARCTIC CIRCUMPOLAR

ARCTIC OCEAN

Tacoma

CALIFORNIA

NORTH AMERICA

Frobisher Bay

GULF STREAM

NORTH EQUATORIAL

EQUATOR

SOUTH EQUATORIAL

PERU

SOUTH AMERICA

EQUATORIAL COUNTERCURRENT

SOUTH EQUATORIAL

ATLANTIC OCEAN

BENGUELA

ANTARCTIC CIRCUMPOLAR

NORTH ATLANTIC DRIFT

Trondheim

EUROPE

CANARY

AFRICA

ANTARCTICA

✎ **Compare and Contrast** Use the space below to compare and contrast the effects of warm and cold currents on climate.

_____

_____

_____

_____

_____

_____

_____

_____

Gulf Stream The Gulf Stream is the largest and most powerful surface current in the North Atlantic Ocean. This current is caused by strong winds from the west. It is more than 30 kilometers wide and 300 meters deep. The Gulf Stream moves warm water from the Gulf of Mexico to the Caribbean Sea. It then continues northward along the east coast of the United States. Near Cape Hatteras, North Carolina, it curves eastward across the Atlantic, as a result of the Coriolis effect. When the Gulf Stream crosses the Atlantic it becomes the North Atlantic Drift.

Effects on Climate The Gulf Stream has a warming effect on the climate of nearby land areas. **Climate** is the pattern of temperature and precipitation typical of an area over a long period of time. The mid-Atlantic region of the United States, including North Carolina and Virginia, has a more moderate climate because of the Gulf Stream. Winters are very mild and summers are humid.

Currents affect climate by moving cold and warm water around the globe. Currents generally move warm water from the tropics toward the poles and bring cold water back toward the equator. 🔑 **A surface current warms or cools the air above it. This affects the climate of land near the coast.** Winds pick up moisture as they blow across warm-water currents. This explains why the warm Kuroshio Current brings mild, rainy weather to the southern islands of Japan. Cold-water currents cool the air above them. Cold air holds less moisture than warm air. So cold currents tend to bring cool, dry weather to land areas in their path.

apply it!

Trondheim, Norway, and Frobisher Bay, Canada, are shown here in July. They are at roughly the same latitude, but they have very different climates.

Infer Why does Trondheim have a mild climate? _Hint:_ Refer to the map on the previous page.

_____

_____

_____

_____

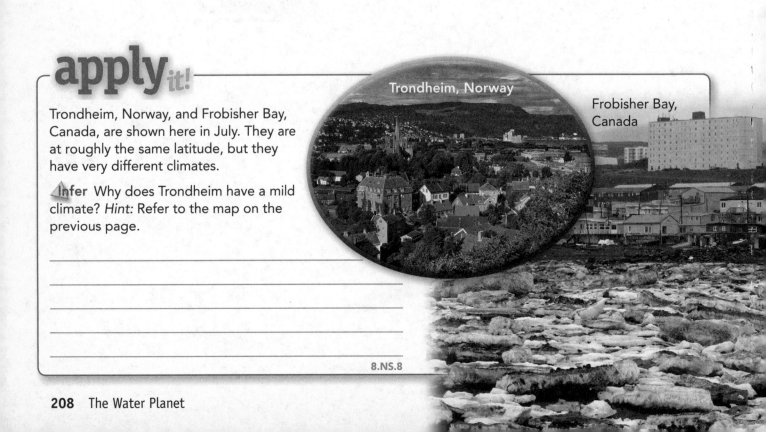

Trondheim, Norway

Frobisher Bay, Canada

8.NS.8

El Niño Changes in wind patterns and currents can have a major impact on the oceans and nearby land. One example of such changes is **El Niño,** a climate event that occurs every two to seven years in the Pacific Ocean. El Niño begins when an unusual pattern of winds forms over the western Pacific. This causes a vast sheet of warm water to move east toward the South American coast, as shown in **Figure 2.** This warm water prevents the cold deep water from moving to the surface. El Niño conditions can last for one to two years before the usual winds and currents return.

El Niño causes shifts in weather patterns. This leads to unusual and often severe conditions in different areas. A major El Niño occurred between 1997 and 1998. It caused an especially warm winter in the northeastern United States. It was also responsible for heavy rains, flooding, and mudslides in California, as well as a string of deadly tornadoes in Florida.

La Niña When surface waters in the eastern Pacific are colder than normal, a climate event known as **La Niña** occurs. A La Niña event is the opposite of an El Niño event. La Niña events typically bring colder than normal winters and greater precipitation to the Pacific Northwest and the north central United States.

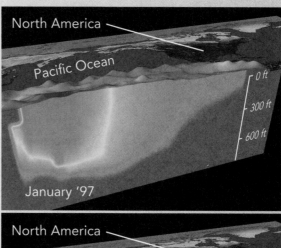

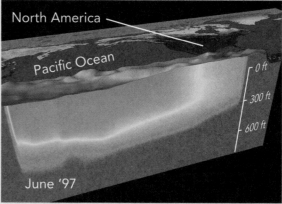

FIGURE 2 ···

>ART IN MOTION **Warming Sea Temperature**
The images show what happens to temperature below the surface of the ocean during an El Niño event. Red indicates a warmer sea surface temperature.

✎ **Draw Conclusions** What happened to the the water temperature over six months? 8.NS.8

_____

_____

Lab®
zone
Do the Lab Investigation
Modeling Ocean Currents.

🗝 Assess Your Understanding

1a. Define What is a current?

_____

_____
8.2.1, 8.2.3

b. Describe What causes surface currents?

_____
8.2.1, 8.2.3

c. CHALLENGE Why is it helpful to a community to be able to predict an El Niño event?

_____

_____

_____
8.2.1, 8.2.3

got it? ···

○ **I get it!** Now I know that currents are driven mainly by _____

_____

○ **I need extra help with** _____

Go to **MY SCIENCE** 🖙 **COACH** *online for help with this subject.* 8.2.1, 8.2.3

Academic Standards for Science

8.2.1 Recognize and demonstrate how the sun's energy drive convection in the atmosphere and in bodies of water, which result in ocean currents and weather patterns.

8.2.3 Describe the characteristics of ocean currents and identify their effects on weather patterns.

8.NS.1 Make predictions and develop testable questions based on research and prior knowledge.

8.NS.8 Analyze data, using appropriate mathematical manipulation as required, and use it to identify patterns and make inferences based on these patterns.

What Causes Deep Currents?

Deep below the ocean surface, another type of current causes chilly waters to creep slowly across the ocean floor. **Deep currents are caused by differences in the density of ocean water.** Recall that cold water is more dense than warm water.

Salinity When a warm surface current moves from the equator toward one of the poles, it gradually cools. As ice forms near the poles, the salinity of the water increases from the salt left behind during freezing. As the water's temperature decreases and its salinity increases, the water becomes denser and sinks. Then, the cold water flows back along the ocean floor as a deep current. Deep currents are affected by the Coriolis effect, which causes them to curve.

Deep currents move and mix water around the world. They carry cold water from the poles toward the equator. Deep currents flow slowly. They may take as long as 1,000 years to circulate between the oceans back to where they started.

Global Ocean Conveyor The simplified pattern of ocean currents in **Figure 3** looks like a conveyor belt, moving water between the oceans. This pattern of ocean currents results from density differences due to temperature and salinity. The currents bring oxygen into the deep ocean that is needed for marine life.

The ocean's deep currents mostly start as cold water in the North Atlantic Ocean. This is the same water that moved north across the Atlantic as part of the Gulf Stream. This cold, salty water, called the North Atlantic Deep Water, is dense. It sinks to the bottom of the ocean and flows southward toward Antarctica. From there it flows northward into both the Indian and Pacific oceans. The deep cold water rises to the surface in the Indian and Pacific oceans, warms, and eventually flows back along the surface into the Atlantic.

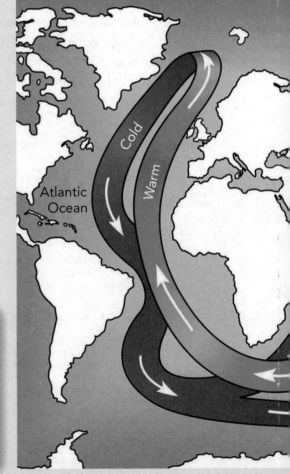

FIGURE 3 ······
Global Conveyor
✎ **Predict** What might happen if the global conveyor stopped?

_____

_____

_____

8.NS.1, 8.NS.8

do the math! Analyzing Data

Calculating Density

Temperature affects the density of ocean water. To calculate the density of a substance, divide the mass of the substance by its volume.

$$\text{Density} = \frac{\text{Mass}}{\text{Volume}}$$

······················ **Practice Problem** ······················

Calculate Find the density of the following 1-L samples of ocean water. Sample A has a mass of 1.01 kg; Sample B has a mass of 1.06 kg. Which sample is likely to have the higher salinity? Why?

_____

_____

_____

8.NS.8

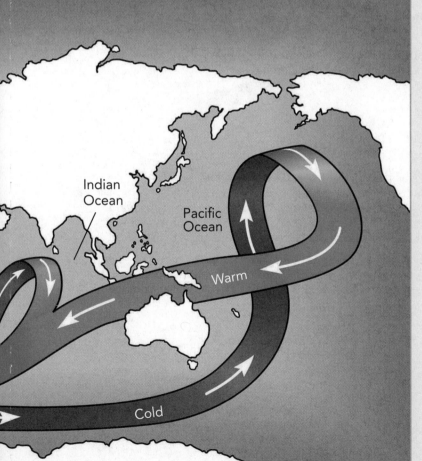

Indian Ocean

Pacific Ocean

Warm

Cold

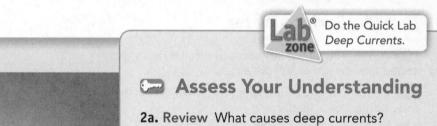

Lab zone® Do the Quick Lab *Deep Currents.*

🔑 Assess Your Understanding

2a. Review What causes deep currents?

_____

_____

8.2.1, 8.2.3

b. Explain How does the temperature of ocean water affect its density?

_____

_____

_____

_____

8.2.1, 8.2.3

got it? ······································

○ **I get it!** Now I know how the global ocean

conveyor moves: _____

_____

_____

○ **I need extra help with** _____

Go to **my science** ⑤ **coach** *online for help with this subject.* 8.2.1, 8.2.3

211

5 Study Guide

Water on Earth cycles between _____, _____, and the atmosphere.

LESSON 1 Water on Earth

8.2.1, 8.2.2, 8.2.7, 8.NS.1, 8.NS.8

🗝 All living things need water in order to carry out their body processes. In addition, many living things live in water.

🗝 Most of Earth's surface water—roughly 97 percent—is salt water found in oceans. Only 3 percent is fresh water.

🗝 In the water cycle, water moves between land, living things, bodies of water on Earth's surface, and the atmosphere.

Vocabulary
• habitat • groundwater • water cycle • evaporation
• transpiration • precipitation

Salt water in oceans and salt lakes **97%** Fresh water **3%**

Water vapor **0.04%**
Ice **69%**
Groundwater **30%**
Lakes and rivers **0.26%**

LESSON 2 Surface Water

8.2.2, 8.NS.8, 8.NS.11

🗝 A river and all the streams and smaller rivers that flow into it together make up a river system.

🗝 Ponds and lakes form when water collects in hollows and low-lying areas of land.

🗝 Natural processes and human activities can cause lakes to disappear.

Vocabulary
• tributary • watershed • divide
• reservoir • eutrophication

LESSON 3 Exploring the Ocean

8.2.2, 8.NS.1, 8.NS.3, 8.NS.8

🗝 The water in Earth's oceans varies in salinity, temperature, and depth.

🗝 Like temperatures on land, temperatures at the surface of the ocean vary with location and the seasons. As you descend through the ocean, the water temperature decreases.

🗝 In the ocean, pressure increases by 1 bar with each 10 meters of depth.

🗝 Major ocean floor features include trenches, the continental shelf, the continental slope, the abyssal plain, and the mid-ocean ridge.

Vocabulary
• salinity • sonar • seamount • trench
• continental slope • continental shelf
• abyssal plain • mid-ocean ridge

LESSON 4 Currents and Climate

8.2.1, 8.2.3, 8.NS.1, 8.NS.8

🗝 Surface currents are driven mainly by winds. A surface current warms or cools the air above it, affecting the climate of the land near the coast.

🗝 Deep currents are caused by differences in the density of ocean water. They move and mix water around the world and carry cold water from the poles toward the equator.

Vocabulary
• current • Coriolis effect • climate
• El Niño • La Niña

Review and Assessment

LESSON 1 Water on Earth

1. Where is most of Earth's total water supply found?

   a. atmosphere

   b. groundwater

   c. ice sheets

   d. oceans
         8.2.2

2. During transpiration, plants _____

_____

_____
         8.2.2

3. Sequence Complete the cycle diagram to show one way in which water can move through the water cycle.

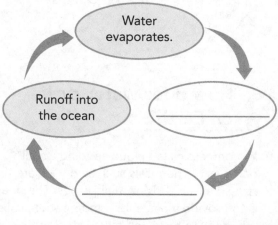

         8.2.1, 8.2.2

4. Apply Concepts Why is so little of Earth's water available for human use?

_____

_____

_____
         8.2.7

5. math! About 3 percent of Earth's water is fresh water. Of that 3 percent, about 69 percent is ice. About what percent of Earth's total water supply is ice?

_____
         8.2.7, 8.NS.8

LESSON 2 Surface Water

6. What is the area that supplies water to a river system called?

   a. reservoir

   b. tributary

   c. watershed

   d. wetland
         8.2.2

7. Two watersheds are separated by a(n)

_____
         8.2.2

8. Relate Cause and Effect Explain why some rivers experience severe springtime flooding as snow and ice melt along small mountain streams.

_____

_____

_____

_____

_____

_____
         8.2.2

9. Compare and Contrast How would the variety of organisms in the center of a pond differ from those in deep water at a lake's center?

_____

_____

_____
         8.2.2

10. Classify How can a large river also be a tributary?

_____

_____

_____

_____
         8.2.2

LESSON 3 Exploring the Ocean

11. Why is ocean water more dense than fresh water at the same temperature?

a. circular winds　　**b.** less pressure

c. deep currents　　**d.** higher salinity

8.2.2, 8.2.3

12. The mid-ocean ridge is _____

_____

_____

8.2.2, 8.2.3

13. Relate Cause and Effect Name two properties of ocean water affected by depth. How does depth affect each?

_____

_____

_____

_____

8.2.2, 8.2.3

14. Apply Concepts Would you expect the salinity of the ocean to be high or low in a rainy region near the mouth of a river?

_____

_____

_____

_____

8.2.2, 8.2.3

15. Sequence Put the following parts of the ocean floor in order from least to greatest depth: abyssal plain, continental shelf, mid-ocean ridge, trench, continental slope.

_____

_____

_____

_____

8.2.2, 8.2.3

16. [Write About It] In what ways is the ocean at 1,000 meters deep different from the ocean at the surface in the same location?

8.2.2, 8.2.3

LESSON 4 Currents and Climate

17. What makes winds and currents move in curved paths?

a. Coriolis effect　　**b.** wave height

c. longshore drift　　**d.** ocean trenches

8.2.1, 8.2.3

18. Compare and Contrast What causes surface currents? Deep currents?

_____

_____

_____

_____

8.2.1, 8.2.3

19. math! A 5-liter container of crude oil spills in the ocean. It has a mass of 4.10 kg. What is its density? If 1 liter of ocean water has a density of 1.03 kg, does the crude oil sink or float? Explain.　　8.2.1, 8.2.3, 8.NS.8

APPLY
THE BIG
?
How does water cycle on Earth?

20. In a process called cloud seeding, small particles of chemicals such as dry ice are spread into clouds from airplanes. The goal is to provide a place for condensation, causing raindrops to form and fall as precipitation. How would increased condensation affect the other processes of the water cycle?

_____

_____

_____

_____

_____

_____

_____

8.2.2

Indiana ISTEP+ Practice

Multiple Choice

Circle the letter of the best answer.

1. Use the diagram to answer the question.

Which of the following is a process that occurs in the water cycle?

A. condensation   B. evaporation

C. precipitation   D. all of the above

8.2.1, 8.2.2

2. What is the shallow, gently sloping area of the ocean floor that extends outward from the shoreline?

A. abyssal plain

B. continental shelf

C. continental slope

D. mid-ocean ridge

8.2.2, 8.2.3

3. A major warm ocean surface current flows along a coastal area. What type of climate would you most likely find in the area influenced by the current?

A. mild and wet   B. very cool and wet

C. cool and dry   D. very hot and dry

8.2.1, 8.2.3

4. How can eutrophication lead to the disappearance of a lake?

A. Waste and nutrients build up in the lake.

B. The amount of oxygen in the lake increases.

C. The lake's water supply dries up.

D. Sediment from streams fills up the lake.

8.2.2

Constructed Response

Write your answer to Question 5 on the lines below.

5. How do surface currents affect climate?

_____

_____

_____

_____

_____

8.2.2, 8.2.3

Extended Response

Use the graph and your knowledge of science to answer Question 6. Write your answer on a separate sheet of paper.

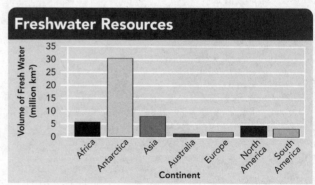

Freshwater Resources

6. The graph shows the total amount of fresh water in all forms found on each continent. Why is so much of Earth's fresh water located in Antarctica? Is that water usable by humans? Explain your answer.

8.2.2, 8.2.7, 8.NS.8

Sustainable Shrimp Farms

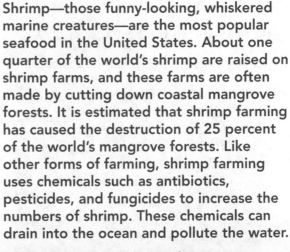

Shrimp—those funny-looking, whiskered marine creatures—are the most popular seafood in the United States. About one quarter of the world's shrimp are raised on shrimp farms, and these farms are often made by cutting down coastal mangrove forests. It is estimated that shrimp farming has caused the destruction of 25 percent of the world's mangrove forests. Like other forms of farming, shrimp farming uses chemicals such as antibiotics, pesticides, and fungicides to increase the numbers of shrimp. These chemicals can drain into the ocean and pollute the water.

Governments and shrimp farmers are working together to solve these problems. For example, farmers are looking into closed production systems. In this kind of farm, the water is filtered and reused, rather than sent back into the ocean. In closed systems, farmers may even be able to raise shrimp organically—without antibiotics. Right now, these high-tech systems are very expensive. But perhaps, with more research, the price tag will come down.

Research It Find out more about the way different shrimp farms work. Compare the economic and ecological impacts of closed production systems with more traditional open systems. Present the costs and benefits and express your opinion in a persuasive essay.

 8.2.6, 8.2.8, 8.NS.2, 8.NS.8, 8.NS.11

What Was Fort Miami?

Ohio's 2,000-Year-Old Aqueduct

▲ Archaeologists use computer-generated images to show what the 2,000-year-old irrigation system might have looked like when it was built.

Archaeologists from the University of Cincinnati have made a startling discovery. They had thought that a 2,000-year-old ruin on a hilltop in southwestern Ohio was a fort used by the Shawnee people native to the region to defend their lands from attack. Recently, however, archaeologists have found evidence that the ruin was actually a complex system of dams and canals.

The Shawnee built the system to collect water from a series of springs and to transport it to farmland, so that they could grow enough food to support their society. Climate records suggest that 2,000 years ago, when the Shawnee built the system, the region was colder and drier than it is now. So this system would have helped the Shawnee survive.

Design It Design a system for collecting and moving water from one place to another. First, brainstorm potential solutions. Choose the best solution and document your design with labeled drawings. Select appropriate materials to develop a prototype. Then, test and evaluate the prototype. Measure a small amount of water and record data about how well your design collects and moves the water. Present the results in a graph or data table. Use this information to redesign your prototype to improve your results. See Appendix A on page 508 for more information about the design process.

▲ Archaeologists sift carefully through dirt removed from the site of the Fort Miami water works.

8.2.8, 8.NS.1–8.NS.11, 8.DP.1–8.DP.11

WHAT KEEPS THIS HANG GLIDER FLYING?

THE BIG ?

How does the sun's energy affect Earth's atmosphere?

Imagine yourself lazily soaring like a bird above Earth. The quiet, gentle winds and warm sun are so relaxing. No noisy engine, no flapping wings, but wait, what's keeping you aloft? Everyone knows that humans can't fly. **Develop Hypotheses** How does this hang glider fly?

_____

_____

_____

_____

_____

_____

> UNTAMED SCIENCE Watch the **Untamed Science** video to learn more about Earth's atmosphere.

The Atmosphere

Academic Standards for Science

8.2.1, 8.2.4, 8.NS.1–8.NS.11, 8.DP.1–8.DP.11

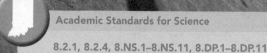

6 Getting Started

Check Your Understanding

1. **Background** Read the paragraph below and then answer the question.

Helen blows up a balloon. She adds it to a large garbage bag already full of balloons. Its low **weight** makes the bag easy to carry, but its large **volume** might be a problem fitting it in the car. Capturing air in a balloon makes it easier to understand that air has **mass.**

Weight is a measure of the force of gravity on an object.

Volume is the amount of space that matter occupies.

Mass is the amount of matter in an object.

- How could the bag's volume make it difficult to fit in the car?

_____

_____

> MY READING WEB If you had trouble completing the question above, visit **My Reading Web** and type in **The Atmosphere.**

Vocabulary Skill

Word Origins Many words come to English from other languages. Learning a few common Greek word parts can help you understand new science words.

Greek Word Part	Meaning	Example
-meter	measure	barometer, n. an instrument that measures air pressure
thermo-	heat	thermosphere, n. the outer layer of Earth's atmosphere

2. **Quick Check** Use the Greek word parts above to write a definition of a thermometer.

_____

_____

atmosphere

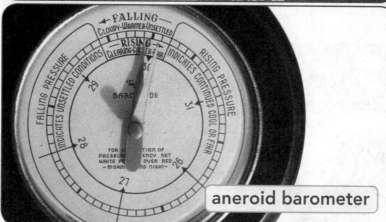

aneroid barometer

troposphere

wind

Chapter Preview

LESSON 1
- weather • atmosphere
- water vapor
- ↻ **Summarize**
- △ **Infer**

LESSON 2
- density • air pressure
- barometer • mercury barometer
- aneroid barometer • altitude
- ↻ **Relate Cause and Effect**
- △ **Develop Hypotheses**

LESSON 3
- troposphere • stratosphere
- mesosphere • thermosphere
- ionosphere • exosphere
- ↻ **Identify Supporting Evidence**
- △ **Interpret Data**

LESSON 4
- electromagnetic waves
- radiation • infrared radiation
- ultraviolet radiation • scattering
- greenhouse effect
- ↻ **Ask Questions**
- △ **Graph**

LESSON 5
- temperature • thermal energy
- thermometer • heat
- convection • conduction
- convection currents
- ↻ **Identify the Main Idea**
- △ **Infer**

LESSON 6
- wind • anemometer
- windchill factor • local winds
- sea breeze • land breeze
- global winds • Coriolis effect
- latitude
- ↻ **Identify Supporting Evidence**
- △ **Draw Conclusions**

1 The Air Around You

UNLOCK THE BIG ?

🔑 **What Is the Composition of Earth's Atmosphere?**
8.2.4, 8.NS.8

🔑 **How Is the Atmosphere a System?**
8.2.4

MY PLANET DIARY

VOICES FROM HISTORY

Antoine Lavoisier

French chemist Antoine Lavoisier was determined to solve a puzzle: How could a metal burned to a powder weigh more than the original metal? In his 1772 lab notes he observed, "Sulphur, in burning . . . gains weight." So did mercury. Lavoisier thought a gas in the air was combining with the mercury as it burned, making it heavier. Then he heated the mercury powder to a higher temperature. It turned back to liquid mercury and a gas. Lavoisier observed that a mouse exposed to the gas could breathe it. He named the gas *principe oxygine*. Today we call it oxygen.

Discuss Lavoisier's experiment with a partner and answer the question below.

Why do you think Lavoisier exposed a mouse to the gas he collected from the mercury?

_____

_____

_____

> **PLANET DIARY** Go to **Planet Diary** to learn more about air.

 Lab zone® Do the Inquiry Warm-Up *How Long Will the Candle Burn?*

Academic Standards for Science

8.2.4 Describe the physical and chemical composition of the atmosphere at different elevations.
8.NS.8 Analyze data.

What Is the Composition of Earth's Atmosphere?

The sun disappears behind thick, dark clouds. In the distance you see a bright flash. Then you hear a crack of thunder. You make it home just as the downpour begins. The weather changed quickly—that was close!

Weather is the condition of Earth's atmosphere at a particular time and place. But what is the atmosphere? Earth's **atmosphere** (AT muh sfeer) is the envelope of gases that surrounds the planet. 🔑 **Earth's atmosphere consists of nitrogen, oxygen, carbon dioxide, water vapor, and other gases, as well as particles of liquids and solids.**

Vocabulary
- weather • atmosphere
- water vapor

Skills
- Reading: Summarize
- Inquiry: Infer

Nitrogen The most abundant gas in the atmosphere is nitrogen. It makes up a little more than three fourths of the air we breathe. Nitrogen occurs in all living things and makes up about 3 percent of the weight of the human body.

Oxygen Although oxygen is the second most abundant gas in the atmosphere, it makes up only about 21 percent of the volume. Plants and animals take oxygen directly from the air and use it to release energy from their food.

Oxygen is also involved in many other processes. A fire uses oxygen rapidly as it burns. Without oxygen, a fire will go out. Some processes use oxygen more slowly. Steel in cars and other objects reacts slowly with oxygen to form iron oxide, or rust.

Carbon Dioxide Carbon dioxide makes up much less than 1 percent of the atmosphere, but it is essential to life. Plants must have carbon dioxide to produce food. The cells of animals break down food and give off carbon dioxide as a waste product.

When fuels like coal and gasoline are burned, they also release carbon dioxide. Burning these fuels increases the amount of carbon dioxide in the atmosphere.

Other Gases Oxygen and nitrogen together make up 99 percent of dry air. Argon makes up most of the other 1 percent. The remaining gases are called trace gases because only small amounts of them are present.

FIGURE 1 ·······························
Gases in the Air
The atmosphere is a thin layer of gases.

✎ Graph **Identify which circle graph shows the correct percentage of gases in the atmosphere. Shade in the key and the graph. Give your graph a title.** 8.NS.8

Key
☐ Nitrogen
☐ Oxygen
☐ Other gases

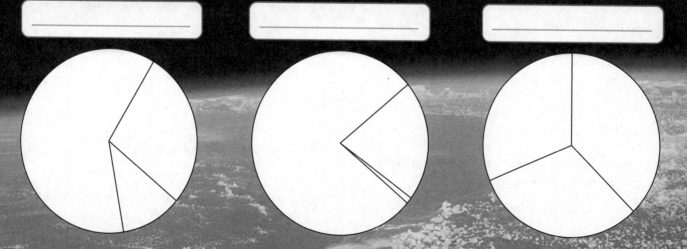

The amount of water vapor in the air can differ from place to place.

1 There is more water vapor in the (desert/rain forest) than in the (desert/rain forest).

2 Infer What evidence do you see for your answer to Question 1?

_____

_____

_____

3 CHALLENGE What factors might affect the amount of water vapor in the air?

_____

_____

_____

8.NS.8

Water Vapor So far, we've discussed the composition of dry air. But in reality, air is not dry. Air contains **water vapor**—water in the form of a gas. Water vapor is invisible. It is not the same thing as steam, which is made up of tiny droplets of liquid water.

The amount of water vapor in the air varies greatly from place to place and from time to time. Water vapor plays an important role in Earth's weather. Clouds form when water vapor condenses out of the air to form tiny droplets of liquid water or crystals of ice. If these droplets or crystals become heavy enough, they fall as rain or snow.

Particles Pure air contains only gases. But pure air exists only in laboratories. In the real world, air contains tiny solid and liquid particles of dust, smoke, salt, and chemicals. You can see some of these particles in the air around you, but most of them are too small to see.

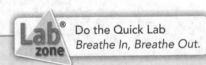
Lab zone® Do the Quick Lab
Breathe In, Breathe Out.

🔑 **Assess Your Understanding**

1a. Define The _____ is the envelope of _____ that surrounds Earth.

8.2.4

b. List What are the four most common gases in dry air?

_____

_____

8.2.4

c. Compare and Contrast What is the difference between wet air and dry air?

_____

_____

8.2.4

got it?

○ I get it! Now I know that the atmosphere is made up of _____

_____

_____

_____

○ I need extra help with _____

_____

Go to **MY SCIENCE** 🄢 **COACH** online for help with this subject.

8.2.4

How Is the Atmosphere a System?

Academic Standards for Science

8.2.4 Describe the physical and chemical composition of the atmosphere at different elevations.

The atmosphere is a system that interacts with other Earth systems, such as the ocean. The atmosphere has many different parts. Some of these parts you can actually see, such as clouds. But most parts of the atmosphere—like air, wind, and energy—you can't see. Instead, you might feel a wind when it blows on you. Or you might feel energy from the sun warming your face on a cool winter day.

At first, the wind that blows and the heat you feel may seem unrelated. But as you'll learn, the different parts of the atmosphere interact with one another. 🗝 **Events in one part of the atmosphere affect other parts of the atmosphere.**

Energy from the sun drives the motions in the atmosphere. A storm such as the hurricane in **Figure 2,** involves a tremendous amount of energy. The spiraling shape of a hurricane is due in part to forces resulting from Earth's rotation. A hurricane also gains energy from warm ocean water. Since the ocean water is warmed by the sun, a hurricane's energy comes mostly from the sun.

⟲ **Summarize** Write a short summary of the third paragraph.

_____
_____
_____
_____

FIGURE 2 ·············

Parts of the Atmosphere
✏ **List** What parts of the atmosphere interact?

_____
_____
_____
_____

Lab zone ® Do the Quick Lab *What Is the Source of Earth's Energy?*

🗝 Assess Your Understanding

got it? ·····················

○ **I get it!** Now I know that events in one part of the atmosphere _____

○ **I need extra help with** _____

Go to **my science** ⊕ **coach** *online for help with this subject.*

8.2.4

Air Pressure

🔑 **What Are Some Properties of Air?**
8.2.4

🔑 **What Instruments Measure Air Pressure?**
8.NS.3, 8.NS.8

🔑 **How Does Altitude Affect Air Pressure and Density?**
8.2.4, 8.NS.1, 8.NS.8, 8.DP.10

my pLaneT DiaRY

Flying High

Astronauts aren't the only people who go into space. High-altitude pilots who fly above 15,250 meters are in a zone with conditions similar to deep space. At these heights, air pressure is so low that blood can boil. A pilot can also pass out in less than a minute from lack of oxygen. To survive, pilots wear pressure suits. These suits weigh about 16 kilograms and are custom-built for each pilot. They inflate in an emergency, keeping air pressure stable for the pilot. The suits are "very, very restrictive," says pilot David Wright. "But it saves your life, so you're able to put up with that."

DISCOVERY

Discuss your answer with a classmate.

Pilots wear pressure suits in addition to flying in a pressurized plane. Why do you think this is so?

_____

_____

_____

> **PLANET DIARY** Go to **Planet Diary** to learn more about air pressure.

Lab zone® Do the Inquiry Warm-Up *Does Air Have Mass?*

Academic Standards for Science

8.2.4 Describe the physical and chemical composition of the atmosphere at different elevations.

What Are Some Properties of Air?

How do you know air exists? You can't see it. Instead, you have to understand what air does. It may seem to you that air has no mass. But the air in the atmosphere consists of atoms and molecules, which have mass. 🔑 **Because air has mass, it also has other properties, including density and pressure.**

Vocabulary
- density • air pressure
- barometer • mercury barometer
- aneroid barometer • altitude

Skills
↪ Reading: Relate Cause and Effect
△ Inquiry: Develop Hypotheses

Density The amount of mass in a given volume of air is its **density.** You calculate the density of a substance by dividing its mass by its volume. If there are more molecules in a given volume, the density is greater. If there are fewer molecules, the density is less.

Pressure The atmosphere is heavy. Its weight exerts a force on surfaces like you. The force pushing on an area or surface is called pressure. **Air pressure** is the result of the weight of a column of air pushing on an area.

As **Figure 1** shows, there is a column of air above you that extends all the way up through the entire atmosphere. In fact, the weight of the column of air above your desk is about the same as the weight of a large school bus. So why doesn't air pressure crush your desk? The reason is that the molecules in air push in all directions—down, up, and sideways. The air pushing down on top of your desk is balanced by the air pushing up on the bottom of your desk.

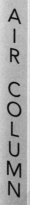

A I R   C O L U M N

FIGURE 1 ⋯⋯⋯⋯⋯⋯⋯⋯⋯⋯⋯⋯⋯
Air Column
The weight of the column of air above you puts pressure on you.

✎ **Answer the questions below.**

1. **Describe** What's an air column?

_____

_____

2. **Apply Concepts** Add arrows to the diagram below to indicate how the pressure from air molecules keeps you from being crushed.

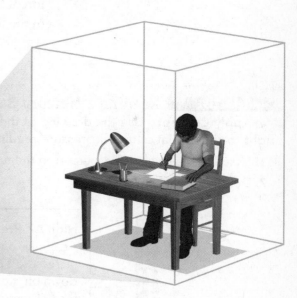

Lab zone® Do the Quick Lab
Properties of Air.

🗝 Assess Your Understanding

got it? ⋯⋯⋯⋯⋯⋯⋯⋯⋯⋯⋯⋯⋯⋯⋯⋯⋯⋯⋯⋯⋯⋯⋯⋯⋯⋯⋯⋯⋯⋯⋯⋯⋯⋯

○ **I get it!** Now I know that air has properties such as _____

_____

○ **I need extra help with** _____

Go to **MY SCIENCE** Ⓢ **COACH** online for help with this subject.

8.2.4

8.NS.3 Collect quantitative data with appropriate tools or technologies and use appropriate units to label numerical data.

8.NS.8 Analyze data.

What Instruments Measure Air Pressure?

Air pressure can change daily. A denser substance has more mass per unit volume than a less dense one. So denser air exerts more pressure than less dense air. A **barometer** (buh RAHM uh tur) is an instrument that is used to measure air pressure. The two **common kinds of barometers are mercury barometers and aneroid barometers.**

Mercury Barometers Look at **Figure 2** to see a mercury barometer model. A **mercury barometer** consists of a long glass tube that is closed at one end and open at the other. The open end of the tube rests in a dish of mercury. The closed end of the tube is almost a vacuum—the space above the mercury contains very little air. The air pressing down on the surface of the mercury in the dish is equal to the pressure exerted by the weight of the column of mercury in the tube. When the air pressure increases, it presses down more on the surface of the mercury. Greater air pressure forces the column of mercury higher. So, the level of the mercury in the tube shows you the pressure of the air that day.

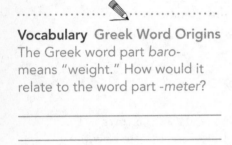

Vocabulary Greek Word Origins
The Greek word part *baro-* means "weight." How would it relate to the word part *-meter*?

_____

_____

_____

FIGURE 2 ···

▶ **INTERACTIVE ART** **Reading a Mercury Barometer**

✎ **Apply Concepts** Use the drawing of the barometer on the right to show what a low air pressure reading looks like.

1. Shade in the level of the mercury in the tube and in the dish.

2. Describe what is happening.   8.NS.8

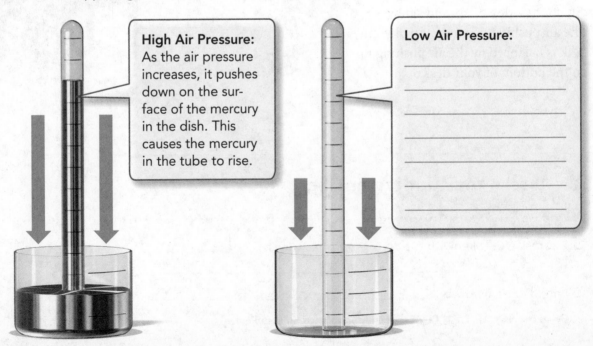

High Air Pressure: As the air pressure increases, it pushes down on the surface of the mercury in the dish. This causes the mercury in the tube to rise.

Low Air Pressure:

_____

_____

_____

_____

_____

_____

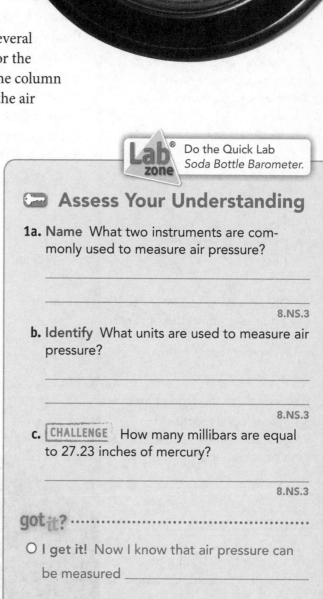

Aneroid Barometers

If you have a barometer at home, it's probably an aneroid barometer. The word *aneroid* means "without liquid." An **aneroid barometer** (AN uh royd) has an airtight metal chamber, as shown in **Figure 3**. The metal chamber is sensitive to changes in air pressure. When air pressure increases, the thin walls of the chamber are pushed in. When the pressure drops, the walls bulge out. The chamber is connected to a dial by a series of springs and levers. As the shape of the chamber changes, the needle on the dial moves.

Units of Air Pressure

Weather reports use several different units for air pressure. Most weather reports for the general public use inches of mercury. For example, if the column of mercury in a mercury barometer is 30 inches high, the air pressure is "30 inches of mercury" or "30 inches."

National Weather Service maps indicate air pressure in millibars. The pressure of the atmosphere is equal to one bar. One inch of mercury is about 33.86 millibars, so 30 inches of mercury is equal to about 1,016 millibars.

FIGURE 3 ···

Inside an Aneroid Barometer

An aneroid barometer has an airtight metal chamber, shown in red, below.

✎ **Identify** Label the diagram that shows the aneroid barometer under high pressure and the diagram that shows it under low pressure.

_____   _____

Lab zone ® Do the Quick Lab *Soda Bottle Barometer.*

🔑 Assess Your Understanding

1a. Name What two instruments are commonly used to measure air pressure?

_____

_____

8.NS.3

b. Identify What units are used to measure air pressure?

_____

_____

8.NS.3

c. CHALLENGE How many millibars are equal to 27.23 inches of mercury?

_____

8.NS.3

got **it**? ···

○ **I get it!** Now I know that air pressure can

be measured _____

_____

○ **I need extra help with** _____

Go to **my science** 🔍 **coach** *online for help with this subject.*   8.NS.3

How Does Altitude Affect Air Pressure and Density?

The higher you hike on a mountain, the more changes you'll notice. The temperature will drop, and the plants will get smaller. But you might not notice another change that is happening. At the top of the mountain, the air pressure is less than the air pressure at sea level—the average level of the oceans. **Altitude,** or elevation, is the distance above sea level. ☞ **Air pressure decreases as altitude increases. As air pressure decreases, so does density.**

Altitude Affects Air Pressure Suppose you have a stack of books. Which book has more weight on it, the second book from the top or the book at the bottom? The second book from the top has the weight of only one book on top of it. The book at the bottom of the stack has the weight of all the books pressing on it.

Air at sea level is like the bottom book. Sea-level air has the weight of the whole atmosphere pressing on it. Air near the top of the atmosphere is like the second book from the top. There, the air has less weight pressing on it and thus has lower air pressure.

apply it!

You're back from a high-altitude hike. As you empty your bag, you notice that the two empty bottles you carried down from the mountain look different.

❶ Observe What observations can you make about the bottles?

_____

_____

_____

❷ Develop Hypotheses What's a possible explanation for your observations?

_____

_____

_____

_____

_____

_____

_____

8.NS.1

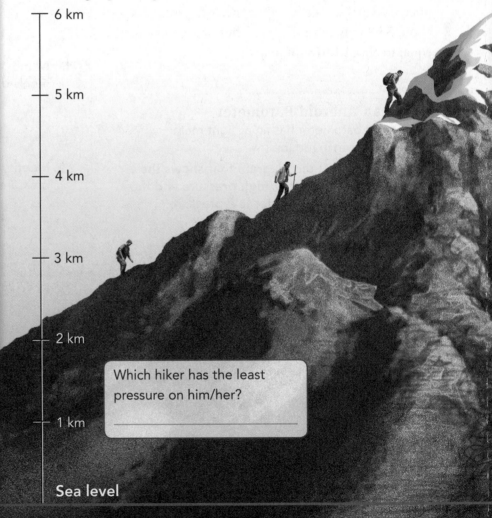

6 km

5 km

4 km

3 km

2 km

Which hiker has the least pressure on him/her?

_____

1 km

Sea level

Altitude Also Affects Density

As you go up through the atmosphere, the density of the air decreases. This means the gas molecules that make up the atmosphere are farther apart at high altitudes than they are at sea level. If you were near the top of a tall mountain and tried to run, you would quickly get out of breath. Why? The air contains 21 percent oxygen, whether you are at sea level or on top of a mountain. However, since the air is less dense at a high altitude, each cubic meter of air you breathe has fewer oxygen molecules than at sea level. So you would become short of breath more quickly at a high altitude.

Relate Cause and Effect
Underline the sentence that explains how altitude can make you short of breath.

FIGURE 4 ·······································

➤ **VIRTUAL LAB** **Effect of Altitude on Pressure and Density**

✎ **Complete the activities below.**

1. **Relate Evidence and Explanation** Draw the air column above each hiker on the mountain. Then answer the question below the hikers.

2. **Make Models** In the empty circles below, draw how densely packed you think the molecules would be at the altitudes shown.

8.NS.8, 8.DP.10

Lab zone Do the Quick Lab *Effects of Altitude on the Atmosphere.*

🔑 Assess Your Understanding

2a. Define What is altitude?

_____

8.2.4

b. Summarize How does air pressure change as altitude increases?

_____

_____

8.2.4

c. Predict What changes in air pressure would you expect if you carried a barometer down a mine shaft?

_____

_____

_____

_____

8.2.4

got it? ·······································

○ I get it! Now I know the properties of air

_____

○ I need extra help with _____

_____

Go to **my science coach** online for help with this subject.

8.2.4

231

Layers of the Atmosphere

UNLOCK
THE BIG
?

🔑 **What Are the Four Main Layers of the Atmosphere?**
8.2.4

🔑 **What Are the Characteristics of the Atmosphere's Layers?**
8.2.4, 8.NS.7, 8.NS.8

MY PLANET DIARY

MISCONCEPTION

Earth's Atmosphere

Misconception: The blanket of gases that makes up Earth's atmosphere is thick.

Fact: Earth's atmosphere extends far out into space, at least as far again as the radius of Earth. However, most of the atmosphere is so thin that it would be hard to tell it apart from the vacuum of space. Most of the gas in the atmosphere is found close to Earth's surface. In fact, half of the gas in the atmosphere is found in the bottom 5.5 kilometers—the height of a tall mountain! The rest of the gas extends thinly out into space for thousands of kilometers.

Evidence: The mass of the atmosphere is surprisingly small. In fact, a thin column of air 1 cm² extending out into space for thousands of kilometers has about the same mass as a 1-liter bottle of water.

Talk about these questions with a classmate and then record your answers.

1. Where is most of the gas in the atmosphere found?

_____

_____

_____

2. Why do you think that people think of the atmosphere as a thick layer around Earth?

_____

_____

▶ PLANET DIARY Go to **Planet Diary** to learn more about layers of the atmosphere.

Lab zone® Do the Inquiry Warm-Up *Is Air There?*

Vocabulary
- troposphere • stratosphere
- mesosphere • thermosphere
- ionosphere • exosphere

Skills
↻ Reading: Identify Supporting Evidence
△ Inquiry: Interpret Data

What Are the Four Main Layers of the Atmosphere?

Academic Standards for Science

8.2.4 Describe the physical and chemical composition of the atmosphere at different elevations.

Imagine taking a trip upward into the atmosphere in a hot-air balloon. You begin on a warm beach near the ocean, at an altitude of 0 kilometers above sea level.

You hear a roar as the balloon's pilot turns up the burner to heat the air in the balloon. The balloon begins to rise, and Earth's surface gets farther away. As the balloon reaches an altitude of 3 kilometers, you realize the air is getting colder. At 6 kilometers you begin to have trouble breathing. The air is becoming less dense. It's time to go back down.

Six kilometers is pretty high. In fact, it's higher than all but the very tallest mountains. But there are still hundreds of kilometers of atmosphere above you. It may seem as though air is the same from the ground to the edge of space. But air pressure and temperature change with altitude. ⚷ **Scientists divide Earth's atmosphere into four main layers classified according to changes in temperature. These layers are the troposphere, the stratosphere, the mesosphere, and the thermosphere.**

✎ ⟳ **Identify Supporting Evidence**
Underline the evidence in the text above that explains how the atmosphere changes as you go up in a hot-air balloon.

Lab zone® Do the Quick Lab *Layers of the Atmosphere.*

⚷ Assess Your Understanding

got it? ....

○ **I get it!** Now I know that the atmosphere has four main layers: _____

_____

_____

○ **I need extra help with** _____

Go to MY SCIENCE COACH online for help with this subject.

8.2.4

Academic Standards for Science

8.2.4 Describe the physical and chemical composition of the atmosphere at different elevations.

8.NS.7 Keep accurate records in a notebook during investigations.

8.NS.8 Analyze data, using appropriate mathematical manipulation as required, and use it to identify patterns and make inferences based on these patterns.

What Are the Characteristics of the Atmosphere's Layers?

Unless you become an astronaut, you won't make a trip to the upper atmosphere. But if you could make that journey, what would you see? Read on to learn more about the conditions you would experience in each layer of the atmosphere.

The Troposphere You live in the inner, or lowest, layer of Earth's atmosphere, the **troposphere** (TROH puh sfeer). *Tropo-* means "turning" or "changing." Conditions in the troposphere are more variable than in the other layers. 🔑 **The troposphere is the layer of the atmosphere in which Earth's weather occurs.** The troposphere is about 12 kilometers thick, as you can see in **Figure 1.** However, it varies from 16 kilometers thick above the equator to less than 9 kilometers thick above the North and South poles. Although it's the shallowest layer, the troposphere is the most dense. It contains almost all the mass of the atmosphere.

As altitude increases in the troposphere, the temperature decreases. On average, for every 1-kilometer increase in altitude, the air gets about 6.5°C cooler. At the top of the troposphere, the temperature stops decreasing and stays at about –60°C. Water here forms thin, feathery clouds of ice.

500 km

400 km

300 km

200 km

FIGURE 1 ·······························
The Atmosphere Layers
✏️ **Observe** Use the journal pages in this lesson to record your observations of the layers of the atmosphere.   8.NS.7

Altitude _____

Temperature _____

_____

Observations _____

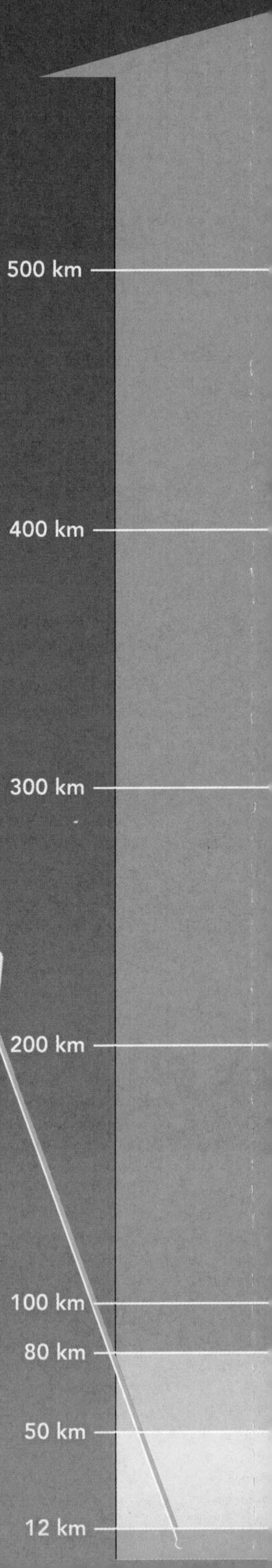

_____

_____

100 km

80 km

50 km

12 km

500 km

400 km

300 km

200 km

100 km

80 km

50 km

12 km

The Stratosphere

The **stratosphere** extends from the top of the troposphere to about 50 kilometers above Earth's surface. *Strato-* means "layer" or "spread out." 🔑 **The stratosphere is the second layer of the atmosphere and contains the ozone layer.**

The lower stratosphere is cold, about −60°C. Surprisingly, the upper stratosphere is warmer than the lower stratosphere. Why is this? The middle portion of the stratosphere has a layer of air where there is much more ozone than in the rest of the atmosphere. Ozone is a form of oxygen that has three atoms in each molecule instead of the usual two. When ozone absorbs energy from the sun, the energy is converted into heat, warming the air. The ozone layer protects living things from ultraviolet radiation from the sun.

Altitude _____

Temperature _____

Observations _____

_____

8.NS.7

do the math!

Changing Temperatures

The graph shows how temperatures in the atmosphere change with altitude. Use it to answer the questions below.

1 Read Graphs What is the temperature at the bottom of the stratosphere?

_____

2 Interpret Data What layer of the atmosphere has the lowest temperature?

_____

8.NS.8

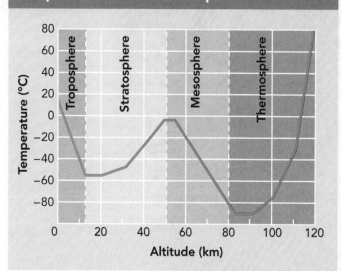

Temperature in the Atmosphere

(Graph: Temperature (°C) vs Altitude (km); layers labeled Troposphere, Stratosphere, Mesosphere, Thermosphere)

3 CHALLENGE How does temperature change with altitude in the troposphere?

_____

235

The Mesosphere

Above the stratosphere, a drop in temperature marks the beginning of the next layer, the **mesosphere.** *Meso-* means "middle," so the mesosphere is the middle layer of the atmosphere. The mesosphere begins 50 kilometers above Earth's surface and ends at an altitude of 80 kilometers. In the upper mesosphere, temperatures approach –90°C.

🔑 **The mesosphere is the layer of the atmosphere that protects Earth's surface from being hit by most meteoroids.** Meteoroids are chunks of stone and metal from space. What you see as a shooting star, or meteor, is the trail of hot, glowing gases the meteoroid leaves behind in the mesosphere as it burns up.

Altitude _____

Temperature _____

_____

Observations _____

_____

_____

_____

_____

8.NS.7

_____

_____

500 km

400 km

300 km

200 km

100 km

80 km

50 km

12 km

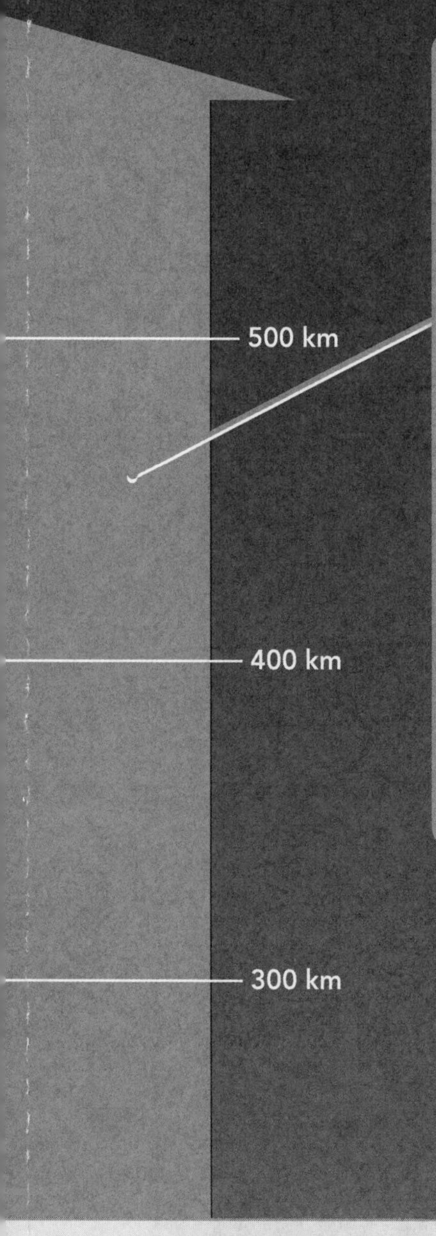
500 km
400 km
300 km

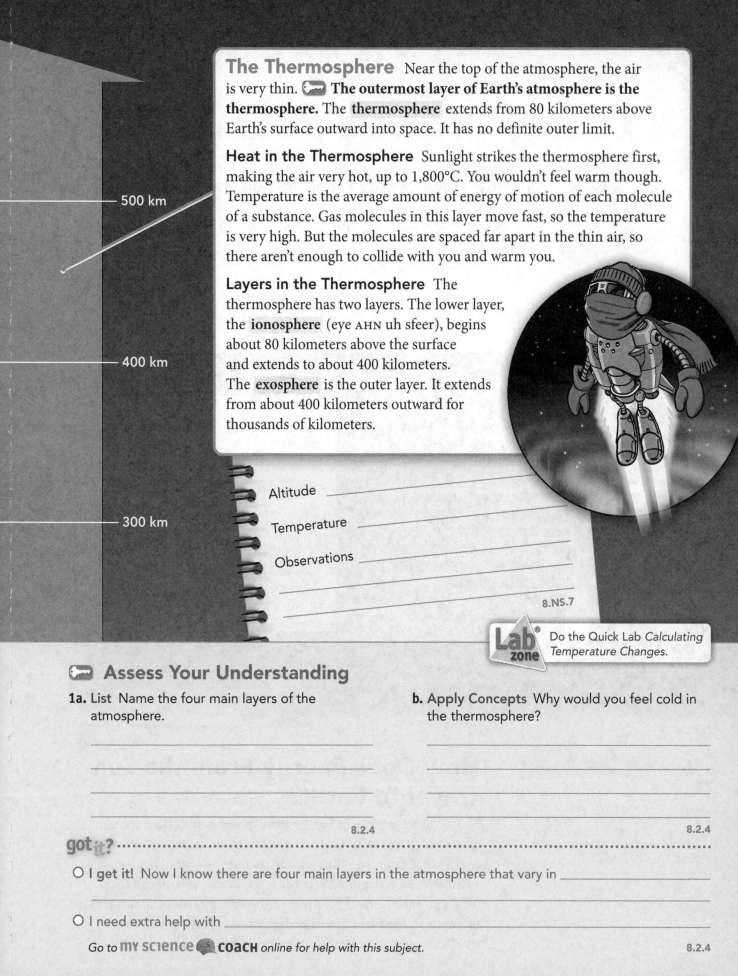

The Thermosphere

Near the top of the atmosphere, the air is very thin. **The outermost layer of Earth's atmosphere is the thermosphere.** The **thermosphere** extends from 80 kilometers above Earth's surface outward into space. It has no definite outer limit.

Heat in the Thermosphere

Sunlight strikes the thermosphere first, making the air very hot, up to 1,800°C. You wouldn't feel warm though. Temperature is the average amount of energy of motion of each molecule of a substance. Gas molecules in this layer move fast, so the temperature is very high. But the molecules are spaced far apart in the thin air, so there aren't enough to collide with you and warm you.

Layers in the Thermosphere

The thermosphere has two layers. The lower layer, the **ionosphere** (eye AHN uh sfeer), begins about 80 kilometers above the surface and extends to about 400 kilometers. The **exosphere** is the outer layer. It extends from about 400 kilometers outward for thousands of kilometers.

Altitude ______________________

Temperature ______________________

Observations ______________________

____

____

8.NS.7

Lab zone Do the Quick Lab *Calculating Temperature Changes.*

Assess Your Understanding

1a. List Name the four main layers of the atmosphere.

____

8.2.4

b. Apply Concepts Why would you feel cold in the thermosphere?

____

8.2.4

got it?

O **I get it!** Now I know there are four main layers in the atmosphere that vary in ______________________

O I need extra help with ______________________

Go to **MY SCIENCE COACH** *online for help with this subject.* 8.2.4

Energy in Earth's Atmosphere

UNLOCK THE BIG ?

🔑 **How Does Energy From the Sun Travel to Earth?**
8.2.1, 8.NS.8

🔑 **What Happens to the Sun's Energy When It Reaches Earth?**
8.2.1, 8.NS.1, 8.NS.8, 8.DP.9

MY PLANET DIARY

BLOG

Posted by: Amanda

Location: Hastings, New York

I love to swim. One time I was swimming at a beach in the summer. I was swimming for a long time. I got out to eat and dried off in about half an hour. Then I went swimming again, and it clouded over. I got out, and it took about an hour to dry off this time. The sun was behind clouds, so it took longer for me to dry off. I found it very interesting.

Read the blog and answer the question.

Why did it take Amanda longer to dry off the second time?

_____

_____

▶ PLANET DIARY Go to **Planet Diary** to learn more about the sun's energy.

Lab zone ® Do the Inquiry Warm-Up *Does a Plastic Bag Trap Heat?*

Academic Standards for Science

8.2.1 Recognize and demonstrate how the sun's energy drives convection in the atmosphere and in bodies of water, which results in ocean currents and weather patterns.

8.NS.8 Analyze data.

How Does Energy From the Sun Travel to Earth?

Nearly all the energy in Earth's atmosphere comes from the sun. This energy travels to Earth as **electromagnetic waves,** a form of energy that can move through the vacuum of space. Electromagnetic waves are classified according to wavelength, or distance between wave peaks. 🔑 **Most of the energy from the sun travels to Earth in the form of visible light and infrared radiation. A smaller amount arrives as ultraviolet radiation.**

Vocabulary
- electromagnetic waves
- radiation
- infrared radiation
- ultraviolet radiation
- scattering
- greenhouse effect

Skills
🔄 Reading: Ask Questions

🔺 Inquiry: Graph

Visible Light Visible light includes all of the colors that you see in a rainbow: red, orange, yellow, green, blue, and violet. The different colors are the result of different wavelengths. Red and orange light have the longest wavelengths, while blue and violet light have the shortest wavelengths, as shown in **Figure 1.**

Nonvisible Radiation The direct transfer of energy by electromagnetic waves is called **radiation.** One form of electromagnetic energy, **infrared radiation,** has wavelengths that are longer than wavelengths for red light. Infrared radiation is not visible by humans, but can be felt as heat. The sun also gives off **ultraviolet radiation,** which is an invisible form of energy with wavelengths that are shorter than wavelengths for violet light. Ultraviolet radiation can cause sunburns.

FIGURE 1 ·····························
Radiation From the Sun
Energy travels to Earth as electromagnetic waves.

✏️ **Identify** Label the types of electromagnetic radiation in the diagram. 8.NS.8

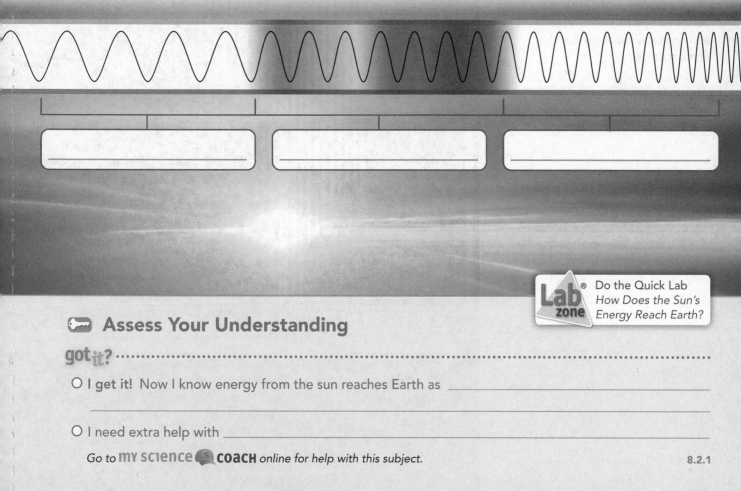

Lab ® Do the Quick Lab
zone *How Does the Sun's Energy Reach Earth?*

🔑 Assess Your Understanding

got **it?** ···

○ I get it! Now I know energy from the sun reaches Earth as _____

_____

○ I need extra help with _____

Go to **my science** ⑤ **coach** *online for help with this subject.*

8.2.1

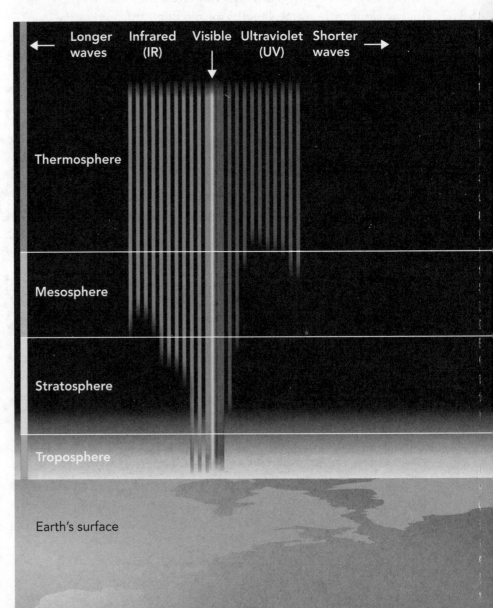

What Happens to the Sun's Energy When It Reaches Earth?

Sunlight must pass through the atmosphere before it reaches Earth's surface. The path of the sun's rays is shown in **Figure 2**. **Some sunlight is absorbed or reflected by the atmosphere before it can reach the surface. The rest passes through the atmosphere to the surface.**

Upper Atmosphere Different wavelengths of radiation are absorbed by different layers in the atmosphere. For example, some ultraviolet radiation is absorbed by the ozone layer in the stratosphere. Infrared radiation penetrates farther into the atmosphere before some of it is absorbed by water vapor and carbon dioxide.

FIGURE 2 ·······························

Energy in the Atmosphere
Some wavelengths reach Earth's surface. Other wavelengths are completely or partially absorbed in the atmosphere.

✎ **Compare and Contrast**
What happens to the radiation as it passes through Earth's atmosphere?

_____

_____

_____

_____

_____

_____

_____

_____

_____

_____

_____

8.NS.8

Longer waves Infrared (IR) Visible Ultraviolet (UV) Shorter waves

Thermosphere

Mesosphere

Stratosphere

Troposphere

Earth's surface

Troposphere

Clouds act as mirrors, reflecting sunlight back into space. Dust-size particles and gases in the atmosphere disperse light in all directions, a process called **scattering**. When you look at the sky, the light you see has been scattered by gas molecules in the atmosphere. Gas molecules scatter short wavelengths of visible light (blue and violet) more than long wavelengths (red and orange). Scattered light looks bluer than ordinary sunlight. That's why the clear daytime sky looks blue.

Earth's Surface

It may seem like a lot of the sun's energy is absorbed by gases in the atmosphere or reflected by clouds and particles. However, about 50 percent of the energy that reaches Earth's surface is absorbed by land and water and changed into heat. Look at **Figure 3** to see what happens to incoming sunlight at Earth's surface.

Ask Questions Before you read, preview the headings on these two pages. Ask a question you'd like to have answered. After you read, answer your question.

_____
_____
_____
_____
_____
_____

apply it!

The materials at Earth's surface shown below reflect different amounts of energy.

1 Graph Use the higher percentages below to draw a bar graph. Give it a title.

2 Based on your graph, which material reflects the most sunlight? Which absorbs the most?

_____

3 CHALLENGE Predict what might happen if a forested area was replaced with an asphalt parking lot.

_____
_____

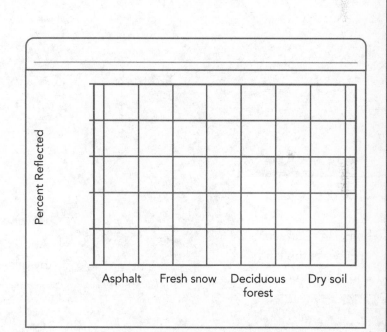

Percent Reflected

Asphalt   Fresh snow   Deciduous forest   Dry soil

8.NS.1, 8.NS.8, 8.DP.9

Asphalt
5–10% reflected

Fresh snow
80–90% reflected

Deciduous forest
15–20% reflected

Dry soil
20–25% reflected

FIGURE 3

Energy at Earth's Surface

✎ **Identify** What's happening to energy in the lower atmosphere and at Earth's surface? Find out by using the words in the word bank below to complete each sentence. **8.NS.8**

Word Bank

reflected   absorbed   radiated

Words may be used more than once.

✎ **Draw Conclusions** Using the diagram below, draw a conclusion about energy at Earth's surface.

_____

_____

_____

About 25 percent of incoming sunlight is _____ by clouds, dust, and gases in the atmosphere.

About 50 percent is _____ by Earth's surface. This heats the land and the water.

About 20 percent is _____ by gases and particles in the atmosphere.

Some absorbed energy is _____ back into the atmosphere.

About 5 percent is _____ by the surface back into the atmosphere.

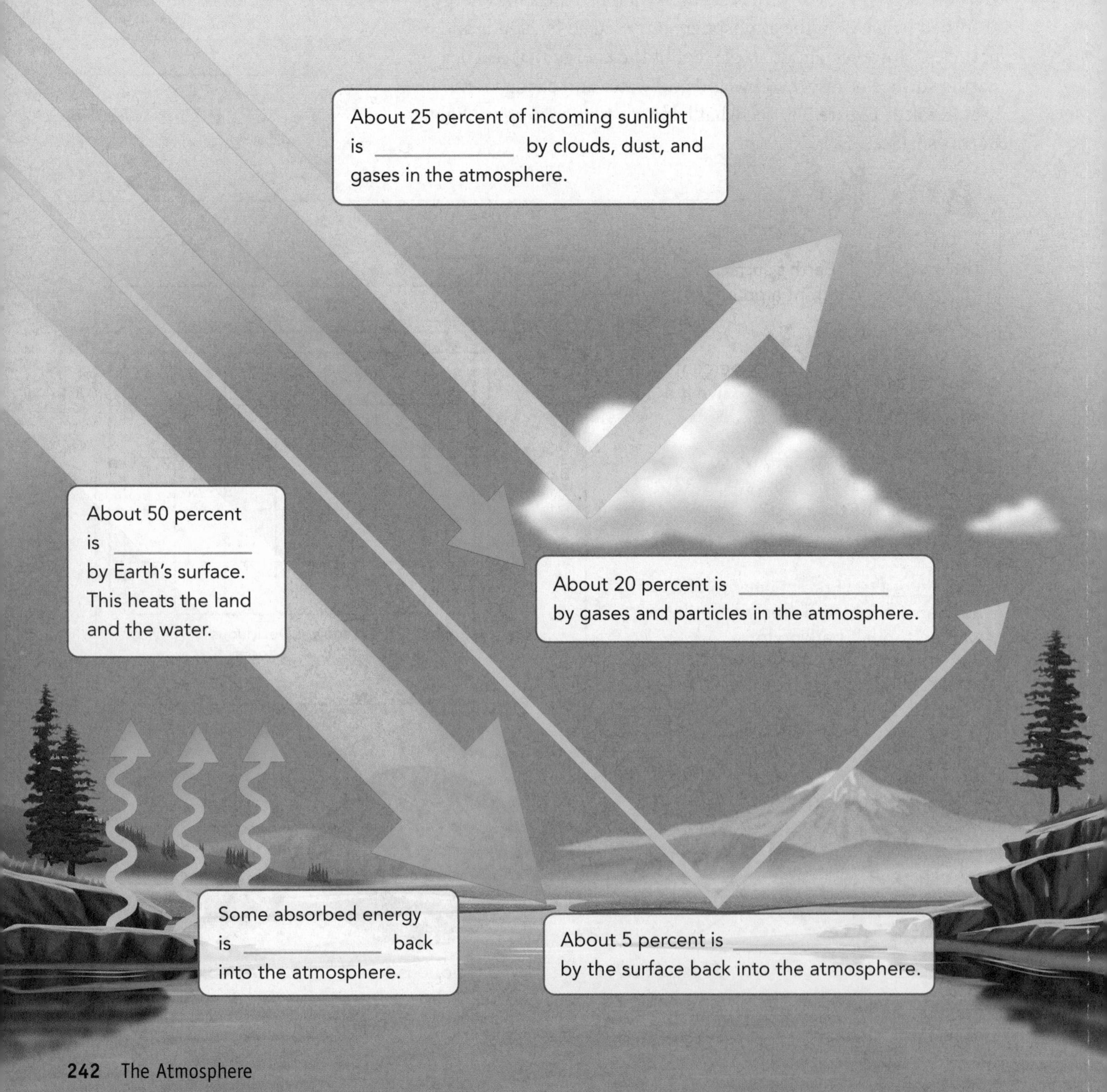

Earth's Energy Budget What happens to the energy that heats the land and water? 🔑 **Earth's surface radiates some energy back into the atmosphere as infrared radiation.** Much of this infrared radiation doesn't immediately travel all the way back into space. Instead, it's absorbed by water vapor, carbon dioxide, methane, and other gases in the air. The energy from the absorbed radiation heats the gases in the air. These gases in turn hold heat in Earth's atmosphere in a process called the **greenhouse effect.**

The greenhouse effect, shown in **Figure 4,** is a natural process. It keeps Earth's atmosphere at a temperature that is comfortable for most living things. Over time, the amount of energy absorbed by the atmosphere and Earth's surface is in balance with the amount of energy radiated into space. In this way, Earth's average temperatures remain fairly constant. But scientists have evidence that human activities may be altering this process.

FIGURE 4 ·····························

> **ART IN MOTION** **Greenhouse Effect**
The greenhouse effect is a natural heat-trapping process.

✏️ **Sequence** Number each step in the diagram to show how the greenhouse effect takes place. Discuss the diagram with a partner.   8.NS.8

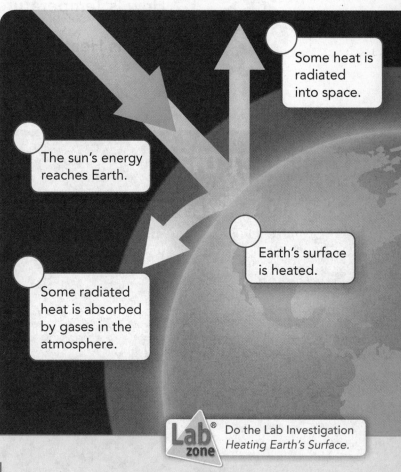

The sun's energy reaches Earth.

Some heat is radiated into space.

Earth's surface is heated.

Some radiated heat is absorbed by gases in the atmosphere.

Lab zone® Do the Lab Investigation *Heating Earth's Surface.*

🔑 Assess Your Understanding

1a. Summarize What happens to most of the sunlight that reaches Earth?

_____

                                                          8.2.1

b. Interpret Diagrams In **Figure 3,** what percentage of incoming sunlight is reflected by clouds, dust, and gases in the atmosphere?

_____

                                                          8.2.1

c. Predict How might conditions on Earth be different without the greenhouse effect?

_____
_____
_____
_____

                                               8.2.1, 8.NS.1

gotit? ···

○ **I get it!** Now I know some energy _____

_____

○ **I need extra help with** _____

Go to MY SCIENCE Ⓢ **COACH** *online for help with this subject.*   8.2.1

Heat Transfer

UNLOCK THE BIG ?

🔑 **How Is Temperature Measured?**
8.2.1, 8.NS.8

🔑 **How Is Heat Transferred?**
8.2.1, 8.NS.8, 8.NS.11, 8.DP.10

my pLaneT DiaRY   SCIENCE IN THE KITCHEN

From the Freezer to the Table

French fries are on many restaurant menus. But have you ever wondered how they get from the freezer to the table? It takes a little science in the kitchen to make it happen.

First, you heat oil in a fryer until it's around 340°F. Then, the frozen potato slices are dropped in. Hot oil moves from the bottom of the fryer and begins to heat the potatoes. Exposure to so much heat causes the water in the potatoes to boil. This is indicated by bubbles rising to the surface of the oil. As the outside of the potato heats up, it transfers heat to the inside of the potato slice. In a matter of minutes it's crunchy on the outside and soft on the inside.

Answer the following question and discuss it with a partner.

Explain in your own words what happens when the potatoes are exposed to heat.

_____

_____

_____

▷ PLANET DIARY Go to **Planet Diary** to learn more about heat transfer.

Lab zone® Do the Inquiry Warm-Up *What Happens When Air Is Heated?*

🇺🇸 **Academic Standards for Science**

8.2.1 Recognize and demonstrate how the sun's energy drives convection in the atmosphere and in bodies of water, which results in ocean currents and weather patterns.

8.NS.8 Analyze data, using appropriate mathematical manipulation.

How Is Temperature Measured?

All substances are made up of tiny particles (atoms and molecules) that are constantly moving. The faster the particles are moving, the more energy they have. **Temperature** is the *average* amount of energy of motion of each particle of a substance. In **Figure 1,** the hot tea in the teapot is the same temperature as the hot tea in the teacup. But do they have the same thermal energy?

Vocabulary
- temperature • thermal energy
- thermometer • heat • convection
- conduction • convection currents

Skills
↺ Reading: Identify the Main Idea
△ Inquiry: Infer

Thermal energy measures the *total* energy of motion in the particles of a substance. This means that the tea in the pot has more thermal energy than the tea in the cup because it has more mass.

Measuring Temperature
Temperature is an important factor affecting weather. 🔑 **Air temperature is usually measured with a thermometer.** A **thermometer** is a device that measures temperature. Some thermometers have a thin glass tube with a bulb on one end that holds liquid mercury or colored alcohol. When the air temperature increases, the temperature of the liquid in the bulb increases. This causes the liquid to expand and rise up the column.

Temperature Scales
Temperature is measured in units called degrees. Two temperature scales are the Celsius scale and the Fahrenheit scale. On the Celsius scale at sea level, the freezing point of water is 0°C, while the boiling point is 100°C. On the Fahrenheit scale at sea level, the freezing point of water is 32°F and the boiling point is 212°F. To convert from Farenheit to Celsius, you would use the following formula:

$$\frac{\text{Fahrenheit} - 32}{1.8} = \text{Celsius}$$

FIGURE 1 ·······················
Measuring Temperature
✏ **Read and then answer the questions.**

1. **Review** Circle the correct word in this sentence: The tea in the cup has (the same/less/more) thermal energy than the tea in the pot.

2. **Calculate** If the tea in the cup cooled to 70°F, what would a Celsius thermometer read?

_____

8.NS.8

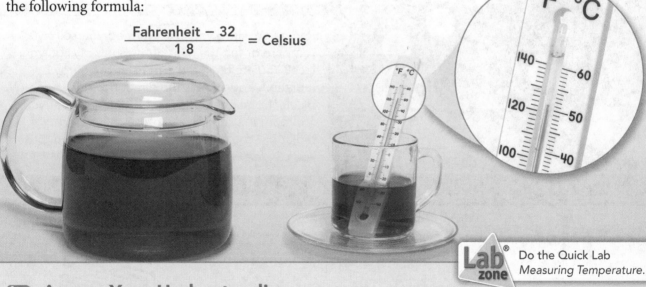

Lab zone® Do the Quick Lab
Measuring Temperature.

🔑 Assess Your Understanding

got it? ···

○ **I get it!** Now I know that temperature and thermal energy are different because _____

_____

○ **I need extra help with** _____

Go to MY SCIENCE ⑤ COACH *online for help with this subject.*

8.2.1

Academic Standards for Science

8.2.1 Recognize and demonstrate how the sun's energy drives convection in the atmosphere and in bodies of water, which results in ocean currents and weather patterns.

8.NS.8 Analyze data.

8.NS.11 Communicate findings using graphs, charts, maps and models through oral and written reports.

8.DP.10 Communicate the solution using drawings.

How Is Heat Transferred?

Heat is thermal energy that is transferred from a hotter object to a cooler one. ➤ Heat is transferred in three ways: convection, conduction, and radiation.

FIGURE 2 ·······················

Heat Transfer

✎ Identify Use the numbers provided in the text to identify each type of heat transfer in the photo.

1 **Convection** In fluids (liquids and gases), atoms and molecules can move easily from one place to another. As they move, their energy moves along with them. The transfer of heat by the movement of a fluid is called **convection.**

2 **Conduction** The transfer of heat between two substances that are in direct contact is called **conduction.** In **Figure 2,** heat is being conducted between the pot and the grate and between the pot and the liquid. When a fast-moving molecule bumps into a slower-moving molecule, the faster molecule transfers some of its energy to the slower one. The closer together the molecules are in a substance, the better they conduct heat. Conduction works well in some solids, such as metals, but not as well in liquids and gases. Air and water do not conduct heat well.

3 **Radiation** Have you ever warmed yourself by a campfire or felt the heat of the sun's rays on your face? You are feeling the transfer of energy by radiation. Radiation is the direct transfer of energy by electromagnetic waves. Most of the heat you feel from the sun travels to you as infrared radiation. You cannot see infrared radiation, but you can feel it as heat.

apply it!

Heat transfer occurs when a warm radiator heats a room.

⚠ Infer What type of heat transfer could keep the paper in the air? Draw arrows on the image to indicate your answer and explain below.

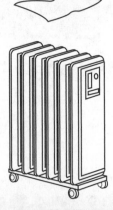

_____

_____

_____

8.NS.8

Heating the Troposphere

Heating the Troposphere Radiation, conduction, and convection work together to heat the troposphere. Notice in **Figure 3** how the sun's radiation heats Earth's surface during the day. The land gets warmer than the air. Air doesn't conduct heat well. So only the first few meters of the troposphere are heated by conduction. When ground-level air warms up, its molecules move more rapidly. As they bump into each other they move farther apart, making the air less dense. Cooler, denser air sinks toward the surface, forcing the warmer air to rise. The upward movement of warm air and the downward movement of cool air form **convection currents.** 🔑 **Heat is transferred mostly by convection within the troposphere.**

> **Identify the Main Idea**
> Underline the main idea in the paragraph at the left.

FIGURE 3 ·····················
Heating the Troposphere
✎ **Summarize** Describe the process of heat transfer taking place in the diagram at the left.

_____
_____
_____
_____
_____
_____
_____
_____
_____
_____

8.NS.11

 Do the Quick Lab
Temperature and Height.

🔑 Assess Your Understanding

1a. Explain Why is convection more important than conduction in the troposphere?

_____
_____
_____

8.2.1

b. Apply Concepts Explain how a convection current can enable a hawk or eagle to soar upward without flapping its wings.

_____
_____
_____

8.2.1

got it? ···

○ **I get it!** Now I know that heat transfer happens in three ways in the atmosphere: _____
_____

○ **I need extra help with** _____

  Go to **my science COACH** online for help with this subject.

8.2.1

What Causes Winds?
8.2.1, 8.2.4

How Do Local Winds and Global Winds Differ?
8.2.1, 8.2.4, 8.NS.8, 8.NS.11

my planeT DiaRY

EXTREME SPORTS

Windsurfing

Imagine being able to ride a wave at almost 81 km/h—not in a boat powered by a motor but on a board powered only by the wind. That's what windsurfing is all about.

Windsurfers stand on a sailboard, which is similar to a surfboard. But the sailboard has a mast and a sail that the surfer can control with his or her hands. It uses a sail to capture wind and move the surfer along the surface of the water. Jim Drake, one of the first inventors of windsurfing, points out:

"It's the simplicity of standing up so you can adjust your weight and move quickly, as well as actively participate in transmitting the sail's forces to the board."

Discuss these questions with a classmate. Write your answers below.

1. How does wind move the sail?

_____

_____

_____

2. How have you experienced the effects of wind?

_____

_____

_____

> PLANET DIARY Go to **Planet Diary** to learn more about winds.

 Do the Inquiry Warm-Up *Does the Wind Turn?*

Vocabulary

- wind • anemometer • windchill factor
- local winds • sea breeze • land breeze
- global winds • Coriolis effect • latitude

Skills

↻ Reading: Identify Supporting Evidence

△ Inquiry: Draw Conclusions

What Causes Winds?

Air is a fluid, so it can move easily from place to place. But how does it do that? **Differences in air pressure cause the air to move.** **Wind** is the movement of air parallel to Earth's surface. Winds move from areas of high pressure to areas of lower pressure.

Most differences in air pressure are caused by the unequal heating of the atmosphere. Recall that convection currents form when an area of Earth's surface is heated by the sun's rays. Air over the heated surface expands and becomes less dense. As the air becomes less dense, its air pressure decreases. If a nearby area is not heated as much, the air above the less-heated area will be cooler and denser. The cool, dense air with a higher pressure flows underneath the warm, less dense air. This forces the warm air to rise.

> **Academic Standards for Science**
>
> **8.2.1** Recognize and demonstrate how the sun's energy drives convection in the atmosphere and in bodies of water, which results in ocean currents and weather patterns.
>
> **8.2.4** Describe the physical and chemical composition of the atmosphere at different elevations.

FIGURE 1 ·····················

Moving Air

Windsurfers need wind in order to move across the water. ✏ **Explain** How do differences in air pressure cause wind?

_____

_____

_____

_____

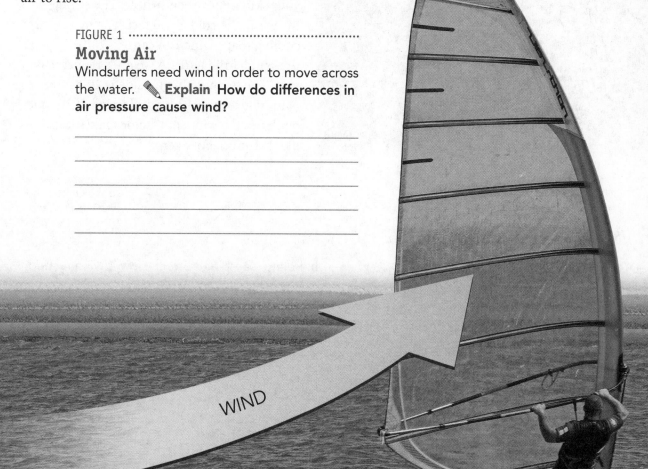

WIND

249

FIGURE 2 ·······························

Wind Direction and Speed

✎ **Identify** Based on the direction of the wind vane, which direction would your kite be flying? Indicate your answer by shading in your kite.

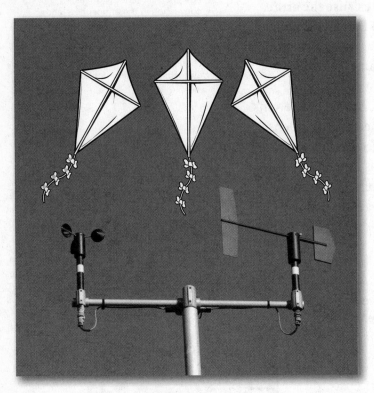

Measuring Wind Winds are described by their direction and speed. Winds can blow from all directions: north, south, east, and west. Wind direction is determined with a wind vane. The wind swings the wind vane so that one end points into the wind. The name of a wind tells you where the wind is coming from. For example, a south wind blows from the south toward the north. A north wind blows to the south.

Wind speed can be measured with an **anemometer** (an uh MAHM uh tur). An anemometer has three or four cups mounted at the ends of spokes that spin on an axle. The force of the wind against the cups turns the axle. A meter connected to the axle shows the wind speed. **Figure 2** shows a wind vane and an anemometer.

Windchill Factor

On a warm day, a cool breeze can be refreshing. But during the winter, the same breeze can make you feel uncomfortably cold. The wind blowing over your skin removes body heat. The stronger the wind, the colder you feel. The increased cooling that a wind can cause is called the **windchill factor.** A weather report may say, "The temperature outside is 20 degrees Fahrenheit. But with a wind speed of 30 miles per hour, the windchill factor makes it feel like 1 degree above zero."

Lab ® Do the Quick Lab
zone *Build a Wind Vane.*

🔑 Assess Your Understanding

1a. Define What is wind?

_____

_____

_____

8.2.1

b. Relate Cause and Effect How is wind related to air pressure and temperature?

_____

_____

_____

8.2.1, 8.2.4

got it? ···

○ I get it! Now I know that wind is _____

_____

○ I need extra help with _____

Go to **MY SCIENCE** 💬 **COACH** *online for help with this subject.*   8.2.1, 8.2.4

How Do Local Winds and Global Winds Differ?

Have you ever noticed a breeze at the beach on a hot summer day? Even if there is no wind inland, there may be a cool breeze blowing in from the water. This breeze is an example of a local wind.

Local Winds Winds that blow over short distances are called **local winds.** 🔑 **The unequal heating of Earth's surface within a small area causes local winds.** These winds form only when large-scale winds are weak. Two types of local winds are sea breezes and land breezes, as shown in **Figure 3**.

Academic Standards for Science

8.2.1 Recognize and demonstrate how the sun's energy drives convection in the atmosphere and in bodies of water, which results in ocean currents and weather patterns.

8.2.4 Describe the physical and chemical composition of the atmosphere at different elevations.

8.NS.8 Analyze data.

8.NS.11 Communicate findings using graphs, charts, maps, and models through oral and written reports.

FIGURE 3 ·······························

Local Winds

✏️ **Relate Text and Visuals** Read about sea breezes. Add arrows to the bottom diagram to indicate how a land breeze develops. Then summarize the process.

Warm air rises

Cooler air moves to take warm air's place

Sea Breeze During the day, the land warms up faster than the water. The air over the land gets warmer than the air over the water. This warm air is less dense. It expands and rises, creating a low-pressure area. Cool air blows inland from over the water and moves underneath the warm air, causing a sea breeze. A **sea breeze** or a lake breeze is a local wind that blows from an ocean or lake.

Land Breeze At night, the process is reversed. The flow of air from land to a body of water forms a **land breeze.**

_____

_____

_____

_____

8.NS.11

251

Global Winds

Global winds are winds that blow steadily from specific directions over long distances. 🔑 **Like local winds, global winds are created by the unequal heating of Earth's surface. But unlike local winds, global winds occur over a large area.** In **Figure 4,** you can see how the sun's radiation strikes Earth. In the middle of the day near the equator, the sun is almost directly overhead. The direct rays from the sun heat Earth's surface intensely. Near the poles, the sun's rays strike Earth's surface at a lower angle. The sun's energy is spread out over a larger area, so it heats the surface less. As a result, temperatures near the poles are much lower than they are near the equator.

Global Convection Currents How do global winds develop? Temperature differences between the equator and the poles produce giant convection currents in the atmosphere. Warm air rises at the equator, and cold air sinks at the poles. Therefore air pressure tends to be lower near the equator and greater near the poles. This difference in pressure causes winds at Earth's surface to blow from the poles toward the equator. Higher in the atmosphere, however, air flows away from the equator toward the poles. Those air movements produce global winds.

FIGURE 4 ·····································

Heating of Earth's Surface

✎ **Interpret Diagrams** The angle of the sun's rays causes temperature differences at Earth's surface.

1. Label the areas where the sun hits Earth most directly (M) and least directly (L).

2. CHALLENGE Draw a convection current in the atmosphere north of the equator.   8.NS.8

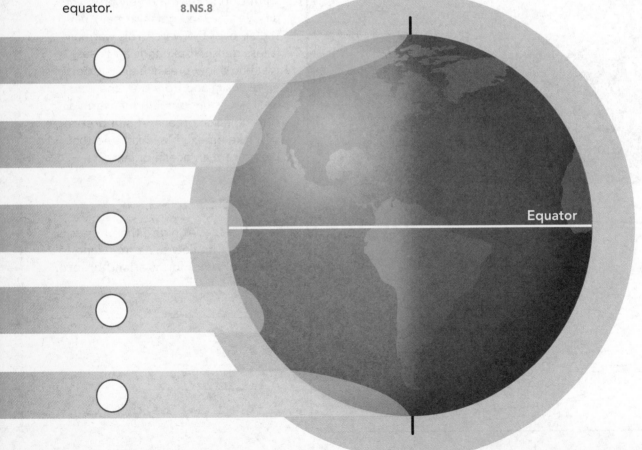

Equator

The Coriolis Effect If Earth did not rotate, global winds would blow in a straight line from the poles toward the equator. Because Earth is rotating, however, global winds do not follow a straight path. As the winds blow, Earth rotates from west to east underneath them, making it seem as if the winds have curved. The way Earth's rotation makes winds curve is called the **Coriolis effect** (kawr ee OH lis). Because of the Coriolis effect, global winds in the Northern Hemisphere gradually turn toward the right. A wind blowing toward the south gradually turns toward the southwest. In the Southern Hemisphere, winds curve toward the left.

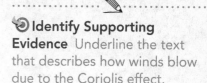

Identify Supporting Evidence Underline the text that describes how winds blow due to the Coriolis effect.

apply it!

8.NS.8

The Coriolis effect determines the direction of global winds.

1 Look at the globe on the left. Shade in the arrows that show the direction the global winds would blow without the Coriolis effect.

2 Look at the globe on the right. Shade in the arrows that show the direction the global winds blow as a result of the Coriolis effect.

3 **Draw Conclusions** Based on your last answer, what direction do global winds blow in the Northern Hemisphere? In the Southern Hemisphere?

_____

_____

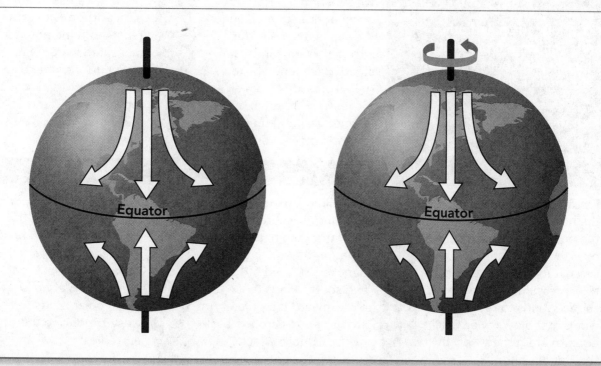

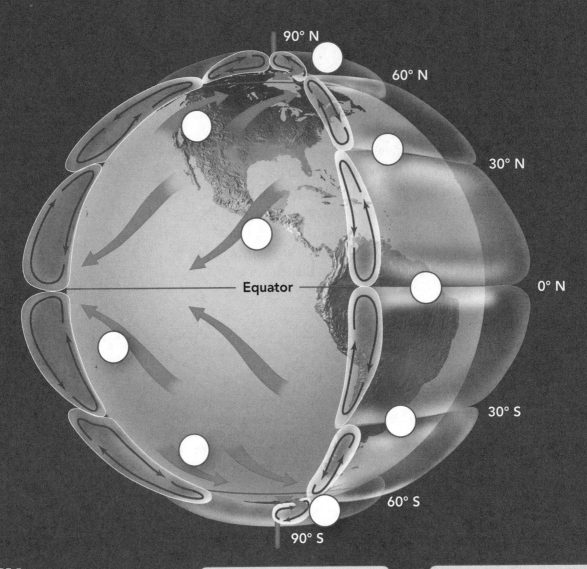

Equator

90° N
60° N
30° N
0° N
30° S
60° S
90° S

FIGURE 5 ·······························
▶ INTERACTIVE ART

Global Wind Belts
The Coriolis effect and other factors combine to produce a pattern of wind belts and calm areas around Earth.

✎ Relate Text and Visuals

Match the descriptions of the global winds with their location on the globe.   8.NS.8

A **Doldrums** are a calm area where warm air rises. They occur at the equator where the sun heats the surface strongly. Warm air rises steadily, creating an area of low pressure. Cool air moves into the area, but is warmed rapidly and rises before it moves very far.

B **Horse Latitudes** are two calm areas of sinking air. **Latitude** is the distance from the equator, measured in degrees. At about 30° north and south latitudes, the air stops moving toward the poles and sinks.

C **Trade Winds** blow from the horse latitudes toward the equator. As cold air over the horse latitudes sinks, it forms a region of high pressure. This causes surface winds to blow. The winds that blow toward the equator are turned west by the Coriolis effect.

D **Prevailing Westerlies** blow from west to east, away from the horse latitudes. In the mid-latitudes, between 30° and 60° north and south, winds that blow toward the poles are turned toward the east by the Coriolis effect.

E **Polar Easterlies** blow cold air away from the poles. Air near the poles sinks and flows back toward lower latitudes. The Coriolis effect shifts these polar winds to the west, producing the polar easterlies.

Parts of the Atmosphere

How does the sun's energy affect Earth's atmosphere?

FIGURE 6 ···

Earth's atmosphere is a system made up of many different parts.

✎ **Communicate** In the space below, draw a picture or a diagram that helps you understand the relationship between the concepts in the word bank. Explain your diagram to a classmate.

8.NS.11, 8.DP.10

Word Bank	
atmosphere	air pressure
convection	radiation
global winds	

Do the Quick Lab
Modeling Global Wind Belts.

🔑 Assess Your Understanding

2a. Summarize What causes local winds?

_____

_____

8.2.1, 8.2.4

b. Identify What is a global wind?

_____

_____

8.2.1, 8.2.4

c. ANSWER THE BIG ? How does the sun's energy affect Earth's atmosphere?

_____

_____

_____

_____

_____

8.2.1, 8.2.4

got it? ··

○ **I get it!** Now I know that winds blow locally and globally due to _____

_____

○ I need extra help with_____

Go to **MY SCIENCE COACH** *online for help with this subject.*

8.2.1, 8.2.4

255

Study Guide

The sun's energy affects Earth's atmosphere by _____ Earth's surface, causing

differences in _____ that result in _____.

LESSON 1 The Air Around You

8.2.4, 8.NS.8

🔑 Earth's atmosphere consists of nitrogen, oxygen, carbon dioxide, water vapor, and other gases, as well as particles of liquids and solids.

🔑 Events in one part of the atmosphere affect other parts of the atmosphere.

Vocabulary
• weather
• atmosphere
• water vapor

LESSON 2 Air Pressure

8.2.4, 8.NS.1, 8.NS.3, 8.NS.8, 8.DP.10

🔑 Because air has mass, it also has other properties, including density and pressure.

🔑 Two common kinds of barometers are mercury barometers and aneroid barometers.

🔑 Air pressure decreases as altitude increases. As air pressure decreases, so does density.

Vocabulary
• density • air pressure • barometer
• mercury barometer • aneroid barometer
• altitude

LESSON 3 Layers of the Atmosphere

8.2.4, 8.NS.7, 8.NS.8

🔑 Scientists divide Earth's atmosphere into four main layers according to changes in temperature.

🔑 Earth's weather occurs in the troposphere. The stratosphere contains the ozone layer.

🔑 The mesosphere protects Earth from meteoroids. The thermosphere is the outermost layer of Earth's atmosphere.

Vocabulary
• troposphere • stratosphere • mesosphere
• thermosphere • ionosphere • exosphere

LESSON 4 Energy in Earth's Atmosphere

8.2.1, 8.NS.1, 8.NS.8, 8.DP.9

🔑 The sun's energy travels to Earth as visible light, infrared radiation, and ultraviolet radiation.

🔑 Some sunlight is absorbed or reflected by the atmosphere. Some of the energy Earth absorbs is radiated back out as infrared radiation.

Vocabulary
• electromagnetic waves • radiation
• infrared radiation • ultraviolet radiation
• scattering • greenhouse effect

LESSON 5 Heat Transfer

8.2.1, 8.NS.8, 8.NS.11, 8.DP.10

🔑 Air temperature is usually measured with a thermometer.

🔑 Heat is transferred in three ways: convection, conduction, and radiation.

🔑 Heat is transferred mostly by convection within the troposphere.

Vocabulary
• temperature • thermal energy • thermometer
• heat • convection • conduction
• convection currents

LESSON 6 Winds

8.2.1, 8.2.4, 8.NS.8, 8.NS.11

🔑 Winds are caused by differences in air pressure.

🔑 The unequal heating of Earth's surface within a small area causes local winds.

🔑 Global winds are caused by the unequal heating of Earth's surface over a large area.

Vocabulary
• wind • anemometer • windchill factor
• local winds • sea breeze • land breeze
• global winds • Coriolis effect • latitude

Review and Assessment

LESSON 1 The Air Around You

1. Which gas forms less than one percent of the atmosphere, but is essential to life?

a. carbon dioxide   **b.** oxygen

c. hydrogen   **d.** nitrogen

8.2.4

2. Weather occurs in Earth's troposphere, which is _____

_____

8.2.4

3. Draw Conclusions Why is it difficult to include water vapor in a graph of the percentages of various gases in the atmosphere? How could you solve the problem?

_____

_____

_____

8.2.4

LESSON 2 Air Pressure

4. When density increases, the number of molecules in a volume

a. increases.   **b.** decreases.

c. stays the same.   **d.** varies.

8.2.4

5. One force affecting an object is air pressure, which is _____

_____

8.2.4

6. Apply Concepts Why can an aneroid barometer measure elevation as well as air pressure?

_____

_____

8.2.4

7. Write About It Suppose you're on a hot-air balloon flight. Describe how air pressure and the amount of oxygen would change during your trip. What would the changes feel like?

8.2.4

LESSON 3 Layers of the Atmosphere

8. The layers of the atmosphere are classified according to changes in

a. altitude.   **b.** air pressure.

c. distance.   **d.** temperature.

8.2.4

9. Sequence List the layers of the atmosphere in order, moving up from Earth's surface.

_____

_____

8.2.4

10. The ozone layer is important because

_____

_____

_____

8.2.4

11. Infer Why are clouds at the top of the troposphere made of ice crystals rather than drops of water?

_____

_____

8.2.4

12. Compare and Contrast How are the upper and lower parts of the stratosphere different?

_____

_____

_____

_____

8.2.4

13. Calculate The table shows the temperature at various altitudes above Omaha, Nebraska, on a January day. Suppose an airplane was 6.8 kilometers above Omaha. What is the approximate temperature at this height?

_____

8.2.4, 8.NS.8

Altitude (kilometers)	0	1.6	3.2	4.8	6.4	7.2
Temperature (°C)	0	−4	−9	−21	−32	−40

257

LESSON 4 **Energy in Earth's Atmosphere**

14. How does most of the energy from the sun travel to Earth's surface?

a. convection   b. conduction

c. radiation   d. scattering

8.2.1

15. What are three forms of radiation that come from the sun?

_____

8.2.1

16. Relate Cause and Effect Why do people need to wear sunscreen at the beach?

_____

_____

_____

_____

8.2.1

LESSON 5 **Heat Transfer**

17. What is the main way heat is transferred in the troposphere?

a. radiation currents   b. reflection currents

c. conduction currents d. convection currents

8.2.1

18. Compare and Contrast A pail of lake water is the same temperature as a lake. Compare the thermal energy of the pail of water with the thermal energy of the lake.

_____

_____

_____

_____

8.2.1

19. Write About It Describe an example of heat transfer in your daily life.

8.2.1

LESSON 6 **Winds**

20. The calm areas near the equator where warm air rises are

a. horse latitudes.   b. trade winds.

c. doldrums.   d. polar easterlies.

8.2.1, 8.2.4

21. Nights often feature land breezes, which blow

_____

8.2.1, 8.2.4

22. Relate Cause and Effect How does the movement of hot air at the equator and cold air at the poles produce global wind patterns?

_____

_____

_____

_____

_____

8.2.1, 8.2.4

 How does the sun's energy affect Earth's atmosphere?

23. Imagine you are sailing around the world. What winds would you expect to find on different parts of your route? Explain the role of the sun's energy in creating those winds.

_____

_____

_____

_____

_____

_____

_____

8.2.1, 8.2.4

Indiana ISTEP+ Practice

Multiple Choice

Circle the letter of the best answer.

1. Use trends in the data table to predict how cold the air temperature would feel if the actual temperature was 0°C and the wind speed was 25 km/h.

Windchill Temperature Index				
Wind Speed	**Equivalent Air Temperature (°C)**			
0 km/h	5°	0°	−5°	−10°
10 km/h	2.7°	−3.3°	−9.3°	−15.3°
15 km/h	1.7°	−4.4°	−10.6°	−16.7°
20 km/h	1.1°	−5.2°	−11.6°	−17.9°

   A. about 0°C   B. about −15°C
   C. about −6°C   D. about 25°C

8.2.1, 8.2.4

2. What is the most abundant gas in the atmosphere?

   A. ozone
   B. water vapor
   C. oxygen
   D. nitrogen

8.2.4

3. Which device is typically used to measure air pressure?

   A. hot-air balloon
   B. barometer
   C. satellite
   D. thermometer

8.NS.3

4. Which layer of the atmosphere protects Earth from meteoroids?

   A. mesosphere
   B. troposphere
   C. ionosphere
   D. stratosphere

8.2.4

Constructed Response

Write your answer to Question 5 on the lines below.

5. What type of energy causes sunburn?

_____

_____

8.2.4

Extended Response

Use the diagram and your knowledge of science to answer Question 6. Write your answer on another sheet of paper.

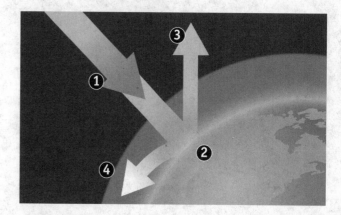

6. Describe the process that results in the greenhouse effect. How does it affect Earth's atmosphere?

8.2.1, 8.NS.8

Everyday Science

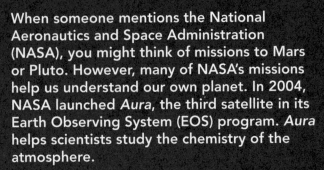

When someone mentions the National Aeronautics and Space Administration (NASA), you might think of missions to Mars or Pluto. However, many of NASA's missions help us understand our own planet. In 2004, NASA launched *Aura*, the third satellite in its Earth Observing System (EOS) program. *Aura* helps scientists study the chemistry of the atmosphere.

The *Aura* mission seeks to answer three questions about our atmosphere.

1. Is the ozone layer recovering? *Aura* helps scientists monitor atmospheric gases, such as chlorofluorocarbons (CFCs), that affect the ozone layer. If the ozone layer does not recover, scientists predict that we will need to learn to better protect ourselves from the sun. In the next 10 years, will we need SPF 100 sunscreen?

2. How do pollutants affect air quality? *Aura* monitors levels of ozone, particulate matter, carbon monoxide, nitrogen dioxide, and sulfur dioxide. The data help scientists understand—and predict—the movement of air pollutants. Are attempts to reduce air pollution working?

3. How is Earth's climate changing? *Aura* checks levels of greenhouse gases in the atmosphere to help scientists build more accurate models of climate change. This way, we will have a better idea of how to plan for long-term climate change. Will you need to invest in a really good raincoat?

Research It Research NASA's EOS program. What are the major satellites in this program? Which Earth systems are they designed to monitor? What discoveries has the EOS program made? Make a display with information and pictures to show what you find out.

 8.NS.2, 8.NS.8, 8.NS.11

Up, Up, and Away!

Bobbing along in the sky, hot air balloons look like a fun way to spend a day. Before the invention of satellites or airplanes, though, scientists used hot air balloons to study the atmosphere. Riding in their balloons, scientists recorded air temperatures and humidity, and even gathered information about cosmic rays. For more than 150 years, balloons were cutting-edge atmospheric observatories.

Research It Find out more about the history of ballooning. How did scientific research using balloons contribute to early space missions? Make a timeline showing balloonists' discoveries.

 8.NS.2, 8.NS.11

PLUGGING INTO THE JET STREAM

About 10 kilometers above Earth's surface, the jet stream winds blow constantly. The winds average 80 to 160 km/h, and they can reach 400 km/h. Scientists are testing designs for high-altitude wind farms. They propose that kite-like wind generators could generate electricity. Cables could then transfer the electricity to Earth.

Design It Design blades to harness the power of the wind by varying blade size or shape. Brainstorm a design and create a prototype. Document your design and create a prototype. Test and evaluate your solution. Record data in graphs or tables. Redesign your prototype to improve the results. See Appendix A on page 508 for more information about the design process.

 8.NS.1-8.NS.11, 8.DP.1-8.DP.11

WHAT CLUES CAN PREDICT A STORM?

 How do meteorologists predict the weather?

This tornado bearing down on this home in Kansas in June of 2004 reached wind speeds of 254–331 km/h. The state of Kansas had 124 tornadoes that year. Although tornadoes can occur anywhere, the United States leads the world with more than 1,000 tornadoes per year. **Observe How could you predict a tornado was coming?**

_____

_____

_____

_____

_____

_____

_____

_____

> **UNTAMED SCIENCE** Watch the **Untamed Science** video to learn more about weather.

Weather

Academic Standards for Science

8.2.1, 8.2.2, 8.2.4, 8.2.5, 8.NS.1, 8.NS.3,
8.NS.7, 8.NS.8, 8.NS.10, 8.NS.11

Check Your Understanding

1. **Background** Read the paragraph below and then answer the question.

"Is that smoke over the baseball field?" Eddie asked Cara in the park. "No," she replied. "It's **fog**." "Ah, water **vapor**," Eddie said. "No," Cara said. "If you can see it, it's water droplets suspended in the **atmosphere**. Water vapor is an invisible gas and can't be seen."

> **Fog** is made up of clouds that form near the ground.
>
> **Vapor** is water in the form of a gas.
>
> The **atmosphere** is the envelope of gases surrounding Earth.

- What does water vapor in the atmosphere look like?

_____

_____

> **MY READING WEB** If you had trouble completing the question above, visit **My Reading Web** and type in *Weather.*

Vocabulary Skill

Prefixes A prefix is a word part that is added at the beginning of a word to change its meaning. For example, the prefix *anti-* means "against" or "opposed to" and is used frequently in science. In the word *antivenom*, the prefix *anti-* is added to the word *venom* to form *antivenom*, meaning "against poison."

Prefix	Meaning	Example
psychro-	cold	psychrometer, *n.*
alto-	high	altocumulus, *n.*; altostratus, *n.*
anti-	against or opposed to	anticyclone, *n.*

2. **Quick Check** Review the prefixes above. Then predict what the word *altocumulus* means using what you know about the prefix *alto-*. After reading the chapter, revise your definition as needed.

_____

_____

_____

_____

cirrus

precipitation

front

tornado

Chapter Preview

LESSON 1
- water cycle • evaporation
- condensation • humidity
- relative humidity • psychrometer

↻ **Sequence**
△ **Interpret Data**

LESSON 2
- dew point • cirrus • cumulus
- stratus

↻ **Summarize**
△ **Predict**

LESSON 3
- precipitation • rain gauge
- flood • drought

↻ **Relate Cause and Effect**
△ **Calculate**

LESSON 4
- air mass • tropical • polar
- maritime • continental
- jet stream • front • occluded
- cyclone • anticyclone

↻ **Relate Text and Visuals**
△ **Classify**

LESSON 5
- storm • blizzard • thunderstorm
- lightning • hurricane
- storm surge • tornado
- evacuate

↻ **Outline**
△ **Infer**

LESSON 6
- meteorologist • isobar
- isotherm

↻ **Compare and Contrast**
△ **Predict**

> **VOCAB FLASH CARDS** For extra help
with vocabulary, visit **Vocab Flash
Cards** and type in **Weather.**

265

Water in the Atmosphere

🔑 **How Does Water Move Through the Atmosphere?**
8.2.1, 8.2.2, 8.NS.8

🔑 **What Is Relative Humidity and How Is It Measured?**
8.2.2, 8.2.4, 8.NS.3, 8.NS.8

Chile

Uruguay

Argentina

Pacific
Ocean

Atlantic
Ocean

my planet Diary

The Driest Place on Earth

The Atacama Desert in Chile is so
dry that there are places where humans
have never measured a single drop of rain. But
even the Atacama has some moisture in the
air. A dense fog along the coastline, known as
camanchaca, often flows inland from the Pacific
Ocean. At one point, the people of the fishing
village Chungungo set up nets above the mountains to catch the fog. Water condensed on the
nets and then was collected and sent through
pipes that brought the water to the village.

Do the Inquiry Warm-Up
Where Did the Water Go?

FUN FACT

Write your answers to each question below.
Then discuss your answers with a partner.

1. Why did the people of Chungungo need
   to use nets to catch moisture in the air?

   _____

   _____

2. What would be one way of collecting
   water where you live?

   _____

 **PLANET DIARY** Go to **Planet Diary** to learn
more about water in the atmosphere.

Academic Standards for Science

8.2.1 Recognize and demonstrate
how the sun's energy drives
convection in the atmosphere and
in bodies of water, which results in
ocean currents and weather patterns.

8.2.2 Describe and model how water
moves through the earth's crust,
atmosphere, and oceans in a cyclic
way, as liquid, vapor, and solid.

8.NS.8 Analyze data.

How Does Water Move Through the Atmosphere?

During a rainstorm, the air feels moist. On a clear, cloudless day,
the air may feel dry. As the sun heats the land and oceans, the sun
provides energy to change the amount of water in the atmosphere.
Water is always moving between Earth's atmosphere and surface.

The movement of water through Earth's systems, powered by
the sun's energy, is the **water cycle**. 🔑 **In the water cycle, water
vapor enters the atmosphere by evaporation from the oceans and
other bodies of water and leaves by condensation.** **Evaporation** is
the process by which molecules of liquid water escape into the air
after becoming water vapor. **Condensation** is the process by which
water vapor becomes liquid water.

Vocabulary

- water cycle • evaporation • condensation
- humidity • relative humidity • psychrometer

Skills

- Reading: Sequence
- Inquiry: Interpret Data

Water vapor is also added to the air by living things. Water enters the roots of plants, rises to the leaves, and is released into the air as water vapor. Animals also release water vapor into the air every time they exhale.

As part of the water cycle, shown in **Figure 1,** some of the water vapor in the atmosphere condenses to form clouds. Rain and snow fall from the clouds toward the surface as precipitation. The water then runs off the surface or moves through the ground, back into lakes, streams, and eventually the oceans. Then the water cycle starts all over again with evaporation.

Sequence Starting with precipitation, list the order of the steps of the water cycle.

_____

_____

_____

_____

8.NS.8

FIGURE 1 ....

> INTERACTIVE ART **The Water Cycle**

In the water cycle, water moves from plants, lakes, rivers, and oceans into the atmosphere and then falls back to Earth.

Summarize Use the word bank to label the parts of the water cycle.

Word Bank

Condensation

Evaporation

Precipitation

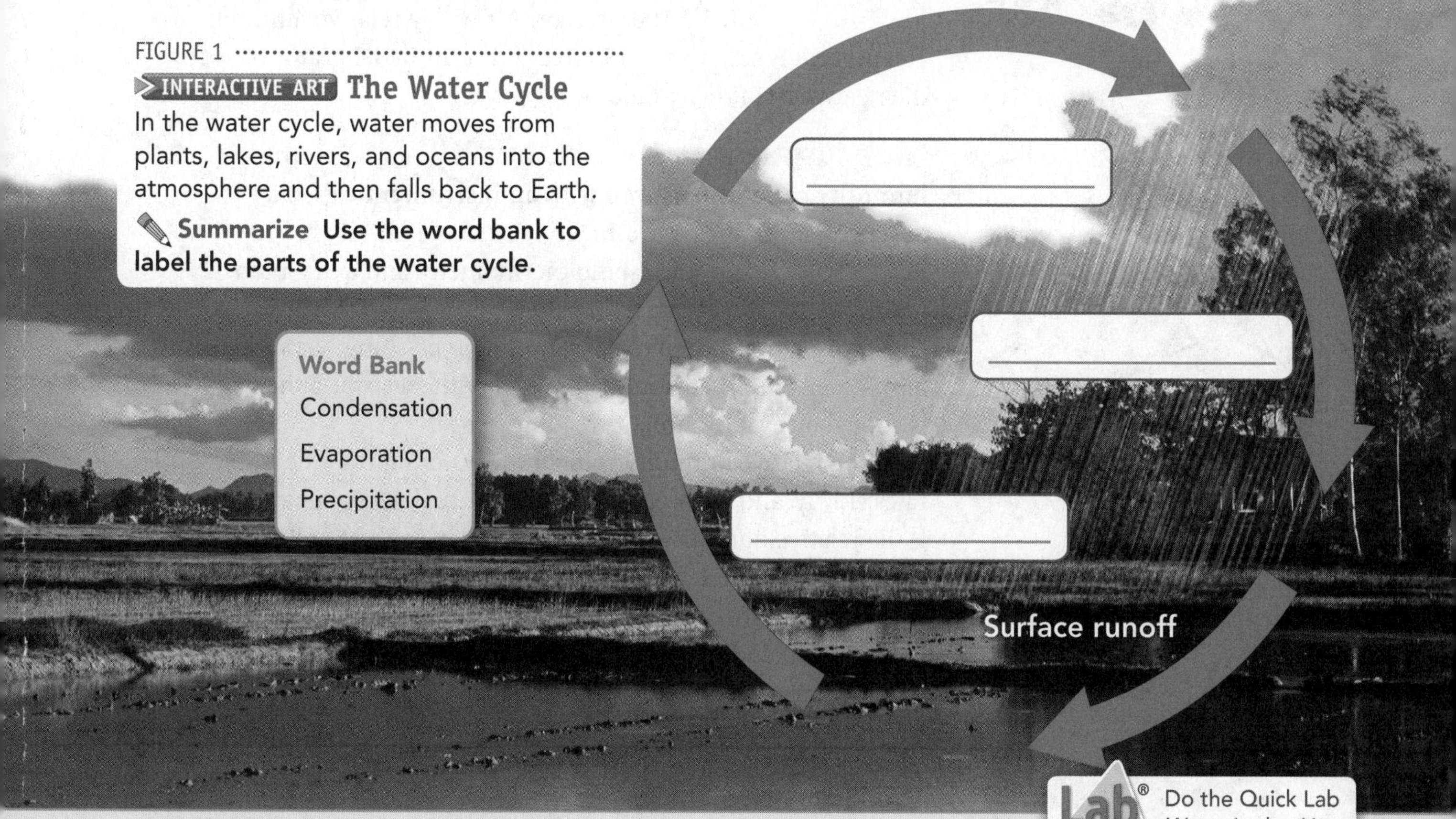

_____

_____

_____

Surface runoff

Lab zone ® Do the Quick Lab
Water in the Air.

Assess Your Understanding

got it? ....

O **I get it!** Now I know that in the water cycle _____

O **I need extra help with** _____

Go to MY SCIENCE COACH *online for help with this subject.*

8.2.1, 8.2.2

267

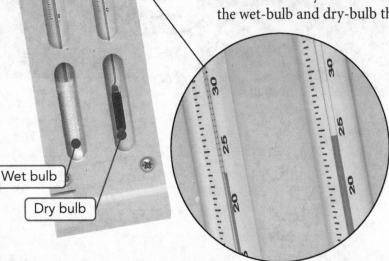
What Is Relative Humidity and How Is It Measured?

How is the quantity of water vapor in the atmosphere measured? **Humidity** is a measure of the amount of water vapor in the air. The ability of air to hold water vapor depends on its temperature. Warm air can hold more water vapor than cool air.

Relative Humidity Weather reports usually refer to the water vapor in the air as relative humidity. **Relative humidity** is the percentage of water vapor that is actually in the air compared to the maximum amount of water vapor the air can hold at a particular temperature. For example, at 10°C, 1 cubic meter of air can hold at most 8 grams of water vapor. If there were 8 grams of water vapor in the air, then the relative humidity of the air would be 100 percent. Air with a relative humidity of 100 percent is said to be saturated. If the air had 4 grams of vapor, the relative humidity would be 50 percent.

Measuring Relative Humidity **Relative humidity can be measured with an instrument called a psychrometer.** A **psychrometer** (sy KRAHM uh tur) has two thermometers, a wet-bulb thermometer and a dry-bulb thermometer. As shown in **Figure 2,** the wet bulb is covered by a moist cloth. When the psychrometer is "slung," or spun, air blows over both thermometers. Because the wet-bulb thermometer is cooled by evaporation, its reading drops.

If the relative humidity is high, the water on the wet bulb evaporates slowly, and the wet-bulb temperature does not change much. If the relative humidity is low, the water on the wet bulb evaporates rapidly, and the wet-bulb temperature drops by a large amount. The relative humidity can be found by comparing the temperatures of the wet-bulb and dry-bulb thermometers.

Wet bulb

Dry bulb

FIGURE 2 ·······················

Sling Psychrometer

✏ **Relate Text and Visuals** Read the psychrometer and compare the two Celsius temperatures. Is the relative humidity low or high? How do you know? **8.NS.3**

_____

_____

_____

_____

do the math!

Relative Humidity

Relative humidity is affected by temperature. Use the data table to answer the questions below. First, find the dry-bulb temperature in the left column of the table. Then find the difference between the wet- and dry-bulb temperatures across the top of the table. The number in the table where these two readings intersect indicates the percentage of relative humidity.

1 ◢ **Interpret Data** At noon the readings on a sling psychrometer are 18°C for the dry bulb and 14°C for the wet bulb. What is the relative humidity?

_____

2 ◢ **Interpret Data** At 5 P.M. the reading on the dry bulb is 12°C and the reading on the wet bulb is 11°C. Determine the new relative humidity.

_____

_____

3 `CHALLENGE` What was the difference in relative humidity between noon and 5 P.M.? How was the relative humidity affected by air temperature?

_____

_____

8.NS.8

Relative Humidity

Dry-Bulb Reading (°C)	Difference Between Wet- and Dry-Bulb Readings (°C)				
	1	2	3	4	5
10	88	76	65	54	43
12	88	78	67	57	48
14	89	79	69	60	50
16	90	80	71	62	54
18	91	81	72	64	56
20	91	82	74	66	58
22	92	83	75	68	60

 **Lab zone** Do the Quick Lab *Measuring to Find the Dew Point.*

🔑 Assess Your Understanding

1a. Review What is humidity?

_____

_____

8.2.2, 8.2.4

b. Calculate Suppose a sample of air can hold at most 10 grams of water vapor. If the sample actually has 2 grams of water vapor, what is its relative humidity?

_____

8.2.2, 8.2.4

c. Compare and Contrast How are humidity and relative humidity different?

_____

_____

_____

_____

_____

8.2.2, 8.2.4

got it? 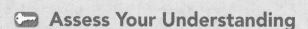 ....

○ **I get it!** Now I know that relative humidity is _____

_____ and it can be measured with _____

○ **I need extra help with** _____

Go to **MY SCIENCE** 💬 **COACH** *online for help with this subject.*

8.2.2, 8.2.4

269

Clouds

UNLOCK THE BIG ?

🔑 **How Do Clouds Form?**
8.2.4, 8.NS.8

🔑 **What Are the Three Main Types of Clouds?**
8.2.4, 8.NS.1, 8.NS.8

my planet diary

Posted by: Chase

Location: Marshfield, Massachusetts

The first time I flew to visit my grandparents, I learned something that really surprised me. When we got above the clouds, I was amazed that something as big as a cloud could float in the sky! I was gazing at the clouds when I asked my mom what they were made of. I was shocked to discover that clouds were mostly fog and mist! I thought they looked like giant piles of mashed potatoes.

Communicate Write your answers to each question below. Then discuss your answers with a partner.

1. Why do you think large clouds can float in the sky?

_____

_____

_____

2. How might you describe what clouds look like?

_____

_____

▷ PLANET DIARY Go to **Planet Diary** to learn more about clouds.

Do the Inquiry Warm-Up
How Does Fog Form?

Academic Standards for Science

8.2.4 Describe the physical and chemical composition of the atmosphere at different elevations.

8.NS.8 Analyze data.

How Do Clouds Form?

When you look at a cloud, you are seeing millions of tiny water droplets or ice crystals. 🔑 **Clouds form when water vapor in the air condenses to form liquid water or ice crystals.** Molecules of water vapor in the air become liquid water in a process called condensation. How does water in the atmosphere condense? Two conditions are required for condensation: cooling of the air and the presence of particles in the air.

Vocabulary
- dew point • cirrus
- cumulus • stratus

Skills
- Reading: Summarize
- Inquiry: Predict

The Role of Cooling

As you have learned, cold air holds less water vapor than warm air. As air cools, the amount of water vapor it can hold decreases. The water vapor condenses into tiny droplets of water or ice crystals. The temperature at which condensation begins is called the **dew point.** If the dew point is above freezing, the water vapor forms droplets. If the dew point is below freezing, the water vapor may change directly into ice crystals.

The Role of Particles

For water vapor to condense and form clouds, tiny particles must be present in the atmosphere so that the water has a surface on which to condense. Most of these particles are salt crystals, dust from soil, or smoke. Water vapor also condenses on solid surfaces, such as blades of grass or window panes. Liquid water that condenses from the air onto a cooler surface is called dew. Ice deposited on a surface that is below freezing is called frost.

Summarize What is the difference between dew and frost?

_____

_____

_____

_____

3 Water vapor condenses on

tiny _____

in the air.

FIGURE 1 ·····················

How Clouds Form
Clouds form when warm, moist air rises and cools.

✏ **Interpret Diagrams**
Fill in the blanks to complete the sentences about cloud formation.
8.NS.8

1 Warm, moist air rises from the surface. As air rises, it

_____

2 At a certain height, air cools to the dew point and

_____ begins.

 Do the Quick Lab *How Clouds Form.*

🔑 Assess Your Understanding

got it? ·····················

○ **I get it!** Now I know that clouds form when _____

_____

○ **I need extra help with** _____

Go to my science *COACH online for help with this subject.*

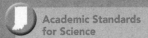

Academic Standards for Science

8.2.4 Describe the physical and chemical composition of the atmosphere.
8.NS.1 Make predictions.
8.NS.8 Analyze data.

What Are the Three Main Types of Clouds?

Scientists classify clouds into three main types based on their shape: cirrus, cumulus, and stratus. Clouds are further classified by their altitude. Each type of cloud is associated with a different type of weather.

(km)
13
12
11
10
9
8
7
6
5
4
3
2
1

Cirrus

Cumulonimbus

Altocumulus

Altostratus

Cumulus

Fog

Cirrus Clouds

Wispy, feathery clouds are called **cirrus** (SEER us) clouds. *Cirrus* comes from a word meaning "a curl." Cirrus clouds form at high altitudes, usually above 6 km, and at low temperatures. They are made of ice crystals and indicate fair weather.

Altocumulus and Altostratus

Clouds that form between 2 and 6 km above Earth's surface have the prefix *alto-*, which means "high." The two main types of these clouds are altocumulus and altostratus. These are "medium-level" clouds that are higher than regular cumulus and stratus clouds, but lower than cirrus clouds. These clouds may indicate precipitation.

Fog

Clouds that form near the ground are called fog. Fog can form when the ground cools at night after a humid day.

CHALLENGE **What happens to fog after sunrise?**

Cumulus Clouds

Clouds that look like cotton are called **cumulus** (KYOO myuh lus) clouds. The word *cumulus* means "heap" in Latin. Cumulus clouds form less than 2 km above the ground, but they may extend upward as much as 18 km. Short cumulus clouds usually indicate fair weather. Towering clouds often spread out in the shape of an anvil. These clouds are called cumulonimbus clouds and often produce thunderstorms. The suffix *-nimbus* means "rain."

FIGURE 2 ···

Cloud Types

There are many different types of clouds.
Predict Read about clouds in the text. Then fill in the table to predict the weather that you would expect with each type of cloud.

Cloud	Weather
Cirrus	
Cirrocumulus	
Cumulus	
Cumulonimbus	
Stratus	
Nimbostratus	

8.NS.1

Cirrocumulus

Cirrocumulus Clouds

Cirrocumulus clouds, which look like cotton balls, often indicate that a storm is on its way.

Stratus Clouds

Clouds that form in flat layers are known as **stratus** (STRAT us) clouds, from the Latin word *strato*, meaning "spread out." Stratus clouds usually cover all or most of the sky and are a dull, gray color. As stratus clouds thicken, they may produce drizzle, rain, or snow. They are then called *nimbostratus* clouds.

Nimbostratus   **Stratus**

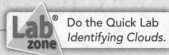

apply it!

① Observe Look out your window and identify the clouds you see. What kind of clouds are they? Circle a cloud on the page that looks most like one of the clouds you see.

_____

_____

② Predict From what you know about this type of cloud, what sort of weather would you expect over the next 24 hours? Why?

_____

_____

8.NS.1, 8.NS.8

Lab zone ® Do the Quick Lab *Identifying Clouds.*

🔑 Assess Your Understanding

1a. Describe Briefly describe the shapes of the three main types of clouds.

_____

_____

_____

8.2.4

b. Classify Classify each of the following cloud types as low-level, medium-level, or high-level.

Altocumulus _____

Altostratus _____

Cirrocumulus _____

Cirrus _____

Cumulus _____

Nimbostratus _____

Stratus _____

8.2.4

got it? ·······································

○ **I get it!** Now I know that the three main

types of clouds are _____

_____

○ **I need extra help with** _____

Go to **MY SCIENCE** 🔵 **COACH** *online for help with this subject.*

8.2.4

273

Precipitation

UNLOCK THE BIG ?

🔑 **What Are the Common Types of Precipitation?**
8.2.4, 8.2.5, 8.NS.1, 8.NS.8

🔑 **What Are the Causes and Effects of Floods and Droughts?**
8.2.5

mY planeT DiaRY *for* Indiana

DISASTER

Too Much Rain, Too Little Time

The first few days of June 2008 weren't very pleasant in Indiana. It all began on June 4th. Rain drenched parts of south-central Indiana and caused flooding around Bloomington. But the worst was yet to come. For the next two days, several more powerful thunderstorms blasted Indiana. Some areas of the state recorded close to 30 cm of rain!

The rainwater flowed into local rivers, causing them to flow over their banks. As a result, Indiana's governor was forced to declare a state of emergency in dozens of counties. The United States Coast Guard was mobilized to help evacuate and rescue stranded Hoosiers.

Write your answer to the question below. Then discuss your answer with a partner.

Do you think the flooding would have been as severe if the same amount of rain fell over a period of a month instead of just a few days? Explain.

_____

_____

_____

_____

_____

▶ PLANET DIARY Go to **Planet Diary** to learn more about precipitation.

Lab zone® Do the Inquiry Warm-Up *How Can You Make Hail?*

Vocabulary
- precipitation
- rain gauge
- flood
- drought

Skills
- Reading: Relate Cause and Effect
- Inquiry: Calculate

What Are the Common Types of Precipitation?

Suppose you could control the weather. If you wanted it to rain, you would have to get the water from somewhere.

Water evaporates from every water surface on Earth and eventually falls back to the surface. **Precipitation** is any form of water that falls from clouds and reaches Earth's surface. It is a vital part of the water cycle. In warm climates, precipitation is almost always rain. In colder regions, it may fall as snow or ice. **Common types of precipitation include rain, sleet, freezing rain, snow, and hail.**

Rain The most common kind of precipitation is rain. As shown in **Figure 1**, drops of water are called rain if they are at least 0.5 millimeters in diameter. Precipitation made up of smaller drops of water is called drizzle. Precipitation of even smaller drops is called mist.

Measuring Rain What if scientists need to measure how much rain has fallen? An open-ended tube that collects rain is called a **rain gauge.** The amount of rain is measured by dipping a ruler into the water or by reading a scale. For rainfall to be measured more accurately, a rain gauge may have a funnel at the top that collects ten times as much rain as the tube alone would without it. The depth is easier to measure. To get the actual depth of rain, it is necessary to divide by ten.

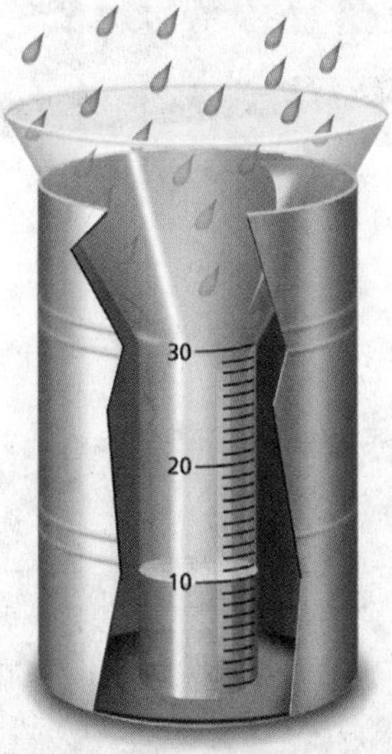

FIGURE 2 ·······················
Rain Gauge
The rain gauge, measuring in centimeters, collects ten times the actual depth of rain that falls.
✏️ **Calculate** How much rain has fallen so far?

8.NS.8

Academic Standards for Science

8.2.4 Describe the physical and chemical composition of the atmosphere at different elevations.

8.2.5 Describe the conditions that cause Indiana weather and weather-related events.

8.NS.1 Make predictions.

8.NS.8 Analyze data using appropriate mathematical manipulation as required.

FIGURE 1 ·······························
Water Droplets
Cloud droplets condense to become larger droplets.
✏️ **Calculate** Determine how many times larger the diameter of a large (5 mm) raindrop is than the diameter of a cloud droplet.

8.NS.8

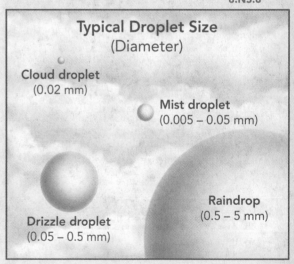

Typical Droplet Size
(Diameter)

Cloud droplet
(0.02 mm)

Mist droplet
(0.005 – 0.05 mm)

Drizzle droplet
(0.05 – 0.5 mm)

Raindrop
(0.5 – 5 mm)

Freezing Rain

On a cold day, raindrops can sometimes fall as liquid water but freeze when they touch a cold surface. This kind of precipitation is called freezing rain.

Snow

You probably know that snow-flakes have an endless number of different shapes and patterns, many with six sides or branches. A snowflake forms when water vapor in a cloud is converted directly into ice crystals. Snow-flakes often join together into large clumps of snow in which the crystals are hard to see.

FIGURE 3 ....

ART IN MOTION Freezing Precipitation

There are four types of freezing precipitation: freezing rain, snow, sleet, and hail.

✎ Circle the temperature range in the air and on the ground for which you would expect each kind of precipitation. In some cases, more than one choice may be correct.

Precipitation	Air Temperature	Ground Temperature
Rain	Above 0 °C / At or below 0 °C	Above 0 °C / At or below 0 °C
Freezing rain	Above 0 °C / At or below 0 °C	Above 0 °C / At or below 0 °C
Sleet	Above 0 °C / At or below 0 °C	Above 0 °C / At or below 0 °C
Snow	Above 0 °C / At or below 0 °C	Above 0 °C / At or below 0 °C
Hail	Above 0 °C / At or below 0 °C	Above 0 °C / At or below 0 °C

Hail

A hailstone is a round pellet of ice larger than 5 millimeters in diameter. If you cut a hailstone in half, you would see layers of ice, like the layers of an onion. Hail forms only inside cumulonimbus clouds during thunderstorms. A hailstone starts as an ice pellet inside a cold region of a cloud. Strong updrafts carry the hailstone up through the cold region many times. Each time the hailstone goes through the cold region, a new layer of ice forms around it. Eventually the hailstone becomes heavy enough to fall to the ground. Because hailstones can grow large, hail can cause damage to crops, buildings, and vehicles.

Sleet

Sometimes raindrops fall through a layer of air that is below 0°C, the freezing point of water. As they fall, the raindrops freeze into solid particles of ice. Ice particles smaller than 5 millimeters in diameter are called sleet.

Measuring Snow Rain is not the only kind of precipitation meteorologists measure. Have you ever walked through a large snowstorm and wanted to know exactly how much snow had fallen?

Snowfall is usually measured in two ways: by using a simple measuring stick or by melting collected snow and measuring the depth of water it produces. On average, 10 centimeters of snow contains about the same amount of water as 1 centimeter of rain. However, light, fluffy snow contains far less water than heavy, wet snow does.

apply it!

A rain gauge with a wide funnel collects ten times the actual depth of rain that falls. After the rain ends, the water level is at 15 centimeters.

1 How much rain actually fell?

_____

2 Calculate If snow had fallen instead, how deep would that snow have been?

_____

8.NS.8

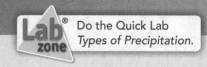
Lab zone® Do the Quick Lab *Types of Precipitation.*

🔑 Assess Your Understanding

1a. Define What is precipitation?

_____

_____

_____

8.2.4, 8.2.5

b. Draw Conclusions What factors determine if precipitation falls as freezing rain or as sleet?

_____

_____

_____

8.2.5

got it? ....

○ **I get it!** Now I know that the common types of precipitation are _____

_____

○ **I need extra help with** _____

Go to **MY SCIENCE COACH** online for help with this subject.

8.2.4, 8.2.5

Academic Standards for Science

8.2.5 Describe the conditions that cause Indiana weather and weather-related events such as tornadoes, lake effect snow, blizzards, thunderstorms, and flooding.

What Are the Causes and Effects of Floods and Droughts?

In September 2008, just three years after Hurricane Katrina, Hurricane Gustav blasted the coasts of Louisiana and Mississippi. Lakes and rivers overflowed. The result was severe flooding.

Floods A **flood** is an overflowing of water in a normally dry area. The floods caused by Gustav fortunately were not as devastating as those caused by Katrina. Because of the flooding caused by Katrina, more than 100,000 homes and businesses were destroyed, along with many bridges and highways.

Causes and Effects of Floods Not all floods are as severe as those caused by a hurricane. **Small or large, many floods occur when the volume of water in a river increases so much that the river overflows its channel.** As rain and melting snow add more water, a river gains speed and strength. A flooding river can uproot trees and pluck boulders from the ground. It can even wash away bridges and buildings.

People who live near rivers try to control floods with dams and levees. A dam is a barrier across a river that may redirect the flow of the river to other channels or store floodwaters so they can be released slowly. A levee is an embankment built along a river to prevent flooding of the surrounding land. People sometimes strengthen levees with sandbags or stones and concrete. But powerful floodwaters can sometimes break through dams and levees.

FIGURE 4 ·····

Flooding Caused by Hurricane Gustav
Hurricane Gustav hit the Gulf Coast in September 2008, causing severe flooding. ✎ **Answer the questions below.**

1. **Infer** What sort of damage would you expect to your home if this flood took place in the area where you live?

_____

_____

2. CHALLENGE A "100-year flood" is the flooding elevation that has a 1% chance of happening each year. Why is the name misleading?

_____

_____

FIGURE 5 ·······················
Drought in Texas
In July 1998, a drought hit Wharton County, Texas. This farmer lost about 50 percent of his normal cereal crop to the drought.

Droughts
If you went away for a month and no one was around to water your plants, what would happen to them? They would probably die from lack of water. A long period of scarce rainfall or dry weather is known as a **drought** (drowt). A drought reduces the supplies of groundwater and surface water. A drought can result in a shortage of water for homes and businesses.

Causes and Effects of Droughts
Droughts are usually caused by dry weather systems that remain in one place for weeks or months at a time. Long-term droughts can devastate a region. Droughts can cause crop failure. A drought can even cause famine in places where people must grow their own food. Streams and ponds dry up, and people and animals suffer.

People can prepare for droughts in several ways. When dry conditions first occur, people can begin conserving water. Farmers can grow drought-resistant plants that have been bred to withstand dry conditions. By practicing water and soil conservation, people can ensure that when droughts do occur, people will be prepared for their effects.

Relate Cause and Effect
What causes a flood? A drought?

_____
_____
_____
_____
_____

Lab® zone   Do the Quick Lab *Floods and Droughts.*

Assess Your Understanding

2a. Explain What are two ways to help reduce the dangers of floods?

_____
                                    8.2.5

b. Make Judgments Your community is considering building a dam on a nearby river to reduce flooding. Would you support this proposal? Explain.

_____
_____
_____
_____
_____
_____
_____
_____
                                    8.2.5

got it? ·····························

O **I get it!** Now I know that floods are caused

by _____

and droughts are caused by _____

_____

O **I need extra help with** _____

Go to MY SCIENCE ⑤ COACH *online for help with this subject.*   8.2.5

279

Air Masses

UNLOCK THE BIG

What Are the Major Air Masses?
8.2.5, 8.NS.8

What Are the Main Types of Fronts?
8.2.5, 8.NS.8

What Weather Do Cyclones and Anticyclones Bring?
8.2.5, 8.NS.8

MY PLANET DIARY

MISCONCEPTION

Cyclones and Tornadoes

Misconception: A cyclone is another name for tornado.

Fact: Both cyclones and tornadoes are spinning storm systems. Both rotate around an area of low pressure. However, tornadoes cover a much smaller area than cyclones do. And tornado winds reach much higher speeds.

Evidence: Outside the tropics, cyclones can be 1,000 to 4,000 kilometers across. Tropical cyclones, which are powerful hurricanes, are smaller, ranging from 100 to 1,000 kilometers across. But tornadoes are smaller still. Tornadoes range in size from a few meters to 1,600 meters across. Tornado winds are the fastest known winds on Earth. They can reach speeds of 480 km/h, but are usually much slower. Cyclone winds are strong, but do not move as fast as the fastest tornado winds. Tropical cyclone winds rarely reach more than 320 km/h.

Think about the cyclones and tornadoes you have heard about as you answer the following questions.

1. Which kind of storm do you think would cause damage over a larger area, a cyclone or a tornado? Why?

_____

_____

_____

2. Have you ever seen water swirl down a drain? How is it related to a tornado?

_____

_____

> PLANET DIARY Go to **Planet Diary** to learn more about violent weather.

Do the Inquiry Warm-Up
How Do Fluids of Different Densities Move?

Vocabulary

- air mass • tropical • polar • maritime
- continental • jet stream • front
- occluded • cyclone • anticyclone

Skills

↻ Reading: Relate Text and Visuals

△ Inquiry: Classify

What Are the Major Air Masses?

When you have a certain type of weather taking place outside, that's because a certain type of air mass is influencing the weather. An **air mass** is a huge body of air in the lower atmosphere that has similar temperature, humidity, and air pressure at any given height. Scientists classify air masses according to temperature and humidity. 🔑 **Four major types of air masses influence the weather in North America: maritime tropical, continental tropical, maritime polar, and continental polar.**

As shown in **Figure 1,** the characteristics of an air mass depend on the temperatures and moisture content of the region over which the air mass forms. Remember that temperature affects air pressure. Cold, dense air has a higher pressure, while warm, less-dense air has a lower pressure. **Tropical,** or warm, air masses form in the tropics and have low air pressure. **Polar,** or cold, air masses form north of 50° north latitude and south of 50° south latitude. Polar air masses have high air pressure.

Whether an air mass is humid or dry depends on whether it forms over water or land. **Maritime** air masses form over oceans. Water evaporates from the oceans, so the air can become very humid. **Continental** air masses form over land. Continental air masses have less exposure to large amounts of moisture from bodies of water. Therefore, continental air masses are drier than maritime air masses.

ℹ **Academic Standards for Science**

8.2.5 Describe the conditions that cause Indiana weather and weather-related events such as tornadoes, lake effect snow, blizzards, thunderstorms, and flooding.

8.NS.8 Analyze data.

FIGURE 1 ·····················

Types of Air Masses

Air masses can be classified according to temperature and humidity.

✎ △ Classify **Fill in the table. Classify each type of air mass as** *maritime* **or** *continental* **and as** *tropical* **or** *polar.*

	Wet	Dry
Warm		
Cool		

FIGURE 2 ·······················

North American Air Masses

Air masses can be warm or cold, and humid or dry. **Classify Identify the two unlabeled air masses on the page by their descriptions.**

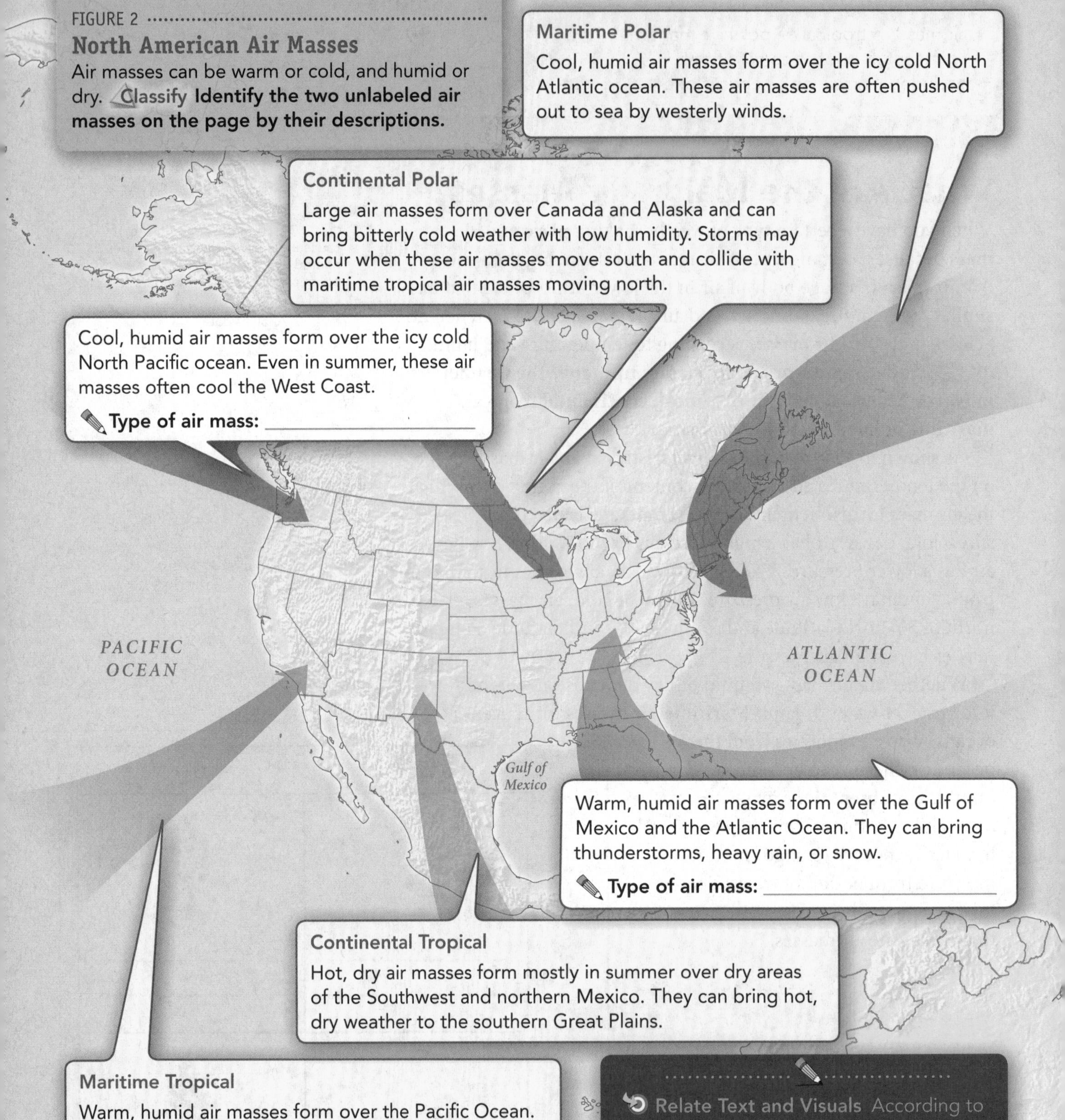

Maritime Polar

Cool, humid air masses form over the icy cold North Atlantic ocean. These air masses are often pushed out to sea by westerly winds.

Continental Polar

Large air masses form over Canada and Alaska and can bring bitterly cold weather with low humidity. Storms may occur when these air masses move south and collide with maritime tropical air masses moving north.

Cool, humid air masses form over the icy cold North Pacific ocean. Even in summer, these air masses often cool the West Coast.

✎ **Type of air mass:** _____

PACIFIC OCEAN

ATLANTIC OCEAN

Gulf of Mexico

Warm, humid air masses form over the Gulf of Mexico and the Atlantic Ocean. They can bring thunderstorms, heavy rain, or snow.

✎ **Type of air mass:** _____

Continental Tropical

Hot, dry air masses form mostly in summer over dry areas of the Southwest and northern Mexico. They can bring hot, dry weather to the southern Great Plains.

Maritime Tropical

Warm, humid air masses form over the Pacific Ocean. In summer, they usually bring hot, humid weather, summer showers, and thunderstorms. In winter, they can bring heavy rain or snow.

✎ **Relate Text and Visuals** According to the map and the text, which two of the following air masses form over water?

8.NS.8

● Maritime tropical
● Maritime polar
● Continental tropical
● Continental polar

How Air Masses Move When an air mass moves into an area and interacts with other air masses, it causes the weather to change, sometimes drastically. In the continental United States, air masses are commonly moved by the prevailing westerlies and jet streams.

Prevailing Westerlies The prevailing westerlies, the major wind belts over the continental United States, generally push air masses from west to east. For example, maritime polar air masses from the Pacific Ocean are blown onto the West Coast, bringing low clouds and showers.

Jet Streams Embedded within the prevailing westerlies are jet streams. **Jet streams** are bands of high-speed winds about 10 kilometers above Earth's surface. As jet streams generally blow from west to east, air masses are carried along their tracks.

Fronts As huge masses of air move across the land and the oceans, they collide with each other, but do not easily mix. Think about a bottle of oil and water. The less-dense oil floats on top. Something similar happens when two air masses of different temperature and humidity collide. They do not easily mix. The boundary where the air masses meet becomes a **front.** Storms and changeable weather often develop along fronts like the one in **Figure 3.**

FIGURE 3 ⋯⋯⋯⋯⋯⋯⋯⋯⋯⋯⋯⋯⋯⋯⋯⋯

How a Front Forms
The boundary where unlike air masses meet is called a front. A front may be 15 to 600 km wide and extend high into the troposphere.
⟳ **Relate Text and Visuals** What kind of weather would develop along the front shown in the photo?

_____

_____

Direction of moving front

Cold air mass   **Warm air mass**

Do the Quick Lab
Tracking Air Masses.

🔑 Assess Your Understanding

1a. Review What two characteristics are used to classify air masses?

_____

_____
                                    8.2.5

b. Apply Concepts What type of air mass would form over the northern Atlantic Ocean?

_____

_____
                                    8.2.5

c. Classify Classify the four major types of air masses according to moisture content.

_____

_____

_____

_____

_____
                                    8.2.5

got it? ⋯⋯⋯⋯⋯⋯⋯⋯⋯⋯⋯⋯⋯⋯⋯⋯⋯⋯⋯⋯⋯⋯⋯⋯⋯⋯⋯⋯⋯⋯⋯⋯⋯⋯⋯

○ **I get it!** Now I know that the four major types of air masses are _____

_____

○ I need extra help with _____

  Go to MY SCIENCE ⓢ COACH *online for help with this subject.*   8.2.5

What Are the Main Types of Fronts?

When you leave school in the afternoon, you may find that the weather is different from when you arrived in the morning. That might be because a front has just recently passed through the area. ⚷ **Colliding air masses can form four types of fronts: cold fronts, warm fronts, stationary fronts, and occluded fronts.** The kind of front that develops depends on the characteristics of the air masses and the direction in which they move.

FIGURE 4 ···

> **INTERACTIVE ART** **Types of Fronts**

✎ **Infer Identify the type of weather brought by each front as it passes through an area.**   8.NS.8

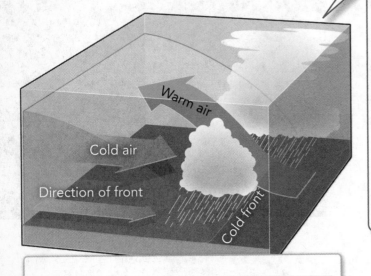

Cold Fronts

Cold air is dense and tends to sink. Warm air is less dense and tends to rise. When a faster cold air mass runs into a slower warm air mass, the denser cold air slides under the lighter warm air. The warm air is pushed upward along the leading edge of the colder air. A cold front forms.

As the warm air rises, it expands and cools. The rising air soon reaches the dew point, the temperature at which water vapor in the air condenses. Clouds form. Heavy rain or snow may fall.

Cold fronts tend to arrive quickly, because their leading edges move along the ground. They can cause abrupt weather changes, including thunderstorms. After a cold front passes, colder, drier air moves in, often bringing clear skies, a shift in wind direction, and lower temperatures.

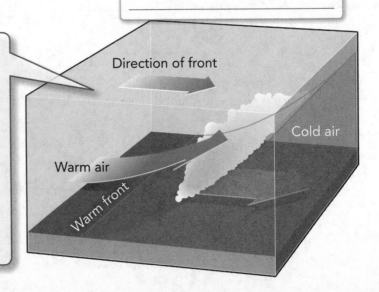

Warm Fronts

Clouds and precipitation also accompany warm fronts. At a warm front, a fast-moving warm air mass overtakes a slower cold air mass. Because cold air is denser than warm air, the warm air moves over the cold air. If the warm air is humid, light rain or snow falls along the front. If the air is dry, scattered clouds form. Because warm fronts arrive slowly, the weather may be rainy or cloudy for several days. After a warm front passes, the weather tends to be warmer and humid.

Occluded Fronts

The most complex weather situation occurs at an occluded front, where a warm air mass is caught between two cooler air masses. The denser cool air masses move underneath the less dense warm air mass and push the warm air upward. The two cooler air masses meet in the middle and may mix. The temperature near the ground becomes cooler. The warm air mass is cut off, or **occluded,** from the ground. As the warm air cools and its water vapor condenses, the weather may turn cloudy and rain or snow may fall.

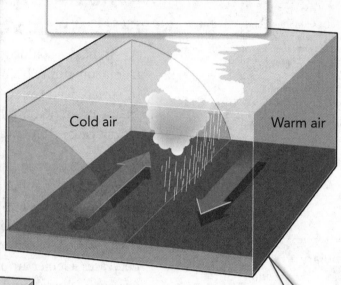

Cold air   Warm air

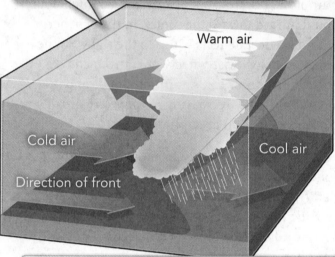

Warm air

Cold air

Direction of front

Cool air

Stationary Fronts

Sometimes cold and warm air masses meet, but neither one can move the other. In this case, the front is called a stationary front. Where the warm and cool air meet, water vapor in the warm air condenses into rain, snow, fog, or clouds. But if a stationary front stalls, it may bring many days of clouds and precipitation.

Lab zone® Do the Quick Lab *Weather Fronts.*

🔑 Assess Your Understanding

2a. Define What is a front?

_____

_____
8.2.5

b. Describe What type of weather occurs as a warm front moves through an area?

_____

_____
8.2.5

c. Classify What types of fronts would cause several days of rain and clouds?

_____

_____
8.2.5

got it?

○ **I get it!** Now I know that the four main types of fronts are _____

_____

_____

○ I need extra help with _____

_____

_____

Go to my science ⑤ coach *online for help with this subject.*
8.2.5

Academic Standards for Science

8.2.5 Describe the conditions that cause Indiana weather and weather-related events such as tornadoes, lake effect snow, blizzards, thunderstorms, and flooding.

8.NS.8 Analyze data.

What Weather Do Cyclones and Anticyclones Bring?

As air masses collide to form fronts, the boundary between the fronts sometimes becomes distorted. This distortion can be caused by surface features, such as mountains, or strong winds, such as the jet stream. When this happens, the air begins to swirl. The swirling air can cause a low-pressure center to form.

Cyclones A circled *L* on a weather map stands for "low," and indicates an area of relatively low air pressure. A swirling center of low air pressure is a **cyclone,** from a Greek word meaning "wheel." You can see a cyclone in **Figure 5.**

As warm air at the center of a cyclone rises, the air pressure decreases. Cooler air blows inward from nearby areas of higher air pressure. Winds spiral inward toward the center. In the Northern Hemisphere, the Coriolis effect deflects winds to the right. So the cyclone winds spin counterclockwise when viewed from above.

As air rises in a cyclone, the air cools, forming clouds and precipitation. 🔑 **Cyclones and decreasing air pressure are associated with clouds, wind, and precipitation.**

Anticyclones As its name suggests, an anticyclone is the opposite of a cyclone. **Anticyclones** are high-pressure centers of dry air, shown by an *H* on a weather map. Winds spiral outward from the center, moving toward areas of lower pressure. Because of the Coriolis effect, winds in an anticyclone spin clockwise in the Northern Hemisphere. As air moves out from the center, cool air moves downward from higher in the troposphere. The cool air warms up, so its relative humidity drops. 🔑 **The descending air in an anticyclone generally causes dry, clear weather.**

Vocabulary Prefixes How does knowing the meaning of the prefix *anti-* help you remember how an anticyclone spins?

_____

_____

_____

FIGURE 5 ·······················

Cyclones and Anticyclones

✏ **Interpret Diagrams** Label each diagram as either a cyclone or an anticyclone. In each circle, draw an arrow to show the direction of air motion for the system as it would be seen from above.

8.NS.8

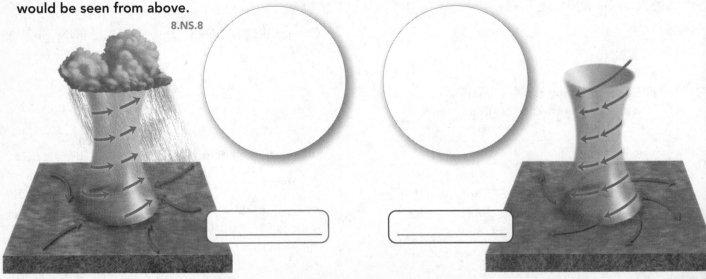

apply it!

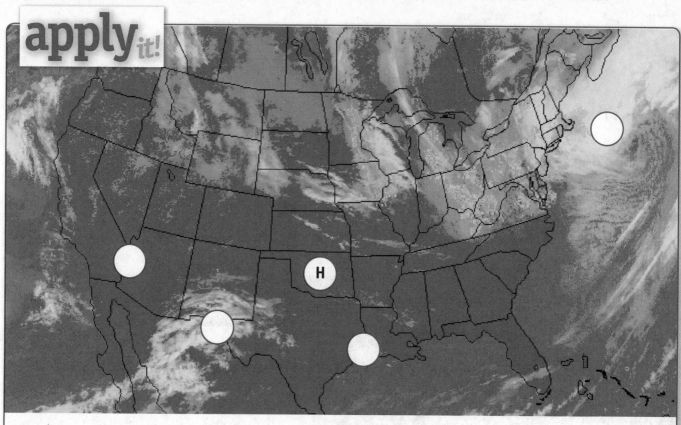

1 Classify Fill in the empty circles with either *L* for a low-pressure center or *H* for a high-pressure center.

2 CHALLENGE What information on the map helped you decide if an area's air pressure was low or high?

_____

_____

8.NS.8

Lab zone Do the Quick Lab *Cyclones and Anticyclones.*

🔑 Assess Your Understanding

3a. Identify What is a cyclone?

_____

8.2.5

b. 🔄 **Relate Text and Visuals** How does air move in a cyclone?

_____

_____

8.2.5

c. Compare and Contrast What kind of weather is associated with a cyclone? What kind of weather is associated with an anticyclone?

_____

_____

_____

8.2.5

got it? ....

○ **I get it!** Now I know that cyclones cause _____

and anticyclones cause _____

○ **I need extra help with** _____

Go to **my science ⓢ coach** *online for help with this subject.*

8.2.5

287

LESSON

5 Storms

UNLOCK
THE BIG
?

🔑 **How Do the Different Types of Storms Form?**
8.2.5, 8.NS.1, 8.NS.8

🔑 **How Can You Stay Safe in a Storm?**
8.2.5, 8.NS.8

mY PLANET DiARY *for* Indiana

DISASTER

The Great Blizzard of 1978

On January 25–26, 1978, a ferocious blizzard hit the central United States. Damaging winds and record-breaking amounts of snow occurred throughout Indiana. Some areas saw as much as 102 cm of snow.

The storm was so bad that the Indianapolis International Airport was forced to close. Travelers were trapped at the airport for three days. The weight of the snow caused many factory and warehouse roofs to collapse. Snowdrifts blocked roads and made travel impossible. Throughout the state, drivers were stranded on roads, workers were stuck in their offices, and homes lost heat and electrical power.

Communicate **Write your answers to each question below. Then discuss your answers with a partner.**

1. What do you think made the blizzard so dangerous?

_____

_____

_____

2. Besides the powerful gusts and the roads filling with snow, what other hazards do you think the blizzard caused?

_____

_____

> PLANET DIARY ⟩ Go to **Planet Diary** to learn more about strong storms.

Lab zone® Do the Inquiry Warm-Up
Can You Make a Tornado?

Vocabulary
- storm • blizzard • thunderstorm • lightning
- hurricane • storm surge • tornado • evacuate

Skills
- Reading: Outline
- Inquiry: Infer

How Do the Different Types of Storms Form?

The Blizzard of 1978 was one of the most intense storms ever to hit the northeastern United States. A **storm** is a violent disturbance in the atmosphere. Storms involve sudden changes in air pressure, which cause rapid air movements. There are several types of severe storms: winter storms, thunderstorms, hurricanes, and tornadoes.

Winter Storms In the winter in the northern United States, a large amount of precipitation falls as snow. 🔑 **All year round, most precipitation begins in clouds as snow. If the air is colder than 0°C all the way to the ground, the precipitation falls as snow.** Heavy snow can block roads, trapping people in their homes and delaying emergency vehicles. Extreme cold can damage crops and cause water pipes to burst.

Some places in Indiana get a lot more snow than others. **Figure 1** shows some areas affected by lake-effect snow. In Indiana, this type of snow is caused by wind that moves across Lake Michigan. In the fall and winter, the land near the Great Lakes cools much more rapidly than the water in the lakes. A cold, dry air mass moves across one of the lakes, picking up water vapor and heat. When it reaches the other side of the lake, the air rises and cools again. The water vapor condenses and falls as snow. Sometimes, Indiana can be affected by a **blizzard,** or a snowstorm with prolonged winds of 56 kilometers per hour or greater and considerable falling or blowing snow that reduces visibility.

Academic Standards for Science

8.2.5 Describe the conditions that cause Indiana weather and weather-related events such as tornadoes, lake effect snow, blizzards, thunderstorms, and flooding.

8.NS.1 Make predictions and develop testable questions based on research and prior knowledge.

8.NS.8 Analyze data.

FIGURE 1 ·······························

Lake-Effect Snow

As cold, dry air moves across the warmer water, it becomes more humid as water vapor evaporates from the lake surface. When the air reaches land and cools, lake-effect snow falls.

✏️ **Interpret Maps** Circle the cities that receive lake-effect snow. In the box on the map, name a city that does not get it and explain why. 8.NS.8

Key
Areas of lake-effect snow
0 — 100 miles
0 — 100 km

Lake Huron
Lake Ontario
Lake Michigan
Lake Erie

Cold, dry air

• Rochester
• Buffalo
Detroit •
• Erie
Cleveland •
Chicago •

289

Thunderstorms Do you find thunderstorms frightening? Exciting? As you watch the brilliant flashes of lightning and listen to long rolls of thunder, you may wonder what causes them.

How Thunderstorms Form A **thunderstorm** is a small storm often accompanied by heavy precipitation and frequent thunder and lightning. 🔑 **Thunderstorms form in large cumulonimbus clouds, also known as thunderheads.** Most cumulonimbus clouds form on hot, humid afternoons or evenings. They also form when warm air is forced upward along a cold front. In both cases, the warm, humid air rises rapidly, as shown in **Figure 2**. The air cools, forming dense thunderheads with water condensing into rain droplets. Heavy rain falls, sometimes along with hail. Within the thunderhead are strong upward and downward winds known as updrafts and downdrafts. Thunderstorms occur very frequently in the summer months in the Midwest.

FIGURE 2 ·········

How Thunderstorms Form
A thunderstorm forms when warm, humid air rises rapidly within a cumulonimbus cloud.
✎ **Interpret Diagrams Fill in the captions noting the direction of the warm, humid air and the cold air.** 8.NS.8

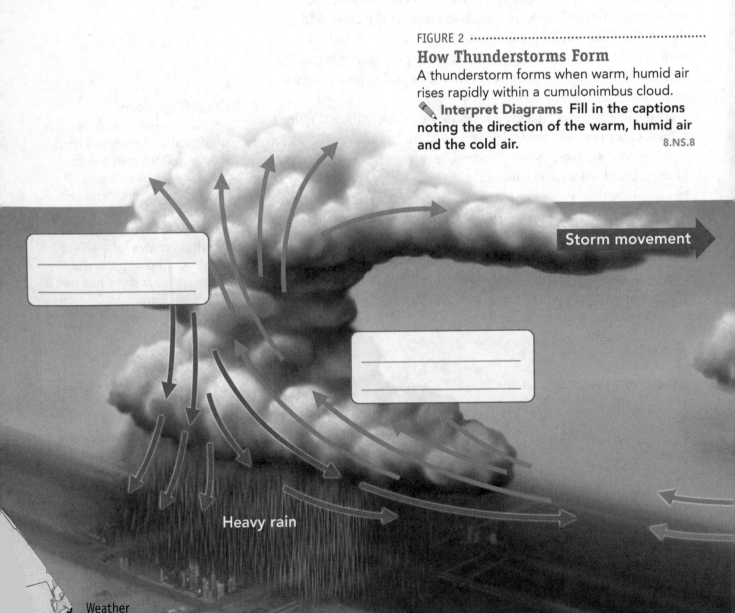

Storm movement

Heavy rain

Lightning and Thunder During a thunderstorm, areas of positive and negative electrical charges build up in the storm clouds. **Lightning** is a sudden spark, or electrical discharge, as these charges jump between parts of a cloud, between nearby clouds, or between a cloud and the ground. Lightning is similar to the shocks you sometimes feel when you touch a metal object on a very dry day. Because lightning is electricity, it is easily conducted by metal.

What causes thunder? A lightning bolt can heat the air near it to as much as 30,000°C, much hotter than the sun's surface. The rapidly heated air expands explosively. Thunder is the sound of the explosion. Because light travels faster than sound, you see lightning before you hear thunder.

Thunderstorm Damage Thunderstorms can cause severe damage. The heavy rains associated with thunderstorms can flood low-lying areas. Lightning can also cause damage. When lightning strikes the ground, the hot, expanding air can shatter tree trunks or start forest fires. When lightning strikes people or animals, it acts like a powerful electric shock. Lightning can cause unconsciousness, serious burns, and heart failure.

Floods A major danger during severe thunderstorms is flooding. Some floods occur when so much water pours into a stream or river that its banks overflow, covering the surrounding land with water. In urban areas, floods can occur when the ground is already saturated by heavy rains. The water can't soak into the water-logged ground or the many areas covered with buildings, roads, and parking lots. A flash flood is a sudden, violent flood that occurs shortly after a storm.

FIGURE 3 ···
Lightning Damage
Lightning can cause fires, serious damage, and injuries. ✏️ △Infer **Which is more likely to be hit by lightning, a metal or a wooden boat? Why?**

Outline After reading the text on this page, complete the outline by adding details about how a hurricane forms.

I. Hurricanes

  A. How a Hurricane Forms

  1. _____
  _____
  _____
  _____

  2. _____
  _____
  _____

  3. _____
  _____
  _____

Hurricanes A **hurricane** is a tropical cyclone with winds of 119 km/h or higher. A typical hurricane is about 600 kilometers across. Hurricanes form in the Atlantic, Pacific, and Indian oceans. In the western Pacific, they are called typhoons. In the Indian ocean, they are simply called cyclones.

How Hurricanes Form A typical hurricane that strikes the United States forms in the Atlantic Ocean north of the equator in August, September, or October. **A hurricane begins over warm ocean water as a low-pressure area, or tropical disturbance.** If the tropical disturbance grows in size and strength, it becomes a tropical storm, which may then become a hurricane.

Look at **Figure 4** to see how a hurricane forms. A hurricane draws its energy from the warm, humid air at the ocean's surface. As this air rises and forms clouds, more air is drawn into the system. Inside the storm are bands of very high winds and heavy rains. Winds spiral inward toward the area of lowest pressure at the center. The lower the air pressure at the center of a storm, the faster the winds blow toward the center. Hurricane winds may be as strong as 320 km/h.

Hurricane winds are strongest in a narrow band around the storm's center. At the center is a ring of clouds, called the eyewall, that encloses a quiet "eye." The wind gets stronger as the eye approaches. When the eye arrives, the weather changes suddenly. The air grows calm and the sky may clear. After the eye passes, the storm resumes, but the wind blows from the opposite direction.

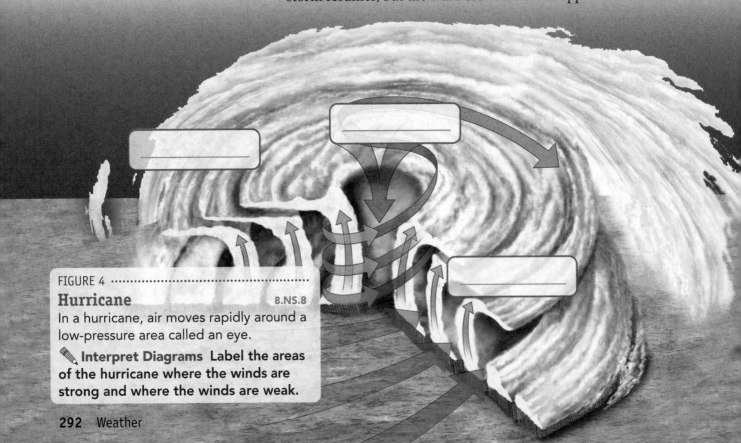

FIGURE 4
Hurricane   8.NS.8
In a hurricane, air moves rapidly around a low-pressure area called an eye.

Interpret Diagrams Label the areas of the hurricane where the winds are strong and where the winds are weak.

August 24, 2005: Katrina approaches Florida.

August 26, 2005: Hurricane Katrina picks up strength over the Gulf of Mexico.

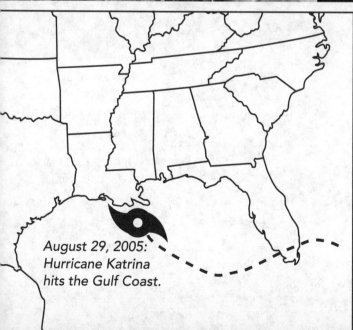

August 29, 2005: Hurricane Katrina hits the Gulf Coast.

How Hurricanes Move Hurricanes can last longer than other storms—a week or more. During that period, they can travel thousands of kilometers. Hurricanes that form in the Atlantic Ocean are steered by easterly trade winds toward the Caribbean islands and the southeastern United States. After a hurricane passes over land, it no longer has warm, moist air to draw energy from. The hurricane gradually weakens, although heavy rainfall may continue for several days.

Hurricane Damage When a hurricane comes ashore, it brings high waves and severe flooding, as well as wind damage. The low pressure and high winds of the hurricane over the ocean raise the level of the water as much as 6 meters above normal sea level. The result is a **storm surge**, a "dome" of water that sweeps across the coast where the hurricane lands. Storm surges can cause great damage, washing away beaches, destroying coastal buildings, and eroding the coastline.

FIGURE 5 ···

Hurricane Katrina

The picture shows the path of Hurricane Katrina.

✎ **Predict** On the picture, draw lines showing the possible paths the hurricane could have taken after reaching land. What happens to a hurricane after it reaches land?

8.NS.1, 8.NS.8

293

On April 11, 1965, 11 tornadoes struck in 20 counties in Indiana, causing 137 deaths, 1,700 injuries, and $30 million in property damage. It was the worst outbreak of tornado activity in Indiana's history.

FIGURE 6 ....
▶ INTERACTIVE ART **Tornado Formation**
About 1,200 tornadoes occur in the United States every year. Weather patterns on the Great Plains result in a "tornado alley."

✏ **Interpret Maps Pick a state on the map (or your home state) and indicate whether its risk of tornadoes is low or high.** 8.NS.8

_____

_____

_____

Tornadoes
A tornado is one of the most frightening and intense types of storms. A **tornado** is a rapidly whirling, funnel-shaped cloud that reaches down from a thunderstorm to touch Earth's surface. If a tornado occurs over a lake or ocean, the storm is called a waterspout. Tornadoes are usually brief, but can be deadly. They may touch the ground for 15 minutes or less and be only a few hundred meters across. But an intense tornado's wind speed may approach 500 km/h.

How Tornadoes Form Tornadoes can form in any situation involving severe weather. 🔑 **Tornadoes most commonly develop in thick cumulonimbus clouds—the same clouds that bring thunderstorms.** Tornadoes often occur when thunderstorms are likely—in spring and early summer, late in the afternoon when the ground is warm.

Tornado Alley Tornadoes occur in nearly every part of the United States. However, the Great Plains often have the kind of weather pattern that is likely to create tornadoes: A warm, humid air mass moves north from the Gulf of Mexico into the lower Great Plains, and a cold, dry air mass moves south from Canada. When the air masses meet, the cold air moves under the warm air, forcing it to rise. A line of thunderstorms called a squall line is likely to form, with storms traveling northeast. A single squall line can produce ten or more tornadoes.

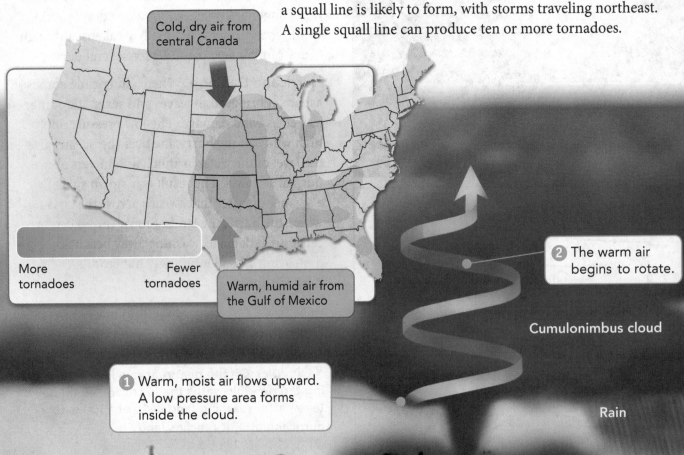

Cold, dry air from central Canada

More tornadoes   Fewer tornadoes

Warm, humid air from the Gulf of Mexico

1 Warm, moist air flows upward. A low pressure area forms inside the cloud.

2 The warm air begins to rotate.

Cumulonimbus cloud

Rain

Tornado Damage Tornado damage comes from both strong winds and flying debris. The low pressure inside the tornado sucks objects into the funnel. Tornadoes can move large objects and scatter debris many miles away. In Indiana, the Palm Sunday tornado outbreak destroyed 90% of the buildings in Russiaville. A tornado can level houses on one street but leave neighboring houses standing.

Tornadoes are ranked on the Enhanced Fujita scale by the amount of damage they cause. The scale was named for the scientist who devised the original scale, Dr. T. Theodore Fujita. As shown in **Figure 7**, the scale goes from light damage (EF0) to extreme damage (EF5). Only about one percent of tornadoes are ranked as EF4 or EF5.

FIGURE 7 ···

Tornado Damage

🖉 CHALLENGE **How would you rank this tornado damage on the Enhanced Fujita scale? Why?**

_____

_____

_____

8.NS.8

Enhanced Fujita Scale	Types of Damage
EF0	Branches broken off trees
EF1	Mobile homes overturned
EF2	Trees uprooted
EF3	Roofs and walls torn down
EF4	Houses leveled
EF5	Houses carried away

Do the Quick Lab *Where Do Hurricanes Come From?*

🗝 **Assess Your Understanding**

1a. Identify What is a hurricane?

_____

_____

_____

8.2.5

b. Explain How do hurricanes form?

_____

_____

_____

8.2.5

c. Compare and Contrast How do hurricanes differ from tornadoes?

_____

_____

_____

_____

_____

_____

_____

8.2.5

got it? ···

○ **I get it!** Now I know that the main kinds of storms are _____

_____

_____

_____

○ I need extra help with _____

_____

Go to **MY SCIENCE** s **COACH** *online for help with this subject.*   8.2.5

FIGURE 8 ·····························

Evacuation Site

In September 2005, the city of Dallas opened up shelters such as the Reunion Arena for people who fled Hurricane Katrina.

✎ **Explain** What is the difference between a hurricane watch and a hurricane warning?

_____

_____

_____

_____

_____

_____

_____

How Can You Stay Safe in a Storm?

A winter storm or a thunderstorm can be fun to watch if you're in a safe place. But you don't want to be near a hurricane or tornado if you can avoid it.

Winter Storm Safety Imagine being caught in a snowstorm when the wind suddenly picks up. High winds can blow falling snow sideways or pick up snow from the ground and suspend it in the air. This situation can be dangerous because the blowing snow limits your vision and makes it easy to get lost. Also, strong winds cool a person's body rapidly. 🔑 **If you are caught in a snowstorm, try to find shelter from the wind.** Cover exposed parts of your body and try to stay dry. If you are in a car, keep the engine running only if the exhaust pipe is clear of snow.

Thunderstorm Safety The safest place to be during a thunderstorm is indoors. Avoid touching telephones, electrical appliances, or plumbing fixtures. It is usually safe to stay in a car. The electricity will move along the metal skin of the car and jump to the ground. However, do not touch any metal inside the car. 🔑 **During thunderstorms, avoid places where lightning may strike. Also, avoid objects that can conduct electricity, such as metal objects and bodies of water.**

How can you remain safe if you are caught outside during a thunderstorm? Do not seek shelter under a tree, because lightning may strike the tree. Instead, find a low area away from trees, fences, and poles. Crouch with your head down. If you are swimming or in a boat, get to shore and find shelter away from the water.

Hurricane Safety Today, weather satellites can track the paths of hurricanes. So people now receive a warning well in advance of an approaching hurricane. A "hurricane watch" indicates that hurricane conditions are possible in an area within the next 36 hours. You should be prepared to **evacuate** (ee VAK yoo ayt), or move away temporarily. A "hurricane warning" means that hurricane conditions are expected within the next 24 hours. 🔑 **If you hear a hurricane warning and are told to evacuate, leave the area immediately.**

apply it!

The two signs in the pictures show warnings about possible storms.

1 Infer Match each safety sign to the appropriate storm.

2 In the space to the right, draw a sign to show how one could stay safe in a thunderstorm or winter storm.

8.NS.8

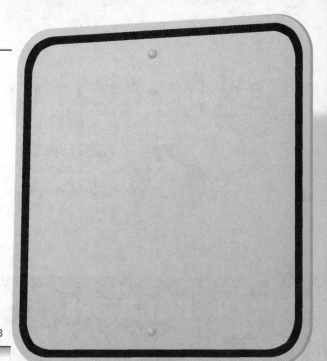

Tornado Safety

A "tornado watch" is an announcement that tornadoes are possible in your area. A "tornado warning" is an announcement that a tornado has been seen in the sky or on weather radar. If you hear a tornado warning, move to a safe area as soon as you can. Do not wait until you actually see the tornado.

🔑 **The safest place to be during a tornado is in a storm shelter or a basement.** If there is no basement, move to the middle of the ground floor. Stay away from windows and doors. Lie under a sturdy piece of furniture. If you are outdoors, lie flat in a ditch.

Lab zone® Do the Quick Lab *Storm Safety.*

🔑 Assess Your Understanding

2a. List Based on the safety steps, list the four storms from least to most dangerous.

_____

_____

_____

_____

8.2.5

b. Solve Problems How can a community make sure people stay safe in a storm?

_____

_____

_____

_____

8.2.5

got it?..

O **I get it!** Now I know that to stay safe in a storm I should either _____

or, in the case of a hurricane, I should _____

O **I need extra help with** _____

Go to **my science** 🔵 **coach** *online for help with this subject.*

8.2.5

Predicting the Weather

UNLOCK THE BIG **?**

🔑 **How Do You Predict the Weather?**
8.2.4, 8.2.5

🔑 **What Can You Learn From Weather Maps?**
8.2.4, 8.2.5, 8.NS.1, 8.NS.8

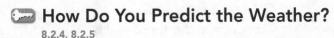

my planet Diary

CAREERS

Meteorologist Mish Michaels

Mish Michaels uses computers in her work every day to sort data from weather satellites, radar, and weather stations from all over the world. Then she shares her weather forecasts with Boston television viewers.

Michaels became interested in weather while in kindergarten in Maryland. She watched a tornado damage her family's apartment complex. Since then, she has been fascinated by storms. Michaels went on to major in meteorology at Cornell University.

Michaels is devoted to educating others about weather. She supports the WINS program (Women in the Natural Sciences) of Blue Hill Weather Observatory in Milton, Massachusetts. The program inspires girls to pursue careers in math, science, and technology.

Communicate After you read about Mish Michaels, answer these questions with a partner.

1. Why do you think that meteorologists depend so heavily on computers?

_____
_____
_____

2. What subjects do you think future meteorologists need to study in school?

_____
_____

▶ PLANET DIARY Go to **Planet Diary** to learn more about predicting the weather.

Lab zone Do the Inquiry Warm-Up *Predicting Weather.*

Vocabulary
- meteorologist
- isobar
- isotherm

Skills
- Reading: Compare and Contrast
- Inquiry: Predict

How Do You Predict the Weather?

The first step in weather forecasting is to collect data, either from direct observations or through the use of instruments. For example, if a barometer shows that the air pressure is falling, you can expect an approaching low-pressure area, possibly bringing rain or snow.

Making Simple Observations You can read weather signs in the clouds, too. Cumulus clouds often form on warm days. If they grow larger and taller, they can become cumulonimbus clouds, which may produce a thunderstorm. If you can see thin cirrus clouds high in the sky, a warm front may be approaching.

Even careful weather observers often turn to meteorologists for weather information. **Meteorologists** (mee tee uh RAHL uh jists) are scientists who study and try to predict weather.

Interpreting Complex Data Meteorologists interpret information from a variety of sources. 🔑 **Meteorologists use maps, charts, computers, and other technology to analyze weather data and to prepare weather forecasts.**

Weather reporters get their information from the National Weather Service, which uses balloons, satellites, radar, and surface instruments to gather data.

Academic Standards for Science

8.2.4 Describe the physical and chemical composition of the atmosphere at different elevations.

8.2.5 Describe the conditions that cause Indiana weather and weather-related events such as tornadoes, lake effect snow, blizzards, thunderstorms, and flooding.

FIGURE 1 ·····

Red Sky
Many people have their own weather sayings. Many of these sayings are based on long-term observations.

✏ **Write your own weather poem in the space below.**

Red sky at night,
Sailors delight;
Red sky at morning,
Sailors take warning.

Evening red and morning gray
Will send the travelers on their way;
Evening gray and morning red
Will bring down rain upon their head.

Using Technology Techniques for predicting weather have changed dramatically in recent years. Short-range forecasts—forecasts for up to five days—are now fairly reliable. Meteorologists can also make somewhat accurate long-range predictions. Technological improvements in gathering weather data and using computers have improved the accuracy of weather forecasts.

FIGURE 2 ···
Weather Technology

✎ **Explain** why better technology leads to improved weather forecasting.

_____

_____

_____

Automated Weather Stations

Weather stations gather data from surface locations for temperature, air pressure, relative humidity, rainfall, and wind speed and direction. The National Weather Service has established a network of more than 1,700 surface weather observation sites.

Weather Balloons

Weather balloons carry instruments into the troposphere and lower stratosphere. The instruments measure temperature, air pressure, and humidity.

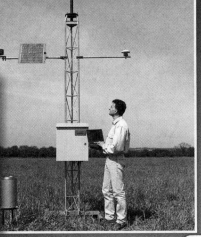

Weather Satellites

Satellites orbit Earth in the exosphere, the uppermost layer of the atmosphere. Cameras on weather satellites can make images of Earth's surface, clouds, storms, and snow cover. Satellites also collect data on temperature, humidity, solar radiation, and wind speed and direction.

Computer Forecasts

Computers process weather data quickly to help forecasters make predictions. The computer works through thousands of calculations using equations from weather models to make forecasts.

Lab ® Do the Quick Lab
zone *Modeling Weather Satellites.*

🔑 Assess Your Understanding

got it? ··

○ **I get it!** Now I know that meteorologists prepare weather forecasts using _____

_____

○ **I need extra help with** _____

Go to my science 🔵 coach *online for help with this subject.*

8.2.4, 8.2.5

What Can You Learn From Weather Maps?

A weather map is a "snapshot" of conditions at a particular time over a large area. There are many types of weather maps.

Weather Service Maps Data from many local weather stations all over the country are assembled into weather maps at the National Weather Service. The way maps display data is shown in the Apply It feature below. The simplified weather map at the end of this lesson includes a key that shows weather station symbols.

On some weather maps you see curved lines. These lines connect places with similar conditions of temperature or air pressure. **Isobars** are lines joining places on the map that have the same air pressure. (*Iso* means "equal" and *bar* means "weight.") The numbers on the isobars are the pressure readings. These readings may be given in inches of mercury or in millibars.

Isotherms are lines joining places that have the same temperature. The isotherm may be labeled with the temperature in degrees Fahrenheit, degrees Celsius, or both.

Academic Standards for Science

8.2.4 Describe the physical and chemical composition of the atmosphere at different elevations.

8.2.5 Describe the conditions that cause Indiana weather and weather-related events.

8.NS.1 Make predictions.

8.NS.8 Analyze data.

↺ **Compare and Contrast**
How are isobars and isotherms alike? How do they differ?

_____

_____

_____

_____

_____

apply it!

The tables below show what various weather symbols represent.

❶ **Apply Concepts** According to the weather map symbol below, what are the amount of cloud cover and the wind speed?

_____

❷ **Predict** Would you expect precipitation in an area marked by this weather symbol? Why?

8.NS.1, 8.NS.8

Cloud Cover (%)	Symbol
0	○
10	◐
20–30	◔
40	◕
50	◑
60	◒
70–80	◕
90	◗
100	●

Weather Map Symbol

Atmospheric pressure (millibars)

Temperature (°F) 38   ●   1018

Wind direction (from the southwest)

Wind Speed (mi/h)	Symbol
1–2	
3–8	
9–14	
15–20	
21–25	
26–31	
32–37	
38–43	
44–49	
50–54	
55–60	
61–66	
67–71	
72–77	

FIGURE 3 ....

Newspaper Weather Map
The symbols on this map show fronts, high- and low-pressure areas, the high and low temperature readings for different cities, and precipitation. The color bands indicate different temperature ranges.

✎ **Answer the questions below.**

1. **Interpret Maps** Identify the weather that will occur in Denver according to this map. **8.NS.8**

_____

_____

2. **[CHALLENGE]** Can you predict the weather in Denver a week later? Explain.

_____

_____

_____

Newspaper Weather Maps

Maps in newspapers are simplified versions of maps produced by the National Weather Service. **Figure 3** shows a typical newspaper weather map. From what you have learned in this lesson, you can probably interpret most symbols on this map. 🔑 **Standard symbols on weather maps show fronts, areas of high and low pressure, types of precipitation, and temperatures.** Note that the high and low temperatures are given in degrees Fahrenheit instead of Celsius.

Limits of Weather Forecasts

As computers have grown more powerful, and new satellites and radar technologies have been developed, scientists have been able to make better forecasts. But even with extremely powerful computers, it is unlikely that forecasters will ever be able to predict the weather accurately a month in advance. This has to do with the so-called "butterfly effect." The atmosphere works in such a way that a small change in the weather today can mean a larger change in the weather a week later! The name refers to a scientist's suggestion that even the flapping of a butterfly's wings causes a tiny disturbance in the atmosphere. A tiny event might cause a larger disturbance that could—eventually—grow into a large storm.

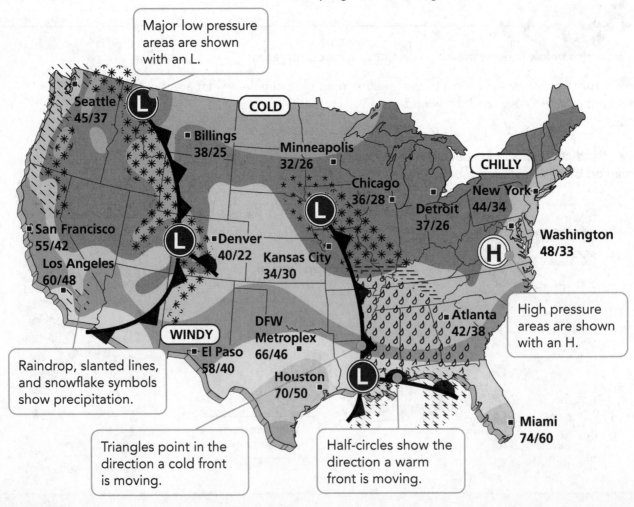

Major low pressure areas are shown with an L.

High pressure areas are shown with an H.

Raindrop, slanted lines, and snowflake symbols show precipitation.

Triangles point in the direction a cold front is moving.

Half-circles show the direction a warm front is moving.

Predicting the Weather
How do meteorologists predict the weather?

FIGURE 4 ·······················

> REAL-WORLD INQUIRY Using a Weather Map

✏️ What would you tell the people of Miami, Kansas City, and Seattle about tomorrow's weather? Explain why.   8.NS.1, 8.NS.8

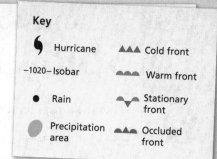

Key

Hurricane · ▲▲▲ Cold front

−1020− Isobar · ︵︵ Warm front

● Rain · ⌄⌄ Stationary front

Precipitation area · ▲▲▲ Occluded front

_____
_____
_____

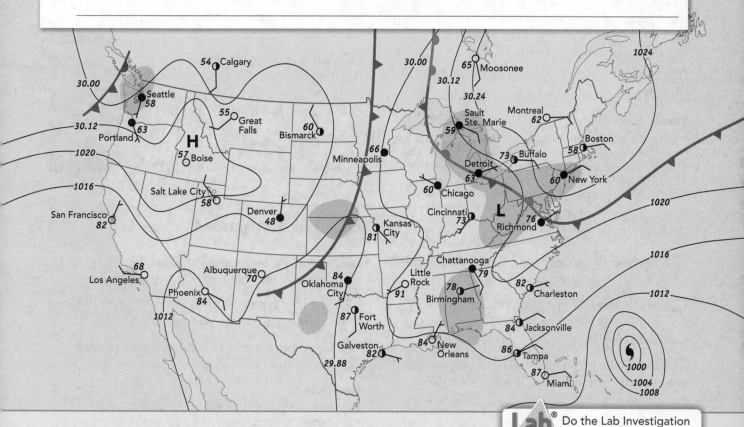

🗝️ **Assess Your Understanding**

1a. Explain What is a weather map?

_____

_____

_____

_____

8.2.4, 8.2.5

b. ANSWER THE BIG ? How do meteorologists predict the weather?

_____

_____

_____

_____

_____

8.2.4, 8.2.5

Lab zone® Do the Lab Investigation *Reading a Weather Map.*

got it? ···

○ **I get it!** Now I know that standard symbols on weather maps show _____

_____

○ **I need extra help with** _____

Go to MY SCIENCE ⓢ COACH *online for help with this subject.*   8.2.4, 8.2.5

7 Study Guide

Meteorologists predict the weather by collecting data about _____, _____, _____, and _____.

LESSON 1 Water in the Atmosphere
8.2.1, 8.2.2, 8.2.4, 8.NS.3, 8.NS.8

🔑 In the water cycle, water vapor enters the atmosphere by evaporation from the oceans and other bodies of water and leaves by condensation.

🔑 Relative humidity can be measured with an instrument called a psychrometer.

Vocabulary
• water cycle • evaporation
• condensation • humidity
• relative humidity • psychrometer

LESSON 2 Clouds
8.2.4, 8.NS.1, 8.NS.8

🔑 Clouds form when water vapor in the air condenses to form liquid water or ice crystals.

🔑 Scientists classify clouds into three main types based on their shape: cirrus, cumulus, and stratus. Clouds are further classified by their altitude.

Vocabulary
• dew point • cirrus
• cumulus • stratus

LESSON 3 Precipitation
8.2.4, 8.2.5, 8.NS.1, 8.NS.8

🔑 Common types of precipitation include rain, sleet, freezing rain, snow, and hail.

🔑 Many floods occur when the volume of water in a river increases so much that the river overflows its channel.

🔑 Droughts are usually caused by dry weather systems that remain in one place for weeks or months at a time.

Vocabulary
• precipitation • rain gauge • flood • drought

LESSON 4 Air Masses
8.2.5, 8.NS.8

🔑 The major air masses are classified as maritime or continental and as tropical or polar.

🔑 The four types of fronts are cold fronts, warm fronts, stationary fronts, and occluded fronts.

🔑 Cyclones come with wind and precipitation. An anticyclone causes dry, clear weather.

Vocabulary
• air mass • tropical • polar
• maritime • continental • jet stream
• front • occluded • cyclone • anticyclone

LESSON 5 Storms
8.2.5, 8.NS.1, 8.NS.8

🔑 Most precipitation begins in clouds as snow.

🔑 Thunderstorms and tornadoes form in cumulonimbus clouds.

🔑 A hurricane begins over warm ocean water as a low-pressure area, or tropical disturbance.

🔑 Always find proper shelter from storms.

Vocabulary
• storm • blizzard • thunderstorm • lightning
• hurricane • storm surge • tornado • evacuate

LESSON 6 Predicting the Weather
8.2.4, 8.2.5, 8.NS.1, 8.NS.8

🔑 Meteorologists use maps, charts, computers, and other technology to prepare weather forecasts.

🔑 Standard symbols on weather maps show fronts, air pressure, precipitation, and temperature.

Vocabulary
• meteorologist • isobar
• isotherm

Review and Assessment

LESSON 1 Water in the Atmosphere

1. Infer What is the energy source for the water cycle?

_____

8.2.1, 8.2.2

2. math! At 3 P.M., a dry-bulb thermometer reading is 66°F. The wet-bulb reading is 66°F. What is the relative humidity? Explain.

_____
_____
_____
_____
_____
_____
_____

8.2.2, 8.2.4, 8.NS.8

LESSON 2 Clouds

3. What type of cloud forms at high altitudes and appears wispy and feathery?

a. stratus   b. altocumulus

c. cumulus   d. cirrus

8.2.4

4. One type of cloud is a nimbostratus, which is

_____
_____
_____

8.2.4

5. Infer Why do clouds usually form high in the air instead of near Earth's surface?

_____
_____
_____
_____

8.2.4

LESSON 3 Precipitation

6. What is the name for raindrops that freeze as they fall through the air?

a. dew   b. sleet

c. hail   d. frost

8.2.4, 8.2.5

7. Rain and hail are both precipitation, which is

_____
_____
_____

8.2.4, 8.2.5

8. **Write About It** It is winter where Jenna lives. It's been snowing all day, but now the snow has changed to sleet and then to freezing rain. What is happening to cause these changes? In your answer, explain how snow, sleet, and freezing rain form.

8.2.4, 8.2.5

LESSON 4 Air Masses

9. What do you call a hot air mass that forms over land?

_____

8.2.5

10. Predict What type of weather is most likely to form at the front shown below?

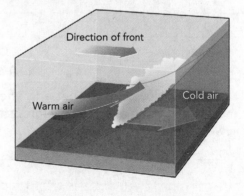

_____
_____
_____

8.2.5, 8.NS.1, 8.NS.8

305

CHAPTER
7

LESSON 5 **Storms**

11. What are very large tropical cyclones with high winds called?

   a. storm surges   **b.** tornadoes

   c. hurricanes   **d.** thunderstorms

                    8.2.5

12. Thunderstorms usually contain lightning, which is _____

_____

_____

_____

                    8.2.5

13. Make Judgments What do you think is the most important thing people should do to reduce the dangers of storms?

_____

_____

_____

_____

                    8.2.5

LESSON 6 **Predicting the Weather**

14. On a weather map, lines joining places with the same temperature are called

   a. low-pressure systems.   **b.** isotherms.

   c. high-pressure systems.   **d.** isobars.

                8.2.4, 8.2.5

15. To predict weather, meteorologists use

_____

_____

_____

                8.2.4, 8.2.5

16. Apply Concepts How does the butterfly effect keep meteorologists from accurately forecasting the weather a month in advance?

_____

_____

_____

_____

_____

                8.2.4, 8.2.5

APPLY THE BIG ?

How do meteorologists predict the weather?

17. Meteorologists use information from many sources to make predictions about the weather. The weather map shows that right now it is sunny in Cincinnati, but the weather report for tomorrow shows a major snowstorm. Using the map, explain how a meteorologist is able to make this prediction. Include details on weather technology used and the atmospheric conditions that lead to a snowstorm. Make sure to discuss clouds, air masses, fronts, temperature, and pressure.

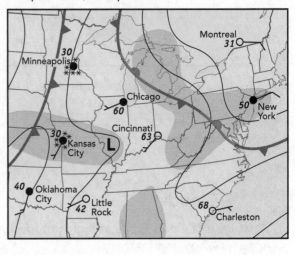

_____

_____

_____

_____

_____

_____

_____

_____

_____

_____

_____

_____

              8.2.4, 8.2.5, 8.NS.11

Indiana ISTEP+ Practice

Multiple Choice

Circle the letter of the best answer.

1. The table below shows the amount of rainfall in different months.

Average Monthly Rainfall			
Month	**Rainfall**	**Month**	**Rainfall**
January	1 cm	July	49 cm
February	1 cm	August	57 cm
March	1 cm	September	40 cm
April	2 cm	October	20 cm
May	25 cm	November	4 cm
June	52 cm	December	1 cm

Which two months had the most rainfall?

A. June and August   **B.** January and March

C. June and July   **D.** August and May

8.2.4, 8.2.5, 8.NS.8

2. When the temperature equals the dew point, what is the relative humidity?

A. zero   **B.** 10%

C. 50%   **D.** 100%

8.2.4

3. How are air masses classified?

A. by temperature and pressure

B. by pressure and humidity

C. by temperature and density

D. by temperature and humidity

8.2.5

4. Which of the following map symbols identifies places with the same air pressure?

A. jet streams   **B.** isobars

C. degrees   **D.** isotherms

8.2.4, 8.2.5

Constructed Response

Write your answer to Question 5 on the lines below.

5. What equipment would you need to design an experiment that measures relative humidity?

_____

_____

_____

8.2.2, 8.2.4

Extended Response

Use the diagram below and your knowledge of science to help you answer Question 6. Write your answer on a separate piece of paper.

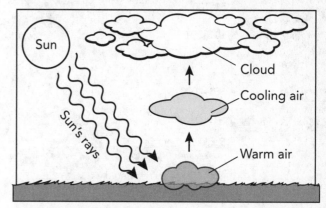

6. Describe the process by which a cloud forms. What two conditions are necessary for this process to occur? How does this process compare to the process by which dew or frost form?

8.2.1, 8.2.2, 8.2.4, 8.NS.11

The S'COOL Project

Schools around the world are teaming up to help scientists at the National Aeronautics and Space Administration (NASA). Since 1998, students have been helping NASA check satellite observations through a project called Students' Cloud Observations On-Line (S'COOL).

NASA tells schools in the program the date and time when the project satellites will be passing over different regions of the world. When a satellite passes over their school, students observe the clouds in the sky. Students can also measure weather data such as temperature and relative humidity. These observations are uploaded to the project Web site. Then NASA scientists compare the satellite data with the students' observations. This process, called ground truthing, helps scientists determine how accurate the satellite data are.

◀ Students' observations are compared to data collected by satellites like this one.

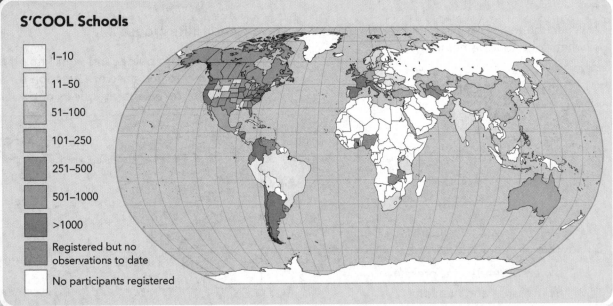

S'COOL Schools

- 1–10
- 11–50
- 51–100
- 101–250
- 251–500
- 501–1000
- >1000
- Registered but no observations to date
- No participants registered

▲ Schools around the world participate in the S'COOL program. The map above shows where they are. If you had to recruit schools to help NASA get complete data, where would you look for schools?

Research It Make a record book. Use it to keep a weeklong log of cloud formations and weather conditions, including photos or sketches, at a specific time each day.

 8.NS.3, 8.NS.7, 8.NS.11

Tracking Hurricanes
with Latitude and Longitude

Do you understand the important bulletin on the computer screen? Lines of latitude and longitude are imaginary lines that crisscross Earth's surface. Because the lines cross, they can help you describe any location on Earth, including the location of hurricanes. A location's latitude is always written before its longitude.

Hurricane Hilda is located in the Atlantic Ocean off the southeastern coast of the United States.

Write About It Assume that Hurricane Hilda is following a straight path. Using the information in the bulletin and the map, try to predict the path the hurricane will take to reach land, and how long it will take to get there. Compare your predicted path with the path of a real hurricane. Evaluate your prediction. Does the bulletin provide enough information for you to make a precise prediction? Write a paragraph explaining why or why not.

 8.NS.1, 8.NS.8, 8.NS.10, 8.NS.11

ATTENTION

HURRICANE HILDA IS CURRENTLY LOCATED AT 30°N, 74°W. IT IS MOVING 21 KM/H NW. ALL RESIDENTS OF NEARBY COASTAL AREAS ARE ADVISED TO EVACUATE IMMEDIATELY.

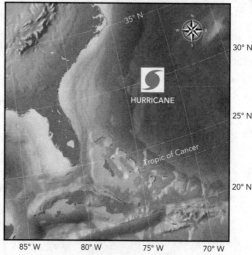

Hurricane Hilda is currently located at 30° N, 74° W. You can plot the hurricane's location on a map. What information do you need to predict where it will reach land? ▶

WHAT DOES THIS MACAW CHICK NEED TO SURVIVE?

How do people use Earth's resources?

People aren't the only living things that need resources to survive. How we use our planet's resources has an impact on all of Earth's species. Small and helpless, this baby scarlet macaw cannot live on its own. This chick was born featherless and with its eyes closed. Macaw parents feed the chick until it is at least three months old. △Infer **What basic things does this chick need to live?**

_____

_____

_____

_____

_____

> UNTAMED SCIENCE Watch the **Untamed Science** video to learn more about natural resources.

Resources and Living Things

Academic Standards for Science

8.2.6, 8.2.7, 8.2.8, 8.NS.1–8.NS.4, 8.NS.7,
8.NS.8, 8.NS.11, 8.DP.7–8.DP.10

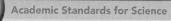

8 Getting Started

Check Your Understanding

1. Background Read the paragraph below and then answer the question.

Ed is observing his **ecology** project for the tenth day in a row. He holds the bottle up to see the **habitat** inside. The snails, fish, and plants inside the bottle all look healthy. He can even see some baby snails. It is a whole **ecosystem** in a bottle!

Ecology is the study of how organisms interact with each other and their environment.

A **habitat** is an environment that provides the things a specific organism needs to live, grow, and reproduce.

An **ecosystem** is the community of organisms that live in a particular area, along with their nonliving environment.

- How are the terms *ecosystem* and *ecology* related?

_____

_____

> **MY READING WEB** If you had trouble completing the question above, visit **My Reading Web** and type in *Resources and Living Things*.

Vocabulary Skill

Identify Related Word Forms You can increase your vocabulary by learning related forms of a word. For example, if you know the verb *produce* means "to make," you can figure out that the meaning of the noun *product* is "something that is made." The table below shows two vocabulary words in this chapter and their related word forms.

Verb	Noun	Adjective
pollute to contaminate Earth's land, water, or air	**pollution** the contamination of Earth's land, water, or air	**pollutive** contaminating Earth's land, water, or air
conserve to manage resource use wisely	**conservation** the practice of managing resource use wisely	**conservational** managing resource use wisely

2. Quick Check Complete the sentence with the correct form of the word from the table above.

- Air _____ is a problem in many of the world's major cities.

natural resource

nonrenewable resource

exponential growth

keystone species

Chapter Preview

LESSON 1
- natural resource
- pollution • point source
- nonpoint source
- environmental science
- 🔁 **Relate Cause and Effect**
- 🔺 **Draw Conclusions**

LESSON 2
- renewable resource
- nonrenewable resource
- sustainable use
- ecological footprint
- conservation
- 🔁 **Relate Text and Visuals**
- 🔺 **Calculate**

LESSON 3
- exponential growth
- 🔁 **Identify the Main Idea**
- 🔺 **Predict**

LESSON 4
- clear-cutting
- selective cutting
- sustainable yield
- fishery
- aquaculture
- 🔁 **Summarize**
- 🔺 **Communicate**

LESSON 5
- biodiversity • keystone species
- gene • extinction
- endangered species
- threatened species
- habitat destruction
- habitat fragmentation
- poaching • captive breeding
- 🔁 **Compare and Contrast**
- 🔺 **Infer**

▷ **VOCAB FLASH CARDS** For more help with vocabulary, visit **Vocab Flash Cards** and type in *Resources and Living Things.*

313

Indiana

LESSON

1

Introduction to Environmental Issues

UNLOCK THE BIG
?

🔑 **What Are the Types of Environmental Issues?**
8.2.6, 8.2.7, 8.2.8

🔑 **How Are Environmental Decisions Made?**
8.2.8, 8.NS.11

MY PLANET DIARY *for* Indiana

DISCOVERY

Living Fossil in Lake Michigan

Think about the creatures that lived at the time of the dinosaurs. Did you know the lake sturgeon found in Lake Michigan, was one of them? The largest fish in the Great Lakes, it can grow to nearly 3 meters long and weigh over 135 kilograms. Lake sturgeons look fierce with bony plates and pointy snouts, but they have no teeth!

Once plentiful in all of the Great Lakes, the lake sturgeon unfortunately is now a threatened species. Local scientists and citizens are joining together to bring back the population of this awesome fish.

Communicate Discuss the question with a partner. Then write your answer below.

Why do you think the lake sturgeon became a threatened species?

_____

_____

_____

▷ PLANET DIARY Go to **Planet Diary** to learn more about environmental issues.

Lab zone® Do the Inquiry Warm-Up
How Do You Decide?

Vocabulary

- natural resource
- nonpoint source
- pollution
- environmental science
- point source

Skills

- Reading: Relate Cause and Effect
- Inquiry: Draw Conclusions

What Are the Types of Environmental Issues?

Here is a riddle for you: what place is bigger than the United States and Mexico combined? This place is covered with ice more than two kilometers thick. It is a habitat for many animals and is a source of oil, coal, and iron. Stumped? The answer is Antarctica. Some people think of Antarctica as a useless, icy wasteland, but there are unique wildlife habitats in Antarctica. There are also valuable minerals beneath its thick ice.

What is the best use of Antarctica? Many people want access to its rich deposits of minerals and oil. Others worry that mining will harm its delicate ecosystems. Some people propose building hotels, parks, and ski resorts. Others think that Antarctica should remain undeveloped. Who should decide Antarctica's fate?

In 1998, 26 nations agreed to ban mining and oil exploration in Antarctica for at least 50 years. As resources become more scarce elsewhere in the world, the debate will surely continue.

Antarctica's future is just one environmental issue that people face today. 🔑 **Environmental issues fall into three general categories: population growth, resource use, and pollution.** Because these three types of issues are interconnected, they are very difficult to study and resolve.

Academic Standards for Science

8.2.6 Identify, explain, and discuss some effects human activities have on the biosphere, such as air, soil, light, noise and water pollution.

8.2.7 Recognize that some of Earth's resources are finite and describe how recycling, reducing consumption and the development of alternatives can reduce the rate of their depletion.

8.2.8 Explain that human activities, beginning with the earliest herding and agricultural activities, have drastically changed the environment and have affected the capacity of the environment to support native species. Explain current efforts to reduce and eliminate these impacts and encourage sustainability.

FIGURE 1

Arguing Over Antarctica
Some people want to leave Antarctica wild. Others want it developed.

✏ **Summarize** Fill in the boxes with points outlining each argument.

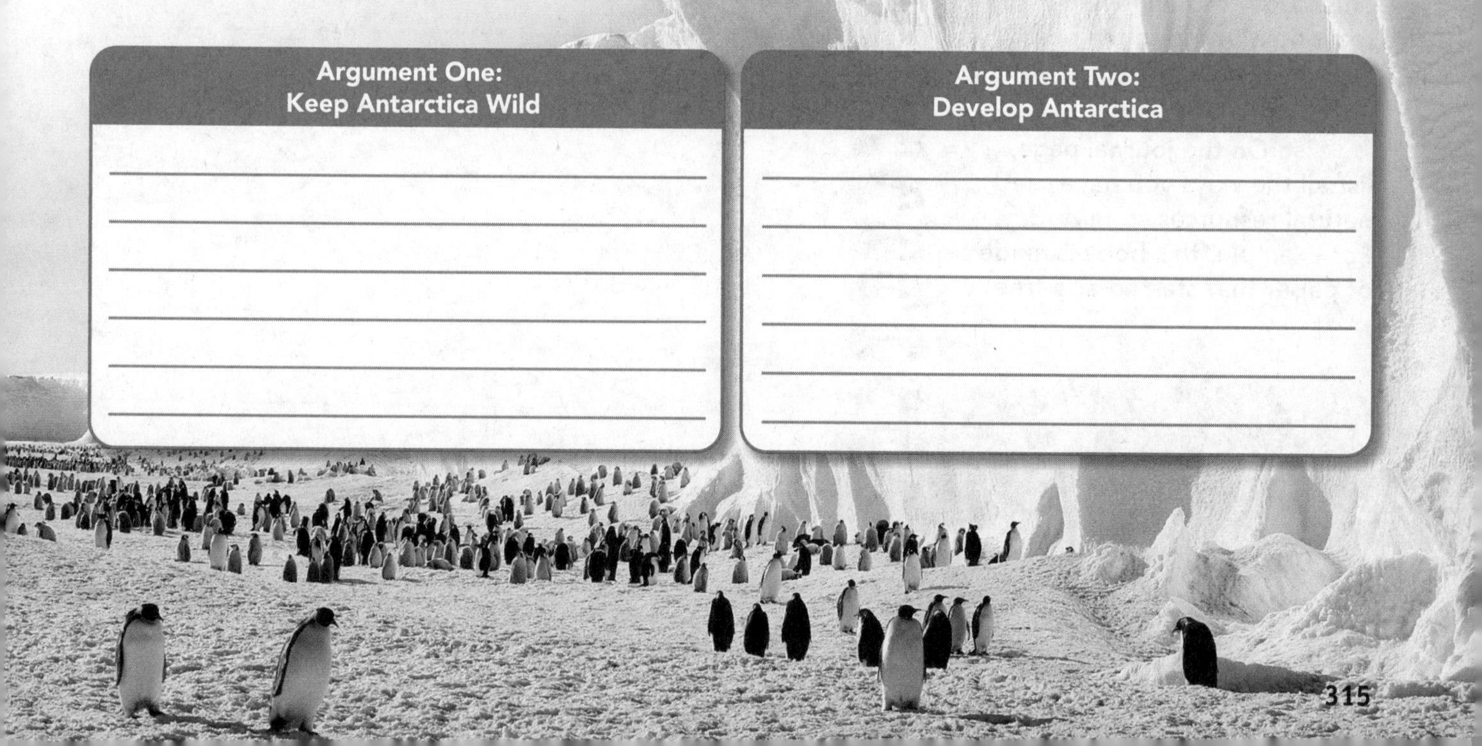

Argument One: Keep Antarctica Wild	Argument Two: Develop Antarctica
_____	_____
_____	_____
_____	_____
_____	_____
_____	_____
_____	_____

Vocabulary Identify Related Word Forms The word *conflict* means a disagreement between people, ideas, or interests. What causes conflicting opinions about natural resource use?

_____

_____

_____

_____

_____

_____

Population Growth

The human population grew very slowly until about A.D. 1650. Around that time, improvements in medicine, agriculture, and waste disposal led to people's living longer. The human population has been growing faster and faster since then.

When a population grows, the demand for resources also grows. Has your town or city ever experienced a water shortage? If so, you might have noticed that people have been asked to restrict their water use. This sometimes happens in areas with fast-growing populations. The water supplies in such areas were designed to serve fewer people than they now do, so shortages can occur during unusually dry weather.

Resource Use

Earth provides many materials people use throughout their lives. Anything that occurs naturally in the environment and is used by people is called a **natural resource.** Natural resources include trees, water, oil, coal, and other things. However, people do not use resources in the same way. In some areas of the world, people use a wide variety of resources. In other areas, people have little or no access to certain natural resources. For example, people in central Asia live too far away from ocean waters that provide fish and other resources. Conflict arises when a natural resource is scarce or used in a way that people feel is unfair.

FIGURE 2

Everyday Natural Resources

We use natural resources many times a day without even realizing it! A trip to the beach uses land, water, fuel, and many other resources.

✎ **List** On the journal page, list all the ways you have used natural resources so far today. For example, this book is made of paper that started as a tree.

My Resources Journal

Pollution Many environmental factors can contribute to less than ideal conditions on Earth for people or other organisms. The contamination of Earth's land, water, or air is called **pollution.** Pollution can be caused by wastes, chemicals, noise, heat, light, and other sources. Pollution can destroy wildlife and cause human health problems.

Pollution is usually related to population growth and resource use. As you probably know, the burning of gasoline releases pollutants into the air. With more cars on the road, more gasoline is used, so more pollutants are released into the air. As populations grow and more people need to be fed, more fertilizers and other chemicals may be used to produce that food. As these chemicals run off the land, they can pollute bodies of water.

Pollution sources can be grouped into two categories. A **point source** is a specific pollution source that can be identified. A pipe gushing polluted water into a river is an example of a point source. A nonpoint source of pollution is not as easy to identify. A **nonpoint source** is widely spread and cannot be tied to a specific origin. For example, the polluted air that can hang over urban areas comes from vehicles, factories, and other polluters. The pollution cannot be tied to any one car or factory.

✏️
➲ Relate Cause and Effect
Use what you have read about pollution so far to fill in the boxes below.

Some Causes of Pollution
_____
_____
_____
_____
_____

Some Effects of Pollution
_____
_____
_____
_____
_____

Lab zone® Do the Quick Lab _Environmental Issues._

🔑 **Assess Your Understanding**

1a. Define What is a natural resource?

_____
_____
_____
_____

8.2.7

b. Make Generalizations How is population growth related to resource use and pollution?

_____
_____
_____
_____

8.2.6, 8.2.8

got**it?**

○ **I get it!** Now I know that the types of environmental issues are_____

○ I need extra help with _____

Go to **MY SCIENCE COACH** online for help with this subject.   8.2.6, 8.2.7, 8.2.8

Academic Standards for Science

8.2.8 Explain that human activities, beginning with the earliest herding and agricultural activities, have drastically changed the environment and have affected the capacity of the environment to support native species. Explain current efforts to reduce and eliminate these impacts and encourage sustainability.

8.NS.11 Communicate findings using graphs, charts, maps and models through oral and written reports.

How Are Environmental Decisions Made?

Dealing with environmental issues means making decisions. Decisions can be made at many levels. Your decision to walk to your friend's house rather than ride in a car is made at a personal level. A town's decision about how to dispose of its trash is made at a local level. A decision about whether the United States should allow oil drilling in a wildlife refuge is made on a national level. Decisions about how to protect Earth's atmosphere are made on a global level. Your personal decisions have a small impact. But when the personal decisions of millions of people are combined, they have a huge impact on the environment.

Balancing Different Needs Lawmakers work with many groups to make environmental decisions. One such group is environmental scientists. **Environmental science** is the study of natural processes in the environment and how humans can affect them. Data provided by environmental scientists are only part of the decision-making process. Environmental decision making requires a balance between the needs of the environment and the needs of people. **To help balance the different opinions on an environmental issue, decision makers weigh the costs and benefits of a proposal for change before making a decision.**

apply it!

Suppose you are a member of a city planning board. A company wants to buy a piece of land outside the city and build a factory on it. When you go into work one day, you are met by protesters demanding that the land be turned into a wildlife park.

1 **Solve Problems** How should you decide what to do with the land?

_____

_____

2 [CHALLENGE] What are some ways you could find out people's opinions about the issue?

_____

_____

_____

Types of Costs and Benefits

Costs and benefits are often economic. Will a proposal provide jobs? Will it cost too much money? Costs and benefits are not measured only in terms of money. For example, suppose a state must decide whether to allow logging in a certain area. Removing trees changes the ecosystem, which is an ecological cost. However, the wood and jobs provided by the logging are economic benefits.

It is also important to consider the short-term and long-term costs and benefits of an environmental decision. A plan's short-term costs might be outweighed by its long-term benefits.

Costs of Offshore Drilling	Benefits of Offshore Drilling
• Setting up sites is expensive.	• Creates jobs
• Transporting the oil is risky and expensive.	• A larger oil supply lowers oil prices.
• Oil supply is limited and will not meet energy demands.	• Provides new oil supply to fight shortages
• Oil spills and leaks harm marine organisms and the environment.	• Reduces dependence on foreign oil

FIGURE 3 ························

> INTERACTIVE ART **Weighing Costs and Benefits**
Once you have identified the potential costs and benefits of a decision, you must analyze them. **Draw Conclusions Read the chart. Based on these costs and benefits, write a brief letter to your senator explaining your opinion either in favor of or against offshore drilling.**

8.NS.11

Lab zone Do the Quick Lab *Comparing Costs and Benefits.*

Assess Your Understanding

got it? ························

○ **I get it!** Now I know that environmental decisions are made by _____

_____

○ **I need extra help with** _____

Go to MY SCIENCE s COACH *online for help with this subject.*

8.2.8

319

Introduction to Natural Resources

UNLOCK THE BIG ?

🔑 **What Are Natural Resources?**
8.2.7, 8.2.8

🔑 **Why Are Natural Resources Important?**
8.2.7, 8.2.8, 8.NS.8

my planet diary

VOICES FROM HISTORY

"It was a spring without voices. On the mornings that had once throbbed with the dawn chorus of robins . . . there was now no sound; only silence lay over the fields and woods and marsh."

—Rachel Carson

In the twentieth century, farmers began to use chemicals to fight insects that killed their crops. People didn't realize that these chemicals were hurting other animals as well. Rachel Carson, born in 1907, was a scientist who wrote about sea life and nature. Carson began to worry about these chemicals. In 1962, she wrote the book *Silent Spring*. She explained what was happening to animals on land, in the air, and in the sea. Today, people are more careful to protect living things.

Write your answers below.

1. What dangers did Rachel Carson warn people about?

_____

_____

_____

2. Do you think the spring Carson wrote about would look different now that some harmful chemicals are banned? Why or why not?

_____

_____

_____

_____

_____

_____

> PLANET DIARY Go to **Planet Diary** to learn more about natural resources.

Lab zone® Do the Inquiry Warm-Up *Using Resources.*

Vocabulary

- renewable resource
- nonrenewable resource
- sustainable use
- ecological footprint
- conservation

Skills

↻ **Reading:** Relate Text and Visuals
△ **Inquiry:** Calculate

What Are Natural Resources?

Did you turn on a light or use an alarm clock today? Flush a toilet or take a shower? Ride in a car or bus? Eat some food? Use any paper—other than this page that you are reading right now? All of these things—and so much more—depend on Earth's resources.

Recall that anything that occurs naturally in the environment and is used by people is called a natural resource. **Natural resources include organisms, water, sunlight, minerals, and oil.**

Renewable Resources A **renewable resource** is either always available or is naturally replaced in a relatively short time. Some renewable resources, like wind and sunlight, are almost always available. Other renewable resources, like water and trees, are renewable only if they are replaced as fast as they are used.

Academic Standards for Science

8.2.7 Recognize that some of Earth's resources are finite and describe how recycling, reducing consumption and the development of alternatives can reduce the rate of their depletion.

8.2.8 Explain that human activities, beginning with the earliest herding and agricultural activities, have drastically changed the environment and have affected the capacity of the environment to support native species. Explain current efforts to reduce and eliminate these impacts and encourage sustainability.

Original trees on land

Trees after first harvest

Trees after replanting

↻ **Relate Text and Visuals** The trees in the first diagram are being harvested for wood. The landowner tells you the trees are a renewable resource. Based on the number of trees being harvested and replanted, is the landowner right? Why?

_____

_____

_____

_____

_____

_____

_____

_____

_____

_____

Nonrenewable Resources Over millions of years, natural processes changed the remains of organisms into the substances now called oil and coal. Today's world is powered by these fuels. Humans use these resources much faster than they are naturally replaced. Resources that are not replaced in a useful time frame are **nonrenewable resources.** Metals and minerals are also nonrenewable. Remember that some resources, such as trees, may be renewable or nonrenewable, depending on how quickly they are replaced.

FIGURE 1 ·····················
Categorizing Resources
Resources are grouped into two main categories: renewable and nonrenewable. Gold, shown above, is nonrenewable.

✎ **Summarize** Use what you have read to fill in the table comparing renewable and nonrenewable resources.

Renewable Resources	Nonrenewable Resources	Both
Replaced in a short time or always available	Not replaced in a useful time frame	Fits both natural resource categories
Examples:_____ _____ _____ _____ _____	Examples:_____ _____ _____ _____ _____	Examples:_____ _____ _____ _____ _____

Do the Quick Lab
Natural Resources.

🗝 Assess Your Understanding

1a. Define What is a renewable resource?

_____
_____
_____
_____

8.2.7, 8.2.8

b. Compare and Contrast Sunlight and trees are both natural resources. How are they different?

_____
_____
_____

8.2.7, 8.2.8

got it? ·······································

○ **I get it!** Now I know that natural resources include _____

_____

○ **I need extra help with** _____

Go to **MY SCIENCE** ⓢ **COACH** *online for help with this subject.*

8.2.7, 8.2.8

Why Are Natural Resources Important?

Humans cannot live without some natural resources, such as sunlight and fresh water. Others, such as metals, are necessary to sustain modern life. ⚿ **Humans depend on Earth's natural resources for survival and for development.**

How People Use Resources Around the world, people rely on natural resources for the same basic needs. Not all resources are equally available in all parts of the world. In some areas, there is a plentiful supply of clean fresh water. In other areas, water is scarce. In some places, pollution threatens the water supply.

Globally, fuels are used for cooking, heating, and power. Different fuels are common in different parts of the world. Coal is plentiful in some areas of the world and oil is plentiful in others. See **Figure 2.** In some areas, wood is the main fuel, not coal or oil.

Academic Standards for Science

8.2.7 Recognize that some of Earth's resources are finite.

8.2.8 Explain that human activities, have drastically changed the environment and have affected the capacity of the environment to support native species.

8.NS.8 Analyze data.

FIGURE 2 ·······················

Resources Around the World

People use natural resources in different ways around the world.

✎ **Describe** In the blank box below, draw or describe one way you use natural resources.

In Sierra Leone, entire communities get their drinking water from a main well.

In China, coal is delivered to homes by bicycle to be burned for heat.

In Iceland, most homes get hot water and heat from the energy of the hot, liquidlike rock under Earth's surface.

FIGURE 3 ··························

Ecological Footprint

Everything you do contributes to your ecological footprint, from how you travel, to the food you eat, to the home you live in. Ecological footprints vary among individuals and among nations, depending on how people live.

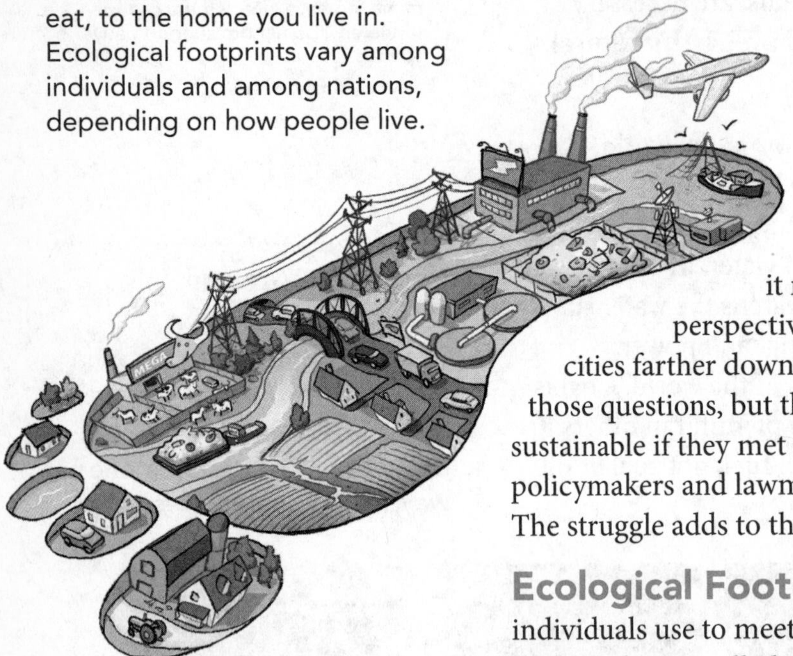

Sustainable Use How long a resource lasts depends on how people use it. **Sustainable use** of a resource means using it in ways that maintain the resource at a certain quality for a certain period of time. For example, a city may want to manage a river. Does the city want the water to be clean enough to drink or clean enough to swim in? Does the city want the water to be clean for fifty years, two hundred years, or indefinitely? The answers to these questions define what would be considered sustainable use of the river. However, it may not be sustainable from an ecological perspective even if it meets human needs. Other cities farther down the river may have different answers to those questions, but their plans could also be considered sustainable if they met their goals. Because of these differences, policymakers and lawmakers struggle to define sustainable use. The struggle adds to the challenge of regulating resources.

Ecological Footprint The amount of land and water that individuals use to meet their resource needs and absorb the waste they produce is called an **ecological footprint.** A high level of resource use means a larger footprint. A low level of resource use means a smaller footprint. Refer to **Figure 3.**

apply it!

The chart below gives the average ecological footprints for the people of several countries. It also gives the footprint for each country as a whole. Ecological footprints are measured in global hectares. A global hectare (gha) is a unit of area. It is adjusted to compare how much life different places on Earth can support.

Country	Average Ecological Footprint (gha/person)	Total Ecological Footprint (million gha)
United States	9.6	2,819
United Kingdom	5.6	333
Germany	4.5	375
Mexico	2.6	265
China	1.6	2,152

❶ **Interpret Tables** Which country has the largest ecological footprint? _____

❷ **Calculate** About how many times larger is the average ecological footprint per person in the United States than per person in Mexico?

_____

❸ CHALLENGE China has a smaller ecological footprint per person than the United Kingdom, but a much larger total ecological footprint. Why?

_____
_____
_____
_____
_____
_____

8.NS.8

Conservation While we cannot avoid using resources, there are better ways to use them. Resource **conservation** is the practice of managing the use of resources wisely so the resources last longer. Conservation cannot make resources last forever, but it can make resources last longer.

Governments and industries greatly affect resource conservation. Even individuals can make a difference. Walking, riding a bike, or riding the bus conserves fuel resources. People can also conserve resources when they turn off lights and unplug equipment that they are not using. Taking shorter showers saves water. When many people make small changes, the results can be huge.

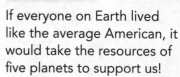

did you
know?

If everyone on Earth lived like the average American, it would take the resources of five planets to support us!

Resource Conservation at My School

FIGURE 4

Conserving Resources at School

Students like you can take action to conserve natural resources.

 List On the notebook paper, write ways your school can conserve resources.

Lab zone Do the Lab Investigation
Recycling Paper.

🔑 Assess Your Understanding

2a. Review Resources (are/are not) equally available around the world.

8.2.7, 8.2.8

b. Summarize What two factors determine whether or not a resource is being used sustainably?

_____

8.2.7, 8.2.8

c. Evaluate the Impact on Society As the human population continues to grow, how do you think it will affect the use of natural resources?

_____

_____

_____

8.2.7, 8.2.8

got it?

○ **I get it!** Now I know that natural resources are important because_____

_____

○ I need extra help with _____

_Go to_ **MY SCIENCE** 🅢 **COACH** _online for help with this subject._

8.2.7, 8.2.8

Human Population Growth

UNLOCK THE BIG ?

🔑 **How Has the Human Population Grown Over Time?**
8.2.8, 8.NS.1, 8.NS.8

🔑 **What Factors Allow the Human Population to Grow?**
8.2.8, 8.NS.8

my PLANET DiARY

DISASTERS

Dangerous Disease

In the mid-1300s, nearly one third of the European population died from a disease known as "black plague." Around 25 million people died, reducing the regional population from 75 million to 50 million. No treatment was available, and the disease spread. Today, the disease can be treated.

Plague is carried by rodents and rodent fleas. It can be passed to humans by a bite from a rodent flea or by handling infected rodents. The most recent outbreak in the United States occurred in 1925. Since then, only 10 to 15 cases have been reported in the United States each year. Around the world, 1,000 to 3,000 cases are reported annually.

Communicate Discuss the question with a group of classmates. Then write your answer below.

Is plague a concern today?

_____

_____

_____

_____

_____

_____

_____

 PLANET DIARY Go to **Planet Diary** to learn more about human population growth.

Lab zone® Do the Inquiry Warm-Up *Doubling Time.*

◀ Rodent flea

Vocabulary
- exponential growth

Skills
- ⤴ Reading: Identify the Main Idea
- ⚠ Inquiry: Predict

How Has the Human Population Grown Over Time?

Five hundred years ago, there were approximately 480 million people on Earth. Today, there are more than 6.7 billion people.

Exponential growth occurs when a population grows at an ever-increasing rate. In exponential growth, the larger a population gets, the faster it grows. 🔑 **Over time, the human population has grown exponentially.** Today, the human population continues to grow, but the growth rate is decreasing. Some experts predict that the human population will stop growing, and possibly decline in the future. Other experts strongly disagree.

Academic Standards for Science

8.2.8 Explain that human activities, beginning with the earliest herding and agricultural activities, have drastically changed the environment and have affected the capacity of the environment to support native species. Explain current efforts to reduce and eliminate these impacts and encourage sustainability.

8.NS.1 Make predictions and develop testable questions based on research and prior knowedge.

8.NS.8 Analyze data, using appropriate mathematical manipulation as required, and use it to identify patterns and make inferences based on these patterns.

do the math!

❶ Interpret Graphs What is the predicted world population for the year 2050?

_____

❷ ⚠ **Predict** How might this graph look in 500 years?

_____

_____

_____

_____

_____

8.NS.1, 8.NS.8

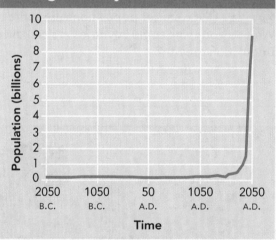

World Population Growth Through History

Population (billions) vs Time

Time axis: 2050 B.C., 1050 B.C., 50 A.D., 1050 A.D., 2050 A.D.

 Lab zone Do the Quick Lab *Human Population Growth.*

🔑 Assess Your Understanding

got it? ....

O **I get it!** Now I know that the human population _____

_____

O **I need extra help with** _____

Go to **my science** 🔊 **coach** *online for help with this subject.*

8.2.8

327

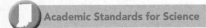
8.2.8 Explain that human activities, beginning with the earliest herding and agricultural activities, have drastically changed the environment and have affected the capacity of the environment to support native species. Explain current efforts to reduce and eliminate these impacts and encourage sustainability.

8.NS.8 Analyze data.

What Factors Allow the Human Population to Grow?

A population needs food and other resources to survive. Health and disease can determine life or death. Over time, people have affected these conditions of human survival. 🔑 **Advances in medicine and technology have improved human health and allowed for exponential human population growth.**

Birth and Death Rates A population's birthrate is the number of babies born each year per 1,000 people. The death rate of a population is the number of people who die each year per 1,000 people. The global population grows because more people are born each year than die each year. In most areas of the world today, people also live longer than ever before in human history.

apply it!

❶ **Interpret Tables** Circle the countries in the table with decreasing populations.

❷ CHALLENGE Larger populations use more resources. Why do you think some countries are still encouraging population growth?

_____

_____

8.NS.8

Country	Birthrate (per 1,000 people)	Death Rate (per 1,000 people)
Japan	7.9	9.2
United States	14.0	8.2
Italy	8.4	10.6
Argentina	18.1	7.4
Egypt	22.1	5.1

Medical Care and Technology

Today human survival has increased greatly because of advances in medical care and technology. Antibiotics, vaccines, sanitation, and improved nutrition have lowered death rates and increased birthrates. New technologies have allowed people to build cities, maintain clean water supplies, and produce and distribute more food than ever anticipated. As a result, today's population size is much larger than most experts in the past had predicted.

Population Growth and Natural Resources

As the human population grows, so does the demand for natural resources. If current trends continue, humans will be using resources twice as fast as Earth can replace them within this century. New technologies may allow for a larger human population than ever imagined, but Earth does not have an endless supply of resources. At some point, if it isn't already, the population size will be too large for Earth to support.

FIGURE 1 ....
> ART IN MOTION **Crowded City**
The photo across these pages is of Hong Kong, China. More than seven million people live in this city of only about 1,100 square kilometers. That's more than 6,000 people per square kilometer!

Healthcare technology	↑	Population	↑
Death rate	↑	Population	
Food production and distribution	↑	Population	
Population	↑	Natural resources	
Birthrate	↑	Population	

✎ **Identify the Main Idea**
Draw arrows in the chart to show the effect of each condition on the human population or natural resources. For example, as healthcare technology improves, the population will increase.

Lab zone ® Do the Quick Lab *Comparing Populations.*

Assess Your Understanding

got it? ....

○ **I get it!** Now I know that the human population has grown exponentially because of _____

_____

_____

○ **I need extra help with** _____

Go to **my science coach** online for help with this subject.

8.2.8

Forests and Fisheries

UNLOCK THE BIG ?

🔑 **How Can Forests Be Managed as Renewable Resources?**
8.2.7, 8.2.8, 8.NS.8

🔑 **How Can Fisheries Be Managed for a Sustainable Yield?**
8.2.7, 8.2.8

my planet diary

What happened to all the trees?

We get all kinds of things from forests, from food to oxygen to medicine to beautiful places for exploring. The world's forests are disappearing at an alarming rate. We lose a piece of forest the size of a soccer field every two seconds. In a year, that's about an area as big as the state of Illinois! Many people are trying to save the forests. Some countries have passed laws to stop farmers, miners, loggers, and ranchers from cutting down the forests. And some organizations are replanting trees.

SCIENCE STATS

Communicate Discuss the questions with a group of classmates. Then write your answers below.

1. Why should people care about losing trees?

_____

_____

_____

_____

_____

2. How could your class raise awareness about the importance of trees in your community?

_____

_____

_____

_____

> **PLANET DIARY** Go to **Planet Diary** to learn more about forests and fisheries.

Lab zone® Do the Inquiry Warm-Up
What Happened to the Tuna?

Vocabulary

- clear-cutting • selective cutting • sustainable yield
- fishery • aquaculture

Skills

🔊 Reading: Summarize

△ Inquiry: Communicate

How Can Forests Be Managed as Renewable Resources?

Forests contain many valuable resources. Many products are made from the fruits, seeds, and other parts of forest plants. Some of these products, such as maple syrup, rubber, and nuts, come from living trees. Other products, such as lumber and wood pulp for making paper, require cutting trees down. Coniferous trees, including pine and spruce, are used for construction and for making paper. Hardwoods, such as oak, cherry, and maple, are used for furniture because of their strength and beauty. Some products made from trees are shown in **Figure 1.**

Trees and other plants produce oxygen that organisms need to survive. They also absorb carbon dioxide and many pollutants from the air. Trees help prevent flooding and control soil erosion. Their roots absorb rainwater and hold the soil together.

There are about 300 million hectares of forests in the United States. That's nearly a third of the nation's area! Many forests are located on public land. Others are owned by individuals or by private timber and paper companies. Forest industries in the United States provide jobs for more than 1.5 million people.

🗝 **Because new trees can be planted to replace trees that are cut down, forests can be renewable resources.** The United States Forest Service and environmental organizations work with forestry companies to conserve forest resources. They try to develop logging methods that maintain forests as renewable resources.

 Academic Standards for Science

8.2.7 Recognize that some of Earth's resources are finite and describe how recycling, reducing consumption and the development of alternatives can reduce the rate of their depletion.

8.2.8 Explain that human activities have drastically changed the environment and have affected its capacity to support native species.

8.NS.8 Analyze data.

FIGURE 1 ································

Forest Products

Many common products have at least one thing in them that came from trees. The soles on the shoes below came from the sap of the rubber tree.

✎ **Identify** Besides the shoes, circle the three items that were made from tree products. Pick one of the items and explain why you think it contains tree products.

_____

_____

_____

331

Logging Methods

There are two major methods of logging: clear-cutting and selective cutting. **Clear-cutting** is the process of cutting down all the trees in an area at once. Cutting down only some trees in a forest and leaving a mix of tree sizes and species behind is called **selective cutting.** See **Figure 2.**

Each logging method has advantages and disadvantages. Clear-cutting is usually quicker and cheaper than selective cutting. It may also be safer for the loggers. In selective cutting, the loggers must move the heavy equipment and logs around the remaining trees in the forest. But selective cutting is usually less damaging to the forest environment than clear-cutting. When an area of forest is clear-cut, the ecosystem changes. After clear-cutting, the soil is exposed to wind and rain. Without the protection of the trees, the soil is more easily blown or washed away. Soil washed into streams may harm the fish and other organisms that live there. However, clear-cutting can provide habitats for species such as rabbits and some birds.

FIGURE 2 ·······························

▶ INTERACTIVE ART **Tree Harvest**
Clear-cutting and selective cutting are two methods of tree harvesting.

✎ **Relate Text and Visuals**
Based on what you have read, label the original forest, the clear-cut forest, and the selectively cut forest.

8.NS.8

Replanted Growth

Diverse Growth

Sustainable Forestry Forests can be managed to provide a sustainable yield. A **sustainable yield** is an amount of a renewable resource such as trees that can be harvested regularly without reducing the future supply. Sustainable forestry works sort of like a book swap: as long as you donate a book each time you borrow one, the total supply of books does not change. Planting a tree to replace one that was cut down is like donating a book to replace a borrowed one.

In sustainable forestry, after trees are harvested, young trees are planted. Trees must be planted frequently enough to keep a constant supply. Different species grow at different rates. Forests containing faster-growing trees, such as pines, can be harvested and replanted every 20 to 30 years. On the other hand, some forests containing hardwood trees, such as hickory, oak, and cherry, may be harvested only every 40 to 100 years. One sustainable approach is to log small patches of forest. This way, different sections of forest can be harvested every year.

Certified Wood

The Forest Stewardship Council is an international organization dedicated to sustainable forest management. This organization oversees certification of forests that are well managed and that provide good working conditions for their employees. Once a forest is certified, its wood may carry a "well-managed" label. This label allows businesses and individuals to select wood from forests that are managed for sustainable yields.

apply it!

You are an advertising writer for a company that makes products from sustainable wood.

❶ **Communicate** Write a slogan to help sell the products.

_____

_____

_____

_____

❷ Design a company logo.

Lab zone ® Do the Quick Lab *Shelterwood Cutting.*

⚷ Assess Your Understanding

1a. Define What is a sustainable yield of a natural resource like trees?

_____

_____

_____

_____

8.2.7, 8.2.8

b. CHALLENGE Should the government buy only certified wood for construction projects? Why?

_____

_____

_____

_____

8.2.7, 8.2.8

got it? ···

○ **I get it!** Now I know that forests can be managed as renewable resources by _____

_____

○ I need extra help with _____

Go to MY SCIENCE ⓢ COACH *online for help with this subject.*

8.2.7, 8.2.8

Academic Standards for Science

8.2.7 Recognize that some of Earth's resources are finite and describe how recycling, reducing consumption and the development of alternatives can reduce the rate of their depletion.

8.2.8 Explain that human activities, beginning with the earliest herding and agricultural activities, have drastically changed the environment and have affected the capacity of the environment to support native species. Explain current efforts to reduce and eliminate these impacts and encourage sustainability.

Summarize Explain the effect of large-scale fishing (as in the scene below) on major fish populations.

_____

_____

_____

_____

_____

_____

_____

_____

How Can Fisheries Be Managed for a Sustainable Yield?

Fish are an important global food resource. An area with a large population of valuable ocean organisms is called a **fishery.**

Until recently, fisheries seemed to have unlimited resources. The waters held such huge schools of fish, and fish reproduce in incredible numbers. A single codfish can lay as many as nine million eggs in one year! But people have discovered that this resource has limits. After many years of big catches, the number of sardines off the California coast suddenly declined. The same thing happened to the huge schools of cod off the New England coast. What caused these changes?

The fish were caught faster than they could breed, so the population decreased. This situation is known as overfishing. Scientists estimate that 70 percent of the world's major fisheries have been overfished. But if fish populations recover, a sustainable yield can again be harvested. ⬤ **Managing fisheries for a sustainable yield includes strategies such as setting fishing limits, changing fishing methods, developing aquaculture techniques, and finding new resources.**

Fishing Limits Laws can ban the fishing of certain species. Laws can also limit the number or size of fish that can be caught. These laws ensure that all of the largest adult fish aren't caught and that young fish survive long enough to reproduce. If a fishery has been severely overfished, however, the government may ban fishing completely until the populations recover.

Fishing Methods Today many fishing crews use nets with a larger mesh size that allow small, young fish to escape. Many other fishing practices are also regulated by laws. Some harmful fishing methods have been outlawed. These methods include poisoning fish with cyanide and stunning them by exploding dynamite under water. These techniques harm all the fish in an area rather than targeting certain fish.

Aquaculture The practice of raising fish and other water-dwelling organisms for food is called **aquaculture.** The fish may be raised in artificial ponds or bays. Salmon, catfish, and shrimp are farmed in this way in the United States.

However, aquaculture is not a perfect solution. The artificial ponds and bays often replace natural habitats such as salt marshes. Maintaining the farms costs money, and the farms can cause pollution and spread diseases into wild fish populations.

New Resources Today about 9,000 different fish species are harvested for food. More than half the animal protein eaten by people throughout the world comes from fish. One way to help feed a growing human population is to fish for new species. Scientists and chefs are working together to introduce people to deep-water species such as monkfish and tile fish, as well as easy-to-farm freshwater fish such as tilapia.

FIGURE 3 ·······················

Aquaculture
Fish like tilapia, shown below, can be farmed.

✎ **Analyze Costs and Benefits** Fill in the boxes to explain the costs and benefits of aquaculture.

Benefits of Aquaculture

Costs of Aquaculture

Lab zone®   Do the Quick Lab
Managing Fisheries.

🔑 **Assess Your Understanding**

got it? ···

○ **I get it!** Now I know managing fisheries for a sustainable yield includes _____

_____

○ **I need extra help with** _____

Go to MY SCIENCE ⑤ COACH *online for help with this subject.*   8.2.7, 8.2.8

335

Biodiversity

UNLOCK
THE BIG

🔑 **What Is Biodiversity's Value?**
8.2.8, 8.NS.8

🔑 **What Factors Affect Biodiversity?**
8.2.8, 8.NS.8

🔑 **How Do Humans Affect Biodiversity?**
8.2.6, 8.2.8, 8.NS.8, 8.DP.10

my planet diary

BLOG

Posted by: Max

Location: Hagerstown, Maryland

I went to summer camp to learn about wildlife and how to protect it. One of the activities that I liked the most was making "bat boxes." These are wooden homes for brown bats, which often need places to nest. Making these houses is important, because without brown bats, there would be too many mosquitoes. I hope the bats like their new homes as much as I loved making them.

Communicate Discuss the question with a group of classmates. Then write your answers below.

How do you think helping the bats in an area helps other species nearby?

_____

_____

_____

_____

_____

_____

_____

▶ PLANET DIARY Go to **Planet Diary** to learn more about biodiversity.

 Do the Inquiry Warm-Up
How Much Variety Is There?

What Is Biodiversity's Value?

Academic Standards for Science

8.2.8 Explain that human activities, have drastically changed the environment and have affected its capacity to support native species. Explain current efforts to reduce and eliminate these impacts and encourage sustainability.

8.NS.8 Analyze data.

No one knows exactly how many species live on Earth. As you can see in **Figure 1,** scientists have identified more than 1.6 million species so far. The number of different species in an area is called the area's **biodiversity.** It is difficult to estimate the total biodiversity on Earth because many areas have not been thoroughly studied.

Vocabulary

- biodiversity • keystone species • gene • extinction
- endangered species • threatened species
- habitat destruction • habitat fragmentation
- poaching • captive breeding

Skills

↻ Reading: Compare and Contrast

△ Inquiry: Infer

There are many reasons why preserving biodiversity is important. One reason to preserve biodiversity is that wild organisms and ecosystems are a source of beauty and recreation. 🔑 **In addition, biodiversity has both economic value and ecological value within an ecosystem.**

Economic Value Many plants, animals, and other organisms are economically valuable for humans. These organisms provide people with food and supply raw materials for clothing, medicine, and other products. No one knows how many other useful species have not yet been identified. Ecosystems are economically valuable, too. Many companies now run wildlife tours to rain forests, savannas, mountains, and other places. This ecosystem tourism, or ecotourism, is an important source of jobs and money for such nations as Brazil, Costa Rica, and Kenya.

Ecological Value All the species in an ecosystem are connected to one another. Species may depend on each other for food and shelter. A change that affects one species can affect all the others.

Some species play a particularly important role in their ecosystems. A **keystone species** is a species that influences the survival of many other species in an ecosystem. Sea otters, as shown in **Figure 2,** are one example of a keystone species.

FIGURE 1 ·····························

Species Diversity

There are many more species of insects than plant or other animal species on Earth!

✎ **Calculate** What percentage of species shown on the pie graph do insects represent? Round your answer to the nearest tenth.

8.NS.8

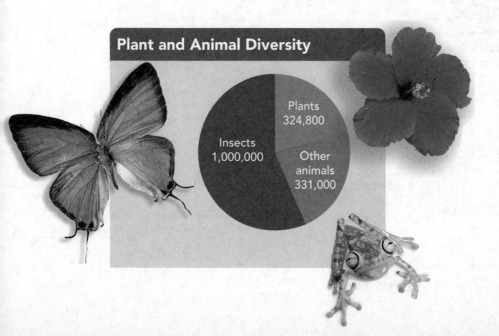

Plant and Animal Diversity

Plants
324,800

Insects
1,000,000

Other animals
331,000

FIGURE 2 ·······························

Keystone Otters

Sea otters are a keystone species in the kelp forest ecosystem.

✎ **Describe** Read the comic. In the empty panel, draw or explain what happened to the kelp forest when the otters returned. Write a caption for your panel. **8.NS.8**

The sea otter is a keystone species in a kelp forest ecosystem.

In the 1800s, many otters were killed for their fur.

Without otters preying on them, the population of kelp-eating sea urchins exploded, destroying kelp forests.

Under new laws that banned the hunting of sea otters, the sea otter population grew again.

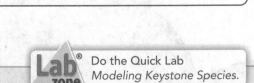

Lab zone ® Do the Quick Lab *Modeling Keystone Species.*

🔑 Assess Your Understanding

got it? ···

○ **I get it!** Now I know that biodiversity has _____

_____

○ **I need extra help with** _____

Go to **MY SCIENCE** ⑤ **COACH** *online for help with this subject.*

What Factors Affect Biodiversity?

Biodiversity varies from place to place on Earth. **Factors that affect biodiversity in an ecosystem include climate, area, niche diversity, genetic diversity, and extinction.**

Climate The tropical rain forests of Latin America, southeast Asia, and central Africa are the most diverse ecosystems in the world. The reason for the great biodiversity in the tropics is not fully understood. Many scientists hypothesize that it has to do with climate. For example, tropical rain forests have fairly constant temperatures and large amounts of rainfall throughout the year. Many plants grow year-round. This continuous growing season means that food is always available for other organisms.

Area See **Figure 3.** Within an ecosystem, a large area will usually contain more species than a small area. For example, you would usually find more species in a 100-square-meter area than in a 10-square-meter area.

Academic Standards for Science

8.2.8 Explain that human activities, beginning with the earliest herding and agricultural activities, have drastically changed the environment and have affected the capacity of the environment to support native species. Explain current efforts to reduce and eliminate these impacts and encourage sustainability.

8.NS.8 Analyze data, using appropriate mathematical manipulation as required, and use it to identify patterns and make inferences based on these patterns.

did you know?

Rain forests cover only about seven percent of the Earth's land surface. But they contain more than half of the world's species, including the chimpanzee!

FIGURE 3

Park Size

A park manager has received three park plans. The dark green area represents the park.

✎ **Complete each task.**

1. **Identify** Circle the plan the manager should choose to support the most biodiversity.

2. **Calculate** Suppose that 15 square meters of the park could support seven species of large mammals. About how many species could the park you circled support?

10 m / 10 m

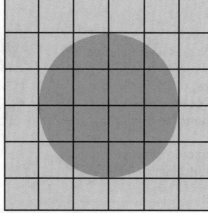

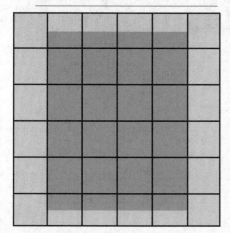

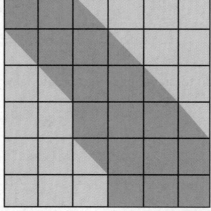

Niche Diversity Coral reefs are the second most diverse ecosystems in the world. Found only in shallow, warm waters, coral reefs are often called the rain forests of the sea. A coral reef supports many different niches. Recall that a niche is the role of an organism in its habitat, or how it makes its living. A coral reef enables a greater number of species to live in it than a more uniform habitat, such as a flat sandbar, does.

Genetic Diversity Diversity is very important within a species. The greatest genetic diversity exists among species of unicellular organisms. Organisms in a healthy population have diverse traits such as color and size. **Genes** are located within cells and carry the hereditary information that determines an organism's traits. Organisms inherit genes from their parents.

The organisms in one species share many genes. But each organism also has some genes that differ from those of other individuals. Both the shared genes and the genes that differ among individuals make up the total gene pool of that species. Species that lack a diverse gene pool are less able to adapt to and survive changes in the environment.

apply it!

New potato plants are created from pieces of the parent plant. So a potato crop has the same genetic makeup as the parent plant. In 1845, Ireland was struck by a potato famine. A rot-causing fungus destroyed potato crops, which were an important part of the Irish diet. Many people died of starvation, and many more left the country to find food.

1 Apply Concepts How did a potato crop without a variety of different genes lead to the Irish potato famine of 1845?

_____

_____

_____

2 CHALLENGE What could farmers do to prevent another potato famine?

_____

_____

_____

_____

Extinction of Species The disappearance of all members of a species from Earth is called **extinction.** Extinction is a natural process that occurs when organisms do not adapt to changes in their environment. In the last few centuries, the number of species becoming extinct has increased dramatically. Once a population drops below a certain level, the species may not recover. People have directly caused the extinction of many species through habitat destruction, hunting, or other actions.

Species in danger of becoming extinct in the near future are called **endangered species.** Species that could become endangered in the near future are called **threatened species.** Endangered and threatened species are found on every continent and in every ocean.

Green sea turtle ▲

FIGURE 4 ···
Endangered Species
Large animals, like the green sea turtle, are the most publicized endangered species. Did you know insects and plants can also be endangered? ✎ **Infer Why do you think some endangered species get more attention than others?**

_____

_____

_____

_____

_____

Blackburn's ▲
sphinx moth

Hawaiian alula ▲

Do the Quick Lab
Grocery Gene Pool.

⚷ Assess Your Understanding

1a. Review A (smaller/larger) area will contain more species than a (smaller/larger) area. **8.2.8**

b. Explain How is biodiversity related to niches?

_____

_____

_____

8.2.8

c. ↻ **Compare and Contrast** What is the difference between an endangered species and a threatened species?

_____

_____

_____

8.2.8

got**it?** ···

○ **I get it!** Now I know that the factors that affect biodiversity include _____

_____

○ **I need extra help with** _____

Go to **MY SCIENCE** 💬 **COACH** *online for help with this subject.*

8.2.8

How Do Humans Affect Biodiversity?

Humans interact with their surroundings every day. The many choices people make impact the environment and affect species. 🔑 **Biodiversity can be negatively or positively affected by the actions of humans.**

Damaging Biodiversity

A natural event, such as a hurricane, can damage an ecosystem, wiping out populations or even entire species. Human activities can also threaten biodiversity and cause extinction. These activities include habitat destruction, poaching, pollution, and the introduction of exotic species.

Habitat Destruction The major cause of extinction is **habitat destruction,** the loss of a natural habitat. Clearing forests or filling in wetlands changes those ecosystems. Breaking larger habitats into smaller, isolated pieces, or fragments, is called **habitat fragmentation.** See **Figure 5.** Some species may not survive such changes to their habitats.

Poaching The illegal killing or removal of wildlife from their habitats is called **poaching.** Some endangered species are valuable to poachers. Animals can be sold as pets or used to make jewelry, coats, belts, or shoes. Plants can be sold as houseplants or used to make medicines.

Pollution Some species are endangered because of pollution. Pollution may reach animals through the water they drink, the air they breathe, or the food they eat. Pollutants may kill or weaken organisms or cause birth defects.

Exotic Species Introducing exotic species into an ecosystem can threaten biodiversity. Exotic species can outcompete and damage native species. The gypsy moth was introduced into the United States in 1869 to increase silk production. Gypsy moth larvae have eaten the leaves off of millions of acres of trees in the northeastern United States.

FIGURE 5 ·

Habitat Fragmentation

Breaking habitats into pieces can have negative effects on the species that live there.

✏️ **Interpret Diagrams** In the first diagram below, a road divides a habitat in two. On the second diagram, redraw the road so it divides the habitat's resources equally. **8.NS.8, 8.DP.10**

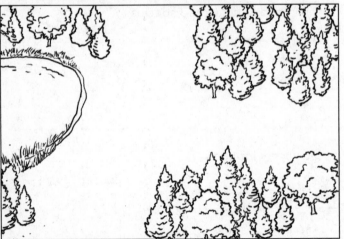

Protecting Biodiversity

Some people who preserve biodiversity focus on protecting individual endangered species. Others try to protect entire ecosystems. Three methods of protecting biodiversity are captive breeding, laws and treaties, and habitat preservation.

Captive Breeding

Captive breeding is the mating of animals in zoos or on wildlife preserves. Scientists care for the young, and then release them into the wild. Much of the sandhill crane habitat in the United States has been destroyed. To help the population, some cranes have been taken into captivity. The young are raised and trained by volunteers to learn the correct behaviors, such as knowing how and where to migrate. They are then released into the wild.

Compare and Contrast
The photos on top show young sandhill cranes being raised by their parents. The photos on the bottom show humans copying this process to increase the crane population. What is a possible disadvantage of the human approach?

_____

_____

_____

_____

_____

Same Land, Different Use

EXPLORE THE BIG ?

How do people use Earth's resources?

FIGURE 6 ··························

> VIRTUAL LAB The cattle ranch in this photo is in Wyoming. You may think the photo on the opposite page is of a completely different place, but it was also taken in Wyoming, in Yellowstone National Park. As you can see, the same land resources can be used in two very different ways to meet very different needs.

✎ **Make Judgments** Write one benefit and one cost of each of the land uses in the boxes. Then answer the question.

Ranch

Benefit _____

_____

Cost _____

_____

Laws and Treaties In the United States, the Endangered Species Act prohibits trade of products made from threatened or endangered species. This law also requires the development of plans to save endangered species. The Convention on International Trade in Endangered Species is an international treaty that lists more than 800 threatened and endangered species that cannot be traded for profit or other reasons anywhere in the world.

Habitat Preservation The most effective way to preserve biodiversity is to protect whole ecosystems. Protecting whole ecosystems saves endangered species, the species they depend upon, and those that depend upon them. Many countries have set aside wildlife habitats as parks and refuges. Today, there are about 7,000 nature parks, preserves, and refuges in the world.

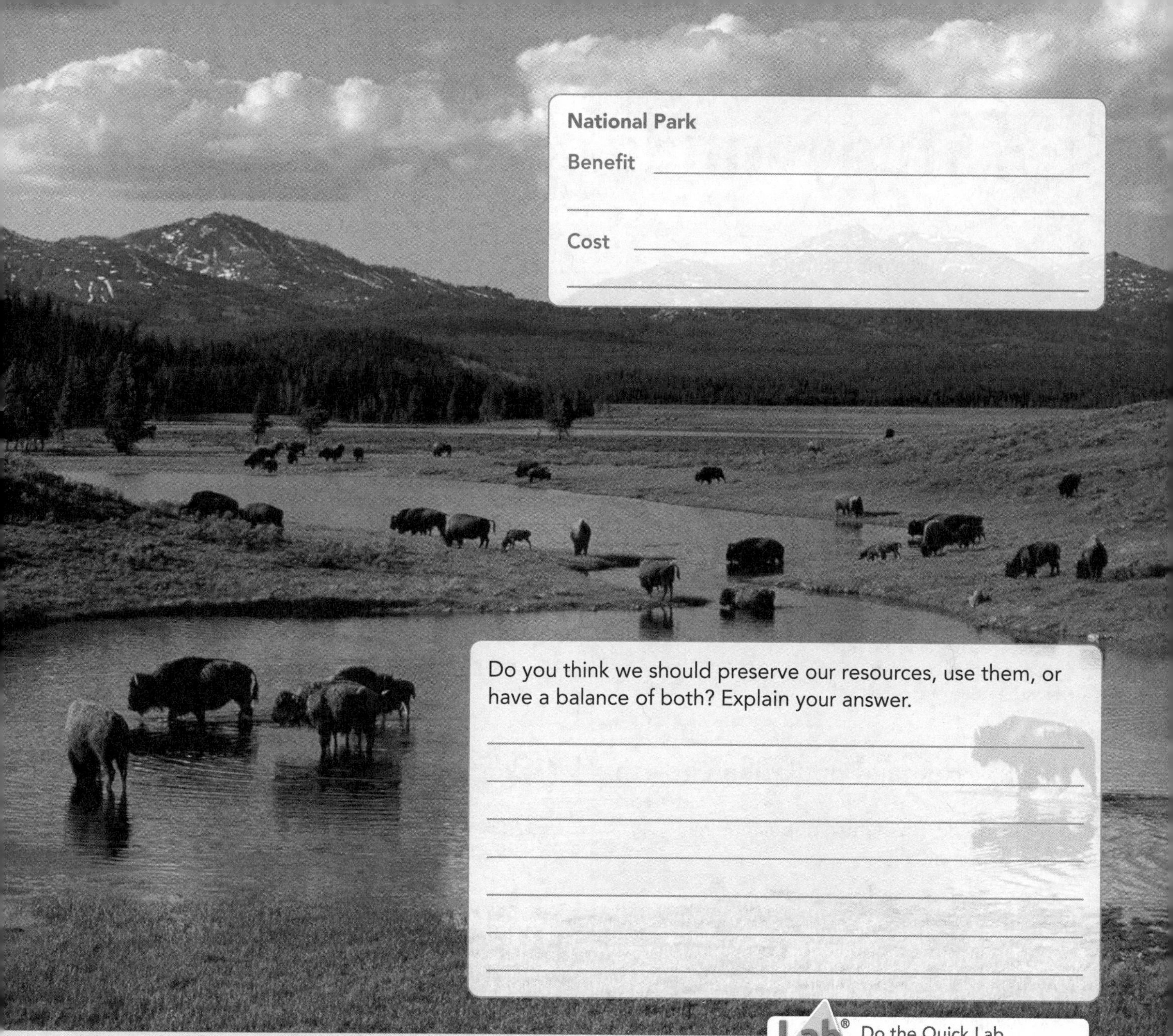

National Park

Benefit _____

_____

Cost _____

_____

Do you think we should preserve our resources, use them, or have a balance of both? Explain your answer.

_____
_____
_____
_____
_____
_____

Lab zone Do the Quick Lab
Humans and Biodiversity.

Assess Your Understanding

2a. Define What is poaching?

_____
_____
_____
_____

8.2.6, 8.2.8

b. **ANSWER THE BIG ?** How do people use Earth's resources?

_____
_____
_____
_____

8.2.6, 8.2.8

got it?

○ **I get it!** Now I know that humans affect biodiversity_____

○ I need extra help with _____

Go to **MY SCIENCE COACH** *online for help with this subject.*

8.2.6, 8.2.8

345

8 Study Guide

People use both _____ and nonrenewable resources. Reducing

resource use through _____ can help make resources last longer.

LESSON 1 Introduction to Environmental Issues

8.2.6, 8.2.7, 8.2.8, 8.NS.11

🔑 Environmental issues fall into three main categories: resource use, population growth, and pollution.

🔑 To balance opinions, decision makers weigh the costs and benefits of a proposal.

Vocabulary
- natural resource • pollution
- point source • nonpoint source
- environmental science

LESSON 2 Introduction to Natural Resources

8.2.7, 8.2.8, 8.NS.8

🔑 Natural resources include organisms, water, sunlight, minerals, and oil.

🔑 Humans depend on Earth's natural resources for survival and for development.

Vocabulary
- renewable resource • nonrenewable resource
- sustainable use • ecological footprint
- conservation

LESSON 3 Human Population Growth

8.2.8, 8.NS.1, 8.NS.8

🔑 Over time, the human population has grown exponentially.

🔑 Advances in medicine and technology have improved human health and allowed for exponential human population growth.

Vocabulary
- exponential growth

LESSON 4 Forests and Fisheries

8.2.7, 8.2.8, 8.NS.8

🔑 Forests can be renewable resources if new trees are planted to replace trees that are cut.

🔑 Managing fisheries for a sustainable yield includes setting fishing limits, changing fishing methods, developing aquaculture techniques, and finding new resources.

Vocabulary
- clear-cutting • selective cutting • sustainable yield
- fishery • aquaculture

LESSON 5 Biodiversity

8.2.6, 8.2.8, 8.NS.8, 8.DP.10

🔑 Biodiversity has both economic value and ecological value within an ecosystem.

🔑 Factors that affect biodiversity include climate, area, niche diversity, genetic diversity, and extinction.

🔑 Biodiversity can be negatively or positively affected by the actions of humans.

Vocabulary
- biodiversity • keystone species • gene • extinction
- endangered species • threatened species • habitat destruction
- habitat fragmentation • poaching • captive breeding

Review and Assessment

LESSON 1 Introduction to Environmental Issues

1. Coal and sunlight are examples of

   a. environmental sciences.

   b. pollution.

   c. natural resources.

   d. extinction.

8.2.7

2. _____ can take many forms, including chemical wastes, noise, heat, and light.

8.2.6

3. **Relate Cause and Effect** Fill in the blank circles with the other main categories of environmental issues. How are they related?

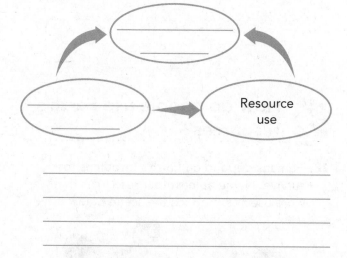

Resource use

_____

_____

_____

_____

_____

_____

8.2.6, 8.2.8

4. **Write About It** Suppose your town is considering building a new coal-burning power plant. The benefits of the new facility include providing power and jobs for the town's growing population. What are some of the costs of this project? What do you think your town should do?

8.2.6, 8.2.7, 8.2.8

LESSON 2 Introduction to Natural Resources

5. Which of the following actions can increase an individual's ecological footprint?

   a. riding a bicycle more often

   b. reducing the use of plastic bags

   c. reusing materials before disposal

   d. turning on the air conditioner

8.2.7

6. Like oil, metals are an example of

_____

8.2.7

7. **Apply Concepts** When is water a renewable resource? When is it nonrenewable?

_____

_____

_____

_____

8.2.7, 8.2.8

LESSON 3 Human Population Growth

8. Under which of the following conditions would the global population decrease?

   a. birthrate > death rate

   b. birthrate = death rate

   c. death rate > birthrate

   d. death rate = birthrate

8.2.8

9. _____, or growth at an ever-increasing rate, describes the pattern of human population growth.

8.2.8

10. **Infer** How would continued population growth affect Earth's natural resources?

_____

_____

_____

_____

8.2.8

LESSON 4 **Forests and Fisheries**

11. The practice of raising fish for food is called

    a. poaching.

    b. overfishing.

    c. captive breeding.

    d. aquaculture.

                                    8.2.8

12. A _____ is the amount of a resource that can be harvested regularly without reducing the future supply.

                                8.2.7, 8.2.8

13. Compare and Contrast How does selective cutting compare with clear-cutting?

_____

_____

_____

_____

_____

_____

                                8.2.7, 8.2.8

14. Make Judgments Do you think the government should encourage more aquaculture, the use of new fish species, or both? Explain your answer.

_____

_____

_____

_____

_____

_____

_____

_____

_____

                                8.2.7, 8.2.8

LESSON 5 **Biodiversity**

15. The most effective way to preserve biodiversity is through

    a. captive breeding.

    b. habitat destruction.

    c. habitat preservation.

    d. habitat fragmentation.

                                8.2.6, 8.2.8

16. _____ occurs when all members of a species disappear from Earth.

                                8.2.6, 8.2.8

17. Predict How could the extinction of a species today affect your life in 20 years?

_____

_____

_____

_____

_____

                                8.2.8, 8.NS.1

 APPLY THE BIG ?

How do people use Earth's resources?

18. Humans depend on Earth's resources to survive. Name at least four resources that were used to produce the scene below.

_____

_____

_____

_____

_____

                                8.2.6, 8.2.8

Indiana ISTEP+ Practice

Multiple Choice

Circle the letter of the best answer.

1. Study the table below. Then choose the list that correctly ranks each country's ecological footprint per person, from smallest to largest.

Country	Average Ecological Footprint (gha/person)
United States	9.6
Germany	4.5
Mexico	2.6
China	1.6

A. China, Germany, Mexico, United States
B. United States, Mexico, Germany, China
C. China, Mexico, Germany, United States
D. Mexico, China, United States, Germany

8.2.6

2. Which words best describe the growth patterns of the human population?

A. decreasing growth
B. exponential growth
C. extended growth
D. incremental growth

8.2.6

3. In some areas, foresters plant one tree for every tree they cut. This activity is an example of

A. a sustainable approach to a renewable resource.
B. an unsustainable approach to a renewable resource.
C. a sustainable approach to a nonrenewable resource.
D. an unsustainable approach to a nonrenewable resource.

8.2.7

4. Which of the following terms describes a species that is in danger of becoming extinct in the near future?

A. captive species
B. keystone species
C. threatened species
D. endangered species

8.2.8

Constructed Response

Write your answer to Question 5 on the lines below.

5. How do conservation practices affect natural resources?

_____

_____

_____

8.2.7

Extended Reponse

Use the chart below to help you answer Question 6. Write your answer on a separate sheet of paper.

Some Costs	Some Benefits
• Changes ecosystem	• Provides jobs
• Makes forest less attractive	• Provides wood

6. A city is considering whether or not to allow logging in a large forest nearby. Based on the costs and benefits of this decision, what do you think the city should do? Give at least three reasons to support your answer.

8.2.7, 8.2.8, 8.NS.11

CAN YOU HEAR ME NOW?

CRASH! BANG! BEEP BEEP! In cities all across the world, noise pollution is part of everyday life. Noise pollution is loud, distracting sound.

There are many different types of noise pollution. Some of the most common are residential noise, road traffic noise, and air traffic noise. Residential noise pollution occurs in places where people live. It includes noisy neighbors, high-pitched car alarms, and power tools from renovations. Road traffic noise pollution is common at busy intersections or on highways. Helicopters and airplanes cause air traffic noise pollution. Air traffic noise is especially troublesome for people who live or work near airports.

Too much noise can cause hearing loss, lack of sleep, and increased stress. Studies show that students who go to school in areas that have high levels of noise pollution have lower test scores. The noise affects students' ability to concentrate.

More than 100 million Americans are regularly exposed to noise levels higher than 55 decibels—the common standard for background noise levels. As a result, governments are passing laws to reduce noise pollution.

Design It Present evidence of noise pollution by listening carefully to the sounds around you. Document the sounds you hear. Now rate the volume of each sound on a scale of 1–10. Brainstorm ways that you can record the sounds so that you can take precise measurements. Present evidence using graphs or data tables. Communicate your results.

8.2.6, 8.NS.2–8.NS.4, 8.NS.7, 8.DP.1–8.DP.3, 8.DP.7–8.DP.10

THE CONSERVATION PRESIDENT

In 1901, if you wanted to go camping or hiking, you might run into a mine or a logging site. Although a lot of natural space existed in the United States when Theodore Roosevelt became president, the country had only five national parks. Years of uncontrolled mining, logging, and hunting threatened many of the country's natural areas. Roosevelt, at left in the photograph, was a passionate conservationist. He signed laws that protected over 93 million hectares of land in the United States. Today, the area of the United States that is protected as wilderness is greater than the area of France, Belgium, and the Netherlands combined!

 8.NS.2, 8.NS.11

Map It Create a map of national parks in your state or region. Your map should include interesting details about each park.

Environmental Lawyer

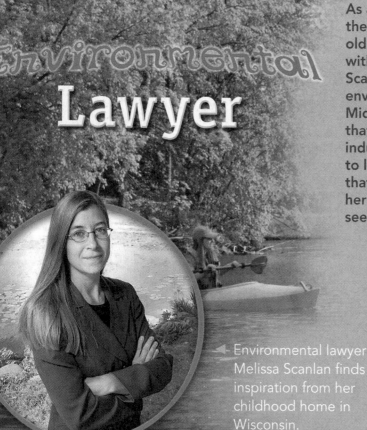

As a child, Melissa Scanlan loved boating on the Fox River with her family. As she grew older, she learned that the river was polluted with industrial and agricultural chemicals. Scanlan went to law school and became an environmental lawyer. As a lawyer, she formed Midwest Environmental Advocates—a law firm that helps midwestern communities work with industries and the government to find solutions to local environmental problems. Scanlan says that seeing her work affect the world around her "is like dropping a pebble into water and seeing the rings echo out."

Environmental lawyer Melissa Scanlan finds inspiration from her childhood home in Wisconsin.

Debate It Research an environmental issue in your region. Choose a possible solution and stage a class debate. Make sure you support your opinion with facts and evidence from your research.

 8.2.6, 8.2.7, 8.2.8, 8.NS.2, 8.NS.11, 8.DP.1, 8.DP.2, 8.DP.4, 8.DP.9, 8.DP.10

HOW IS THIS HOUSE SAVING OUR PLANET?

What can people do to use resources wisely?

Have you ever thought of ways to reuse something you would normally throw away? This home is made from the shipping containers you see transporting goods on ships and trucks. These containers would have been thrown away but an architect thought of a new way to use them.

Infer How can reusing shipping containers and other objects help our planet?

_____

_____

_____

_____

_____

▶ UNTAMED SCIENCE Watch the **Untamed Science** video to learn more about reusing resources.

Land, Air, and Water Resources

Academic Standards for Science

8.2.6, 8.2.7, 8.2.8, 8.NS.1, 8.NS.2, 8.NS.8, 8.NS.11

my science online.com

Land, Air, and Water Resources >UNTAMED SCIENCE >THE BIG QUESTION

Getting Started

Check Your Understanding

1. Background Read the paragraph below and then answer the question.

> On a lazy summer day, Mia pours water on the hot sidewalk and imagines where the water will go as it travels through the **water cycle.** After the water **evaporates,** it may float through the **atmosphere** and fall as rain in faraway lands or the ocean.

- What makes the water cycle a *cycle*?

_____

_____

The **water cycle** is the continuous process by which water moves from Earth's surface to the atmosphere and back.

Evaporation is the process by which molecules of liquid water absorb energy and change to a gas.

The **atmosphere** is the envelope of gases that surrounds the planet.

▶ **MY READING WEB** If you had trouble answering the question above, visit **My Reading Web** and type in *Land, Air, and Water Resources.*

Vocabulary Skill

Prefixes Some words can be divided into parts. A root is the part of the word that carries the basic meaning. A prefix is a word part placed in front of the root to change the word's meaning. The prefixes below will help you understand some of the vocabulary in this chapter.

Prefix	Meaning	Example
bio-	life	biodegradable, *adj.* describes a material that can be broken down and recycled by bacteria and other decomposers
aqua-	water	aquaculture, *n.* the farming of saltwater and freshwater organisms

2. Quick Check In the definitions of the example words in the table, circle the part that includes the prefix meaning.

topsoil

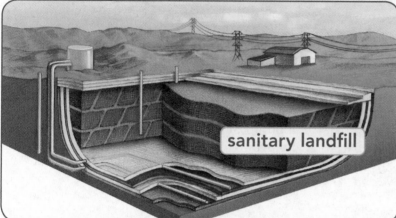

sanitary landfill

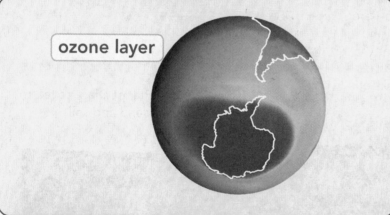

ozone layer

pesticide

Chapter Preview

LESSON 1

- litter • topsoil • subsoil
- bedrock • erosion
- nutrient depletion • fertilizer
- desertification • drought
- land reclamation

↻ Relate Cause and Effect

△ Infer

LESSON 2

- municipal solid waste
- incineration • pollutant
- leachate
- sanitary landfill
- recycling • biodegradable
- hazardous waste

↻ Compare and Contrast

△ Graph

LESSON 3

- emissions • photochemical smog
- ozone • temperature inversion
- acid rain • radon • ozone layer
- chlorofluorocarbon

↻ Relate Text and Visuals

△ Communicate

LESSON 4

- groundwater • pesticide
- sewage • sediment

↻ Outline

△ Design Experiments

LESSON 5

- greenhouse gas
- fossil fuel
- global warming

↻ Ask Questions

△ Make Models

> VOCAB FLASH CARDS For extra help with vocabulary, visit **Vocab Flash Cards** and type in *Land, Air, and Water Resources.*

Conserving Land and Soil

UNLOCK THE BIG

🔑 **How Do People Use Land?**
8.2.6, 8.2.8

🔑 **Why Is Soil Management Important?**
8.2.6, 8.2.8, 8.NS.8, 8.NS.11

my PLANeT DiaRY

VOICES FROM HISTORY

Land Inspiration

Conservation is a state of harmony between men and land.
—Aldo Leopold

Aldo Leopold spent his life in beautiful landscapes. He was so inspired by what he saw that he sought to better understand it. Leopold realized that land and all it contains—living and nonliving—are connected. He believed people should use land in a way that protects it for all living things as well as for future generations. Leopold called his idea the "land ethic." He wrote several books on conservation using this philosophy, including his most famous book, *A Sand County Almanac*.

Communicate Discuss this question with a group of classmates. Write your answer below.

How do you think land should be used?

_____

_____

_____

_____

_____

▶ PLANET DIARY Go to **Planet Diary** to learn more about conserving land and soil.

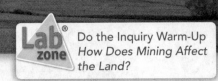
Lab zone
Do the Inquiry Warm-Up *How Does Mining Affect the Land?*

Academic Standards for Science

8.2.6 Identify, explain, and discuss some effects human activities have on the biosphere, such as soil pollution.

8.2.8 Explain that human activities have drastically changed the environment and have affected the capacity of the environment to support native species.

How Do People Use Land?

Less than a quarter of Earth's surface is dry, ice-free land. All people on Earth must share this limited amount of land to produce their food, build shelter, and obtain resources. As the American author Mark Twain once said about land, "They don't make it anymore."

People use land in many ways. 🔑 **Three uses that change the land are agriculture, mining, and development.** See **Figure 1.**

Vocabulary

- litter   • topsoil   • subsoil   • bedrock   • erosion
- nutrient depletion   • fertilizer   • desertification
- drought   • land reclamation

Skills

↩ Reading: Relate Cause and Effect

△ Inquiry: Infer

Agriculture

Strip Mining

Development

Agriculture Land provides most of the food that people eat. Crops such as wheat require lots of fertile land, but less than a third of Earth's land can be farmed. The rest is too dry, too salty, or too mountainous. New farmland is created by clearing forests, draining wetlands, and irrigating deserts. Land can also be used to grow food for animals, to provide grazing for livestock, or to grow crops such as cotton.

Mining Mining is the removal of nonrenewable resources from the land. Resources just below the surface are strip mined. Strip mining removes a strip of land to obtain minerals. The strip is then replaced. Strip mining exposes soil, which can then be blown or washed away. The area may remain barren for years. Resources can also be removed from deeper underground by digging tunnels to bring the minerals to the surface.

Development People settled in areas that had good soil near fresh water. As populations grew, the settlements became towns and cities. People developed the land by constructing buildings, bridges, and roads. In the United States, an area half the size of New Jersey is developed each year.

FIGURE 1 ·

Land Use

The ways that people use land vary greatly. For example, about 93 percent of land in Nebraska is used for agriculture, while only 10 percent of land in Massachusetts is used for agriculture.

✎ **Describe** How is land used in your area?

_____

_____

Lab zone ® Do the Quick Lab *Land Use.*

🔑 Assess Your Understanding

got it? ·

○ **I get it!** Now I know the ways people use and change land include _____

_____

○ **I need extra help with** _____

Go to **my science** ⑤ **coach** *online for help with this subject.*

8.2.6, 8.2.8

Academic Standards for Science

8.2.6 Identify, explain, and discuss some effects human activities have on the biosphere, such as soil pollution.

8.2.8 Explain that human activities have drastically changed the environment and have affected the capacity of the environment to support native species.

8.NS.8 Analyze data.

8.NS.11 Communicate findings.

Why Is Soil Management Important?

To understand why soil management is important, you need to know about the structure and function of fertile soil. It can take hundreds of years to form just a few centimeters of new soil. Soil contains the minerals and nutrients that plants need to grow. Soil also absorbs, stores, and filters water. Bacteria, fungi, and other organisms in soil break down the wastes and remains of living things. See **Figure 2.**

FIGURE 2 ························

Structure of Fertile Soil

Fertile soil is made up of several layers, including litter, topsoil, and subsoil.

✎ **Identify** Underline the organisms that make up or play a role in each soil layer.

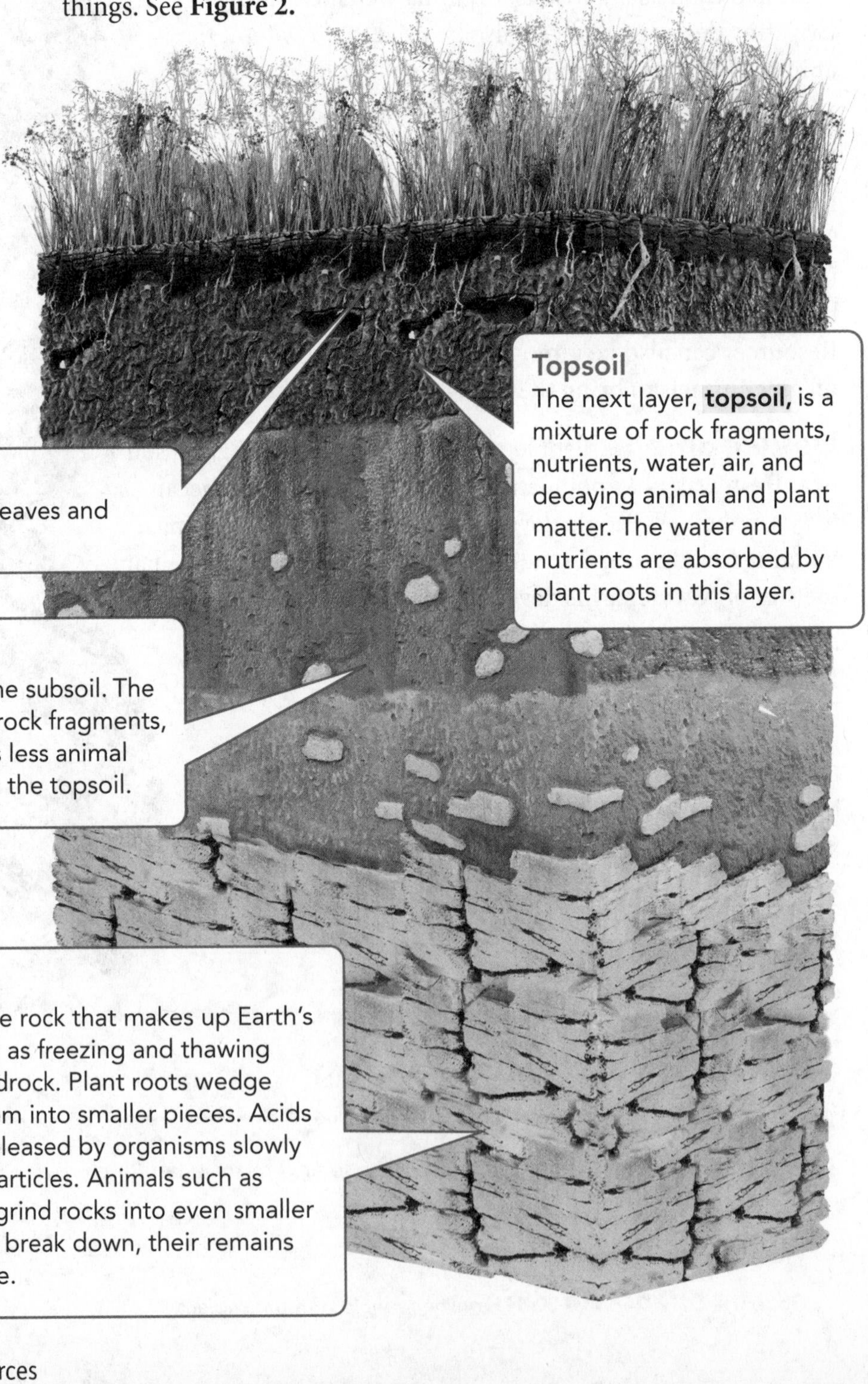

Topsoil
The next layer, **topsoil,** is a mixture of rock fragments, nutrients, water, air, and decaying animal and plant matter. The water and nutrients are absorbed by plant roots in this layer.

Litter
The top layer of dead leaves and grass is called **litter.**

Subsoil
Below the topsoil is the subsoil. The **subsoil** also contains rock fragments, water, and air, but has less animal and plant matter than the topsoil.

Bedrock
All soil begins as **bedrock,** the rock that makes up Earth's crust. Natural processes such as freezing and thawing gradually break apart the bedrock. Plant roots wedge between rocks and break them into smaller pieces. Acids in rainwater and chemicals released by organisms slowly break the rock into smaller particles. Animals such as earthworms and moles help grind rocks into even smaller particles. As dead organisms break down, their remains also contribute to the mixture.

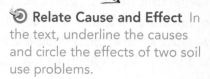
Soil Use Problems Because rich topsoil takes so long to form, it is important to protect Earth's soil. 🔑 **Without soil, most life on land could not exist. Poor soil management can result in three problems: erosion, nutrient depletion, and desertification.** Fortunately, damaged soil can sometimes be restored.

Erosion Normally, plant roots hold soil in place. But when plants are removed during logging, mining, or farming, the soil is exposed and soil particles can easily move. The process by which water, wind, or ice moves particles of rocks or soil is called **erosion.** Terracing, one farming method that helps reduce erosion, is shown in **Figure 3.**

.................................🖉.................................
🔄 **Relate Cause and Effect** In the text, underline the causes and circle the effects of two soil use problems.

Nutrient Depletion Plants make their own food through photosynthesis. Plants also need nutrients such as the nitrogen, potassium, and phosphorus found in soil to grow. Decomposers supply these nutrients to the soil as they break down the wastes and remains of organisms. But if a farmer plants the same crops in a field every year, the crops may use more nutrients than the decomposers can supply. The soil becomes less fertile, a situation called **nutrient depletion.**

When soil becomes depleted, farmers usually apply **fertilizers,** which include nutrients that help crops grow better. Farmers may choose other methods of soil management, too. They may periodically leave fields unplanted. The unused parts of crops, such as cornstalks, can be left in fields to decompose, adding nutrients to the soil. Farmers also can alternate crops that use many nutrients with crops that use fewer nutrients.

FIGURE 3 ·····································
Terracing
🖉 A terrace is a leveled section of a hill used to grow crops and prevent erosion. The flat surfaces allow crops to absorb water before the water flows downhill.

1. **Interpret Photos** Draw the path of water down the first hill and the terraced hill.

2. 🔺**Infer** Why do you think terracing helps prevent erosion?

_____

_____

_____

8.NS.8

359

Desertification If the soil in a once-fertile area becomes depleted of moisture and nutrients, the area can become a desert. The advance of desertlike conditions into areas that previously were fertile is called **desertification** (dih zurt uh fih KAY shun).

One cause of desertification is climate. For example, a **drought** is a period when less rain than normal falls in an area. During droughts, crops fail. Without plant cover, the exposed soil easily blows away. Overgrazing of grasslands by cattle and sheep and cutting down trees for firewood can cause desertification, too.

Desertification is a serious problem. People cannot grow crops and graze livestock where desertification has occurred. As a result, people may face famine and starvation. Desertification is severe in central Africa. Millions of rural people there are moving to the cities because they can no longer support themselves on the land.

apply it!

Desertification affects many areas around the world.

1 Name Which continent has the most existing desert?

_____

2 Interpret Maps Where in the United States is the greatest risk of desertification?

_____

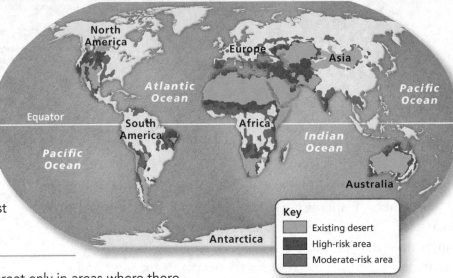

Key
- Existing desert
- High-risk area
- Moderate-risk area

3 ⚠ Infer Is desertification a threat only in areas where there is existing desert? Explain. Circle an area on the map to support your answer.

_____

_____

4 CHALLENGE If an area is facing desertification, what are some things people could do to possibly limit its effects?

_____

_____

8.NS.8

Land Reclamation Fortunately, it is possible to replace land damaged by erosion or mining. The process of restoring an area of land to a more productive state is called **land reclamation.** In addition to restoring land for agriculture, land reclamation can restore habitats for wildlife. Many different types of land reclamation projects are currently underway all over the world. But it is generally more difficult and expensive to restore damaged land and soil than it is to protect those resources in the first place. In some cases, the land may not return to its original state.

FIGURE 4 ······························

Land Reclamation
These pictures show land before and after it was mined.   8.NS.11

✎ **Communicate** Below the pictures, write a story about what happened to the land.

_____

_____

_____

 Lab zone   Do the Quick Lab
Modeling Soil Conservation.

🔑 Assess Your Understanding

1a. Review Subsoil has (less/more) plant and animal matter than topsoil.   8.2.6

b. Explain What can happen to soil if plants are removed?

_____

_____

_____

c. Apply Concepts What are some problems that could prevent people from supporting land reclamation?

_____

_____

_____

_____

8.2.6

got it? ·· 8.2.6 ··

○ **I get it!** Now I know that soil management is important because _____

_____

_____

○ **I need extra help with** _____

Go to **MY SCIENCE COACH** *online for help with this subject.*   8.2.6, 8.2.8

Waste Disposal and Recycling

🔑 **What Are Three Solid Waste Disposal Methods?**
8.2.6, 8.2.7, 8.NS.8, 8.NS.11

🔑 **What Are the Major Categories of Recycling?**
8.2.6, 8.2.7, 8.NS.8

🔑 **How Are Hazardous Wastes Safely Disposed Of?**
8.2.6, 8.2.7, 8.NS.8

my planet Diary
for Indiana

SCIENCE STATS

Trash Talk

Here are some interesting facts about trash:

- Hoosiers generate about 7 million metric tons of municipal solid waste every year.

- Annually, Indiana residents generate almost 1 million metric tons of yard waste. That's about 136 kilograms of trimmings and brush, 91 kilograms of leaves, and 453 kilograms of grass clippings per household.

- The average Indiana resident throws away about 308 kilograms of paper a year, including cardboard, magazines, and newspapers. That's about 2 billion kilograms of paper thrown away each year!

- Paper makes up about 39% of the trash in a landfill.

Communicate Discuss these questions with a group of classmates. Write your answers below.

1. Do you think the amount of trash we produce will increase or decrease in the future? Explain.

_____

_____

_____

2. What can you do to reduce the amount of trash you create?

_____

_____

_____

> **PLANET DIARY** Go to **Planet Diary** to learn more about waste disposal and recycling.

 Lab zone Do the Inquiry Warm-Up *What's in the Trash?*

Vocabulary
- municipal solid waste
- incineration
- pollutant
- leachate
- sanitary landfill
- recycling
- biodegradable
- hazardous waste

Skills
⟳ Reading: Compare and Contrast
△ Inquiry: Graph

What Are Three Solid Waste Disposal Methods?

People generate many types of waste, including empty packaging, paper, and food scraps. The wastes produced in homes, businesses, schools, and in the community are called **municipal solid waste.** Other sources of solid waste include construction debris, agricultural wastes, and industrial wastes. **Three methods of handling solid waste are burning, burying, and recycling.** Each method has its advantages and disadvantages.

Incineration The burning of solid waste is called **incineration** (in sin ur AY shun). The burning facilities, or incinerators, do not take up much space. They do not directly pollute groundwater. The heat produced by burning solid waste can be used to produce electricity. Incinerators supply electricity to many homes.

Unfortunately, incinerators do have drawbacks. Even the best incinerators create some air pollution. Although incinerators reduce the volume of waste by as much as 90 percent, some waste still remains and needs to be disposed of somewhere. Incinerators are also expensive to build.

Academic Standards for Science

8.2.6 Identify, explain, and discuss some effects human activities have on the biosphere, such as soil pollution.

8.2.7 Recognize that some of Earth's resources are finite and describe how recycling, reducing consumption and the development of alternatives can reduce the rate of their depletion.

8.NS.8 Analyze data.

8.NS.11 Communicate findings using graphs and charts.

apply it!

What happens to all the trash?

1 ◢ **Graph** Use the data in the table and the key to fill in the bar graph. The graph represents the methods of municipal waste disposal in the United States in 2007. Give the graph a title.

Disposal Method	Waste (Percent)
Incineration	13%
Landfills	54%
Recycling	33%

2 **CHALLENGE** Why do you think incineration is the least popular method of solid waste disposal?

_____

_____

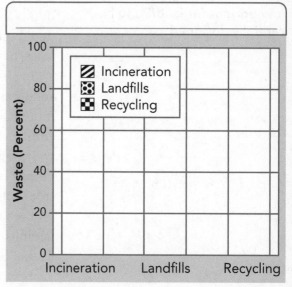

8.NS.8, 8.NS.11

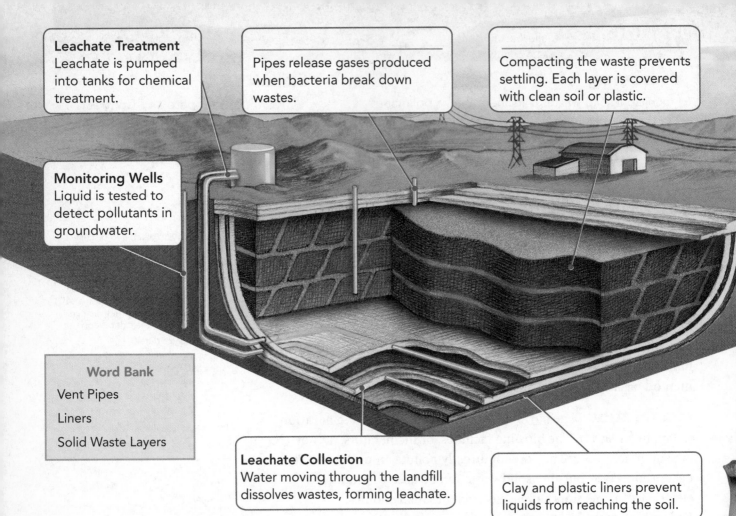

Leachate Treatment
Leachate is pumped into tanks for chemical treatment.

Pipes release gases produced when bacteria break down wastes.

Compacting the waste prevents settling. Each layer is covered with clean soil or plastic.

Monitoring Wells
Liquid is tested to detect pollutants in groundwater.

Word Bank
Vent Pipes
Liners
Solid Waste Layers

Leachate Collection
Water moving through the landfill dissolves wastes, forming leachate.

Clay and plastic liners prevent liquids from reaching the soil.

FIGURE 1 ·······························

Sanitary Landfill Design

Sanitary landfills are designed to protect the surrounding area.

✎ **Interpret Diagrams** Use the terms listed in the word bank to fill in the missing labels on the diagram. Why is it important for landfills to be carefully designed? 8.NS.8

_____

_____

_____

_____

_____

Landfills Until fairly recently, people disposed of waste in open holes in the ground called dumps. Some of this waste polluted the environment. Any substance that causes pollution is a **pollutant.** Dumps were dangerous and unsightly. Rainwater falling on a dump dissolved chemicals from the wastes, forming a polluted liquid called **leachate.** Leachate could run off into streams and lakes, or trickle down into the groundwater.

In 1976, the government banned open dumps. Now much solid waste is buried in landfills that are built to hold the wastes more safely. A **sanitary landfill** holds municipal solid waste, construction debris, and some types of agricultural and industrial waste. **Figure 1** shows the parts of a well-designed sanitary landfill. Once a landfill is full, it is covered with a clay cap to keep rainwater from entering the waste.

Even well-designed landfills can pollute groundwater. Capped landfills can be reused as parks and sites for sports arenas. They cannot be used for housing or agriculture.

Recycling You may have heard of the "three R's"—reduce, reuse, and recycle. *Reduce* refers to creating less waste from the beginning, such as using cloth shopping bags rather than disposable ones. *Reuse* refers to finding another use for an object rather than discarding it, such as refilling reusable bottles with drinking water instead of buying new bottled water.

The process of reclaiming raw materials and reusing them to create new products is called **recycling.** You can recycle at home and encourage others to recycle. You can buy products made from recycled materials. Your purchase makes it more profitable for companies to use recycled materials in products.

Another way to reduce solid waste is to start a compost pile. The moist, dark conditions in a compost pile allow natural decomposers to break down grass clippings, leaves, and some food wastes. Compost is an excellent natural fertilizer for plants.

✏️ **Compare and Contrast**
In the table below, write one pro and one con for each of the three solid waste disposal methods. **8.NS.11**

	Incineration	Sanitary Landfills	Recycling
Pro			
Con			

Lab zone Do the Lab Investigation *Waste, Away!*

🔑 **Assess Your Understanding**

1a. Define What is incineration?

_____

8.2.6, 8.2.7

b. Design a Solution What could be some possible uses for the space over a landfill once it is capped? _____

_____

8.2.6, 8.2.7

c. Make Judgments Which solid waste disposal method do you think is best? Why?

_____
_____
_____
_____

8.2.6, 8.2.7

got it? ....

O **I get it!** Now I know solid waste can be disposed of through _____

O **I need extra help with** _____

Go to **MY SCIENCE** Ⓢ **COACH** *online for help with this subject.*

8.2.6, 8.2.7

Academic Standards for Science

8.2.6 Identify, explain, and discuss some effects human activities have on the biosphere, such as soil pollution.

8.2.7 Recognize that some of Earth's resources are finite and describe how recycling, reducing consumption and the development of alternatives can reduce the rate of their depletion.

8.NS.8 Analyze data.

Vocabulary Prefixes The prefix *bio-* means "life." A material is biodegradable if it can be broken down and recycled by living things such as

_____

_____

What Are the Major Categories of Recycling?

Recycling reduces the volume of solid waste by reusing materials. Recycling uses energy, but it also saves the energy that would be needed to obtain, transport, and process raw materials. Recycling is also cheaper than making new materials. Additionally, recycling conserves nonrenewable resources and limits the environmental damage caused by mining for raw materials.

Materials that can be broken down and recycled by bacteria and other decomposers are **biodegradable** (by oh dih GRAY duh bul). Many products people use today are not biodegradable, such as plastic containers, metal cans, rubber tires, and glass jars. Instead, people have developed different ways to recycle the raw materials in these products.

A wide range of materials can be recycled. ☞ **Most recycling focuses on four major categories of products: metal, glass, paper, and plastic.**

Material	Recycling Process	Products Made From Recycling
Metal	Metals are melted in furnaces and rolled into sheets.	Cars, cans, bicycles, jewelry, office supplies, house siding
Glass	Glass pieces are melted in furnaces and cast into new glass.	Bottles, floor tiles, countertops, jewelry, jars
Paper	Paper is shredded and mixed with water to form pulp. The pulp is washed, dried, and rolled into new sheets.	Toilet paper, notebook paper, paper cups, paper plates, napkins, envelopes
Plastic	Plastic containers are chopped, washed, and melted. The molten plastic is turned into pellets that can be heated and molded.	Picnic tables, park benches, speed bumps, recycling bins, playground equipment, deck lumber, fleece (see girl's jacket at left)

Is recycling worthwhile? Besides conserving resources, recycling saves energy. Making aluminum products from recycled aluminum rather than from raw materials uses about 90 percent less energy overall. For certain materials, recycling is usually worthwhile. However, recycling is not a complete answer to the solid waste problem. For some cities, recycling is not cost-effective. Scientists have not found good ways to recycle some materials, such as plastic-coated paper and plastic foam. Some recycled products, such as low-quality recycled newspaper, have few uses. All recycling processes require energy and create pollution. The value of recycling must be judged on a case-by-case basis.

RECYCLED TIRE BELT

FACT: One of the largest tire dumps is so big it can actually be seen from the moon.

MADE IN CANADA

recycled

FIGURE 2 ·······················

⟩ INTERACTIVE ART **Like New**

Did you know that old tires can be made into belts? Or jeans into insulation?

✎ **Apply Concepts** Besides the examples shown, name other objects that could be made from these recyclables. 8.NS.8

Lab® zone

Do the Quick Lab *It's in the Numbers.*

🔑 Assess Your Understanding

2a. Explain How does recycling save energy?

_____

_____

_____

_____

8.2.6, 8.2.7

b. Solve Problems How could your community solve its solid waste problem?

_____

_____

_____

_____

8.2.6, 8.2.7

got it?

○ **I get it!** Now I know recyclable materials are categorized as _____

_____

_____

_____

_____

○ **I need extra help with** _____

_____

Go to **my science** 💬 **coach** *online for help with this subject.*

8.2.6, 8.2.7

How Are Hazardous Wastes Safely Disposed Of?

Many people picture hazardous wastes as bubbling chemicals or oozing slime. Any material that can be harmful to human health or the environment if it is not properly disposed of is a **hazardous waste.**

Types of Hazardous Wastes Toxic wastes can damage the health of humans and other organisms. Explosive wastes can react very quickly when exposed to air or water, or explode when dropped. Flammable wastes easily catch fire. Corrosive wastes can dissolve many materials. Everyday hazardous wastes include electronic devices, batteries, and paint.

Other wastes that require special disposal are radioactive wastes. Radioactive wastes give off radiation that can cause cancer and other diseases. Some radioactive waste can remain dangerous for millions of years.

Health Effects A person can be exposed to hazardous wastes by breathing, eating, drinking, or touching them. Even short-term exposure to hazardous wastes can cause problems such as skin irritation or breathing difficulties. Long-term exposure can cause diseases such as cancer, damage to body organs, or death.

FIGURE 3 ·······························

Sort It Out!

Wastes can be thrown away, recycled, or disposed of as hazardous waste.

✎ **Summarize** Draw a line from each object to its appropriate disposal container.

8.NS.8

FIGURE 4 ·······························

Hazardous Wastes
Hazardous waste can be harmful if improperly handled.

✎ **Review** What is the best way to manage hazardous wastes?

○ Store waste in small facilities.

○ Produce less waste to start.

○ Incinerate waste.

Disposal Methods It is difficult to safely dispose of hazardous wastes. Hazardous wastes are most often disposed of in carefully designed landfills. The landfills are lined and covered with clay and plastic. These materials prevent chemicals from leaking into the soil and groundwater. ⊶ **Hazardous wastes that are not disposed of in carefully designed landfills may be incinerated or broken down by organisms. Liquid wastes may be stored in deep rock layers.**

Scientists are still searching for methods that will provide safe and permanent disposal of radioactive wastes. Some wastes are currently stored in vaults dug hundreds of meters underground or in concrete and steel containers above ground.

Disposal Sites It is a challenge to decide where to build hazardous waste disposal facilities. In general, people would prefer to have a single large facility located in an area where few people live. However, it may be safer, cheaper, and easier to transport wastes to small local facilities instead.

Reducing Hazardous Waste The best way to manage hazardous wastes is to produce less of them in the first place. Industries are eager to develop safe alternatives to harmful chemicals. At home, you can find substitutes for some hazardous household chemicals. For example, you could use citronella candles instead of insect spray to repel insects.

Do the Quick Lab
Half-Life.

⊶ **Assess Your Understanding**

3a. Name What are some negative health effects of exposure to hazardous wastes?

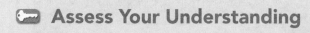

_____

_____

8.2.6, 8.2.7

b. Make Judgments Do you think hazardous wastes should be disposed of at one large central facility? Explain.

_____

_____

_____

8.2.6, 8.2.7

got it? ··

○ **I get it!** Now I know that hazardous wastes are disposed of by_____

_____

○ I need extra help with _____

Go to **my science** ⓢ **coach** *online for help with this subject.*

8.2.6, 8.2.7

369

3 Air Pollution and Solutions

UNLOCK THE BIG ?

🔑 **What Causes Outdoor and Indoor Air Pollution?**
8.2.6, 8.2.8, 8.NS.8

🔑 **What Causes Damage to the Ozone Layer?**
8.2.6, 8.2.8, 8.NS.8, 8.NS.11

🔑 **How Can Air Pollution Be Reduced?**
8.2.6, 8.2.8, 8.NS.11

MY PLANET DIARY

PROFILE

Drawing for a Difference

Some people may think that kids can't help the environment. Kids in the San Joaquin Valley of California know better! Each year, students enter their drawings into a contest for a Clean Air Kids Calendar sponsored by the San Joaquin Valley Air Pollution Control District. Lisa Huang (bottom right drawing) and Saira Delgada (bottom left drawing) are two middle school students whose work was chosen to be a part of the 2008 calendar. Their drawings show people why healthy air is important. Every time people looked at the calendar, the drawings reminded them of the simple ways they can help the planet.

Communicate Discuss the question with a group of classmates. Then, write your answer below.

How could you raise awareness about air pollution in your community?

_____

_____

_____

_____

> PLANET DIARY Go to **Planet Diary** to learn more about air pollution and solutions.

 Do the Inquiry Warm-Up
How Does the Scent Spread?

Vocabulary
- emissions
- photochemical smog
- ozone
- temperature inversion
- acid rain
- radon
- ozone layer
- chlorofluorocarbon

Skills
- Reading: Relate Text and Visuals
- Inquiry: Communicate

What Causes Outdoor and Indoor Air Pollution?

You can't usually see it, taste it, or smell it, but you are surrounded by air. Air is a mixture of nitrogen, oxygen, carbon dioxide, water vapor, and other gases. Almost all living things depend on these gases to survive. Recall that these gases cycle between living things and the atmosphere. These cycles guarantee that the air supply will not run out, but they don't guarantee that the air will be clean.

Outdoor Air Pollution What causes air pollution? Until the mid-1900s in the United States, factories and power plants that burned coal produced most of the pollutants, or **emissions,** that were released into the air. **Today, a large source of emissions resulting in air pollution outdoors comes from motor vehicles such as cars and trucks.** There are also some natural causes of air pollution. Methane released from animals such as cows also sends pollutants into the atmosphere.

Air pollution sources can be grouped as point or nonpoint sources. A point source is a specific source of pollution that is easy to identify, such as a smokestack. A nonpoint source is a source that is widely spread and cannot be tied to a specific origin, such as vehicle emissions. So the pollution cannot be traced to any specific vehicle.

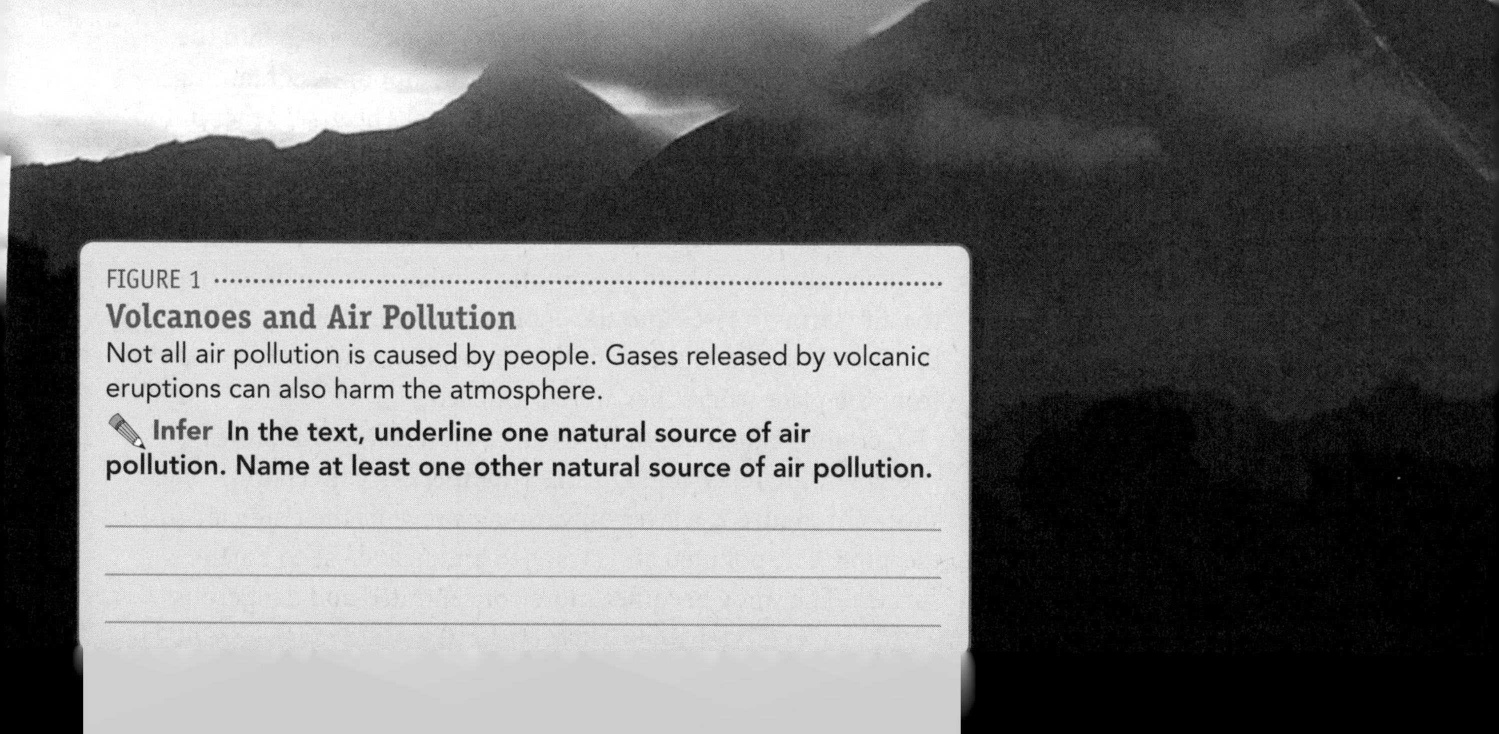

Academic Standards for Science

8.2.6 Identify, explain, and discuss some effects human activities have on the biosphere, such as soil pollution.

8.2.8 Explain that human activities, have drastically changed the environment and have affected the capacity of the environment to support native species.

8.NS.8 Analyze data.

FIGURE 1 ·······················

Volcanoes and Air Pollution

Not all air pollution is caused by people. Gases released by volcanic eruptions can also harm the atmosphere.

✎ **Infer** In the text, underline one natural source of air pollution. Name at least one other natural source of air pollution.

_____

_____

_____

FIGURE 2 ·····················

Temperature Inversion
Normally, pollutants rise into the atmosphere and blow away. During a temperature inversion, warm air traps the pollution close to the ground.

✎ **Interpret Photos** On the photo above, label the warm air, cool air, and polluted air.

8.NS.8

Smog Have you ever heard a weather forecaster talk about a "smog alert"? A smog alert is a warning about a type of air pollution called photochemical smog. **Photochemical smog** is a thick, brownish haze formed when certain gases in the air react with sunlight. When the smog level is high, it settles as a haze over a city. Smog can cause breathing problems and eye and throat irritation. Exercising outdoors can make these problems worse.

The major sources of smog are the gases emitted by cars and trucks. Burning gasoline in a car engine releases gases into the air. These gases include hydrocarbons (compounds containing hydrogen and carbon) and nitrogen oxides. The gases react in the sunlight and produce a form of oxygen called **ozone.** Ozone, which is toxic, is the major chemical found in smog. Ozone can cause lung infections and damage the body's defenses against infection.

Normally, air close to the ground is heated by Earth's surface. As the air warms, it rises into the cooler air above it. Any pollutants in the air are carried higher into the atmosphere and are blown away from the place where they were produced.

Certain weather conditions can cause a condition known as a temperature inversion. During a **temperature inversion,** as shown in **Figure 2,** a layer of warm air prevents the rising air from escaping. The polluted air is trapped and held close to Earth's surface. The smog becomes more concentrated and dangerous.

Acid Rain Precipitation that is more acidic than normal because of air pollution is called **acid rain.** Acid rain can also take the form of snow, sleet, or fog. Acid rain is caused by the emissions from power plants and factories that burn coal and oil. These fuels produce nitrogen oxides and sulfur oxides when they are burned. The gases that are released react with water vapor in the air, forming nitric acid and sulfuric acid. The acids dissolve in precipitation and return to Earth's surface.

As you can imagine, acid falling from the sky has some negative effects. When acid rain falls into a pond or lake, it changes the conditions there. Many fish, particularly their eggs, cannot survive in more acidic water. When acid rain falls on plants, it can damage their leaves and stems. Acid rain that falls on the ground can also damage plants by affecting the nutrient levels in the soil. Whole forests have been destroyed by acid rain. Fortunately, some of the effects of acid rain are reversible. Badly damaged lakes have been restored by adding lime or other substances that neutralize the acid.

Acid rain doesn't just affect living things. The acid reacts with stone and metal in buildings and statues. Statues and stonework damaged by acid rain may look as if they are melting, as seen in **Figure 3.** Automobiles rust more quickly in areas with acid rain. These effects are not reversible and the damage can be costly.

FIGURE 3 ·······················

Acid Rain
Acid rain harms plants, animals, buildings, and statues.

✎ **Review** In the text, underline the cause of acid rain.

apply it!

You are a scientist called to testify before Congress about acid rain. The government is proposing putting limits on emissions that lead to acid rain.

1 **Communicate** Some of the members of Congress do not think acid rain causes real damage. What do you tell them?

_____

_____

2 **Explain** Is rain the only form of precipitation you would identify as being potentially acidic? Explain.

_____

3 CHALLENGE What could you tell a company that was unwilling to reduce its emissions because the initial cost was high?

_____

_____

FIGURE 4 ·······················

Indoor Air Pollution

Indoor air pollution has many sources. ✎ **Identify** Circle the sources of indoor air pollution in this room.

Indoor Air Pollution You might think that you can avoid air pollution by staying inside. The air inside buildings can be polluted, too. 🔑 **Some substances that cause indoor air pollution, such as dust and pet hair, bother only those people who are sensitive to them. Other indoor air pollutants, such as toxic chemicals, can affect anyone.** Glues and cleaning supplies may give off toxic fumes. Cigarette smoke, even from another person's cigarette, can damage the lungs and heart. **Figure 4** shows some sources of air pollution that can be found in homes.

Carbon Monoxide One particularly dangerous indoor air pollutant is carbon monoxide. Carbon monoxide is a colorless and odorless gas that forms when fuels are not completely burned. When carbon monoxide builds up in an enclosed space, like a house, it can be deadly. Any home heated by wood, coal, oil, or gas needs a carbon monoxide detector.

Radon Another indoor air pollutant that is difficult to detect is radon. **Radon** is a colorless, odorless gas that is radioactive. It is formed naturally by certain rocks underground. Radon can enter homes through cracks in basement walls or floors. Breathing radon gas over many years may cause lung cancer and other health problems. Homeowners can install ventilation systems to prevent radon from building up in their homes.

Lab ® Do the Quick Lab
zone *How Acid Is Your Rain?*

🔑 **Assess Your Understanding**

1a. Name (Photochemical smog/Methane) is a thick, brownish haze formed when gases in the air are exposed to sunlight. 8.2.6, 8.2.8

b. Make Judgments Do you think the government should regulate sources of air pollution such as factory and car emissions? Explain.

_____

_____

_____

_____

8.2.6, 8.2.8

got it? ······················

O **I get it!** Now I know outdoor air pollution is caused by _____

_____

and indoor air pollution is caused by _____

_____

O **I need extra help with** _____

_____

Go to **MY SCIENCE** Ⓢ **COACH** *online for help with this subject.* 8.2.6, 8.2.8

What Causes Damage to the Ozone Layer?

If you have ever had a sunburn, you have experienced the painful effects of the sun's ultraviolet radiation. But did you know that sunburns would be even worse without the protection of the ozone layer? The **ozone layer** is a layer of the upper atmosphere about 15 to 30 kilometers above Earth's surface. The amount of ozone in this layer is very small. Yet even this small amount of ozone in the ozone layer protects people from the effects of too much ultraviolet radiation. These effects include sunburn, eye diseases, and skin cancer.

Because you read earlier that ozone is a pollutant, the fact that ozone can be helpful may sound confusing. The difference between ozone as a pollutant and ozone as a helpful gas is its location in the atmosphere. Ozone close to Earth's surface in the form of smog is harmful. Ozone higher in the atmosphere, where people cannot breathe it, protects us from too much ultraviolet radiation.

The Source of Ozone
Ozone is constantly being made and destroyed. See **Figure 5.** When sunlight strikes an ozone molecule, the energy of the ultraviolet radiation is partly absorbed. This energy causes the ozone molecule to break apart into an oxygen molecule and an oxygen atom. The oxygen atom soon collides with another oxygen molecule. They react to form a new ozone molecule. Each time this cycle occurs, some energy is absorbed. That energy does not reach Earth's surface.

Academic Standards for Science

8.2.6 Identify, explain, and discuss some effects human activities have on the biosphere, such as soil pollution.

8.2.8 Explain that human activities, have drastically changed the environment and have affected the capacity of the environment to support native species.

8.NS.8 Analyze data, and use it to identify patterns and make inferences based on these patterns.

8.NS.11 Communicate findings using models.

FIGURE 5 ·······································

Ozone Cycle
The ozone cycle prevents harmful ultraviolet radiation from reaching Earth's surface.

✎ **Sequence** Explain the ozone cycle in your own words.

_____

_____

_____

_____

_____

_____

_____

_____

_____

_____

_____

_____

_____

_____

_____

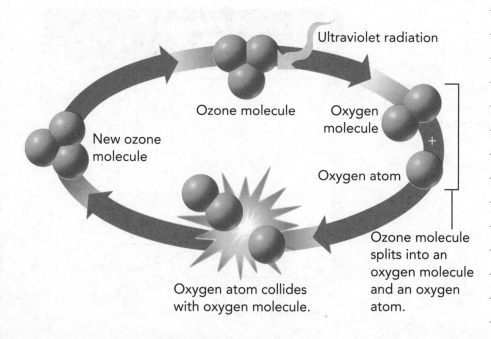

Ultraviolet radiation

New ozone molecule

Ozone molecule

Oxygen molecule

Oxygen atom

+

Ozone molecule splits into an oxygen molecule and an oxygen atom.

Oxygen atom collides with oxygen molecule.

8.NS.11

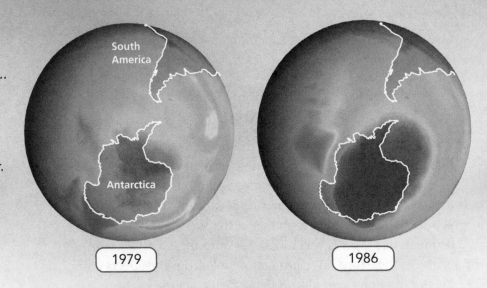

1979　　1986

FIGURE 6
Ozone Hole
The ozone hole (shown in blue) is over Antarctica. The hole has grown over time, but it varies seasonally and from year to year.

The Ozone Hole In the late 1970s, scientists observed from satellite images that the ozone layer over Antarctica was growing thinner each spring. The amount of ozone in the ozone layer was decreasing. This caused an area of severe ozone depletion, or an ozone hole. In **Figure 6,** you can see the size of the ozone hole in five selected years.

What is to blame for the ozone hole? 🗝 **Scientists determined that the major cause of the ozone hole is a group of gases called CFCs.** CFCs, or **chlorofluorocarbons,** are human-made gases that contain chlorine and fluorine. CFCs had been used in air conditioners, aerosol spray cans, and other household products. CFCs reach high into the atmosphere, and react with ozone molecules. The CFCs block the cycle in which ozone molecules absorb ultraviolet radiation. As a result, more ultraviolet light reaches Earth's surface.

FIGURE 7
Ozone and Ultraviolet Radiation
✏️ The amount of ozone in the atmosphere and the amount of UV radiation reaching Earth are linked.

1. **Read Graphs** Label the curve on the graph representing ozone and the curve representing UV radiation.

2. **Summarize** Explain the graph in your own words.

_____

_____

_____

_____

8.NS.8

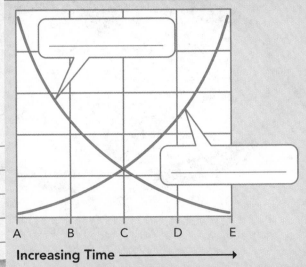

Ozone and UV Radiation Resulting From CFCs

A　B　C　D　E

Increasing Time ⟶

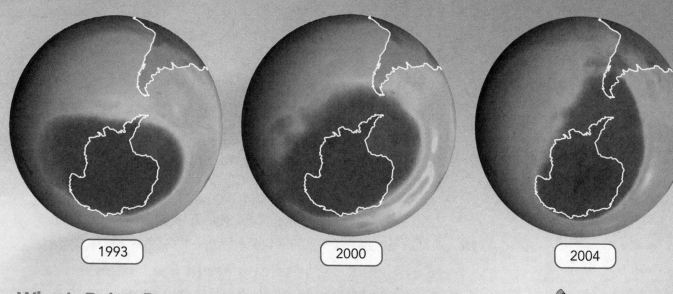

| 1993 | 2000 | 2004 |

What's Being Done In 1990, many nations signed an agreement to eventually ban the use of ozone-depleting substances, including CFCs. Most uses of CFCs were banned in 2000. Some uses of CFCs are still allowed, but compared to the 1970s, few CFCs now enter the atmosphere. Unfortunately, CFC molecules remain in the atmosphere for a long time. Scientists predict that if the ban on ozone-depleting substances is maintained, the ozone layer will gradually recover.

When scientists discovered that CFCs were harming the atmosphere, they immediately began to search for substitutes. Refrigerators and air conditioners were redesigned to use less-harmful substances. Most spray cans were either replaced by pump sprays or redesigned to use other gases. Researchers developed new ways to make products such as plastic foam without using CFCs. As a result of this research and the development of CFC substitutes, far less CFCs now enter the atmosphere.

Relate Text and Visuals

Based on the photos, describe what happened to the hole in the ozone layer before CFCs were banned. What do you think could happen if the ban is maintained and enforced?

_____

_____

_____

_____

_____

_____

8.NS.8

Do the Quick Lab
Analyzing Ozone.

Assess Your Understanding

2a. Explain How can ozone be both a pollutant and something beneficial to Earth?

_____

_____

_____

8.2.6, 8.2.8

b. Solve Problems What can countries do to help the ozone layer recover?

_____

_____

_____

8.2.6, 8.2.8

got it?

○ **I get it!** Now I know the ozone layer was damaged by_____

_____

○ **I need extra help with**_____

Go to **MY SCIENCE COACH** online for help with this subject.

8.2.6, 8.2.8

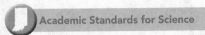
Academic Standards for Science

8.2.6 Identify, explain, and discuss some effects human activities have on the biosphere, such as soil pollution.

8.2.8 Explain that human activities, have drastically changed the environment and have affected the capacity of the environment to support native species.

8.NS.11 Communicate findings.

FIGURE 8 ·······················

> INTERACTIVE ART

Your Solutions

✎ Communicate With a partner, list ways you can reduce air pollution in your everyday life.

_____

_____

_____

_____

_____

_____

How Can Air Pollution Be Reduced?

Air pollution can be reduced if we examine the sources. 🗝 **The key to reducing air pollution is to control emissions.** In the United States, laws such as the Clean Air Act regulate the amount of certain pollutants that can be released into the air. Laws also encourage the development of new technology that reduces air pollution. Reducing emissions also requires your efforts.

Controlling Emissions From Factories
At one time, industries dealt with emissions by building tall smokestacks. The stacks released wastes high into the air where they could blow away, but the pollutants still ended up somewhere. Now factories remove pollutants from their emissions with devices known as scrubbers that release water droplets. Pollutants dissolve in the water and fall into a container. The use of scrubbers explains why "smoke" from factories is white—it's not smoke, it's steam.

Controlling Emissions From Vehicles
Cars and trucks now contain pollution-control devices. A catalytic converter is a part of the exhaust system that reduces emissions of carbon monoxide, hydrocarbons, and nitrogen oxides. This device causes the gases to react, forming less-harmful carbon dioxide and water. Laws can ensure that people use pollution-control devices. For example, in many states, cars must pass emissions tests to be allowed on the road.

What You Can Do You may not think there is much you can do to reduce air pollution. However, even small changes in your behavior can make a big difference.

You can help reduce air pollution by reducing certain types of energy use. Much air pollution is a result of burning fuels to provide electricity and transportation. Using less energy conserves fuel resources and reduces emissions. Turning off lights, computers, and televisions in empty rooms uses less energy and reduces emissions. When you take public transportation, carpool, walk, or ride a bicycle, there are fewer cars on the road. This means there are less emissions that contribute to air pollution.

Apple Imports

Apples are grown in an orchard in Chile.

Trucks carry apples from the orchard to the airport.

Airplanes carry the apples from Chile to the United States.

More trucks bring the apples from the airport to shipping centers and grocery stores around the country.

FIGURE 9 ·······································

Where Does an Apple Really Come From?

Many things in our everyday lives, even where food comes from, can contribute to air pollution. ✏ **Analyze Costs and Benefits** Read the comic strip above. Then, fill in the boxes with pros and cons of buying apples that were grown locally instead of those grown in another country.

8.NS.11

Pros

Cons

Lab® zone | Do the Quick Lab *It's in the Air.*

🔑 Assess Your Understanding

got it? ·····································

○ **I get it!** Now I know the key to reducing air pollution is _____

_____

○ **I need extra help with** _____

_____

Go to **MY SCIENCE ⑤ COACH** online for help with this subject.   8.2.6, 8.2.8

379

Water Pollution and Solutions

UNLOCK THE BIG

?

🔑 **Why Is Fresh Water a Limited Resource?**
8.2.6, 8.2.8

🔑 **What Are the Major Sources of Water Pollution?**
8.2.6, 8.2.8

🔑 **How Can Water Pollution Be Reduced?**
8.2.6, 8.2.8, 8.NS.1

MY PLANET DIARY

DISASTERS

A Flood of Sludge

In December 2008, over 4.5 billion liters of polluted water flooded the area around Kingston, Tennessee. A nearby coal-powered electric plant produced polluted water containing arsenic, lead, and other toxic chemicals. The toxic chemicals and coal ash mixed with water in a holding pond to form a thick sludge. When the dam holding back the pond broke, the water poured into rivers. The sludge water spilled over the land, damaging trees, homes, and other buildings. Local residents feared the flood would be dangerous to their health as well.

Communicate Discuss the question with a group of classmates. Then write your answer below.

Is water pollution a problem in your community? Why or why not?

_____

_____

_____

_____

_____

> **PLANET DIARY** Go to **Planet Diary** to learn more about water pollution and solutions.

 Do the Inquiry Warm-Up *How Does the Water Change?*

Why Is Fresh Water a Limited Resource?

Most of Earth's surface is covered by some form of water. Oceans cover nearly three fourths of Earth's surface. Around the poles are vast sheets of ice. From space you cannot even see many parts of Earth because they are hidden behind clouds of tiny water droplets. There seems to be so much water—it's hard to believe that it is a scarce resource in much of the world.

Vocabulary

• groundwater • pesticide • sewage • sediment

Skills

↻ **Reading:** Outline

△ **Inquiry:** Design Experiments

How can water be scarce when there is so much of it on Earth's surface? 🔑 **Water is scarce on Earth because most of it—about 97 percent—is salt water.** Salt water cannot be used for drinking or watering crops. Also, about three quarters of the fresh water on Earth is ice. Most liquid fresh water is **groundwater,** water stored in soil and rock beneath Earth's surface. People use groundwater for drinking, but it is not always found near where people live. Cities in dry areas may draw their drinking water from hundreds of kilometers away.

Renewing the Supply

Fortunately, Earth's fresh water is renewable. Remember that water continually moves between the atmosphere and Earth's surface in the water cycle. Even though fresh water is renewable, there is not always enough of it in a given place at a given time.

Water Shortages

Water shortages occur when people use water faster than the water cycle can replace it. This is likely to happen during a drought when an area gets less rain. Many places never receive enough rain to meet their needs and use other methods to get water. Desert cities in Saudi Arabia get more than half of their fresh water by removing salt from ocean water, which is very expensive.

FIGURE 1 ·······························

Water

Most of Earth's surface is covered with water, but fresh water is still a limited resource.

✎ **Identify** Reread the text. Then, underline the reasons why fresh water is scarce.

Lab ® Do the Quick Lab
zone *Where's the Water?*

🔑 Assess Your Understanding

got it? ·······································

○ **I get it!** Now I know that fresh water is limited on Earth because _____

_____

○ **I need extra help with** _____

Go to **MY SCIENCE COACH** *online for help with this subject.*

8.2.6, 8.2.8

Academic Standards for Science

8.2.6 Identify, explain, and discuss some effects human activities have on the biosphere, such as soil pollution.

8.2.8 Explain that human activities, have drastically changed the environment and have affected the capacity of the environment to support native species.

What Are the Major Sources of Water Pollution?

Since fresh water is scarce, water pollution can be devastating. Some pollutants, such as iron and copper, make water unpleasant to drink or wash in. Other pollutants, such as mercury or benzene, can cause sickness or even death.

🔑 **Most water pollution is the result of human activities. Wastes produced by agriculture, households, industry, mining, and other human activities can end up in water.** Water pollutants can be point or nonpoint pollution sources, classified by how they enter the water. A pipe gushing wastewater directly into a river or stream is an example of a point source. The pipe is a specific pollution source that can be easily identified. Nonpoint pollution sources include farm, street, and construction site runoff. The exact pollution source is hard to trace and identify.

Agricultural Wastes Animal wastes, fertilizers, and pesticides are also sources of pollution. **Pesticides** are chemicals that kill crop-destroying organisms. Rain washes animal wastes, fertilizers, and pesticides into ponds, causing algae to grow. The algae block light and deplete the oxygen in the pond.

Household Sewage The water and human wastes that are washed down sinks, showers, and toilets are called **sewage.** If sewage is not treated to kill disease-causing organisms, the organisms quickly multiply. People can become ill if they drink or swim in water containing these organisms.

FIGURE 2 ·······························

Farm Pollution

This scene may show common things found on a farm, but even common things can lead to water pollution.

✏️ **Relate Text and Visuals**
Circle the potential sources of water pollution in this scene.

Industry and Mining Wastes Some plants, mills, factories, and mines produce wastes that can pollute water. Chemicals and metal wastes can harm organisms that live in bodies of water. Animals that drink from polluted bodies of water or eat the organisms that live in the water can also become ill.

Sediments Water that causes erosion picks up **sediments,** or particles of rock and sand. Sediments can cover up the food sources, nests, and eggs of organisms in bodies of water. Sediments also block sunlight, preventing plants from growing.

Heat Heat can also have a negative effect on a body of water. Some factories and power plants release water that has been used to cool machinery. This heated water can kill organisms living in the body of water into which it is released. This type of pollution is also known as thermal pollution.

Oil and Gasoline An oil spill is a very dramatic form of water pollution. It can take many years for an area to recover from an oil spill because the oil floats on water and is difficult to collect. Another water pollution problem is caused by oil and gasoline that leak out of damaged underground storage tanks. The pollution can be carried far away from a leaking tank by groundwater.

⟲ Outline Look back in the text and fill in the graphic organizer below to outline causes of water pollution.

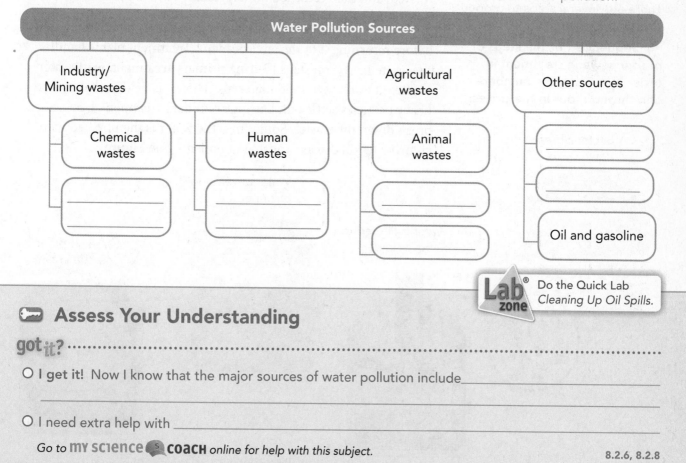

Lab zone ® Do the Quick Lab *Cleaning Up Oil Spills.*

🗝 Assess Your Understanding

got it?

○ **I get it!** Now I know that the major sources of water pollution include _____

_____

○ **I need extra help with** _____

Go to **MY SCIENCE ⓢ COACH** *online for help with this subject.*

8.2.6, 8.2.8

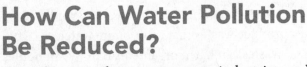
How Can Water Pollution Be Reduced?

By working together, governments, industries, and individuals can improve water quality. Federal and state laws in the United States regulate the use of certain substances that can pollute water.

🔑 **The keys to keeping water clean are effective cleanup of oil and gasoline spills, proper sewage treatment, and reduction of pollutants.** There are also some important ways that people can reduce water pollution at home.

Cleaning Up Oil and Gasoline Spills

Nature can handle oil in small amounts. A natural cleaning process slowly takes place after oil spills. Certain bacteria living in the ocean feed on the oil. Of course, oil can cause much damage to an area in the time it takes the bacteria to work, so people often help clean up large spills. The hard work of many scientists and volunteers can minimize environmental damage from large spills.

Gasoline or oil that leaks from an underground tank is hard to clean up. If the pollution has not spread far, the soil around the tank can be removed. But pollution that reaches groundwater may be carried far away. Groundwater can be pumped to the surface, treated, and then returned underground. This can take many years.

Sewage Treatment

Most communities treat wastewater before returning it to the environment. Treatment plants handle the waste in several steps. During primary treatment, wastewater is filtered to remove solid materials. Then it is held in tanks where heavy particles settle out. During secondary treatment, bacteria break down the wastes. Sometimes the water is then treated with chlorine to kill disease-causing organisms. See **Figure 3.**

FIGURE 3 ·····························

Wastewater Treatment
There are several steps to proper sewage treatment.

✎ **Sequence** Put the steps of proper sewage treatment in order by writing the numbers one through four in the circles.

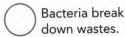
◯ Bacteria break down wastes.

◯ Water is filtered to remove solids.

◯ Water is treated with chlorine.

◯ Heavy particles settle in tank.

Reducing Pollutants Instead of releasing wastes into the environment, industries can recycle their wastes. Once such programs are underway, companies often find they save money as well as reduce pollution. Other companies change their processes to produce less waste or less-harmful waste by using fruit acids as cleaning agents instead of toxic chemicals.

What You Can Do It is easy to prevent water pollution at home. Some common household water pollutants are paints and paint thinner, motor oil, and garden chemicals. You can avoid causing water pollution by never pouring these chemicals down the drain. Instead, save these materials for your community's next hazardous waste collection day.

know?

The Exxon *Valdez* oil tanker spilled 40.9 million liters of oil into the Pacific Ocean on March 24, 1989. The oil eventually covered 28,000 square kilometers of ocean!

apply it! Bacteria can be used to clean up oil spills. Some companies specialize in creating bacteria for cleaning up oil.

❶ Analyze Costs and Benefits Fill in the boxes with some pros and cons of using bacteria to clean oil spills.

Pros	Cons

❷ Design Experiments If you were creating bacteria for cleaning oil spills, what characteristics would you want to test the bacteria for? _____

Pollution and Solutions

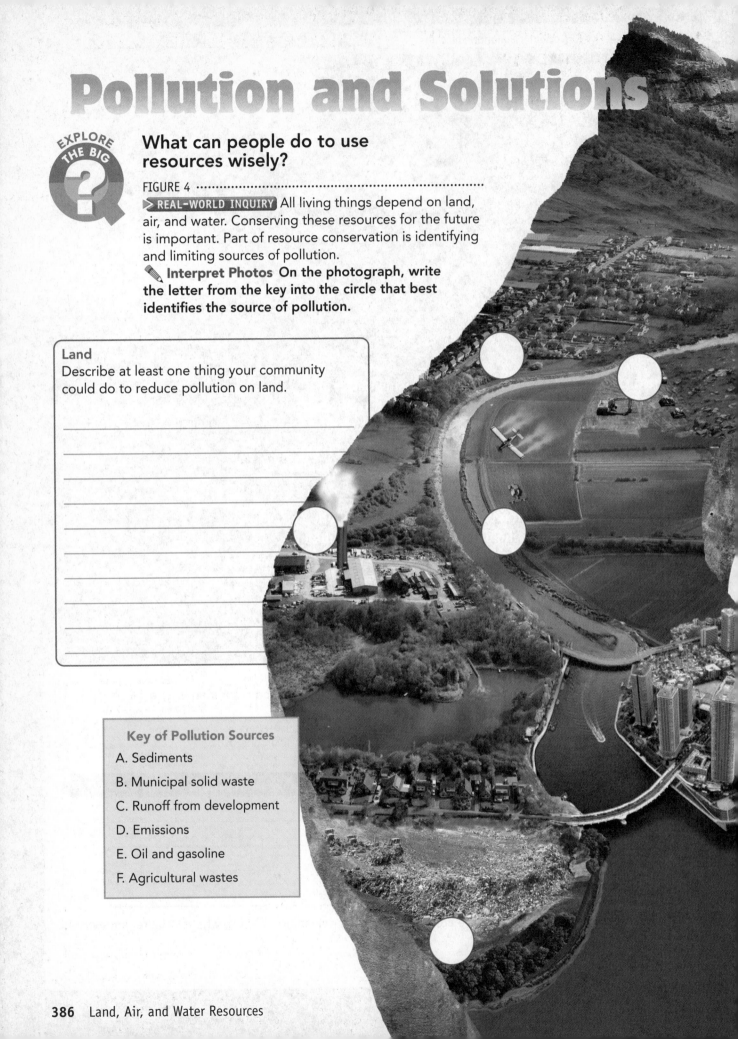

EXPLORE THE BIG ?

What can people do to use resources wisely?

FIGURE 4 ·····································

> REAL-WORLD INQUIRY   All living things depend on land, air, and water. Conserving these resources for the future is important. Part of resource conservation is identifying and limiting sources of pollution.

✎ **Interpret Photos** On the photograph, write the letter from the key into the circle that best identifies the source of pollution.

Land
Describe at least one thing your community could do to reduce pollution on land.

_____

_____

_____

_____

_____

_____

_____

Key of Pollution Sources

A. Sediments

B. Municipal solid waste

C. Runoff from development

D. Emissions

E. Oil and gasoline

F. Agricultural wastes

Air
Describe at least one thing your community could do to reduce air pollution.

_____

_____

_____

_____

_____

_____

_____

Water
Describe at least one thing your community could do to reduce water pollution.

_____

_____

_____

_____

_____

_____

_____

Do the Quick Lab _Getting Clean._

🔑 Assess Your Understanding

1a. Define What are sediments?

_____

_____

8.2.6

b. Explain How can bacteria help clean an oil spill in the ocean?

_____

_____

_____

8.2.6, 8.2.8

c. ANSWER THE BIG ? What can people do to use resources wisely?

_____

_____

_____

8.2.6, 8.2.8

d. CHALLENGE Why might a company not want to recycle the waste they produce even if it would reduce water pollution?

_____

_____

_____

_____

_____

_____

8.2.6, 8.2.8

got it? ....

○ **I get it!** Now I know that water pollution can be reduced by _____

_____

_____

○ **I need extra help with** _____

_____

Go to **MY SCIENCE COACH** online for help with this subject.   8.2.6, 8.2.8

387

Indiana

LESSON 5

Human Activities and Climate Change

🔑 **How Are Human Activities Affecting Earth's Climate?**

8.2.6, 8.2.8, 8.NS.2, 8.NS.8, 8.NS.11

my planet Diary

EVERYDAY SCIENCE

How Big Is Your Footprint?

Today people are measuring their effect on the environment by looking at their carbon footprint. Carbon is found in two of the greenhouse gases most responsible for warming Earth's climate. Your carbon footprint measures the total amount of greenhouse gases you emit directly and indirectly. Cars, factories, and home heating all rely on fuels that release carbon into the atmosphere. The manufacturing of products you use, like food and clothing, does, too. When people know how big their carbon footprints are, they can make changes that improve their own lives and the environment.

Brainstorm with a classmate and answer the questions below.

What activities affect your carbon footprint? How big is your carbon footprint?

_____
_____
_____
_____
_____
_____

▶ **PLANET DIARY** Go to **Planet Diary** to learn more about global warming.

Lab zone Do the Inquiry Warm-Up *What Is the Greenhouse Effect?*

Academic Standards for Science

8.2.6 Identify, explain, and discuss some effects human activities have on the biosphere.

8.2.8 Explain that human activities, have drastically changed the environment.

8.NS.2 Plan and carry out investigations.

8.NS.8 Analyze data.

8.NS.11 Communicate findings using models.

How Are Human Activities Affecting Earth's Climate?

You may not realize it, but you are a powerful geologic force. Humans change the land, air, and water of Earth's surface faster than most geologic processes. In fact, human activities are causing a major change in the temperature of Earth's atmosphere. It's important to understand this impact because the atmosphere controls our climate and weather.

Vocabulary

- greenhouse gas
- fossil fuel
- global warming

Skills

- Reading: Ask Questions
- Inquiry: Make Models

Greenhouse Effect Outer space is incredibly cold: −270°C. If you were in a spaceship, you would rely on the insulated walls of the ship to keep you from freezing to death. Now think of Earth as a spaceship, moving through space as it orbits the sun. Earth's atmosphere is like the walls of the ship. It insulates us from the cold of space. How does it do this? The atmosphere keeps Earth's surface warm through a process called the greenhouse effect, as shown in **Figure 1.**

When the sun warms Earth's surface, this heat is radiated back to space as infrared waves. The infrared waves pass easily through nitrogen and oxygen, which make up 99 percent of Earth's atmosphere. However, **greenhouse gases,** such as water vapor, carbon dioxide, methane, and absorb the heat leaving Earth's surface. These gases then radiate some energy back toward Earth, trapping heat in the lower atmosphere. Greenhouse gases make up less than 1 percent of the atmosphere. But as you can see, it only takes a small amount of them to absorb heat, keeping Earth warm.

Ask Questions What questions do you have about the greenhouse effect? Before you read about it, write one question below. Try to answer your question after you read.

_____
_____
_____
_____
_____
_____

FIGURE 1 ·····················
> ART IN MOTION **Greenhouse Effect**
Communicate Use the word bank to fill in the blanks. Then talk about the steps in the greenhouse effect with a classmate.   8.NS.11

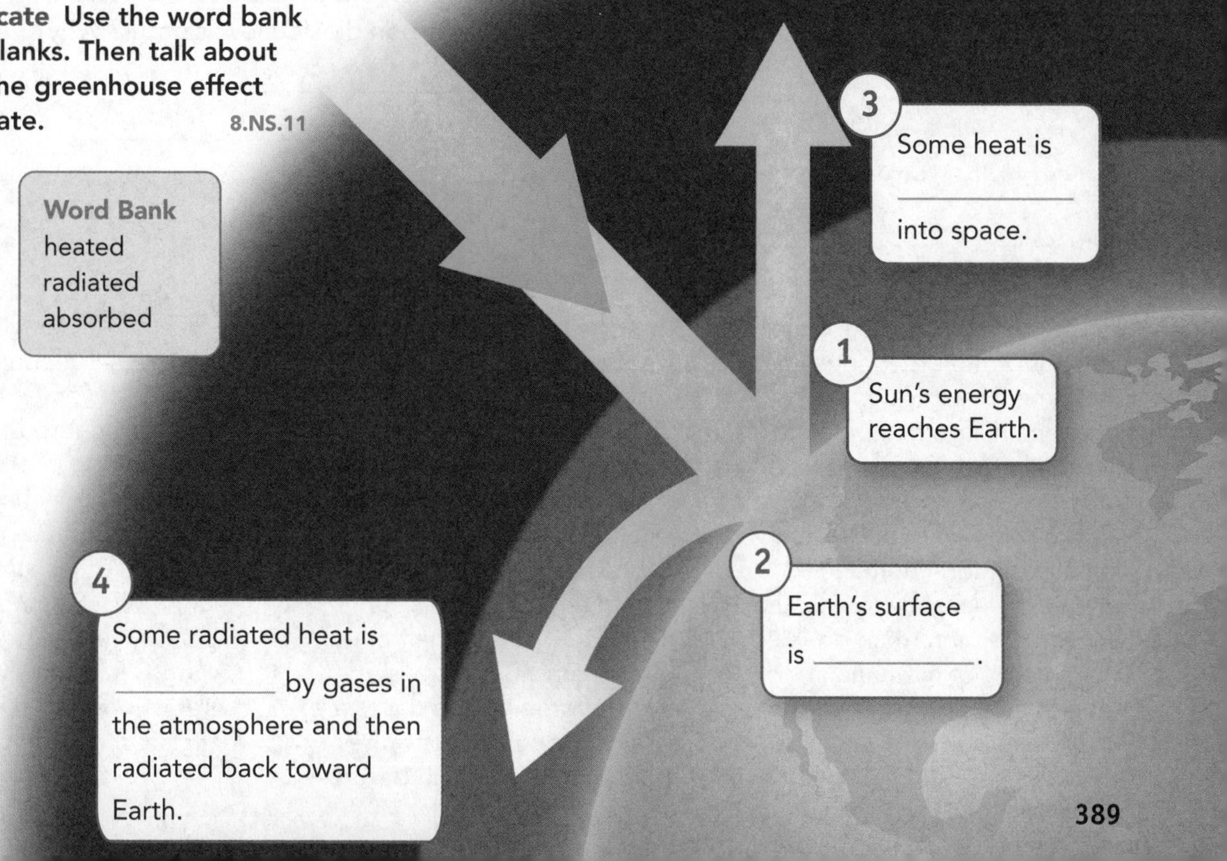

Word Bank
heated
radiated
absorbed

3 Some heat is _____ into space.

1 Sun's energy reaches Earth.

2 Earth's surface is _____.

4 Some radiated heat is _____ by gases in the atmosphere and then radiated back toward Earth.

Levels of Greenhouse Gases We need the greenhouse effect, but you can have too much of a good thing. 🔑 **Many human activities are increasing the level of greenhouse gases in the atmosphere and producing changes in climate worldwide. This increase is causing global temperatures to rise.** This conclusion is based on our observations and measurements of the greenhouse gases humans release. It's also based on an understanding of how greenhouse gases affect the temperature at Earth's surface.

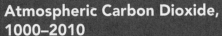

FIGURE 2

Carbon Dioxide Levels
The graph shows the levels of carbon dioxide in the atmosphere over time.

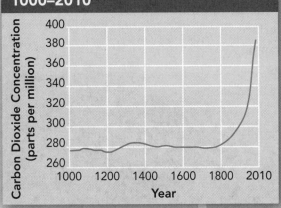

Atmospheric Carbon Dioxide, 1000–2010

Carbon Dioxide One of the most abundant greenhouse gases is carbon dioxide. Humans release billions of tons of it into the atmosphere each year. Most of this carbon dioxide is released by burning **fossil fuels**—energy-rich substances formed from the remains of organisms. Humans burn fossil fuels such as coal, natural gas, and gasoline to generate electricity, heat homes, and power cars.

✏️ **Read Graphs Study the graph and answer the questions below.**

1. Describe what the level of carbon dioxide was like about 500 years ago.

_____

2. When did the biggest increase in carbon dioxide levels occur? Why?

_____

8.NS.8

Methane

Human activities increase the amount of the greenhouse gas methane. Livestock emit methane. Large numbers of livestock, such as cattle, are raised for food production. As the population of livestock increases, more methane is released. In past centuries, this activity has more than doubled the amount of methane in the atmosphere.

Temperature Increase

Over the last 120 years, the average temperature of the troposphere has increased by about 0.7°C. This gradual increase in the temperature of Earth's atmosphere is called **global warming.** The effect is the same as it would be if the heat from the sun increased by about half of one percent. But increasing levels of greenhouse gases are causing global temperatures to rise more quickly than before.

Climate Models

Some models of climate change predict that global temperatures may rise several degrees over the next hundred years. Climate models are complex computer programs. They use data to predict temperature, precipitation, and other atmospheric conditions. Scientists are trying to improve climate models. They want to make more specific predictions about how warming will affect different regions.

Effects of Global Warming

Over the past 800,000 years, global temperatures have gone up and down. Scientists look at past events to predict the possible effects of global warming. 🔑 **The effects of global warming include melting glaciers, rising sea levels, drought, desertification, changes to the biosphere, and regional changes in temperature. Global warming is part of larger set of changes to Earth's climate that together are called climate change.**

FIGURE 3 ·······················

Sea Level Rise

This satellite image shows how sea level rise could affect the eastern United States.

Key
- Low vulnerability
- Moderate vulnerability
- High vulnerability
- Very high vulnerability

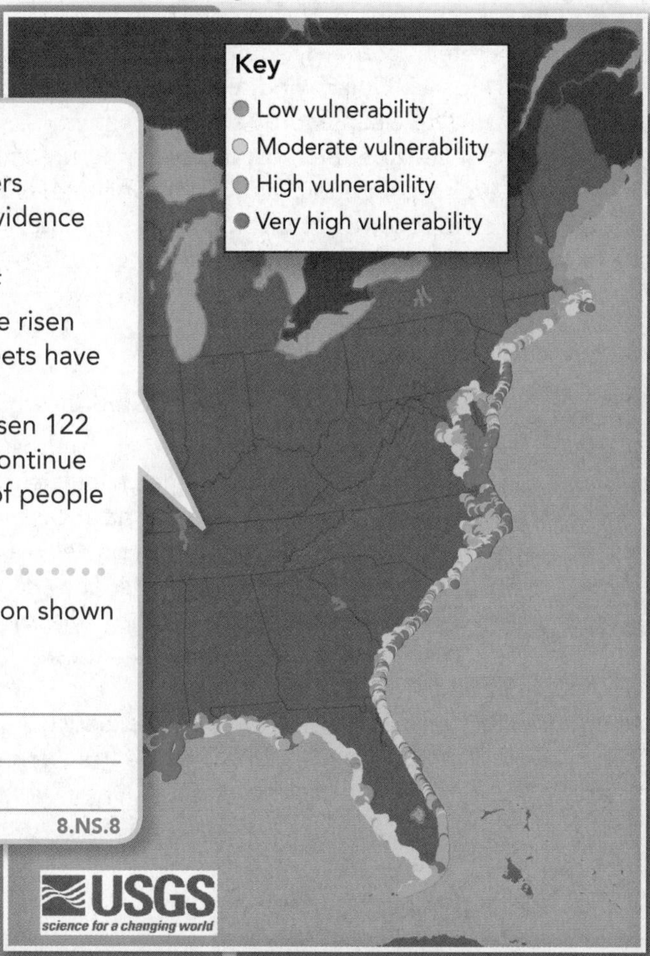

Melting Glaciers and Rising Sea Levels

Over the last century, scientists have observed glaciers retreating in many mountain regions. Now there is evidence that mountain glaciers are melting worldwide.

Records also indicate that temperatures in parts of Antarctica, which is covered by a thick ice sheet, have risen 6 degrees over 50 years. In fact, several giant ice sheets have collapsed and tumbled into the sea.

Since the end of the last ice age, sea levels have risen 122 meters. As glaciers continue to melt, sea levels will continue to rise. This rise poses a threat to the large number of people who live near the ocean.

✏️ **Interpret Data** How would the sea level prediction shown here affect people in the eastern United States?

_____

_____

_____

8.NS.8

USGS
science for a changing world

Droughts and Desertification

When global temperatures rise, some regions get very warm and dry. This can lead to water shortages or periods of drought. Today the southwestern United States is experiencing a severe drought at a time when global temperatures are warming. Severe droughts also cause some lands to become deserts. This process of desertification can lead to food shortages.

Changes to the Biosphere

Each climate region has its own communities of living organisms that are adapted to that climate. As global climates warm, organisms are often pushed to new locations to find familiar climates. Organisms that can't adapt may become extinct. Species that can adapt to warmer conditions will survive.

Regional Changes in Temperature

Global temperature changes affect regions differently. During the twentieth century, global temperatures increased by an average of less than one degree. Yet some parts of the world got warmer by more than five degrees, while others got cooler. In some areas, temperature changes have led to longer growing seasons.

Limiting Global Warming Scientists think human activities that release greenhouse gases are responsible for our recent episode of global warming. The solution might sound simple: Reduce greenhouse gas emissions. But how do we do that? Solutions for limiting global warming and climate change include finding clean, renewable sources of energy, being more energy efficient, and removing carbon from fossil fuel emissions.

Clean Energy Sources

Clean energy refers to energy sources that release very small amounts of greenhouse gases. Solar, wind, hydroelectric, geothermal, nuclear, and tidal energy are clean energy sources.

Solar energy might be the most important future energy source. The sun provides a continuous and nearly unlimited supply of energy. In one hour, Earth receives as much energy from the sun as all humans use in one year. Solar energy drives the water cycle behind hydroelectric power and the air motions behind wind power.

Efficient Energy

One of the best ways to reduce global warming is to develop more energy-efficient technologies. Clean energy power plants can power electric and hydrogen fuel cell cars. And factories can run on steam from power plants. People can also practice energy-efficient habits. They can turn off lights when they leave a room or use public transportation.

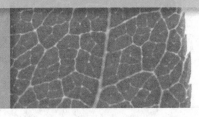

Carbon Capture

When fossil fuels are burned, they release exhaust. Technologies are being developed to remove carbon dioxide from exhaust. The carbon dioxide could then be buried underground. This process takes more energy and is a bit more expensive, but the result is that fewer greenhouse gases are released.

apply it!

△ **Make Models** How can you help limit global warming? Pick one item from your home. Come up with a plan to make it more energy efficient. Use the space provided to draw or explain your idea. 8.NS.11

CLIMATE IN THE MEDIA

FIGURE 4 ···

> INTERACTIVE ART ✎ Evaluate Science in the Media **Working with a group, choose at least three different media sources. Spend a week collecting stories about climate change from these sources. Discuss the stories with your group. Evaluate how they cover the topic of climate change. Present your findings to the class. Use the space below to jot down ideas about sources you might use and some of the questions you might explore as you evaluate these sources.**

8.NS.2

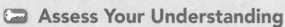

Do the Quick Lab
*Greenhouse Gases
and Global Warming.*

🔑 Assess Your Understanding

1a. Define What is a greenhouse gas?

_____

_____

8.2.6, 8.2.8

b. List What are some solutions for reducing greenhouse gases?

_____

8.2.6, 8.2.8

c. What factors affect Earth's climate?

_____

_____

_____

_____

_____

_____

8.2.6, 8.2.8

got **it?** ···

○ **I get it!** Now I know that human activities can affect Earth's climate by _____

_____

○ I need extra help with _____

Go to **MY SCIENCE ⑤ COACH** *online for help with this subject.*

8.2.6, 8.2.8

9 Study Guide

To use resources wisely, people can reuse or _____ materials and they can properly dispose of hazardous wastes and other _____.

LESSON 1 Conserving Land and Soil
8.2.6, 8.2.8, 8.NS.8, 8.NS.11

🔑 Three uses that change the land are agriculture, mining, and development.

🔑 Without soil, most life on land could not exist. Poor soil management results in three problems: erosion, nutrient depletion, and desertification.

Vocabulary
- litter • topsoil • subsoil • bedrock
- erosion • nutrient depletion • fertilizer
- desertification • drought • land reclamation

LESSON 2 Waste Disposal and Recycling
8.2.6, 8.2.7, 8.NS.8, 8.NS.11

🔑 Solid waste is burned, buried, or recycled.

🔑 Recycling categories include metal, glass, paper, and plastic.

🔑 Hazardous wastes are stored depending on the type and potential danger.

Vocabulary
- municipal solid waste • incineration
- pollutant • leachate • sanitary landfill
- recycling • biodegradeable • hazardous waste

LESSON 3 Air Pollution and Solutions
8.2.6, 8.2.8, 8.NS.8, 8.NS.11

🔑 A major source of outdoor air pollution is vehicle emissions. Indoor air pollution has a variety of causes.

🔑 The major cause of the ozone hole is CFCs.

🔑 Reducing air pollution requires reducing emissions.

Vocabulary
- emissions • photochemical smog • ozone
- temperature inversion • acid rain
- radon • ozone layer • chlorofluorocarbon

LESSON 4 Water Pollution and Solutions
8.2.6, 8.2.8, 8.NS.1

🔑 Earth's water is about 97 percent salt water.

🔑 Most water pollution is caused by human activities.

🔑 The keys to keeping water clean include cleaning oil spills, proper sewage treatment, and the reduction of pollutants.

Vocabulary
- groundwater • pesticide • sewage • sediment

LESSON 5 Human Activities and Climate Change
8.2.6, 8.2.8, 8.NS.2, 8.NS.8, 8.NS.11

🔑 Many human activities are increasing the level of greenhouse gases in the atmosphere, causing global temperatures to rise.

🔑 The effects of global warming include melting glaciers, rising sea levels, drought, desertification, changes in the biosphere, and regional changes in temperature.

🔑 Solutions for limiting global warming include finding clean, renewable sources of energy, being more energy efficient, and removing carbon from fossil fuel emissions.

Vocabulary
- greenhouse gas • fossil fuel • global warming

Review and Assessment

LESSON 1 Conserving Land and Soil

1. What is an agricultural use of land?

a. growing crops on land

b. collecting water from land

c. building structures on land

d. removing minerals from land

8.2.6

2. Plant roots absorb nutrients and water from the layer of soil called _____.

8.2.6

3. Relate Cause and Effect What type of land use can result in nutrient depletion? Explain.

_____

_____

_____

_____

8.2.8

LESSON 2 Waste Disposal and Recycling

4. What is one benefit of recycling?

a. It increases the volume of solid waste.

b. If it is recycled, a material won't biodegrade.

c. It conserves resources and energy.

d. It uses more raw materials that need to be mined.

8.2.7

5. A _____ is a waste that can be harmful to human health or the environment.

8.2.6

6. Write About It How could your school reduce the amount of municipal solid waste it produces? Include where you think the most waste is produced in your school and propose at least two ways to reduce it.

8.2.7

LESSON 3 Air Pollution and Solutions

7. Which of the following describes a pollutant that has been released into the air?

a. sewage   **b.** leachate

c. sediment   **d.** emissions

8.2.6

8. The _____ in the upper atmosphere prevents some of the sun's ultraviolet radiation from reaching Earth.

8.2.6

9. Predict Do you think the hole in the ozone layer will increase or decrease in size? Why?

_____

_____

_____

8.2.8, 8.NS.1

10. Solve Problems Describe two ways a large city can reduce air pollution.

_____

_____

_____

_____

_____

_____

8.2.8

LESSON 4 Water Pollution and Solutions

11. Why is fresh water a limited resource?

   a. because most water on Earth is in lakes

   b. because most water on Earth is in clouds

   c. because most water on Earth is in the ground

   d. because most water on Earth is salt water

8.2.6

12. A _____ is a chemical that kills crop-destroying organisms.   8.2.6

13. Draw Conclusions Rain may wash fertilizers into bodies of water, such as ponds. How might fertilizer affect a pond?

_____

_____

_____

_____

8.2.6, 8.2.8, 8.NS.1

LESSON 5 Human Activities and Climate Change

14. Which change in the atmosphere appears to contribute to global warming?

   a. decreased moisture

   b. decreased heat

   c. increased oxygen

   d. increased carbon dioxide

8.2.6, 8.2.8

15. Identify Greenhouse gases absorb _____

_____

8.2.6, 8.2.8

16. Compare and Contrast How is global warming different from earlier changes in Earth's climate?

_____

_____

_____

8.2.6, 8.2.8

 APPLY THE BIG ? ## What can people do to use resources wisely?

17. Every individual, including young people, can make decisions to use resources wisely. **Use the terms *reduce*, *reuse*, and *recycle* to explain how the students in the picture below can help minimize solid waste.**

_____

_____

_____

_____

_____

_____

_____

_____

_____

_____

_____

_____

_____

_____

_____

_____

_____

_____

_____

8.2.6, 8.2.7, 8.2.8, 8.DP.2

Indiana ISTEP+ Practice

Multiple Choice

Circle the letter of the best answer.

1. According to the circle graph, what is the most common method of waste disposal in the United States?

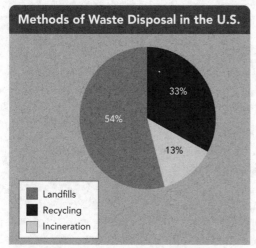

Methods of Waste Disposal in the U.S.

33%
54%
13%

- Landfills
- Recycling
- Incineration

   A. composting   B. recycling
   C. incineration   D. landfills

8.2.7, 8.NS.8

2. In which layer of soil would you expect to find rock fragments, nutrients, and decaying plant and animal matter?

   A. litter   B. topsoil
   C. subsoil   D. bedrock

8.2.6

3. What types of materials could be broken down in a compost pile?

   A. all recyclable materials

   B. biodegradable materials

   C. all materials that can be incinerated

   D. glass, metal, and other raw materials

8.2.7

4. Which of the following is an effect of global warming?

   A. increased frequency of droughts

   B. falling sea levels

   C. decreased coastal flooding

   D. spreading glaciers

8.2.8

Constructed Response

Write your answer to Question 5 on the lines below.

5. How can sediments negatively affect an aquatic ecosystem?

_____

_____

_____

8.2.6, 8.2.8

Extended Response

Use the diagram below and your knowledge of science to help you answer Question 6. Write your answer on a separate sheet of paper.

6. Compare and contrast the role of ozone in each of the images shown above.

8.NS.11

The Human Effect

Many people think that human activities haven't had much of an impact on the environment until recently. But in reality humans have had a great effect on their local environments for thousands of years.

Indiana has a long and varied history. Many different people have lived in the area since the end of the last ice age about 10,000 years ago. The first people to settle the area hunted large animals, such as mastodons and giant bison, for food and clothing. Eventually, these large animals were hunted to extinction.

European-Americans arrived in the area about three hundred years ago. These settlers developed commercial hunting, logging, herding, and farming. Animals were hunted to feed or clothe local villages. But they were also hunted so that their fur could be traded for other goods. This fur trade eventually led to the near extinction of animals such as the beaver.

Commercial farming required a great deal of land. The primary building material and fuel at the time was wood. As a result, large tracts of forest were cut down to clear land for crops and to provide timber for construction and fuel. As these forests disappeared, so too did the animals that called them home.

Today, we have a better understanding of the effects of our activities on the environment. We can act to control or reverse those damaging effects.

Research It Find out more about how humans are currently changing the environment in Indiana. Create an informational poster that details these changes.

 8.2.8, 8.NS.2, 8.NS.11

Save the Seeds, Save the World

Bananas may be in trouble. So may some species of wheat. In fact a number of species of plants face threats to their survival. Scientists think that Earth's climate is changing. And as it changes, so does the biosphere. Some plants are becoming more vulnerable to disease or to insect pests. Human development also threatens some plants' habitats. With all these changes to the biosphere, plant species are becoming extinct at an increasing rate.

The Svalbard Global Seed Vault may be helping to preserve samples of important resources. Tucked into the permafrost in Svalbard—an island north of Norway that is farther north than almost any other landmass on Earth—the Seed Vault protects seeds that come from almost every important food crop in the world. The seeds of bananas, strawberries, rice, and beans are all preserved (along with many other species) in case they go extinct. Many seeds come from developing countries, which have a lot of biodiversity. Because the Seed Vault is in the cryosphere—the frozen portion of the hydrosphere—scientists think that Svalbard will remain frozen even if climate change continues to cause the glaciers farther south to melt.

The Seed Vault can store up to 4.5 million seeds at –18°C. Even if the power goes out, the seeds will stay frozen because the permafrost will keep the temperature of the vaults below –3.5°C.

Inside the Svalbard Global Seed Vault ▲

Write About It Scientists have observed signs of global climate change. Changes to Earth's climate are affecting many other Earth systems. For example, sea levels are rising, and sea ice is melting. Write an essay explaining how these changes might lead to the extinction of a specific plant species.

 8.2.6, 8.2.8, 8.NS.1, 8.NS.11

HOW ARE THIS MANATEE AND HYRAX ALIKE?

How are living things alike yet different?

Living in Florida waters, a manatee can grow to be longer than 3 meters and weigh over 350 kilograms. A rock hyrax is a small, tailless, rodentlike animal that lives in rocky areas of Africa. While these animals appear to be very different, they are actually related.

Develop Hypotheses **What could these two animals have in common?**

_____

_____

_____

_____

_____

> **UNTAMED SCIENCE** Watch the **Untamed Science** video to learn more about living things.

Introduction to Living Things

Academic Standards for Science

8.3.1, 8.3.2, 8.3.6, 8.NS.1–8.NS.11, 8.DP.1–8.DP.11

10 Getting Started

Check Your Understanding

1. **Background** Read the paragraph below and then answer the question.

You eat **microscopic** organisms all the time without realizing it! Some microscopic organisms are necessary to prepare common foods. **Yeast,** for example, is a tiny organism that is used to make bread. **Bacteria** are used to make yogurt, sauerkraut, and many other foods.

Something **microscopic** is so small that it cannot be seen without a magnifying lens or a microscope.

Yeast is a single-celled organism that has a nucleus.

Bacteria are single-celled organisms that do not have nuclei.

• What is one kind of food that bacteria are used to make?

> **MY READING WEB** If you had trouble completing the question above, visit **My Reading Web** and type in *Introduction to Living Things.*

Vocabulary Skill

Greek Word Origins Many science words come from ancient Greek words. Learning the word parts that have Greek origins can help you understand some of the vocabulary in this chapter.

Greek Word Part	Meaning	Example
autos	self	autotroph, *n.* an organism that makes its own food
taxis	order, arrangement	taxonomy, *n.* the scientific study of how living things are classified
homos	similar, same	homeostasis, *n.* the maintenance of stable internal conditions

2. **Quick Check** Circle the part of the word *taxonomy* that lets you know that the word's meaning has something to do with ordering or classifying things.

organism

species

eukaryote

branching tree diagram

Chapter Preview

LESSON 1
- organism
- cell
- unicellular
- multicellular
- metabolism
- stimulus
- response
- development
- asexual reproduction
- sexual reproduction
- spontaneous generation
- controlled experiment
- autotroph
- heterotroph
- homeostasis

↻ **Compare and Contrast**
▲ **Control Variables**

LESSON 2
- classification
- taxonomy
- binomial nomenclature
- genus
- species

↻ **Ask Questions**
▲ **Observe**

LESSON 3
- prokaryote
- nucleus
- eukaryote

↻ **Identify the Main Idea**
▲ **Classify**

LESSON 4
- evolution
- branching tree diagram
- shared derived characteristic
- convergent evolution

↻ **Summarize**
▲ **Infer**

▶ **VOCAB FLASH CARDS** For extra help with vocabulary, visit **Vocab Flash Cards** and type in *Introduction to Living Things.*

403

What Is Life?

UNLOCK THE BIG ?

🔑 **What Are the Characteristics of All Living Things?**
8.3.1, 8.3.2, 8.3.6, 8.NS.8

🔑 **Where Do Living Things Come From?**
8.3.6, 8.NS.1, 8.NS.2, 8.NS.4, 8.NS.9

🔑 **What Do Living Things Need to Survive?**
8.3.6

my planet diary

TECHNOLOGY

It's Kismet!

If you hear a loud noise, do you turn toward the sound to see what caused it? When someone smiles at you, do you smile back? If somebody shook something in front of your face, would you back away? Most people react in these ways, and so does Kismet, a humanlike robot! Scientists developed Kismet to interact with, cooperate with, and learn from humans. Kismet can understand information that it sees and hears as if it were a young child. When responding to information, Kismet's face changes so that it seems interested, happy, or frightened. Kismet's expressions are so convincing that it is sometimes hard to remember that Kismet isn't really alive!

Answer the questions below.

1. What does Kismet do that makes it seem human?

_____

_____

_____

2. What are some things you think Kismet might not be able to do that humans can?

_____

_____

_____

▶ PLANET DIARY Go to **Planet Diary** to learn more about living things.

Lab zone® Do the Inquiry Warm-Up
Is It Living or Nonliving?

Vocabulary

- organism • cell • unicellular • multicellular • metabolism
- stimulus • response • development • asexual reproduction
- sexual reproduction • spontaneous generation
- controlled experiment • autotroph • heterotroph • homeostasis

Skills

↻ Reading: Compare and Contrast

△ Inquiry: Control Variables

What Are the Characteristics of All Living Things?

If you were asked to name some living things, or **organisms**, you might name yourself, a pet, and some insects or plants. You would probably not mention a moss growing in a shady spot, the mildew on bathroom tiles, or the slime molds that ooze across lawns. But all of these things are organisms that share several important characteristics with all other living things. ⚷ **All living things have a cellular organization, contain similar chemicals, use energy, respond to their surroundings, grow and develop, and reproduce.**

> **Academic Standards for Science**
>
> **8.3.1** Explain that reproduction is essential for the continuation of every species and is the mechanism by which all organisms transmit genetic information.
>
> **8.3.2** Compare and contrast the transmission of genetic information in sexual and asexual reproduction.
>
> **8.3.6** Observe anatomical structures of a variety of organisms and describe their similarities and differences.
>
> **8.NS.8** Analyze data.

FIGURE 1 ·······································

It's Alive . . . or Is It?

✎ **Look at the photos. Then answer the questions.**

1. **Identify** List the letter of the photo(s) that you think show living thing(s). _____

2. **Describe** What characteristics helped you decide whether or not the things shown were living or nonliving?

_____

_____

_____

8.NS.8

405

Cellular Organization

All organisms are made of small building blocks called cells. A **cell,** like the one shown here, is the basic unit of structure and function in an organism. Organisms may be composed of only one cell or of many cells.

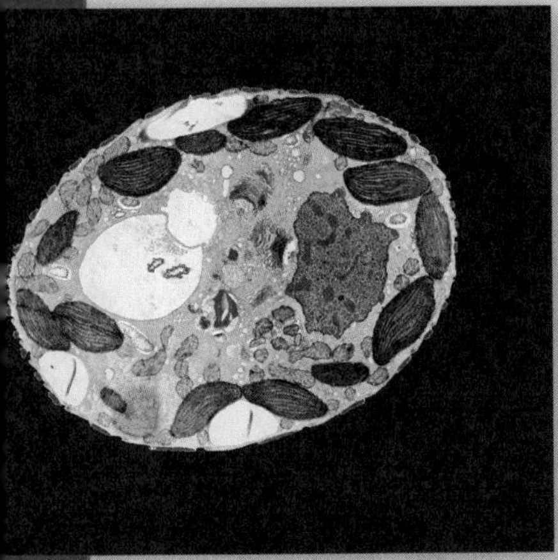

Single-celled organisms, like bacteria (bak TIHR ee uh), are **unicellular** organisms. The single cell is responsible for carrying out all of the functions necessary to stay alive. Organisms that are composed of many cells are **multicellular.** For example, you are made of trillions of cells. In many multicellular organisms, the cells are specialized to do certain tasks. Specialized cells in your body, such as muscle and nerve cells, work together to keep you alive. Nerve cells carry messages to your muscle cells, making your body move.

Characteristics of Living Things

The Chemicals of Life

The cells of living things are made of chemicals. The most abundant chemical in cells is water. Other chemicals, called carbohydrates (kahr boh HY drayts) are a cell's main energy source. Two other chemicals, proteins and lipids, are the building materials of cells, much as wood and bricks are the building materials of houses. Finally, nucleic (noo KLEE ik) acids are the genetic material of cells—the chemical instructions that cells need to carry out the functions of life.

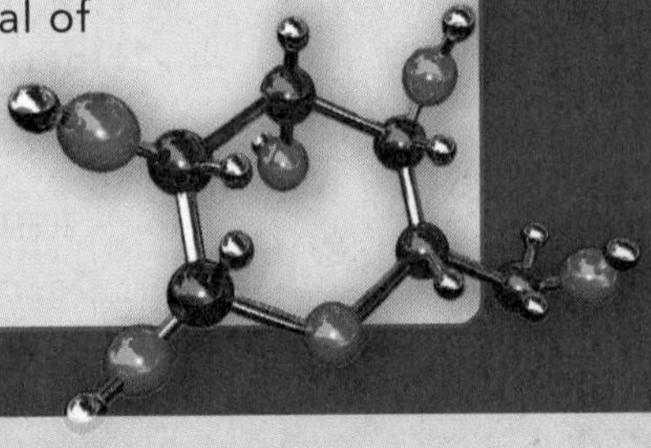

Energy Use

Organisms get energy from taking in and breaking down materials. The combination of chemical reactions through which an organism builds up or breaks down materials is called **metabolism.** The cells of organisms use energy to do what living things must do, such as grow and repair injured parts. An organism's cells are always hard at work. For example, as you read these words, not only are your eye and brain cells busy, but most of your other cells are working, too. Young sooty terns, like the one shown above, need lots of energy to fly. These birds can fly four to five years without ever setting foot on land!

FIGURE 2 ....

Living Things

All living things share the same characteristics.

✎ **Make Judgments** Which characteristic on these two pages do you think best identifies an object as a living thing? Explain your choice.

Response to Surroundings

If you've ever seen a plant in a sunny window, you may have observed that the plant's stems have bent so that the leaves face the sun. Like a plant bending toward the light, all organisms react to changes in their environment. A change in an organism's surroundings that causes the organism to react is called a **stimulus** (plural *stimuli*). Stimuli include changes in light, sound, and other factors.

An organism reacts to a stimulus with a **response**—an action or a change in behavior. For example, has someone ever knocked over a glass of water by accident during dinner, causing you to jump? The sudden spilling of water was the stimulus that caused your startled response.

 Lab **zone** Do the Quick Lab *React!*

Growth and Development

All living things grow and develop. Growth is the process of becoming larger. **Development** is the process of change that occurs during an organism's life, producing a more complex organism. As they develop and grow, organisms use energy and make new cells.

Reproduction

Another characteristic of organisms is the ability to reproduce, or produce offspring that are similar to the parents. Organisms reproduce in different ways. **Asexual reproduction** involves only one parent and produces offspring that are identical to the parent. **Sexual reproduction** involves two parents and combines their genetic material to produce a new organism that differs from both parents. Mammals, birds, and most plants sexually reproduce. Penguins lay eggs that develop into young penguins that closely resemble their parents.

Assess Your Understanding

1a. Review A change in an organism's surroundings is a (stimulus/response).

8.3.6

b. Infer A bird sitting in a tree flies away as you walk by. Which of the life characteristics explains the bird's behavior?

_____

8.3.6

c. CHALLENGE Trees do not move like birds do, but they are living things. Why?

_____
_____
_____
_____
_____

8.3.6

got it? ....

○ I get it! Now I know that all living things

_____
_____
_____
_____

○ I need extra help with _____

_____

Go to **MY SCIENCE COACH** *online for help with this subject.* 8.3.1, 8.3.2, 8.3.6

407

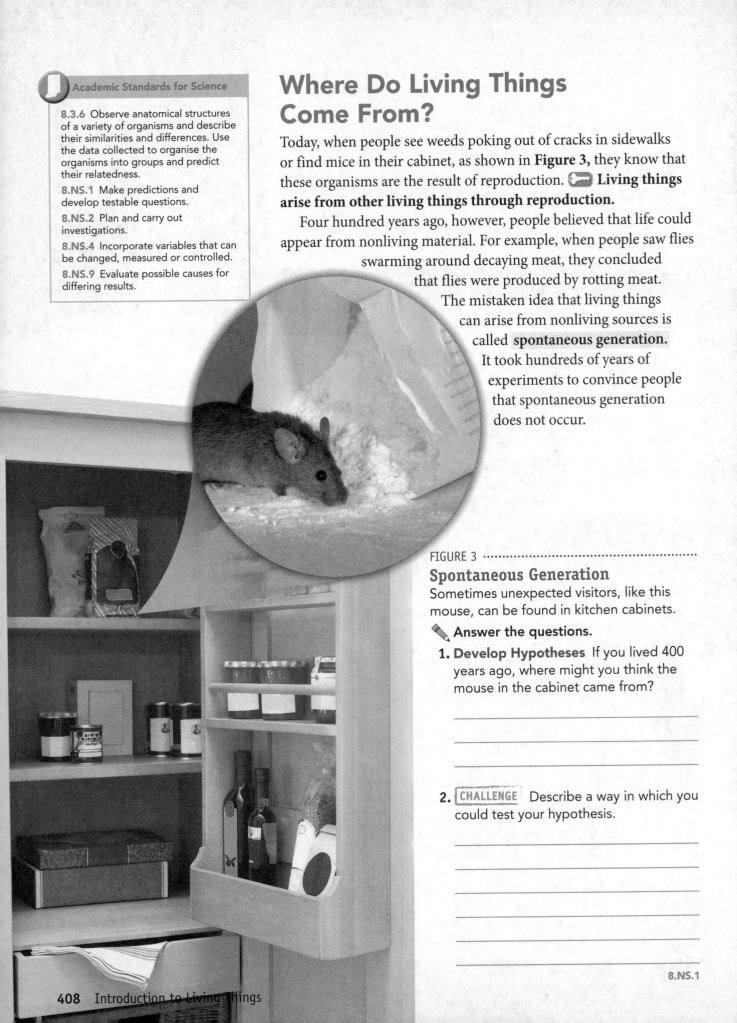
Where Do Living Things Come From?

Today, when people see weeds poking out of cracks in sidewalks or find mice in their cabinet, as shown in **Figure 3,** they know that these organisms are the result of reproduction. 🔑 **Living things arise from other living things through reproduction.**

Four hundred years ago, however, people believed that life could appear from nonliving material. For example, when people saw flies swarming around decaying meat, they concluded that flies were produced by rotting meat. The mistaken idea that living things can arise from nonliving sources is called **spontaneous generation.** It took hundreds of years of experiments to convince people that spontaneous generation does not occur.

FIGURE 3 ·······························

Spontaneous Generation

Sometimes unexpected visitors, like this mouse, can be found in kitchen cabinets.

✏ **Answer the questions.**

1. **Develop Hypotheses** If you lived 400 years ago, where might you think the mouse in the cabinet came from?

_____

_____

_____

2. CHALLENGE Describe a way in which you could test your hypothesis.

_____

_____

_____

_____

_____

8.NS.1

Redi's Experiment

In the 1600s, an Italian doctor named Francesco Redi helped to disprove spontaneous generation. Redi designed a controlled experiment to show that maggots, which develop into new flies, do not arise from decaying meat. In a **controlled experiment,** a scientist carries out a series of tests that are identical in every respect except for one factor. The one factor that a scientist changes in an experiment is called the manipulated variable. The factor that changes as a result of changes to the manipulated variable is called the responding variable. Redi's experiment is shown in **Figure 4.**

FIGURE 4 ·······································

Redi's Experiment

Francesco Redi designed one of the first controlled experiments. Redi showed that flies do not spontaneously arise from decaying meat. Here's how he did it:

Uncovered jar   **Covered jar**

STEP 1 Redi placed meat in two identical jars. He left one jar uncovered. He covered the other jar with a cloth that let in air.

STEP 2 After a few days, Redi saw maggots (young flies) on the decaying meat in the open jar. There were no maggots on the meat in the covered jar.

STEP 3 Redi reasoned that flies had laid eggs on the meat in the open jar. The eggs hatched into maggots. Because flies could not lay eggs on the meat in the covered jar, there were no maggots there. Redi concluded that decaying meat did not produce maggots.

apply it!

Use **Figure 4** to answer the following questions about Redi's experiment.   8.NS.4, 8.NS.9

1 Control Variables What is the manipulated variable in this experiment?

_____

_____

_____

2 Control Variables What is the responding variable?

_____

_____

_____

3 Analyze Sources of Error Name two factors that would need to be kept constant in this experiment to avoid causing error. Why?

_____

_____

_____

_____

_____

_____

_____

Pasteur's Experiment Even after Redi's experiment, many people continued to believe in spontaneous generation. In the mid-1800s, Louis Pasteur, a French chemist, designed another experiment to test spontaneous generation. That experiment, shown in **Figure 5**, along with Redi's work, finally disproved spontaneous generation.

FIGURE 5 ···

> INTERACTIVE ART **Pasteur's Experiment**

Louis Pasteur's carefully controlled experiment demonstrated that bacteria arise only from existing bacteria. ✎ **Design Experiments Read each step of the experiment below. Why do you think flasks with curved necks were important?**

_____

_____

_____

8.NS.2

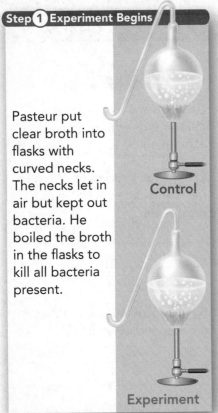

Step ❶ Experiment Begins

Pasteur put clear broth into flasks with curved necks. The necks let in air but kept out bacteria. He boiled the broth in the flasks to kill all bacteria present.

Control

Experiment

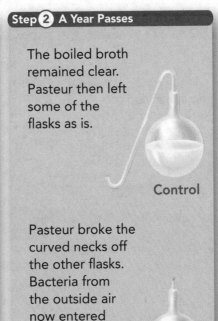

Step ❷ A Year Passes

The boiled broth remained clear. Pasteur then left some of the flasks as is.

Control

Pasteur broke the curved necks off the other flasks. Bacteria from the outside air now entered these flasks.

Experiment

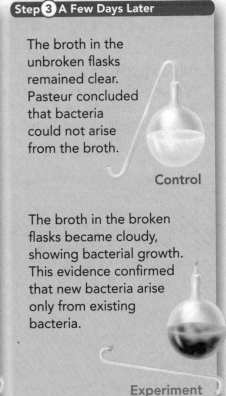

Step ❸ A Few Days Later

The broth in the unbroken flasks remained clear. Pasteur concluded that bacteria could not arise from the broth.

Control

The broth in the broken flasks became cloudy, showing bacterial growth. This evidence confirmed that new bacteria arise only from existing bacteria.

Experiment

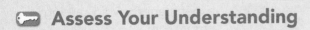

Lab Do the Quick Lab
zone *Compare Broth Samples.*

🔑 **Assess Your Understanding**

2a. Identify A _____ is the one factor that changes in a controlled experiment.　　8.3.6

b. Explain Why is the idea of spontaneous generation incorrect?

_____

_____

8.3.6

gotit**?**

○ **I get it!** Now I know that living things come from _____

_____

○ **I need extra help with** _____

Go to **MY SCIENCE** 🅢 **COACH** *online for help with this subject.*　　8.3.6

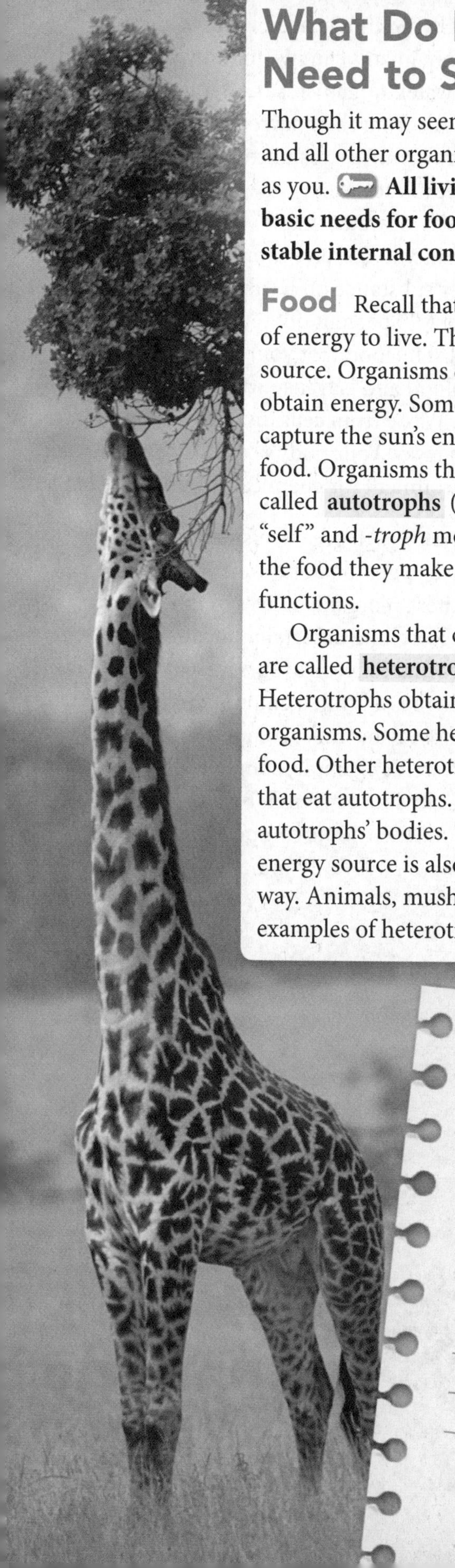

What Do Living Things Need to Survive?

Though it may seem surprising, flies, bacteria, and all other organisms have the same basic needs as you. **All living things must satisfy their basic needs for food, water, living space, and stable internal conditions.**

Food Recall that organisms need a source of energy to live. They use food as their energy source. Organisms differ in the ways they obtain energy. Some organisms, such as plants, capture the sun's energy and use it to make food. Organisms that make their own food are called **autotrophs** (AW toh trohfs). *Auto-* means "self" and *-troph* means "feeder." Autotrophs use the food they make to carry out their own life functions.

Organisms that cannot make their own food are called **heterotrophs** (HET uh roh trohfs). Heterotrophs obtain energy by feeding on other organisms. Some heterotrophs eat autotrophs for food. Other heterotrophs consume heterotrophs that eat autotrophs. They use the energy in the autotrophs' bodies. Therefore, a heterotroph's energy source is also the sun—but in an indirect way. Animals, mushrooms, and slime molds are examples of heterotrophs.

Academic Standards for Science

8.3.6 Observe anatomical structures of a variety of organisms and describe their similarities and differences. Use the data collected to organize the organisms into groups and predict their relatedness.

Compare and Contrast As you read, circle how autotrophs and heterotrophs are similar and underline how they are different.

Vocabulary Greek Word Origins The Greek word part *hetero-* means "other." How does this word help you to understand how heterotrophs get their food?

_____

_____

_____

_____

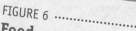

FIGURE 6

Food

This giraffe, a heterotroph, obtains its energy by feeding on trees and shrubs.

Identify From your own habitat, name two examples of autotrophs and two examples of heterotrophs.

_____

_____

_____

_____

know?......................

During the summer, when desert temperatures can exceed 47°C, a camel only needs to drink water every five days. At that time, a camel can drink up to 189 liters of water in just a few hours!

FIGURE 7 ....

Desert Oasis
You might be surprised to see so much green in the middle of a desert. In a desert oasis, there is water beneath the surface. The groundwater can bubble to the surface and create springs.

✎ **Draw Conclusions** How can a small area in the middle of a desert provide an organism what it needs to survive?

_____

_____

_____

_____

_____

Water All living things need water to survive. In fact, most organisms can live for only a few days without water. Organisms need water to obtain chemicals from their surroundings, break down food, grow, move substances within their bodies, and reproduce.

One property of water that is vital to living things is its ability to dissolve more chemicals than any other substance on Earth. In fact, water makes up about 90 percent of the liquid part of your blood. The food that your cells need dissolves in blood and is transported to all parts of your body. Waste from cells dissolves in blood and is carried away. Your body's cells also provide a watery environment for chemicals to dissolve.

Living Space All organisms need a place to live—a place to get food and water and find shelter. Whether an organism lives in the freezing Arctic or the scorching desert, its surroundings must provide what it needs to survive.

Because there is a limited amount of space on Earth, some organisms must compete for space. Trees in a forest, for example, compete with other trees for sunlight above ground. Below ground, their roots compete for water and minerals.

FIGURE 8 ··
Homeostasis
During the winter months, birds rely on their feathers to maintain homeostasis. By fluffing its feathers, this bluebird is able to trap body heat to keep warm. ✎ **Make Generalizations** How do people maintain homeostasis when exposed to cold temperatures?

_____

_____

_____

Lab ® Do the Lab
zone Investigation *Please Pass the Bread.*

🔑 Assess Your Understanding

3a. Describe Which basic need is a fox meeting by feeding on berries?

_____

_____

8.3.6

b. Apply Concepts The arctic fox has thick, dense fur in the winter and much shorter fur in the summer. How does this help the fox maintain homeostasis?

_____

_____

_____

_____

_____

8.3.6

got it? ···

○ **I get it!** Now I know that to survive, living things need _____

_____

_____

○ **I need extra help with** _____

_____

_____

_____

Go to **MY SCIENCE** 🔊 **COACH** *online for help with this subject.* 8.3.6

Stable Internal Conditions

Organisms must be able to keep the conditions inside their bodies stable, even when conditions in their surroundings change significantly. For example, your body temperature stays steady despite changes in the air temperature. The maintenance of stable internal conditions is called **homeostasis** (hoh mee oh STAY sis).

Homeostasis keeps internal conditions just right for cells to function. Think about your need for water after a hard workout. When water levels in your body decrease, chemicals in your body send signals to your brain, which cause you to feel thirsty.

Other organisms have different mechanisms for maintaining homeostasis. Consider barnacles, which as adults are attached to rocks at the edge of the ocean. At high tide, they are covered by water. But at low tide, the watery surroundings disappear, and barnacles are exposed to hours of sun and wind. Without a way to keep water in their cells, they would die. Fortunately, a barnacle can close up its hard outer plates, trapping some water inside. In this way, a barnacle can keep its body moist until the next high tide. Refer to **Figure 8** to see another example of how an organism maintains homeostasis.

Classifying Life

UNLOCK THE BIG ?

🔑 **Why Do Biologists Classify Organisms?**
8.3.6, 8.NS.8

🔑 **What Are the Levels of Classification?**
8.3.6

🔑 **How Are Taxonomic Keys Useful?**
8.3.6, 8.NS.8

my planeт Diary

CAREER

Birds of a Feather

When people first began to travel in airplanes, birds often caused crashes. In 1960, 62 people were killed when birds flew into an airplane's engine. Something had to be done, but no one knew what kinds of birds were causing the crashes. Usually only a tiny, burnt piece of feather remained. Engineers didn't know how big or heavy the birds were, so they couldn't design planes to keep birds out of the engines. Then a scientist named Roxie Laybourne invented a way to classify birds using a tiny piece of feather. She identified the birds from many crashes. Her work helped engineers design engines to reduce bird collisions. She also helped develop bird management programs for major airports. Roxie's work has saved passengers' lives!

Answer the questions below.

1. What did Roxie Laybourne invent?

_____

_____

_____

2. Why was her invention so important?

_____

_____

_____

_____

_____

_____

> **PLANET DIARY** Go to **Planet Diary** to learn more about classification.

Lab zone® Do the Inquiry Warm-Up Can You Organize a Junk Drawer?

Vocabulary
- classification • taxonomy • binomial nomenclature
- genus • species

Skills
↻ Reading: Ask Questions

△ Inquiry: Observe

Why Do Biologists Classify Organisms?

So far, scientists have identified more than one million kinds of organisms on Earth. That's a large number, and it keeps growing as scientists discover new organisms. Imagine how difficult it would be to find information about one particular organism if you had no idea even where to begin. It would be a lot easier if similar organisms were placed into groups.

Organizing living things into groups is exactly what biologists have done. Biologists group organisms based on similarities, just as grocers group milk with dairy products and tomatoes with other produce. **Classification** is the process of grouping things based on their similarities, as shown in **Figure 1**.

🔑 **Biologists use classification to organize living things into groups so that the organisms are easier to study.** The scientific study of how organisms are classified is called **taxonomy** (tak SAHN uh mee). Taxonomy is useful because once an organism is classified, a scientist knows a lot of information about that organism. For example, if you know that a crow is classified as a bird, then you know that a crow has wings, feathers, and a beak.

Academic Standards for Science

8.3.6 Observe anatomical structures of a variety of organisms and describe their similarities and differences. Use the data to organize the organisms into groups and predict their relatedness.

8.NS.8 Analyze data, using appropriate mathematical manipulation as required, and use it to identify patterns and make inferences based on these patterns.

↻ **Ask Questions** Before you read, preview the headings. Ask a *what*, *why*, or *how* question that you would like answered. As you read, write the answer to your question.

_____
_____
_____
_____
_____

FIGURE 1 ······························

Classifying Insects

These bees and wasps belong to a large insect collection in a natural history museum. They have been classified according to the characteristics they share.

✎ **Observe** What characteristics do you think may have been used to group these insects?

_____
_____
_____
_____
_____

8.NS.8

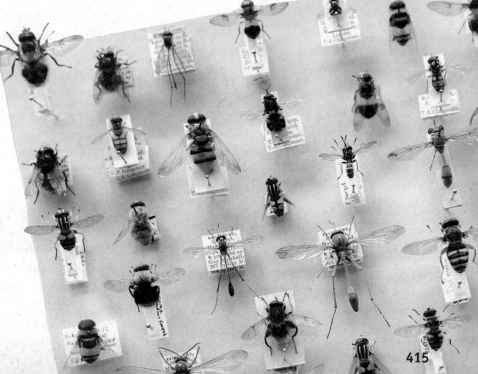

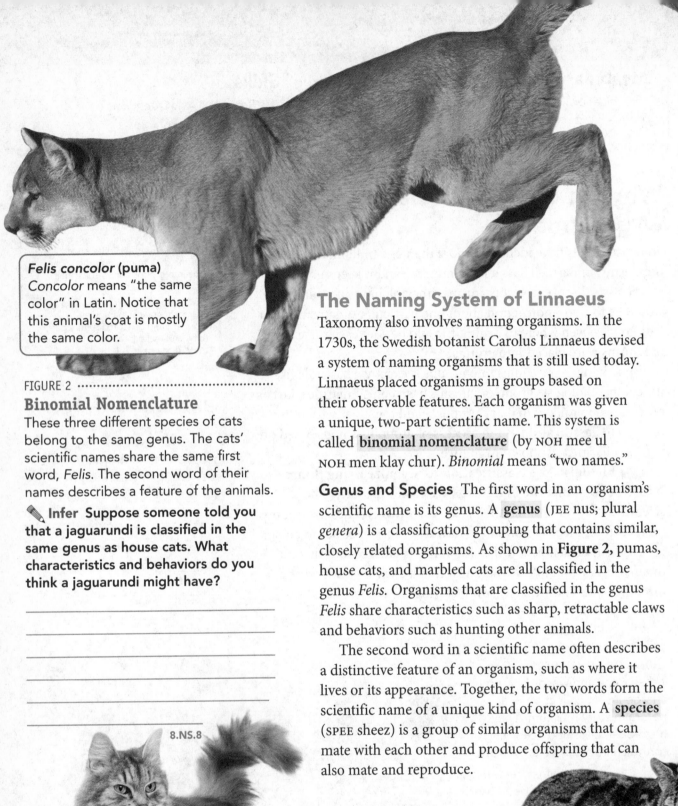

Felis concolor (puma)
Concolor means "the same color" in Latin. Notice that this animal's coat is mostly the same color.

FIGURE 2 ·······································

Binomial Nomenclature
These three different species of cats belong to the same genus. The cats' scientific names share the same first word, *Felis*. The second word of their names describes a feature of the animals.

✎ **Infer** Suppose someone told you that a jaguarundi is classified in the same genus as house cats. What characteristics and behaviors do you think a jaguarundi might have?

_____

_____

_____

_____

_____

_____

8.NS.8

Felis domesticus (house cat)
Domesticus means "of the house" in Latin.

The Naming System of Linnaeus
Taxonomy also involves naming organisms. In the 1730s, the Swedish botanist Carolus Linnaeus devised a system of naming organisms that is still used today. Linnaeus placed organisms in groups based on their observable features. Each organism was given a unique, two-part scientific name. This system is called **binomial nomenclature** (by NOH mee ul NOH men klay chur). *Binomial* means "two names."

Genus and Species The first word in an organism's scientific name is its genus. A **genus** (JEE nus; plural *genera*) is a classification grouping that contains similar, closely related organisms. As shown in **Figure 2,** pumas, house cats, and marbled cats are all classified in the genus *Felis*. Organisms that are classified in the genus *Felis* share characteristics such as sharp, retractable claws and behaviors such as hunting other animals.

The second word in a scientific name often describes a distinctive feature of an organism, such as where it lives or its appearance. Together, the two words form the scientific name of a unique kind of organism. A **species** (SPEE sheez) is a group of similar organisms that can mate with each other and produce offspring that can also mate and reproduce.

Felis marmorata (marbled cat)
Marmorata means "marble" in Latin. Notice the marbled pattern of this animal's coat.

Using Binomial Nomenclature A complete scientific name is written in italics. Only the first letter of the first word in a scientific name is capitalized. Notice that scientific names contain Latin words. Linnaeus used Latin words in his naming system because Latin was the language that scientists used during that time.

Binomial nomenclature makes it easy for scientists to communicate about an organism because everyone uses the same scientific name for the same organism. Using different names or common names for the same organism can get very confusing, as **Figure 3** describes.

FIGURE 3 ·········

What Are You Talking About?

Is this animal a groundhog, a woodchuck, a marmot, or a whistlepig? Depending on where you live, all of these names are correct. Luckily, this animal has only one scientific name, *Marmota monax.*

✏️ **Describe** How is a scientific name written?

_____

_____

_____

do the math!

8.NS.8

Aristotle and Classification

Aristotle, an ancient Greek scholar, also developed a classification system for animals.

Animals With Blood

32%

46%

22%

- ■ Animals that swim (sharks, bass, dolphins)
- ■ Animals that fly (eagles, gulls, pigeons)
- ■ Animals that walk, run, or hop (tortoises, frogs, lions)

❶ **Read Graphs** Which group made up the largest percentage of animals?

_____

❷ **Calculate** _____ percent of these animals either fly or swim.

❸ **Classify** What new categories would you use to make a graph that classifies animals that move in more than one way?

_____

_____

_____

Lab zone ® Do the Quick Lab *Classifying Seeds.*

🔑 Assess Your Understanding

1a. Define The scientific study of how living things are classified is called

_____

8.3.6

b. Make Generalizations What is the advantage of using scientific names instead of using common names, like cat or dog?

_____

_____

_____

_____

_____

_____

8.3.6

got it? ·····························

○ **I get it!** Now I know that organisms are

classified _____

_____

_____

○ **I need extra help with** _____

_____

Go to MY SCIENCE ⓢ COACH *online for help with this subject.*

8.3.6

417

What Are the Levels of Classification?

The classification system that scientists use today is based on the contributions of Linnaeus. But today's classification system uses a series of many levels to classify organisms.

To help you understand the levels of classification, imagine a room filled with everybody who lives in your state. First, all of the people who live in your town raise their hands. Then those who live in your neighborhood raise their hands. Then those who live on your street raise their hands. Finally, those who live in your house raise their hands. Each time, fewer people raise their hands. The more levels you share with others, the more you have in common with them.

The Major Levels of Classification Of course, organisms are not grouped by where they live, but by their shared characteristics. Most biologists today classify organisms into the levels shown in **Figure 4.** First, an organism is placed in a broad group, which in turn is divided into more specific groups.

🔑 **A domain is the broadest level of organization. Within a domain, there are kingdoms. Within kingdoms, there are phyla (FY luh; singular *phylum*). Within phyla are classes. Within classes are orders. Within orders are families. Each family contains one or more genera. Finally, each genus contains one or more species.** The more classification levels two organisms share, the more characteristics they have in common and the more closely related they are.

FIGURE 4 ···

▷ **VIRTUAL LAB** **Levels of Classification**
The figure on the facing page shows how the levels of organization apply to a great horned owl.

✎ **Answer the questions.**

1. ◢**Observe** List the characteristics that the organisms share at the kingdom level.

_____

_____

2. ◢**Observe** List the characteristics that the organisms share at the class level.

_____

_____

_____

3. ◢**Observe** List the characteristics that the organisms share at the genus level.

_____

_____

_____

_____

4. **Draw Conclusions** How does the number of shared characteristics on your list change at each level? _____

_____

_____

5. **Interpret Diagrams** Robins have more in common with (lions/owls).

Levels of Classification

Domain Eukarya

Kingdom Animalia

Phylum Chordata

Class Aves

Order Strigiformes

Family Strigidae

Genus *Bubo*

Species *Bubo virginianus*

> As you move down these levels of classification, the number of organisms decreases. The organisms that remain share more characteristics with one another and are more related.

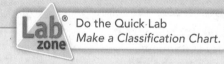 Do the Quick Lab
Make a Classification Chart.

🔑 Assess Your Understanding

got it? ··

○ **I get it!** Now I know that the levels of classification are _____
_____
_____
_____

○ **I need extra help with** _____
_____

Go to **my science** Ⓢ **coach** *online for help with this subject.*

8.3.6

Academic Standards for Science

8.3.6 Observe anatomical structures of a variety of organisms and describe their similarities and differences. Use the data to organize the organisms into groups and predict their relatedness.

8.NS.8 Analyze data.

How Are Taxonomic Keys Useful?

Why should you care about taxonomy? Suppose that you are watching television and feel something tickling your foot. Startled, you look down and see a tiny creature crawling across your toes. Although it's only the size of a small melon seed, you don't like the looks of its two claws waving at you. Then, in a flash, it's gone.

How could you find out what the creature was? You could use a field guide. Field guides are books with illustrations that highlight differences between similar-looking organisms. You could also use a taxonomic key. 🔑 **Taxonomic keys are useful tools that help determine the identity of organisms.** A taxonomic key consists of a series of paired statements that describe the various physical characteristics of different organisms. The taxonomic key shown in **Figure 5** can help you identify the mysterious organism.

FIGURE 5 ···

> INTERACTIVE ART **Identifying Organisms**   8.NS.8

The six paired statements in this taxonomic key describe physical characteristics of different organisms.

✎ **Identify** _____ different organisms can be identified using this key. The mysterious organism is a _____

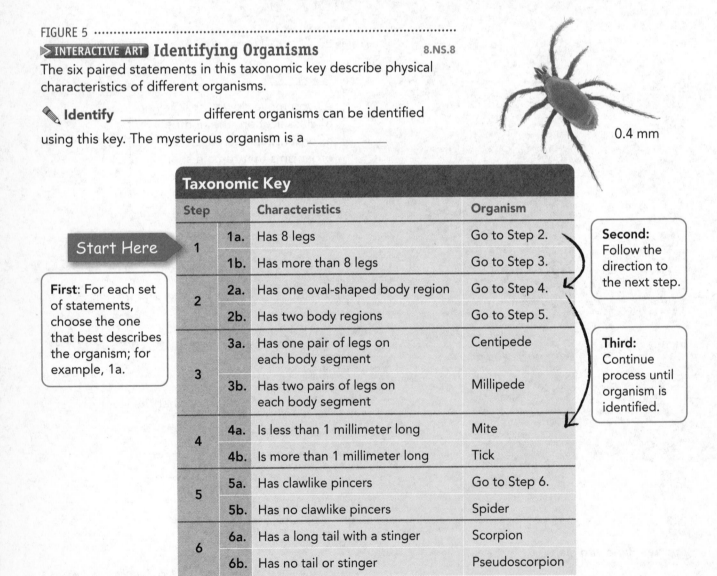

0.4 mm

Start Here →

First: For each set of statements, choose the one that best describes the organism; for example, 1a.

Second: Follow the direction to the next step.

Third: Continue process until organism is identified.

Taxonomic Key			
Step		**Characteristics**	**Organism**
1	**1a.**	Has 8 legs	Go to Step 2.
	1b.	Has more than 8 legs	Go to Step 3.
2	**2a.**	Has one oval-shaped body region	Go to Step 4.
	2b.	Has two body regions	Go to Step 5.
3	**3a.**	Has one pair of legs on each body segment	Centipede
	3b.	Has two pairs of legs on each body segment	Millipede
4	**4a.**	Is less than 1 millimeter long	Mite
	4b.	Is more than 1 millimeter long	Tick
5	**5a.**	Has clawlike pincers	Go to Step 6.
	5b.	Has no clawlike pincers	Spider
6	**6a.**	Has a long tail with a stinger	Scorpion
	6b.	Has no tail or stinger	Pseudoscorpion

apply it!

Use the taxonomic key in **Figure 5** to answer the following questions.

1 Interpret Tables Identify each pictured organism.

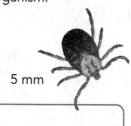

5 mm

64 mm

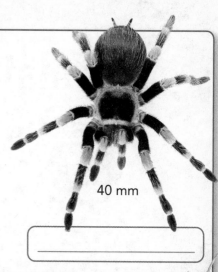

40 mm

50 mm

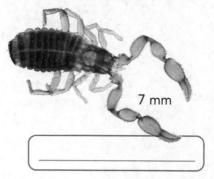

7 mm

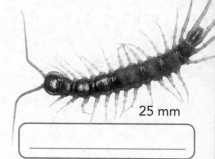

25 mm

2 Draw Conclusions What other information could have been helpful in identifying these organisms?

_____

_____

_____

_____

3 CHALLENGE Is this information necessary for the key in **Figure 5**? Explain your answer.

_____

_____

_____

8.NS.8

 Do the Quick Lab
Living Mysteries.

🔑 Assess Your Understanding

got it? ....

○ **I get it!** Now I know that taxonomic keys are used to _____

_____

○ **I need extra help with** _____

Go to **MY SCIENCE COACH** online for help with this subject.

8.3.6

421

Indiana

LESSON

3 Domains and Kingdoms

UNLOCK THE BIG

? How Are Organisms Classified Into Domains and Kingdoms?

8.3.6, 8.NS.8

my planeT DiaRY

Unbeelievable!

If you were classifying organisms, would you expect there to be more bees, more birds, or more mammals in the world? The table below shows the number of species of bees, mammals, and birds that scientists have found so far!

Number of Species		
Bees	Mammals	Birds
19,200	5,400	10,000

SCIENCE STATS

Answer the question below.

Why do you think that bee species outnumber mammal and bird species combined?

_____

_____

_____

_____

▷ PLANET DIARY   Go to **Planet Diary** to learn more about domains and kingdoms.

Lab zone® Do the Inquiry Warm-Up
What Organism Goes Where?

Academic Standards for Science

8.3.6 Observe anatomical structures of a variety of organisms and describe their similarities and differences. Use the data to organize the organisms into groups and predict their relatedness.

8.NS.8 Analyze data.

How Are Organisms Classified Into Domains and Kingdoms?

Suppose you helped Linnaeus classify organisms. You probably would have identified organisms as either plants or animals. That's because in Linnaeus' time there were no microscopes to see the tiny organisms that are known to exist today. Microscopes helped to discover new organisms and identify differences among cells.

Today, a three-domain system of classification is commonly used. As shown in the table on the top of the next page, the three domains are Bacteria, Archaea, and Eukarya. Within the domains are kingdoms. ☞ **Organisms are placed into domains and kingdoms based on their cell type, their ability to make food, and the number of cells in their bodies.**

Vocabulary
- prokaryote
- nucleus
- eukaryote

Skills
- Reading: Identify the Main Idea
- Inquiry: Classify

Three Domains of Life

Bacteria	Archaea	Eukarya			
		Protists	Fungi	Plants	Animals

Domain Bacteria Although you may not know it, members of the domain Bacteria are all around you. You can find them on the surfaces you touch and inside your body. Some bacteria are autotrophs, while others are heterotrophs.

Members of the domain Bacteria are called prokaryotes (proh KA ree ohtz). **Prokaryotes** are unicellular organisms whose cells lack a nucleus. A **nucleus** (NOO klee us; plural *nuclei*) is a dense area in a cell that contains nucleic acids—the chemical instructions that direct the cell's activities. In prokaryotes, nucleic acids are not contained within a nucleus.

Domain Archaea Deep in the Pacific Ocean, hot gases and molten rock spew out from a vent in the ocean floor. It is hard to imagine that any living thing could exist in such harsh conditions. Surprisingly, a group of tiny organisms thrives in such a place. They are members of the domain Archaea (ahr KEE uh), whose name comes from the Greek word for "ancient."

Like bacteria, archaea are unicellular prokaryotes. And like bacteria, some archaea are autotrophs and others are heterotrophs. Archaea are classified in their own domain because their chemical makeup differs from that of bacteria. Bacteria and archaea also differ in the structure of their cells. The bacteria in **Figure 1** and the archaea in **Figure 2** have been stained and magnified to make them easier to see.

FIGURE 1 ....
Bacteria
Most bacteria, such as *Lactobacillus acidophilus*, are helpful. These bacteria help to produce yogurt and milk for people who are lactose intolerant.

FIGURE 2 ....
Archaea
Archaea can be found in extreme environments such as hot springs, very salty water, and the intestines of cows! Scientists think that the harsh conditions in which archaea live are similar to those of ancient Earth.

✎ **Compare and Contrast** How are archaea and bacteria similar? How are they different?

_____

_____

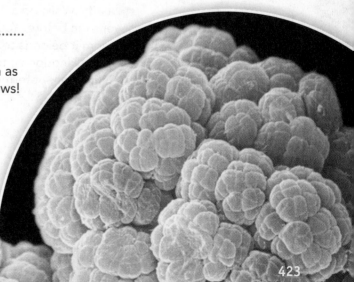

423

FIGURE 3

Eukarya

You can encounter organisms from all four kingdoms of Eukarya on a trip to a salt marsh.

Three Domains of Life					
Bacteria	Archaea	Eukarya			
		Protists	Fungi	Plants	Animals

Domain Eukarya What do seaweeds, mushrooms, tomatoes, and dogs have in common? They are all members of the domain Eukarya. Organisms in this domain are **eukaryotes** (yoo KA ree ohtz)—organisms with cells that contain nuclei. Scientists classify organisms in the domain Eukarya into one of four kingdoms: protists, fungi, plants, or animals.

Marine dinoflagellates

Protists

A protist (PROH tist) is any eukaryotic organism that cannot be classified as a fungus, plant, or animal. Because its members are so different from one another, the protist kingdom is sometimes called the "odds and ends" kingdom. For example, some protists are autotrophs, while others are heterotrophs. Most protists are unicellular, but some, such as seaweeds, are multicellular.

Fungi

If you have eaten mushrooms, then you have eaten fungi (FUN jy). Mushrooms, molds, and mildew are all fungi. The majority of fungi are multicellular eukaryotes. A few, such as the yeast used in baking, are unicellular eukaryotes. Fungi are found almost everywhere on land, but only a few live in fresh water. All fungi are heterotrophs. Most fungi feed by absorbing nutrients from dead or decaying organisms.

Aspergillus fumigatus

apply it!

Classify While on a walk, you find an organism that you've never seen before. You are determined to figure out what kingdom it belongs to. Starting with the first observation below, circle the kingdom(s) the organism could fit into. Using the process of elimination, determine what kingdom the organism belongs to.

1 There are nuclei present.
(Protists/Fungi/Plants/Animals)

2 You can count more than one cell.
(Protists/Fungi/Plants/Animals)

3 The organism cannot make its own food.
(Protists/Fungi/Plants/Animals)

4 The organism gets nutrients from dead organisms. (Protists/Fungi/Plants/Animals)

5 Other members of this kingdom can be unicellular. (Protists/Fungi/Plants/Animals)

8.NS.8

Plants

Dandelions on a lawn, peas in a garden, and the marsh grass shown here are familiar members of the plant kingdom. Plants are all multicellular eukaryotes, and most live on land. Also, plants are autotrophs that make their own food. Plants provide food for most of the heterotrophs on land.

The plant kingdom includes a great variety of organisms. Some plants produce flowers, while others do not. Some plants, such as giant redwood trees, can grow very tall. Others, like mosses, never grow taller than a few centimeters.

✐ **Identify the Main Idea** In the text under Domain Eukarya, underline the main idea.

Snowy egret

Animals

A dog, a flea on the dog's ear, and a cat that the dog chases have much in common because all are animals. All animals are multicellular eukaryotes. In addition, all animals are heterotrophs. Animals have different adaptations that allow them to locate food, capture it, eat it, and digest it. Members of the animal kingdom live in diverse environments throughout Earth. Animals can be found from ocean depths to mountaintops, from hot, scalding deserts to cold, icy landscapes.

Lab zone® Do the Quick Lab *Staining Leaves.*

🔑 Assess Your Understanding

1a. Define A cell that lacks a nucleus is called a (eukaryote/prokaryote).

8.3.6

b. List Two ways that the members of the two domains of prokaryotes differ are in the

_____

_____

8.3.6

c. CHALLENGE You learn that a dandelion is in the same kingdom as pine trees. Name three characteristics that these organisms share.

_____

_____

8.3.6

got it?

○ **I get it!** Now I know that organisms are classified into domains and kingdoms based on their _____

_____

_____

○ **I need extra help with** _____

_____

Go to **MY SCIENCE** 🗨 **COACH** *online for help with this subject.*

8.3.6

Indiana

LESSON

4 Evolution and Classification

🔑 **How Are Evolution and Classification Related?**

8.3.6, 8.3.8, 8.NS.7, 8.NS.8

MY PLANET DIARY

DISCOVERY

If It Looks Like a Duck...

The first scientist to see the pelt of the platypus thought it was a joke. Could a four-legged, duck-billed, egg-laying mammal exist? How had it evolved? Native people from Australia believed that the first platypus was born when a water rat mated with a duck. But scientists put the platypus into a new group of egg-laying mammals. Then many years later, scientists began to argue. Had the platypus really evolved later with younger marsupials such as kangaroos? Would the platypus have to be reclassified? Scientists studied its DNA and discovered that the platypus was in the right place!

Answer the question below.
How did DNA help classify the platypus?

_____

_____

_____

_____

_____

_____

▷ **PLANET DIARY** Go to **Planet Diary** to learn more about evolution and classification.

Lab zone Do the Inquiry Warm-Up *Observing Similarities.*

Academic Standards for Science

8.3.6 Observe anatomical structures of a variety of organisms and describe their similarities and differences. Use the data to organize the organisms into groups and predict their relatedness.

8.3.8 Examine traits of individuals within a population of organisms that may give them an advantage in survival and reproduction in a given environment or when the environment changes.

8.NS.7 Keep accurate records in a notebook.

8.NS.8 Analyze data.

How Are Evolution and Classification Related?

When Linnaeus developed his classification system, people thought that species never changed. In 1859, a British naturalist named Charles Darwin published an explanation for how species could change over time. Recall that the process of change over time is called **evolution.** Darwin thought that evolution occurs by means of natural selection. Natural selection is the process by which individuals that are better adapted to their environment are more likely to survive and reproduce than other members of the same species.

Vocabulary

- evolution
- branching tree diagram
- shared derived characteristic
- convergent evolution

Skills

- Reading: Summarize
- Inquiry: Infer

As understanding of evolution increased, biologists changed how they classify species. Scientists now understand that certain organisms may be similar because they share a common ancestor and an evolutionary history. The more similar the two groups are, the more recent the common ancestor probably is. Today's system of classification considers the history of a species. **Species with similar evolutionary histories are classified more closely together.**

Summarize Name two things that similar organisms share.

_____

_____

_____

Branching Tree Diagrams Two groups of organisms with similar characteristics may be descended from a common ancestor. A **branching tree diagram,** like the one in **Figure 1,** shows probable evolutionary relationships among organisms and the order in which specific characteristics may have evolved. Branching tree diagrams begin at the base with the common ancestor of all the organisms in the diagram. Organisms are grouped according to their shared derived characteristics.

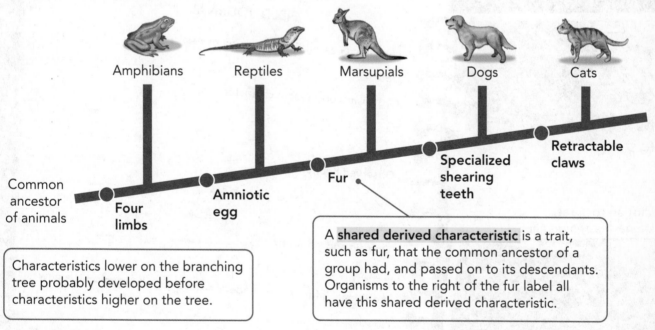

Common ancestor of animals

Four limbs

Amniotic egg

Fur

Specialized shearing teeth

Retractable claws

Amphibians · Reptiles · Marsupials · Dogs · Cats

Characteristics lower on the branching tree probably developed before characteristics higher on the tree.

A **shared derived characteristic** is a trait, such as fur, that the common ancestor of a group had, and passed on to its descendants. Organisms to the right of the fur label all have this shared derived characteristic.

FIGURE 1 ·······

ART IN MOTION **A Branching Tree**   8.NS.8

This branching tree diagram shows how cats have evolved.

Complete the tasks.

1. **Interpret Diagrams** Put squares around the shared derived characteristics.

2. **Interpret Diagrams** Circle the animal(s) that belong to the smallest group.

3. **Apply Concepts** Cats are more closely related to (reptiles/marsupials).

apply it!

Note the characteristics of Figures A, B, C, and D.

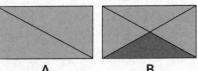

A   B

C   D

1 **Infer** Which figure is the most similar to Figure B?

_____

2 **CHALLENGE** Suppose these shapes are fossils of extinct organisms. Which organism do you think might be the ancestor of all the others? Why?

_____

_____

8.NS.8

Finding a New Species

How are living things alike yet different?

FIGURE 2 ·· 8.NS.7, 8.NS.8

While on an expedition, you photograph what you think is a new species.

✏ **Draw Conclusions** Use the camera image of the new species and the photos of organisms previously identified from the same area to record your observations in your field journal.

Laotian rock rat
Laonastes aenigmanus

Golden-crowned flying fox
Acerodon jubatus

FIELD JOURNAL

Location: Greater Mekong region of Asia

Date: _____

Organism's observable characteristics: _____

_____

_____

Observed habitat(s): _____

_____

_____

Domain and kingdom: _____

_____

Additional information needed to determine if organism is a new

species: _____

_____

_____

Name (assuming it's a new species): _____

_____

Significance/meaning of name: _____

_____

FIGURE 3 ·······························
Convergent Evolution
Birds and insects both use wings to help them fly. However, these two organisms are not closely related.

Determining Evolutionary Relationships How do scientists determine the evolutionary history of a species? One way is to compare the structure of organisms. Scientists can also use information about the chemical makeup of the organisms' cells.

Sometimes unrelated organisms evolve similar characteristics because they evolved in similar environments, like organisms that move through the water or eat similar foods. Because the organisms perform similar functions, their body structures may look similar. Look at **Figure 3.** The process by which unrelated organisms evolve characteristics that are similar is called **convergent evolution.**

When studying the chemical makeup of organisms, sometimes new information is discovered that results in reclassification. For example, skunks and weasels were classified in the same family for 150 years. When scientists compared nucleic acids from the cells of skunks and weasels, they found many differences. These differences suggest that the two groups are not that closely related. As a result, scientists reclassified skunks into a separate family.

Do the Quick Lab
Common Ancestors.

🔑 **Assess Your Understanding**

1a. Identify Look back at **Figure 1.** What characteristics do all reptiles share?

_____

8.3.6

b. ANSWER THE BIG ❓ How are living things alike yet different? _____

_____

_____

_____

got it? ··· 8.3.6

O **I get it!** Now I know that evolution and classification are related because _____

_____

_____

O **I need extra help with** _____

_____

Go to MY SCIENCE 🔵 COACH *online for help with this subject.* 8.3.6

10 Study Guide

Living things can vary. For example, organisms may be prokaryotes or _____.
Yet all living things are made of _____, which grow, develop, and reproduce.

LESSON 1 What Is Life?

8.3.1, 8.3.2, 8.3.6, 8.NS.1, 8.NS.2, 8.NS.4, 8.NS.8, 8.NS.9

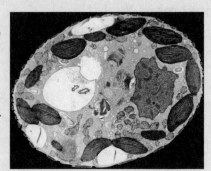

🔑 All living things have a cellular organization, contain similar chemicals, use energy, respond to their surroundings, grow and develop, and reproduce.

🔑 Living things arise from other living things through reproduction.

🔑 All living things must satisfy their basic needs for food, water, living space, and stable internal conditions.

Vocabulary
• organism • cell • unicellular • multicellular • metabolism • stimulus • response • development
• asexual reproduction • sexual reproduction • spontaneous generation • controlled experiment
• autotroph • heterotroph • homeostasis

LESSON 2 Classifying Life

8.3.6, 8.NS.8

🔑 Biologists use classification to organize living things into groups so that the organisms are easier to study.

🔑 The levels of classification are domain, kingdom, phylum, class, order, family, genus, and species.

🔑 Taxonomic keys are useful tools that help determine the identity of organisms.

Vocabulary
• classification • taxonomy • binomial nomenclature
• genus • species

LESSON 3 Domains and Kingdoms

8.3.6, 8.NS.8

🔑 Organisms are placed into domains and kingdoms based on their cell type, ability to make food, and the number of cells in their bodies.

Vocabulary
• prokaryote
• nucleus • eukaryote

LESSON 4 Evolution and Classification

8.3.6, 8.3.8, 8.NS.7, 8.NS.8

🔑 Species with similar evolutionary histories are classified more closely together.

Vocabulary
• evolution
• branching tree diagram
• shared derived characteristic
• convergent evolution

Review and Assessment

LESSON 1 What Is Life?

1. The maintenance of stable internal conditions is called

    a. stimulus.   **b.** autotrophy.

    c. homeostasis.   **d.** response.

8.3.6

2. _____ involves only one parent and produces offspring that are identical to the parent.

8.3.1, 8.3.2

3. Apply Concepts Pick an organism in your home and describe how this organism meets the four basic conditions for survival.

_____

_____

_____

_____

_____

8.3.6

4. Control Variables A student is designing a controlled experiment to test whether the amount of water that a plant receives affects its growth. Which variables should the student hold constant and which variable should the student manipulate?

_____

_____

_____

_____

8.3.6, 8.NS.4

5. Write About It Suppose you are searching for new life forms as part of an expedition in a remote region of Alaska. At one site you find 24 greenish-brown objects, each measuring around 1 cm³. The objects do not appear to have heads, tails, or legs, but you suspect they may be alive. Describe what you would do to determine if the objects are alive.

8.3.6

LESSON 2 Classifying Life

6. Which of the following is the broadest level of classification?

    a. genus   **b.** species

    c. domain   **d.** kingdom

8.3.6

7. The two-part naming system called

_____

was devised by Linnaeus in the 1700s.

8.3.6

8. Predict The scientific name for the red maple tree is *Acer rubrum*. Another organism is called *Acer negundo*. Based on its name, what can you predict about this organism? Explain.

_____

_____

_____

_____

8.3.6, 8.NS.1

9. Make Models Develop a taxonomic key that a person could use to identify each of the plants shown below.   8.3.6, 8.NS.11

White ash   Red oak   White oak   Pasture rose

10 Review and Assessment

 Domains and Kingdoms

10. Which four kingdoms belong to the domain Eukarya?

    a. prokarya, archaea, eukarya, bacteria

    b. protists, fungi, plants, animals

    c. mite, tick, scorpion, spider

    d. class, order, family, genus

                                     8.3.6

11. All eukaryotes belong to domain Eukarya, while _____ belong to domain Bacteria or domain Archaea.

                                       8.3.6

12. Compare and Contrast Both plants and fungi belong to the domain Eukarya. What is one main difference between these organisms?

_____

_____

_____

_____

                                       8.3.6

 Evolution and Classification

13. Which of the following factors is most important when classifying an organism?

    a. size   **b.** shape

    c. habitat   **d.** evolutionary history

                                       8.3.6

14. A diagram that shows probable evolutionary relationships among organisms is called a

_____

                                       8.3.6

15. Apply Concepts If you discovered two unrelated organisms that looked very similar, how could you explain it?

_____

_____

_____

_____

_____

                                       8.3.6

 How are living things alike yet different?

16. With the advances in commercial space travel, some day you may have the opportunity to visit another planet and see things you've never seen before! How would you go about identifying things on the other planet as being living or nonliving? If an object turns out to be living, what characteristics would you look for in order to classify it? Use four vocabulary terms from the chapter in your answer.

_____

_____

_____

_____

_____

_____

_____

_____

_____

_____

_____

_____

_____

                                       8.3.6

Indiana ISTEP+ Practice

Multiple Choice

Circle the letter of the best answer.

1. How many kingdoms are represented by the organisms shown below?

   A. 1   **B.** 2
   C. 3   **D.** 4

8.3.6

2. According to the system of binomial nomenclature, which of the following is a properly written scientific name?

   A. Acer rubrum   **B.** Acer Rubrum
   C. *Acer rubrum*   **D.** *acer rubrum*

8.3.6

3. Which of the following is an example of an autotroph?

   A. a lion   **B.** a tree
   C. an eagle   **D.** a mushroom

8.3.6

4. Which domain does NOT contain prokaryotes?

   A. Archaea
   B. Bacteria
   C. Eukarya
   D. None of the above. All three domains contain prokaryotes.

8.3.6

Constructed Response

Write your answer to Question 5 on the lines below.

5. How does a branching tree diagram show evolutionary relationships?

   _____

   _____

   _____

8.3.6

Extended Response

Use the chart below and your knowledge of science to help you answer Question 6. Write your answer on a separate piece of paper.

Some Types of Trees

Common Name of Tree	Kingdom	Family	Species
Bird cherry	Plants	Rosaceae	*Prunus avium*
Flowering cherry	Plants	Rosaceae	*Prunus serrula*
Smooth-leaved elm	Plants	Ulmaceae	*Ultimus minor*
Whitebeam	Plants	Rosaceae	*Sorbus aria*

6. Which one of the four trees is most different from the other three? Explain your answer.

8.3.6

Museum of Science

TECH & DESIGN

LIGHTS, CAMERA, SHARK ACTION!

In movies, sharks are often scary, toothy costars. Although many people know that sharks have a mean reputation, there is a lot that we don't know about them.

To discover more about these mysterious creatures, Fabien Cousteau and his team created a shark submarine. The one-person submarine has a steel skeleton and a thick rubber skin that makes it look like a great white shark. The 4.25-meter shark sub moves through the water as quietly and quickly as a real shark, and can even wiggle its tail!

In the sub, Cousteau was able to observe shark behavior up close. He saw sharks' feeding habits, how they investigated new things, and how they prepared to attack. He also saw real sharks trying to communicate with the fake one by rolling their eyes and puffing their gills. The submarine's cameras recorded hours of shark action, which will help us understand these creatures better.

Research It Find three articles describing Cousteau's interaction with the sharks. Write your own article comparing and reviewing the science presented in the articles. Describe any new information you learned from each article, and evaluate any bias in the articles. How was the information presented in each article? Did the authors balance their discussions of the risks and benefits of shark research?

8.NS.2, 8.NS.11

Museum of Science

"feet" of engineering

Geckos are tiny lizards that live in warm climates all over the world, including the southwestern United States. If you've ever seen one, you've probably watched it scale a wall in about the time it takes for you to blink. Or you may have seen a gecko hang from one foot.

How do geckos hang from one foot? The answer is their hair! The gecko's feet are covered in millions of tiny hairs. Molecules in the hairs are attracted to molecules in the wall or on any other surface. These forces of attraction, called van der Waals forces, are usually so weak that you can't feel them. However, there are so many tiny hairs on a gecko's feet that geckos can cling to nearly any surface!

Gecko feet have inspired scientists to design artificial super-sticky materials that use the same principle. Scientists will have to see which designs stick!

Design It Technological design inspired by biology is called biomimetic design. Identify a need or problem that could be solved by biomimetic design. Brainstorm potential solutions and choose your best idea. Document your design with labeled drawings and then select materials to create a prototype. Test and evaluate how well your solution meets the goal. Record relevant data in graphs or tables. Use this information to redesign your prototype to improve the results. See Appendix A on page 508 for more information about the design process.

8.NS.1–8.NS.11,
8.DP.1–8.DP.11

DOES THIS FISH HAVE LEGS?

 How do life forms change over time?

This is not your average fish. Besides having bright red lips, the rosy-lipped batfish is a poor swimmer. Instead of using its pectoral fins for swimming, the batfish uses them to crawl along the seafloor.

Develop Hypotheses How do you think the batfish's leglike fins help it survive?

_____

_____

_____

_____

_____

_____

▶ UNTAMED SCIENCE Watch the **Untamed Science** video to learn more about adaptations.

Change Over Time

Academic Standards for Science

8.3.6, 8.3.7, 8.3.8, 8.3.9, 8.3.10, 8.NS.1, 8.NS.2, 8.NS.8, 8.NS.11, 8.DP.1, 8.DP.2, 8.DP.4

Check Your Understanding

1. **Background** Read the paragraph below and then answer the question.

> Last fall, Jerome collected more than 100 seeds from a single sunflower in his garden. In the spring, he planted all the seeds. He was not surprised that the new plants all varied in many **traits.** Jerome knows that, because of **sexual reproduction,** each plant's **DNA** is different.

> A **trait** is a characteristic that an organism passes to offspring through its genes.
>
> **Sexual reproduction** results in offspring that are genetically different from each parent.
>
> **DNA** is genetic material that carries information about an organism and is passed from parent to offspring.

- How are the plants' different traits related to sexual reproduction?

_____

_____

> **MY READING WEB** If you had trouble completing the question above, visit **My Reading Web** and type in *Change Over Time.*

Vocabulary Skill

Identify Multiple Meanings Familiar words may mean something else in science. Look at the different meanings of the words below.

Word	Everyday Meaning	Scientific Meaning
theory	*n.* a guess **Example:** Sue has a theory that soccer is harder to play than basketball.	*n.* a well-tested concept that explains a wide range of observations **Example:** The cell theory says that all organisms are made of cells.
adaptation	*n.* a change in an individual's behavior **Example:** Talia's adaptation to her new school was hard, but she did it.	*n.* a trait that helps an individual survive and reproduce **Example:** Fur is an adaptation to cold.

2. **Quick Check** Circle the sentence that uses the scientific meaning of the word *theory.*

- Evolutionary *theory* describes change over time.
- Do you have a *theory* about why Sarah is a vegetarian?

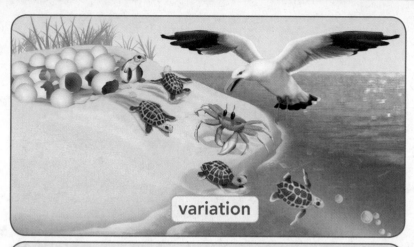

variation

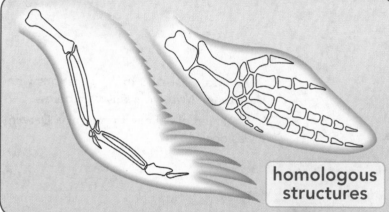

homologous structures

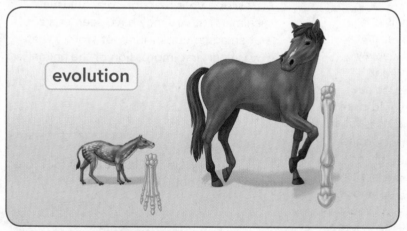

evolution

adaptation

Chapter Preview

LESSON 1

- species
- fossil
- adaptation
- evolution
- scientific theory
- natural selection
- variation

↻ Relate Cause and Effect

△ Develop Hypotheses

LESSON 2

- homologous structures

↻ Identify the Main Idea

△ Communicate

LESSON 3

- gradualism
- punctuated equilibrium

↻ Compare and Contrast

△ Make Models

> **VOCAB FLASH CARDS** For extra help with vocabulary, visit **Vocab Flash Cards** and type in *Change Over Time.*

Darwin's Theory

UNLOCK THE BIG ?

🔑 **What Was Darwin's Hypothesis?**
8.3.8, 8.3.9, 8.3.10, 8.NS.1, 8.NS.8

🔑 **What Is Natural Selection?**
8.3.8, 8.3.9, 8.NS.8, 8.DP.10

my planet Diary

Charles Darwin

In 1839, Charles Darwin published his book *The Voyage of the Beagle.* Read the following excerpt about an animal Darwin encountered while in the Galápagos Islands.

The inhabitants believe that these animals are absolutely deaf; certainly they do not overhear a person walking close behind them. I was always amused when overtaking one of these great monsters, as it was quietly pacing along, to see how suddenly, the instant I passed, it would draw in its head and legs, and uttering a deep hiss fall to the ground with a heavy sound, as if struck dead. I frequently got on their backs, and then giving a few raps on the hinder part of their shells, they would rise up and walk away; — but I found it very difficult to keep my balance.

VOICES FROM HISTORY

Communicate **Discuss these questions with a classmate. Write your answers below.**

1. What kind of animal do you think Darwin was describing?

_____

_____

2. Describe your reaction to an unusual animal that you may have seen at a zoo, at an aquarium, or in a pet store. What was your first impression of the animal?

_____

_____

_____

▶ PLANET DIARY Go to **Planet Diary** for more information about Charles Darwin.

Do the Inquiry Warm-Up
How Do Living Things Vary?

Vocabulary

- species • fossil • adaptation
- evolution • scientific theory
- natural selection • variation

Skills

- Reading: Relate Cause and Effect
- Inquiry: Develop Hypotheses

What Was Darwin's Hypothesis?

In 1831, the British ship HMS *Beagle* set sail from England on a five-year trip around the world. Charles Darwin was on board. Darwin was a naturalist—a person who observes and studies the natural world.

Diversity Darwin was amazed by the diversity of living things that he saw during the voyage. He wondered why they were so different from those in England. Darwin saw insects that looked like flowers. He also observed sloths, slow-moving animals that spent much of their time hanging in trees. Today, scientists know that organisms are even more diverse than Darwin thought. In fact, scientists have identified more than 1.6 million species of organisms on Earth. A **species** is a group of similar organisms that can mate with each other and produce fertile offspring. The exact number of species is unknown because many areas of Earth have not yet been studied.

Fossils Darwin saw fossils of animals that had died long ago. A **fossil** is the preserved remains or traces of an organism that lived in the past. Darwin was puzzled by some of the fossils he observed. For example, he saw fossils that resembled the bones of living sloths but were much larger in size. He wondered what had happened to the ancient, giant ground sloths. See **Figure 1.**

Academic Standards for Science

8.3.8 Examine traits of individuals within a population of organisms that may give them an advantage in survival and reproduction in a given environment or when the environment changes.

8.3.9 Describe the effects of environmental changes on populations of organisms.

8.3.10 Recognize and describe how new varieties of organisms have come about from selective breeding.

8.NS.1 Make predictions.

8.NS.8 Analyze data.

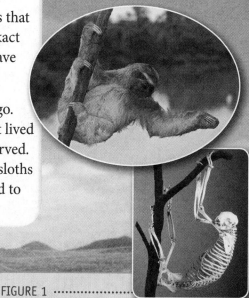

FIGURE 1 ·········

Sloth Similarities

Darwin thought that the fossil bones of the giant ground sloths (left) resembled the bones of modern-day sloths (above).

✎ **Observe** List two similarities that you notice between the two sloths.

Similarities

8.NS.8

441

Galápagos Organisms

The *Beagle* made many stops along the Atlantic and Pacific coasts of South America. From the Pacific coast, the ship traveled west to the Galápagos Islands. Darwin observed many unusual life forms there. He compared organisms from the Galápagos Islands to organisms that lived elsewhere. He also compared organisms living on the different islands.

Comparisons to South American Organisms Darwin discovered many similarities between Galápagos organisms and those found in South America. Many of the birds and plants on the islands resembled those on the mainland. However, he also noted important differences between the organisms. For instance, you can see differences between island and mainland iguanas in **Figure 2**.

Darwin became convinced that species do not always stay the same. Instead, he thought species could change and even produce new species over time. Darwin began to think that maybe the island species were somehow related to South American species. Perhaps, he thought, the island species had become different from their mainland relatives over time.

FIGURE 2 ....

Comparing Iguanas

The iguanas on the Galápagos Islands have large claws that allow them to grip slippery rocks so they can feed on seaweed.

The iguanas on the mainland have smaller claws that allow them to climb trees so they can eat leaves.

✎ **Infer** The color of each iguana is an adaptation to its

○ food.　　○ habitat.

○ predators.　　○ climate.

Explain your answer.

_____

_____

_____

8.NS.8

FIGURE 3 ··

> INTERACTIVE ART **Galápagos Finches**
The structure of each bird's beak is an adaptation
to the type of food the bird eats. Birds with long,
pointed, sharp beaks pick at cacti. Those with
short, thick beaks crush seeds.

Birds with narrow, pointed beaks grasp insects.
Those with short, hooked beaks tear open fruit.

✎ **Interpret Diagrams** **Look at the different
beak structures. Draw a line from each finch to
the type of food you think it eats.**   8.NS.8

Comparisons Among the Islands Darwin also discovered
many differences among organisms on the different Galápagos
Islands. For example, the tortoises on one island had dome-shaped
shells. Those on another island had saddle-shaped shells. A government official in the islands told Darwin that he could tell which
island a tortoise came from just by looking at its shell.

Adaptations Birds were also different from one island to the
next. Look at **Figure 3.** When Darwin returned to England, he
learned that the different birds were all finches. Darwin
concluded that the finch species were all related to a single ancestor
species that came from the mainland. Over time, different finches
developed different beak shapes and sizes that were well suited to
the food that they ate. Beak shape is an example of an **adaptation,**
a trait that increases an organism's ability to survive and reproduce.

·············· ✎ ··············

Vocabulary Identify Multiple
Meanings Write a sentence
using the everyday meaning of
the word *adapt.*

_____

_____

_____

_____

_____

_____

did you **know?** ....

Many species of animals can be traced back to primitive ancestors. For example, this fossil shows primitive amphibian tracks. The balls at the ends of the toes are similar to those on the feet of modern frogs and salamanders. This fossil is displayed at the Indiana Geological Survey.

Darwin's Hypothesis Darwin thought about what he had seen during his voyage on the *Beagle*. By this time, Darwin was convinced that organisms change over time. The process of change over time is called **evolution.** Darwin, however, wanted to know *how* organisms change. Over the next 20 years, he consulted with other scientists and gathered more information. Based on his observations, Darwin reasoned that plants or animals that arrived on the Galápagos Islands faced conditions that were different from those on the nearby mainland. **Darwin hypothesized that species change over many generations and become better adapted to new conditions**.

Darwin's ideas are often referred to as a theory of evolution. A **scientific theory** is a well-tested concept that explains a wide range of observations. From the evidence he collected, Darwin concluded that organisms on the Galápagos Islands had changed over time.

apply it!

The first labradoodle dog was bred in 1989. A labradoodle is a cross between a standard poodle and a Labrador retriever. The poodle is very smart and has fur that sheds very little. The poodle may be less irritating for people allergic to dogs. Labradors are gentle, easily trained, and shed seasonally.

Standard poodle   Labrador retriever   Labradoodle

❶ **Make Generalizations** Why do you think people breed these two dogs together?

_____

_____

❷ **Develop Hypotheses** Would you expect the first labradoodle puppies to be the same as puppies produced several generations later? Explain.

_____

_____

8.NS.1, 8.NS.8

Artificial Selection Darwin studied the offspring of domesticated animals that were produced by artificial selection in an effort to understand how evolution might occur. In artificial selection, only the organisms with a desired characteristic, such as color, are bred. Darwin himself had bred pigeons with large, fan-shaped tails. By repeatedly allowing only those pigeons with many tail feathers to mate, Darwin produced pigeons with two or three times the usual number of tail feathers. Darwin thought that a process similar to artificial selection might happen in nature. But he wondered what natural process selected certain traits.

FIGURE 4 ··
Artificial Selection
The pigeons that Darwin bred were all descended from the rock dove (left). Pigeons can be bred for characteristics such as color, beak shape, wingspan, and feather patterns.

✎ **Describe** If you were to breed an animal, what would it be and what traits would you want it to have?

_____

_____

_____

Lab® Do the Quick Lab
zone *Bird Beak Adaptations.*

🔑 Assess Your Understanding

1a. List Make a list of three observations that Darwin made during the *Beagle's* voyage.

_____

_____

_____

8.3.8, 8.3.9

b. Describe An adaptation is a trait that increases an organism's ability to _____ and _____

8.3.8, 8.3.9

c. Develop Hypotheses How does artificial selection support Darwin's hypothesis?

_____

_____

_____

_____

_____

8.3.10

got it? ··

○ **I get it!** Now I know that Darwin's hypothesis was _____

_____

○ **I need extra help with** _____

Go to MY SCIENCE ⓢ COACH *online for help with this subject.*

8.3.8, 8.3.9, 8.3.10

445

What Is Natural Selection?

In 1858, Darwin and Alfred Russel Wallace, another British biologist, both proposed the same explanation for how evolution occurs. The next year, Darwin described his explanation in his book *The Origin of Species*. In this book, Darwin proposed that evolution occurs by means of natural selection. **Natural selection** is the process by which individuals that are better adapted to their environment are more likely to survive and reproduce more than other members of the same species. Darwin identified factors that affect the process of natural selection: overproduction, variation, and competition. **Figure 5** shows how natural selection might happen in a group of sea turtles.

Overproduction Darwin knew that most species produce far more offspring than can possibly survive. In many species, so many offspring are produced that there are not enough resources—food, water, and living space—for all of them.

Factors That Affect Natural Selection
How do life forms change over time?

EXPLORE THE BIG **?**

FIGURE 5 ···

▶ **REAL-WORLD INQUIRY** Overproduction, variation, and competition are factors that affect the process of natural selection.

✎ **Summarize** Examine the sequence below that shows how natural selection could affect a group of sea turtles over time. Label each factor in the illustration and write a brief caption explaining what is occurring.   8.NS.8

Variation Members of a species differ from one another in many of their traits. Any difference between individuals of the same species is called a **variation.** For example, sea turtles may differ in color, size, the ability to swim quickly, and shell hardness.

Competition Since food, space, and other resources are limited, the members of a species must compete with one another to survive. Competition does not always involve physical fights between members of a species. Instead, competition is usually indirect. For example, some turtles may not find enough to eat. A slower turtle may be caught by a predator, while a faster turtle may escape. Only a few turtles will survive to reproduce.

Selection Darwin observed that some variations make individuals better adapted to their environment. Those individuals are more likely to survive and reproduce. Their offspring may inherit the helpful characteristic. The offspring, in turn, will be more likely to survive and reproduce, and pass the characteristic to their offspring. After many generations, more members of the species will have the helpful characteristic.

In effect, the environment selects organisms with helpful traits to become parents of the next generation. 🔑 **Darwin proposed that, over a long time, natural selection can lead to change. Helpful variations may accumulate in a species, while unfavorable ones may disappear.**

↺ **Relate Cause and Effect**
Fill in the graphic organizer to identify the factors that cause natural selection.

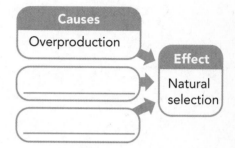

Causes
Overproduction
_____
_____

Effect
Natural selection

Environmental Change A change in the environment can affect an organism's ability to survive and therefore lead to natural selection. For example, monkey flowers are plants that do not normally grow in soil that has a high concentration of copper. However, because of genetic variation, some varieties of monkey flower now grow near copper mines. In **Figure 6** you can see how natural selection might have resulted in monkey flowers that can grow in copper-contaminated soil.

Genes and Natural Selection Without variations, all the members of a species would have the same traits and the same chance of surviving and reproducing. But where do variations come from? How are they passed on from parents to offspring?

Darwin could not explain what caused variations or how they were passed on. As scientists later learned, variations can result from changes in genes and the shuffling of different forms of genes when egg and sperm join. Genes, such as those for hair color and height, are passed from parents to their offspring. Only traits that are inherited, or controlled by genes that are passed on to offspring, can be acted upon by natural selection.

do the math!

The typical clutch size, or number of eggs, a loggerhead sea turtle can lay at once is around 113. Even with producing so many offspring, the loggerhead sea turtle is endangered in many areas. Suppose that scientists counted the number of eggs laid at seven different nesting sites along the southeast coast of the United States. The following year, scientists check the nesting sites to see how many offspring survived and returned.

Loggerhead Sea Turtle Data							
Site	A	B	C	D	E	F	G
Clutch Size	114	103	121	118	107	103	104
Returning Turtles	45	35	55	53	40	66	38

① Calculate Determine the mean for the clutch sizes of the seven nesting sites in the table. _____ How does the mean compare to the typical clutch size for loggerheads? _____

_____

_____

② Interpret Data Do you think clutch size influences the survival rates of the offspring? Use the data to support your answer.

_____

_____

_____

_____

③ CHALLENGE Hypothesize why Site F had the largest number of returning turtles.

_____

_____

_____

_____

8.NS.8

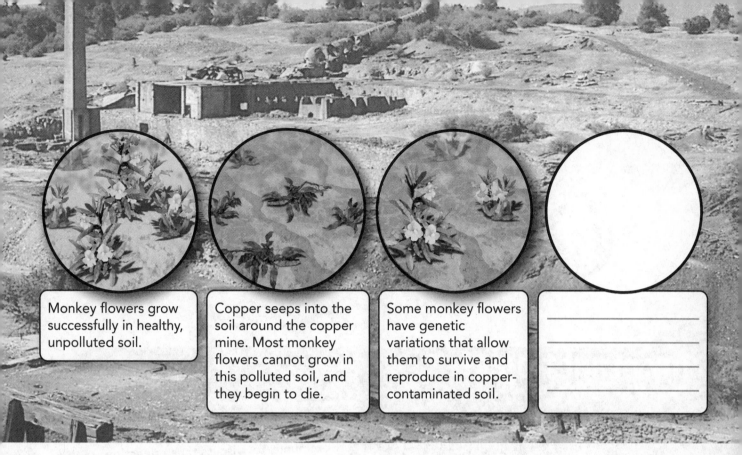

Monkey flowers grow successfully in healthy, unpolluted soil.

Copper seeps into the soil around the copper mine. Most monkey flowers cannot grow in this polluted soil, and they begin to die.

Some monkey flowers have genetic variations that allow them to survive and reproduce in copper-contaminated soil.

_____
_____
_____
_____

FIGURE 6 ··

Environmental Change
When copper contaminated the soil surrounding the monkey flowers, the environment changed. Due to a genetic variation, some varieties of monkey flower are now able to survive in that soil.

✏ **Draw Conclusions** In the last circle, draw what you think the area will look like in ten years' time. Write a caption describing what has taken place. 8.NS.8, 8.DP.10

 Do the Lab Investigation
Nature at Work.

🗝 Assess Your Understanding

2a. Define A variation is any (similarity/ difference) between individuals of the same species. 8.3.8, 8.3.9

b. ANSWER THE BIG ❓ How do life forms change over time?

_____
_____
_____
8.3.8, 8.3.9

c. 🔄 **Relate Cause and Effect** Explain how unfavorable traits can disappear in a species.

_____
_____
_____
_____
_____
8.3.8, 8.3.9

got it? ··

O **I get it!** Now I know that natural selection occurs _____
_____
_____

O I need extra help with _____

Go to **MY SCIENCE** ⓢ **COACH** *online for help with this subject.* 8.3.8, 8.3.9

Evidence of Evolution

🔑 **What Evidence Supports Evolution?**

UNLOCK THE BIG ❓

8.3.8, 8.3.9, 8.NS.8

my plaNeT DiaRY

DISCOVERY

Moving On Up

In 2004, researchers on Ellesmere Island, Nunavut, in the Canadian Arctic, found a fossil that provides information about when fish first came onto land. The fossil, called *Tiktaalik*, is 375 million years old. *Tiktaalik* has characteristics of both fish and four-legged animals. Like other fish, it has fins. However, the fins have interior bones that helped push the animal up in the shallow waters close to shore to find food. The discovery of *Tiktaalik* has provided new fossil evidence to help scientists understand the relationship between marine vertebrates and land vertebrates.

Researcher from Ellesmere Island

Communicate Discuss these questions with a partner. Write your answers below.

1. Do you think the discovery of *Tiktaalik* is important to understanding evolution? Why?

_____

_____

_____

_____

2. Do you think *Tiktaalik* spent most of its time on land or in water? Why?

_____

_____

_____

> PLANET DIARY ◁ Go to **Planet Diary** to learn more about fossil evidence.

This model of *Tiktaalik* shows what it may have looked like 375 million years ago.

 Do the Inquiry Warm-Up
How Can You Classify a Species?

Vocabulary
• homologous structures

Skills
🔊 Reading: Identify the Main Idea
△ Inquiry: Communicate

What Evidence Supports Evolution?

Since Darwin's time, scientists have found a great deal of evidence that supports the theory of evolution. 🔑 **Fossils, patterns of early development, similar body structures, and similarities in DNA and protein structures all provide evidence that organisms have changed over time.**

Fossils By examining fossils, scientists can infer the structures of ancient organisms. Fossils show that, in many cases, organisms that lived in the past were very different from organisms alive today. The millions of fossils that scientists have collected are called the fossil record. The fossil record provides clues about how and when new species evolved and how organisms are related.

Similarities in Early Development Scientists also infer evolutionary relationships by comparing the early development of different organisms. For example, the organisms in **Figure 1** look similar during the early stages of development. All four organisms have a tail. They also have a row of tiny slits along their throats. The similarities suggest that these vertebrate species are related and share a common ancestor.

Academic Standards for Science

8.3.8 Examine traits of individuals within a population of organisms that may give them an advantage in survival and reproduction in a given environment or when the environment changes.

8.3.9 Describe the effect of environmental changes on populations of organisms when their adaptive characteristics put them at a disadvantage for survival. Describe how extinction of a species can ultimately result.

8.NS.8 Analyze data, using appropriate mathematical manipulation as required, and use it to identify patterns and make inferences based on these patterns.

FIGURE 1 ·················

Similarities in Development

These four organisms all look similar during their early development.

✏️ **Complete each task.**

1. **Observe** Circle at least two similarities shared by all four organisms.

2. **Describe** What are some differences between the organisms?

_____

_____

_____

8.NS.8

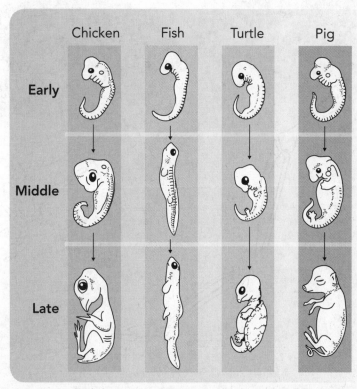

Chicken   Fish   Turtle   Pig

Early

Middle

Late

Similarities in Body Structure

An organism's body structure is its basic body plan, which in vertebrates includes how its bones are arranged. Fishes, amphibians, reptiles, birds, and mammals all have an internal skeleton with a backbone. This similarity provides evidence that these animal groups all evolved from a common ancestor.

Similar structures that related species have inherited from a common ancestor are known as **homologous structures** (hoh MAHL uh gus). In **Figure 2,** you can see some examples of homologous structures. These include a bird's wing, a dolphin's flipper, and a dog's leg.

Sometimes fossils show structures that are homologous with structures in living species. For example, scientists have recently found fossils of ancient whalelike creatures. The fossils show that the ancestors of today's whales had legs and walked on land. This evidence supports other evidence that whales and other vertebrates share a common ancestor that had a skeleton with a backbone.

⟳ **Identify the Main Idea**
Describe the main idea on this page.

_____

_____

_____

_____

_____

FIGURE 2 ··

⟩ INTERACTIVE ART **Homologous Structures**

The bones in a bird's wing, a dolphin's flipper, and a dog's leg have similar structures.

✎ **Interpret Diagrams** Use the drawing of the dog's leg as a guide. Color in the matching bones in the bird's wing and the dolphin's flipper with the appropriate colors.   8.NS.8

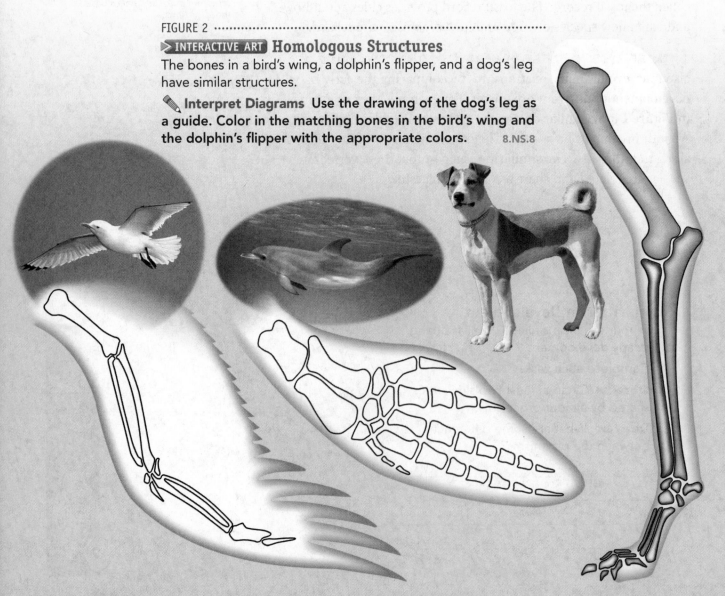

Similarities in DNA and Protein Structure

Why do some species have similar body structures and development patterns? Scientists infer that the species inherited many of the same genes from a common ancestor.

Recall that genes are segments of DNA. Scientists compare the sequence of nitrogen bases in the DNA of different species to infer how closely related the two species are. The more similar the DNA sequences, the more closely related the species are. The DNA bases along a gene specify what type of protein will be produced. Therefore, scientists can also compare the order of amino acids in a protein to see how closely related two species are.

In most cases, evidence from DNA and protein structure has confirmed conclusions based on fossils, embryos, and body structure. For example, DNA comparisons show that dogs are more similar to wolves than to coyotes. Scientists had already reached this conclusion based on similarities in the structure and development of these three species.

apply it!

The table shows the sequence of amino acids in one region of a protein, cytochrome c, for five different animals. Each letter corresponds to a different amino acid in the protein.

Section of Cytochrome c Protein in Animals

Animal	Amino Acid Position in the Sequence											
	39	40	41	42	43	44	45	46	47	48	49	50
Horse	N	L	H	G	L	F	G	R	K	T	G	Q
Donkey	N	L	H	G	L	F	G	R	K	T	G	Q
Rabbit	N	L	H	G	L	F	G	R	K	T	G	Q
Snake	N	L	H	G	L	F	G	R	K	T	G	Q
Turtle	N	L	N	G	L	I	G	R	K	T	G	Q

1 Interpret Tables Which species is most distantly related to the horse? _____

2 Communicate Explain how amino acid sequences provide information about evolutionary relationships among organisms.

_____

_____

_____

_____

_____

_____

8.NS.8

 Do the Quick Lab
Finding Proof.

🔑 Assess Your Understanding

1a. Define _____ structures are structurally similar body parts in related species.   8.3.8, 8.3.9

b. CHALLENGE Insects and birds both have wings. What kinds of evidence might show whether or not insects and birds are closely related? Explain.

_____

_____

_____

_____

8.3.8, 8.3.9

got it?

○ **I get it!** Now I know that the theory of evolution is supported by evidence that includes _____

_____

_____

_____

○ I need extra help with _____

Go to MY SCIENCE COACH *online for help with this subject.*   8.3.8, 8.3.9

3 Rate of Change

UNLOCK THE BIG ?

🗝 **How Do New Species Form?**
8.3.8, 8.3.9, 8.3.10

🗝 **What Patterns Describe the Rate of Evolution?**
8.3.8, 8.3.9, 8.NS.8

MY PLANET DIARY

Crickets, Maggots, and Flies, Oh My!

A male cricket chirps to attract a mate. Unfortunately, chirping also attracts a parasitic fly. Parasitic flies listen for chirping crickets. When a cricket is located, a female fly deposits larvae onto the cricket's back. The larvae, or maggots, burrow into the cricket. The maggots come out seven days later, killing the cricket in the process. Parasitic flies reduced the cricket population on the Hawaiian island of Kauai between 1991 and 2001. By 2003, the cricket population on Kauai had increased. The male crickets were silent! In about 20 cricket generations, the crickets had evolved into an almost silent population.

 Lab zone® Do the Inquiry Warm-Up *Making a Timeline.*

Academic Standards for Science

8.3.8 Examine traits of individuals within a population of organisms that may give them an advantage in survival and reproduction in a given environment or when the environment changes.

8.3.9 Describe the effects of environmental changes on populations of organisms.

8.3.10 Recognize and describe how new varieties of organisms have come about from selective breeding.

FUN FACT

Communicate Discuss these questions with a classmate. Write your answers below.

1. Why do you think the crickets on Kauai evolved so quickly?

_____

_____

_____

2. If most of the male crickets can no longer chirp, how do you think it might affect the size of the cricket population?

_____

_____

_____

_____

▷ **PLANET DIARY** Go to **Planet Diary** to learn more about evolution.

How Do New Species Form?

Natural selection explains how variations can lead to changes in a species. But how could an entirely new species form? 🗝 **A new species can form when a group of individuals remains isolated from the rest of its species long enough to evolve different traits that prevent reproduction.** Isolation, or complete separation, occurs when some members of a species become cut off from the rest of the species. One way this can happen is when a natural barrier, such as a river, separates group members.

Vocabulary
- gradualism
- punctuated equilibrium

Skills
- Reading: Compare and Contrast
- Inquiry: Make Models

FIGURE 1

Kaibab and Abert's Squirrels
The Kaibab squirrel (left) and the Abert's squirrel (right) have been isolated from each other for a long time. Eventually, this isolation may result in two different species.

✎ **Identify** What conditions might differ from one side of the Grand Canyon to the other that would cause the squirrels to be different colors?

_____

_____

As you can see in **Figure 1,** the populations of Kaibab and Abert's squirrels are separated by the Grand Canyon. The two kinds of squirrels are the same species, but they have slightly different characteristics. For example, the Kaibab squirrel has a black belly, while Abert's squirrel has a white belly. It is possible that one day these squirrels will become so different that they will no longer be able to mate with each other and will become separate species.

 Do the Quick Lab *Large-Scale Isolation.*

🔑 **Assess Your Understanding**

got it? ....

○ I get it! Now I know that new species form when _____

_____

○ I need extra help with _____

Go to **my science** **coach** *online for help with this subject.*   8.3.8, 8.3.9, 8.3.10

....

⟳ **Compare and Contrast**
Identify the similarity and the key differences between gradualism and punctuated equilibrium.

- Both describe the

  _____

- Gradualism states that evolution occurs (quickly/slowly) and (steadily/in short bursts).

- Punctuated equilibrium states that evolution occurs (quickly/slowly) over_____ periods of time.

What Patterns Describe the Rate of Evolution?

The fossil record has provided scientists with a lot of important information about past life on Earth. For example, scientists have found many examples of the appearance of new species as older species vanish. Sometimes the new species appear rapidly, and at other times they are the result of more gradual change. ⊶ **Scientists have developed two patterns to describe the pace of evolution: gradualism and punctuated equilibrium.**

Gradual Change
Some species in the fossil record seem to change gradually over time. **Gradualism** involves small changes that add up to major changes over a long period of time. Since the time scale of the fossil record involves hundreds, thousands, or even millions of years, there is plenty of time for gradual changes to produce new species. The fossil record contains many examples of species that are intermediate between two others. One example is the horse relative, *Merychippus*, shown in **Figure 2.** Many such intermediate forms seem to be the result of gradual change.

Equus
Today

Merychippus
35 million years ago

Hyracotherium
53 million years ago

FIGURE 2 ··

▷ **ART IN MOTION** **Horse Evolution**
Horses left a rich and detailed fossil record of their evolution. Many intermediate forms have been found between modern horses and their four-toed ancestors. *Merychippus* is shown here.

✎ **Answer these questions.**

1. List Name two differences between the horses.

_____

_____

2. CHALLENGE How could the evolution of the shape of the leg and the number of toes have benefited *Equus*?

_____

_____

_____

8.NS.8

Rapid Change Scientists have also found that many species remain almost unchanged during their existence. Then, shortly after they become extinct, related species often appear in the fossil record. This pattern, in which species evolve during short periods of rapid change and then don't change much, is called **punctuated equilibrium.** Today most scientists think that evolution can occur rapidly at some times, and more gradually at others.

apply it!

Two patterns that describe the rate of evolution are modeled at the right.

Make Models Look at the shells in the key. For each pattern, decide if—and at what point—each shell belongs on the timelines. Using colored pencils, draw and color in the shells at their correct locations to show how they have evolved over time. 8.NS.8

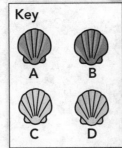

Key

A   B

C   D

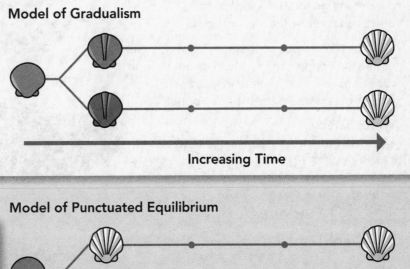

Model of Gradualism

Increasing Time

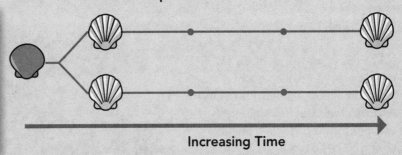

Model of Punctuated Equilibrium

Increasing Time

Lab zone® Do the Quick Lab *Slow or Fast?*

🔑 Assess Your Understanding

1a. Identify The _____ has given scientists information about past life on Earth. 8.3.8, 8.3.9

b. Infer Why are fossils of intermediate life forms likely to be rare if the pattern of punctuated equilibrium explains how evolution occurs?

_____

_____

_____

8.3.8, 8.3.9

got it?

○ **I get it!** Now I know that two patterns of evolution are _____

_____

_____

○ **I need extra help with** _____

_____

Go to my science ⑤ coach *online for help with this subject.* 8.3.8, 8.3.9

11 Study Guide

Living things change over time, or _____, through a process called _____

LESSON 1 Darwin's Theory

8.3.8, 8.3.9, 8.3.10, 8.NS.1, 8.NS.8, 8.DP.10

🔑 Darwin hypothesized that species change over many generations and become better adapted to new conditions.

🔑 Darwin proposed that, over a long time, natural selection can lead to change. Helpful variations may accumulate in a species, while unfavorable ones may disappear.

Vocabulary
• species • fossil • adaptation • evolution
• scientific theory • natural selection • variation

LESSON 2 Evidence of Evolution

8.3.8, 8.3.9, 8.3.10

🔑 Fossils, patterns of early development, similar body structures, and similarities in DNA and protein structures all provide evidence that organisms have changed over time.

Vocabulary
• homologous structures

LESSON 3 Rate of Change

8.3.8, 8.3.9, 8.3.10, 8.NS.8

🔑 A new species can form when a group of individuals remains isolated from the rest of its species long enough to evolve different traits that prevent reproduction.

🔑 Scientists have developed two patterns to describe the pace of evolution: gradualism and punctuated equilibrium.

Vocabulary
• gradualism
• punctuated equilibrium

Review and Assessment

LESSON 1 Darwin's Theory

1. A trait that helps an organism to survive and reproduce is called a(n)

    a. variation.   **b.** adaptation.

    c. species.   **d.** selection.

                                            8.3.8, 8.3.9

2. Two organisms that can mate and produce fertile offspring are members of the same

_____

                                            8.3.8, 8.3.9

3. Infer Why are Darwin's ideas classified as a scientific theory?

_____

_____

_____

_____

                                            8.3.8, 8.3.9

4. Apply Concepts What is one factor that affects natural selection? Give an example.

_____

_____

_____

_____

_____

                               8.3.8, 8.3.9, 8.3.10

5. Compare and Contrast Identify one similarity and one difference between natural selection and artificial selection.

_____

_____

_____

_____

_____

_____

                                            8.3.10

6. Write About It You are a reporter in the 1800s interviewing Charles Darwin about his theory of evolution. Write three questions you would ask him. Then write answers that Darwin might have given.

                          8.3.8, 8.3.9, 8.3.10

LESSON 2 Evidence of Evolution

7. Similar structures that related species have inherited from a common ancestor are called

    a. adaptations.

    b. fossils.

    c. ancestral structures.

    d. homologous structures.

                                            8.3.8, 8.3.9

8. The more _____ the DNA sequences between two organisms are, the more closely related the two species are.

                                      8.3.8, 8.3.9

9. Draw Conclusions Look at the drawing, at the right, of the bones in a crocodile's leg. Do you think that crocodiles share a common ancestor with birds, dolphins, and dogs? Support your answer with evidence.

Crocodile

_____

_____

_____

_____

                                  8.3.8, 8.3.9, 8.NS.8

10. Make Judgments What type of evidence is the best indicator of how closely two species are related? Explain your answer.

_____

_____

_____

_____

_____

_____

                                          8.3.8, 8.3.9

LESSON 3 **Rate of Change**

11. The pattern of evolution that involves short periods of rapid change is called

   a. adaptation.

   b. gradualism.

   c. isolation.

   d. punctuated equilibrium.

                                 8.3.8, 8.3.9

12. _____ involves tiny changes in a species that slowly add up to major changes over time.

                                 8.3.8, 8.3.9

13. **Apply Concepts** A population of deer lives in a forest. Draw a picture that illustrates how a geographic feature could isolate this deer population into two separate groups. Label the geographic feature.

                 8.3.10, 8.NS.11, 8.DP.10

14. **Develop Hypotheses** Describe the conditions that could cause these two groups of deer to become separate species over time.

                             8.3.10, 8.NS.1

APPLY THE BIG Q **How do life forms change over time?**

15. Suppose that over several years, the climate in an area becomes much drier than it was before. How would plants, like the ones shown below, be affected? Using the terms *variation* and *natural selection*, predict what changes you might observe in the plants as a result of this environmental change.

                 8.3.8, 8.3.9, 8.3.10, 8.NS.1

Indiana ISTEP+ Practice

Multiple Choice

Circle the letter of the best answer.

1. The illustration below has no title. Which of the following titles would best describe the concept shown in this drawing?

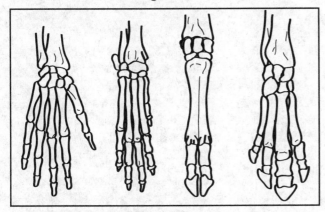

   A. Wrist Bone Adaptations
   B. Similarities in Wrist Bone Development
   C. Evolutionary Change Through Gradualism
   D. Homologous Structures in Four Animals

   8.3.8, 8.3.9, 8.NS.8

2. The process by which individuals that are better adapted to their environment are more likely to survive and reproduce than other members of the same species is called

   A. natural selection.
   B. evolution.
   C. competition.
   D. overproduction.

   8.3.8, 8.3.9

3. Which of the following is the best example of an adaptation that helps organisms survive in their environment?

   A. green coloring in lizards living on gray rocks
   B. a thick coat of fur on animals that live in the desert
   C. an extensive root system in desert plants
   D. thin, delicate leaves on plants in a cold climate

   8.3.8, 8.3.9

4. Which of the following sets of factors did Darwin identify as affecting natural selection?

   A. adaptations, gradualism, and evolution
   B. overproduction, variation, and competition
   C. adaptations, traits, and variations
   D. predation, competition, and mutualism

   8.3.8, 8.3.9

Constructed Response

Write your answer to Question 5 on the lines below.

5. What is the main difference between gradualism and punctuated equilibrium?

   _____

   _____

   _____

   _____

   _____

   _____

   _____

   8.3.8, 8.3.9

Extended Response

Use the diagram below and your knowledge of science to help you answer Question 6. Write your answer on a separate piece of paper.

6. This drawing shows variations in wing size within a species of fly. Describe a situation in which natural selection might favor flies with the smallest wings.

   8.3.8, 8.3.9, 8.3.10, 8.NS.8

THE INCREDIBLE SHRINKING FISH

▲ The practice of commercial fishing may be leading to populations of smaller and smaller fish.

This diagram shows how Dr. Conover and his team set up and performed their experiment. It also shows the results. ▶

Design It If current policies are causing the average size of fish to decrease, what is the best way to help fish populations recover? Design an experiment that would test your method for helping fish populations recover.

8.NS.2, 8.DP.1, 8.DP.2, 8.DP.4

For years, fishers have followed a simple rule: keep the big fish and release the small fish. This practice aims to keep fish populations stable by allowing young fish to reach reproductive age. However, a scientist named David Conover thinks that this practice of throwing back small fish might be affecting the evolution of fish species.

Not all small fish are young. Like humans, adult fish come in different sizes. Conover hypothesized that removing the largest fish from fish populations might result in populations of smaller fish because smaller adult fish would survive to reproduce more often than larger adult fish. To test this hypothesis, Conover's team divided a population of 6,000 fish into different groups. Over four generations, the scientists selectively removed 90 percent of the fish in each group before they could reproduce.

The results showed that over just a few generations, selection pressures can influence not only the size of fish, but also the health of fish populations. Currently, Conover is researching ways to change fishing regulations so fish populations can recover.

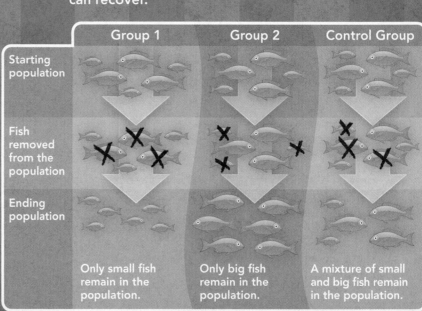

	Group 1	Group 2	Control Group
Starting population			
Fish removed from the population			
Ending population			
	Only small fish remain in the population.	Only big fish remain in the population.	A mixture of small and big fish remain in the population.

WALKING WHALES?

If you could visit Earth 50 million years ago, you would see many amazing sights. One of the strangest things you might see is the ancestor of modern whales—walking on land!

For years, scientists have thought that whales evolved from land-dwelling mammals. About 50 million years ago, the ancestors of modern whales had four legs and were similar to large dogs. Over 50 million years, whales evolved to become the giant marine mammals we recognize today. However, scientists have had difficulty finding fossils of whales that show how this dramatic change occurred. These missing links could reveal how whales lost their legs.

Now, several new discoveries are helping scientists fill in the blanks in the evolutionary history of whales. A fossil whale skeleton discovered in Washington State has a pelvis with large cuplike sockets. These sockets likely held short legs that enabled the whale to move on land. Other whale fossils, found in Alabama, include large hind limbs that probably helped the animals swim. Researchers have also discovered the gene mutation that could have been responsible for whales losing their legs about 35 million years ago.

Design It Find out more about the evolutionary history of whales. How is a whale flipper similar to a bat wing and a human hand? Design a poster that shows the evolutionary history of whales.

 8.3.6, 8.3.7, 8.3.8, 8.NS.2, 8.NS.8, 8.NS.11

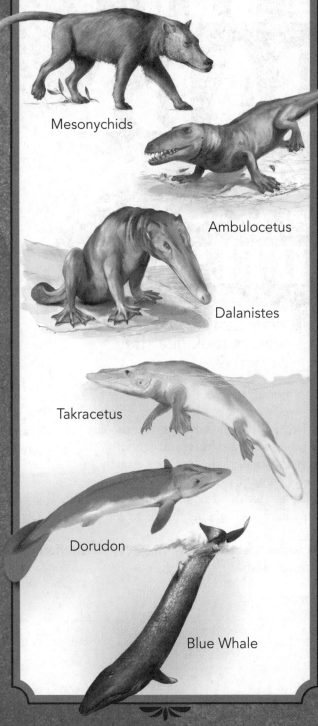

Over 50 million years, whales evolved from a species of doglike land mammals to the aquatic giants we know today.

Mesonychids

Ambulocetus

Dalanistes

Takracetus

Dorudon

Blue Whale

WHAT MAKES THIS BABY KOALA DIFFERENT?

Why don't offspring always look like their parents?

Even though this young koala, or joey, has two fuzzy ears, a long nose, and a body shaped like its mom's, you can see that the two are different. You might expect a young animal to look exactly like its parents, but think about how varied a litter of kittens or puppies can look. This joey is an albino—an animal that lacks the usual coloring in its eyes, fur, and skin.

Observe **Describe how this joey looks different from its mom.**

_____

_____

_____

_____

> UNTAMED SCIENCE Watch the **Untamed Science** video to learn more about heredity.

Genetics: The Science of Heredity

CHAPTER 12

Academic Standards for Science

8.3.3, 8.3.5, 8.NS.1, 8.NS.2, 8.NS.8,
8.NS.11, 8.DP.2, 8.DP.4

12 Getting Started

Check Your Understanding

1. Background Read the paragraph below and then answer the question.

> Kent's cat just had six kittens. All six kittens look different from one another—and from their two parents! Kent knows each kitten is unique because cats reproduce through **sexual reproduction,** not **asexual reproduction.** Before long, the kittens will grow bigger and bigger as their cells divide through **mitosis.**

- In what way are the two daughter cells that form by mitosis and cell division identical?

Sexual reproduction involves two parents and combines their genetic material to produce a new organism that differs from both parents.

Asexual reproduction involves only one parent and produces offspring that are identical to the parent.

During **mitosis,** a cell's nucleus divides into two new nuclei, and one copy of DNA is distributed into each daughter cell.

> MY READING WEB If you had trouble completing the question above, visit **My Reading Web** and type in *Genetics: The Science of Heredity.*

Vocabulary Skill

Suffixes A suffix is a word part that is added to the end of a word to change its meaning. For example, the suffix -*tion* means "process of." If you add the suffix -*tion* to the verb *fertilize,* you get the noun *fertilization.* *Fertilization* means "the process of fertilizing." The table below lists some other common suffixes and their meanings.

Suffix	Meaning	Example
-*ive*	performing a particular action	recessive allele, *n.* an allele that is masked when a dominant allele is present
-*ance* or -*ant*	state, condition of	codominance, *n.* occurs when both alleles are expressed equally

2. Quick Check Fill in the blank with the correct suffix.

- A domin_____ allele can mask a recessive allele.

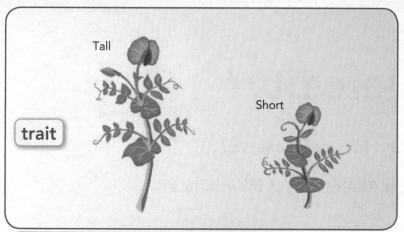

trait

Tall

Short

phenotype

incomplete dominance

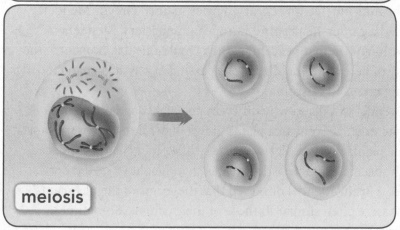

meiosis

Chapter Preview

LESSON 1
- heredity • trait • genetics
- fertilization • purebred • gene
- allele • dominant allele
- recessive allele • hybrid

⟳ **Identify Supporting Evidence**

△ **Predict**

LESSON 2
- probability • Punnett square
- phenotype • genotype
- homozygous • heterozygous

⟳ **Identify the Main Idea**

△ **Draw Conclusions**

LESSON 3
- incomplete dominance
- codominance • multiple alleles
- polygenic inheritance

⟳ **Compare and Contrast**

△ **Interpret Data**

LESSON 4
- meiosis

⟳ **Relate Cause and Effect**

△ **Design Experiments**

LESSON 5
- selective breeding • inbreeding
- hybridization • clone
- genetic engineering
- gene therapy

⟳ **Ask Questions**

△ **Draw Conclusions**

> **VOCAB FLASH CARDS** For extra help with vocabulary, visit **Vocab Flash Cards** and type in *Genetics: The Science of Heredity.*

467

What Is Heredity?

UNLOCK THE BIG ?

What Did Mendel Observe?
8.3.3, 8.NS.8

How Do Alleles Affect Inheritance?
8.3.3, 8.NS.1, 8.NS.8

my planet diary

Almost Forgotten

When scientists make great discoveries, sometimes their work is praised, criticized, or even forgotten. Gregor Mendel was almost forgotten. He spent eight years studying pea plants, and he discovered patterns in the way characteristics pass from one generation to the next. For almost 40 years, people overlooked Mendel's work. When it was finally rediscovered, it unlocked the key to understanding heredity.

BIOGRAPHY

Communicate Discuss the question below with a partner. Then write your answer.

Did you ever rediscover something of yours that you had forgotten? How did you react?

_____

_____

_____

▶ PLANET DIARY Go to **Planet Diary** to learn more about heredity.

 Do the Inquiry Warm-Up *What Does the Father Look Like?*

 Academic Standards for Science

8.3.3 Explain that genetic information is transmitted from parents to offspring mostly by chromosomes.

8.NS.8 Analyze data and use it to identify patterns and make inferences based on these patterns.

What Did Mendel Observe?

In the mid-nineteenth century, a priest named Gregor Mendel tended a garden in a central European monastery. Mendel's experiments in that peaceful garden would one day transform the study of heredity. **Heredity** is the passing of physical characteristics from parents to offspring.

Mendel wondered why different pea plants had different characteristics. Some pea plants grew tall, while others were short. Some plants produced green seeds, while others had yellow seeds. Each specific characteristic, such as stem height or seed color, is called a **trait.** Mendel observed that the forms of the pea plants' traits were often similar to those of their parents. Sometimes, however, the forms differed.

Vocabulary

- heredity • trait • genetics • fertilization
- purebred • gene • allele • dominant allele
- recessive allele • hybrid

Skills

- Reading: Identify Supporting Evidence
- Inquiry: Predict

Mendel's Experiments Mendel experimented with thousands of pea plants. Today, Mendel's discoveries form the foundation of **genetics,** the scientific study of heredity. **Figure 1** shows the parts of a pea plant's flower. The pistil produces female sex cells, or eggs. The stamens produce pollen, which contains the male sex cells, or sperm. A new organism begins to form when egg and sperm cells join in the process called **fertilization.** Before fertilization can happen in pea plants, pollen must reach the pistil of a pea flower. This process is called pollination.

Pea plants are usually self-pollinating. In self-pollination, pollen from a flower lands on the pistil of the same flower. Mendel developed a method by which he cross-pollinated, or "crossed," pea plants. **Figure 1** shows his method.

Mendel decided to cross plants that had contrasting forms of a trait—for example, tall plants and short plants. He started with purebred plants. A **purebred** organism is the offspring of many generations that have the same form of a trait. For example, purebred tall pea plants always come from tall parent plants.

FIGURE 1 ....

Crossing Pea Plants

8.NS.8

Mendel devised a way to cross-pollinate pea plants.

✏ **Use the diagram to answer the questions about Mendel's procedure.**

1. **Observe** How does flower B differ from flower A?

_____

_____

2. **Infer** Describe how Mendel cross-pollinated pea plants.

_____

_____

_____

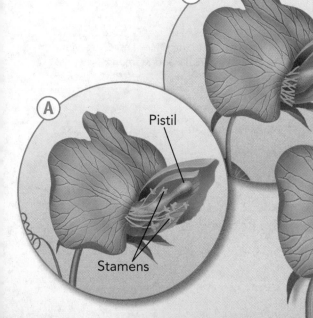

Pistil

Pollen

Stamens

469

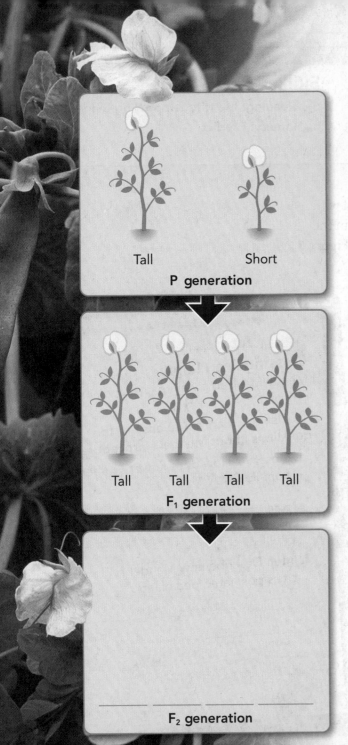

Tall   Short

P generation

Tall   Tall   Tall   Tall

F₁ generation

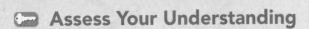

F₂ generation

The F₁ and F₂ Offspring

Mendel crossed purebred tall plants with purebred short plants. Today, scientists call these plants the parental, or P, generation. The resulting offspring are the first filial (FIL ee ul), or F₁, generation. The word *filial* comes from *filia* and *filius*, the Latin words for "daughter" and "son."

Look at **Figure 2** to see the surprise Mendel found in the F₁ generation. All the offspring were tall. The shortness trait seemed to have disappeared!

When these plants were full-grown, Mendel allowed them to self-pollinate. The F₂ (second filial) generation that followed surprised Mendel even more. He counted the plants of the F₂ generation. About three fourths were tall, while one fourth were short.

Experiments With Other Traits

Mendel repeated his experiments, studying other pea-plant traits, such as flower color and seed shape. 🔑 **In all of his crosses, Mendel found that only one form of the trait appeared in the F₁ generation. However, in the F₂ generation, the "lost" form of the trait always reappeared in about one fourth of the plants.**

FIGURE 2 ·······························

Results of a Cross
In Mendel's crosses, some forms of a trait were hidden in one generation but reappeared in the next.

✏️ **Interpret Diagrams** Draw and label the offspring in the F₂ generation.

8.NS.8

Lab zone® Do the Quick Lab *Observing Pistils and Stamens.*

How Do Alleles Affect Inheritance?

Mendel reached several conclusions from his experimental results. He reasoned that individual factors, or sets of genetic "information," must control the inheritance of traits in peas. The factors that control each trait exist in pairs. The female parent contributes one factor, while the male parent contributes the other factor. Finally, one factor in a pair can mask, or hide, the other factor. The tallness factor, for example, masked the shortness factor.

Genes and Alleles Today, scientists use the word **gene** to describe the factors that control a trait. **Alleles** (uh LEELZ) are the different forms of a gene. The gene that controls stem height in peas has one allele for tall stems and one allele for short stems. Each pea plant inherits two alleles—one from the egg and the other from the sperm. A plant may inherit two alleles for tall stems, two alleles for short stems, or one of each.

🔑 **An organism's traits are controlled by the alleles it inherits from its parents. Some alleles are dominant, while other alleles are recessive.** A **dominant allele** is one whose trait always shows up in the organism when the allele is present. A **recessive allele,** on the other hand, is hidden whenever the dominant allele is present. **Figure 3** shows dominant and recessive alleles of the traits in Mendel's crosses.

Academic Standards for Science

8.3.3 Explain that genetic information is transmitted from parents to offspring mostly by chromosomes.

8.NS.1 Make predictions.

8.NS.8 Analyze data.

FIGURE 3 ·······························

Alleles in Pea Plants

Mendel studied the inheritance of seven different traits in pea plants.

✎ **Use the table to answer the questions.**

1. **Draw Conclusions** Circle the picture of each dominant form of the trait in the P generation.

2. **Predict** Under what conditions would the recessive form of one of these traits reappear?

_____

_____

8.NS.1, 8.NS.8

Inheritance of Pea Plants Studied by Mendel

	Seed Shape	Seed Color	Pod Shape	Pod Color	Flower Color	Flower Position	Stem Height
P	Wrinkled  X  Round	Yellow  X  Green	Pinched  X  Smooth	Green  X  Yellow	Purple  X  White	Tip of stem  X  Side of stem	Tall  X  Short
F₁	 Round	 Yellow	 Smooth	 Green	 Purple	 Side of stem	 Tall

471

FIGURE 4 ·····································

▶ VIRTUAL LAB Dominant and Recessive Alleles

Symbols serve as a shorthand way to identify alleles.

✎ **Complete each row of the diagram.**

1. **Identify** Fill in the missing allele symbols and descriptions.

2. **Summarize** Use the word bank to complete the statements. (Terms will be used more than once.)

3. **Relate Cause and Effect** Draw the two possible ways the F_2 offspring could look.

Alleles in Mendel's Crosses In Mendel's cross for stem height, the purebred tall plants in the P generation had two alleles for tall stems. The purebred short plants had two alleles for short stems. But each F_1 plant inherited one allele for tall stems and one allele for short stems. The F_1 plants are called hybrids. A **hybrid** (HY brid) organism has two different alleles for a trait. All the F_1 plants are tall because the dominant allele for tall stems masks the recessive allele for short stems.

Symbols for Alleles Geneticists, scientists who study genetics, often use letters to represent alleles. A dominant allele is symbolized by a capital letter. A recessive allele is symbolized by the lowercase version of the same letter. For example, T stands for the allele for tall stems, and t stands for the allele for short stems. When a plant has two dominant alleles for tall stems, its alleles are written as TT. When a plant has two recessive alleles for short stems, its alleles are written as tt. These plants are the P generation shown in **Figure 4.** Think about the symbols that would be used for F_1 plants that all inherit one allele for tall stems and one for short stems.

P

Tall
T ____
Purebred

Short
t ____
Purebred

Word Bank
dominant
recessive

F₁

____
T ____
____

All plants inherit one _____ allele and one _____ allele. These plants are all tall.

F₂

Plants may inherit two _____ alleles. These plants are tall.

Plants may inherit one _____ allele and one _____ allele. These plants are tall.

Plants may inherit two _____ alleles. These plants are short.

8.NS.8

apply it!

In fruit flies, long wings are dominant over short wings. A scientist crossed a purebred long-winged fruit fly with a purebred short-winged fruit fly.

1 If *W* stands for long wings, write the symbols for the alleles of each parent fly.

_____

2 ⚠ **Predict** What will be the wing length of the F₁ offspring?

_____

3 ⚠ **Predict** If the scientist crosses a hybrid male F₁ fruit fly with a hybrid F₁ female, what will their offspring probably be like?

_____

_____

_____

8.NS.1, 8.NS.8

Significance of Mendel's Contribution Mendel's discovery of genes and alleles eventually changed scientists' ideas about heredity. Before Mendel, most people thought that the traits of an individual organism were simply a blend of the parents' characteristics. Mendel showed that offspring traits are determined by individual, separate alleles inherited from each parent. Unfortunately, the value of Mendel's discovery was not known during his lifetime. But when scientists in the early 1900s rediscovered Mendel's work, they quickly realized its importance. Because of his work, Mendel is often called the Father of Genetics.

✏ **Identify Supporting Evidence** What evidence showed Mendel that traits are determined by separate alleles?

_____

_____

_____

_____

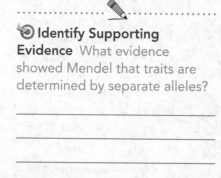 Do the Quick Lab *Inferring the Parent Generation.*

🔑 Assess Your Understanding

2a. Relate Cause and Effect Why is a pea plant that is a hybrid for stem height tall?

_____

_____

_____

8.3.3

b. [CHALLENGE] Can a short pea plant be a hybrid for the trait of stem height? Why or why not?

_____

_____

_____

8.3.3

got it?

○ **I get it!** Now I know that an organism's traits are controlled by _____

_____

_____

_____

_____

○ **I need extra help with** _____

Go to **MY SCIENCE** **COACH** online for help with this subject.

8.3.3

473

Indiana

LESSON

2 Probability and Heredity

UNLOCK THE BIG ?

🔑 **How Is Probability Related to Inheritance?**
8.3, 8.NS.1, 8.NS.8

🔑 **What Are Phenotype and Genotype?**
8.3, 8.NS.8

MY PLANET DIARY

Storm on the Way?

Have you ever watched a hurricane form? Weather forecasters at the National Hurricane Center (NHC) in Miami, Florida, have. From May 15 to November 30, the NHC Operations Area is staffed around the clock with forecasters. They study data from aircraft, ocean buoys, and satellites to develop computer models. These models predict the probable paths of a storm. If the probability of a certain path is high, the NHC issues a warning that helps save lives and reduce damage.

FIELD TRIP

Communicate Answer the question below. Then discuss your answer with a partner.

Local weather forecasters often talk about the percent chance for rainfall. What do you think they mean?

_____

_____

_____

_____

_____

> PLANET DIARY Go to **Planet Diary** to learn more about probability and weather.

Lab® zone Do the Inquiry Warm-Up
What's the Chance?

Academic Standards for Science

8.3 core standard Understand the predictability of characteristics being passed from parents to offspring.

8.NS.1 Make predictions.

8.NS.8 Analyze data, using appropriate mathematical manipulation as required, and use it to identify patterns and make inferences based on these patterns.

How Is Probability Related to Inheritance?

Before the start of a football game, the team captains stand with the referee for a coin toss. The team that wins the toss chooses whether to kick or receive the ball. As the referee tosses the coin, the visiting team captain calls "heads." What is the chance that the visitors will win the toss? To answer this question, you need to understand the principles of probability.

Vocabulary
- probability
- Punnett square
- phenotype
- genotype
- homozygous
- heterozygous

Skills
- Reading: Identify the Main Idea
- Inquiry: Draw Conclusions

What Is Probability? Each time you toss a coin, there are two possible ways it can land—heads up or tails up. **Probability** is a number that describes how likely it is that an event will occur. In mathematical terms, you can say the probability that a tossed coin will land heads up is 1 in 2. There's also a 1 in 2 probability that the coin will land tails up. A 1 in 2 probability is expressed as the fraction $\frac{1}{2}$ or as 50 percent.

The laws of probability predict what is *likely* to occur, not what *will* occur. If you toss a coin 20 times, you may expect it to land heads up 10 times and tails up 10 times. But you may get 11 heads and 9 tails, or 8 heads and 12 tails. The more tosses you make, the closer your actual results will be to those predicted by probability.

Do you think the result of one toss affects the result of the next toss? Not at all. Each event occurs independently. Suppose you toss a coin five times and it lands heads up each time. What is the probability that it will land heads up on the next toss? If you said the probability is still 1 in 2, or 50 percent, you're right. The results of the first five tosses do not affect the result of the sixth toss.

do the math!

Percentage

One way to express probability is as a percentage. A percentage is a number compared to 100. For example, 50 percent, or 50%, means 50 out of 100. Suppose you want to calculate percentage from the results of a series of basketball free throws in which 3 out of 5 free throws go through the hoop.

STEP 1 Write the comparison as a fraction.

$$3 \text{ out of } 5 = \frac{3}{5}$$

STEP 2 Calculate the number value of the fraction.

$$3 \div 5 = 0.6$$

STEP 3 Multiply this number by 100%.

$$0.6 \times 100\% = 60\%$$

.... Practice! ....

❶ **Calculate** Suppose 5 out of 25 free throws go through the hoop. Write this result as a fraction.

_____

❷ **Calculate** Express your answer in Question 1 as a percentage.

_____

_____

_____

_____

8.NS.8

Probability and Genetics How is probability related to genetics? Think back to Mendel's experiments. He carefully counted the offspring from every cross. When he crossed two plants that were hybrid for stem height (*Tt*), about three fourths of the F$_2$ plants had tall stems. About one fourth had short stems.

Each time Mendel repeated the cross, he observed similar results. He realized that the principles of probability applied to his work. He found that the probability of a hybrid cross producing a tall plant was 3 in 4. The probability of producing a short plant was 1 in 4. Mendel was the first scientist to recognize that the principles of probability can predict the results of genetic crosses.

Punnett Squares

A tool that can help you grasp how the laws of probability apply to genetics is called a Punnett square. A **Punnett square** is a chart that shows all the possible ways alleles can combine in a genetic cross. Geneticists use Punnett squares to see these combinations and to determine the probability of a particular outcome, or result. 🔑 **In a genetic cross, the combination of alleles that parents can pass to an offspring is based on probability.**

Figure 1 shows how to make a Punnett square. In this case, the cross is between two hybrid pea plants with round seeds (*Rr*). The allele for round seeds (*R*) is dominant over the allele for wrinkled seeds (*r*). Each parent can pass either one allele or the other to an offspring. The boxes in the Punnett square show the possible combinations of alleles that the offspring can inherit.

FIGURE 1 ···
▶ INTERACTIVE ART **How to Make a Punnett Square**

You can use a Punnett square to find the probabilities of a genetic cross.

✏️ **Follow the steps in the figure to fill in the Punnett square.**

1. **Predict** What is the probability that an offspring will have wrinkled seeds?

_____

2. **Interpret Tables** What is the probability that an offspring will have round seeds? Explain your answer.

_____

_____

_____

8.NS.1, 8.NS.8

2 The male parent's alleles are written along the top of the square. Fill in the female parent's alleles along the left side.

1 Start by drawing a box and dividing it into four squares.

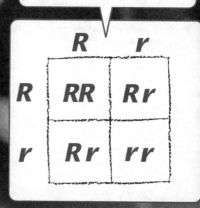

5 The completed square shows all the possible allele combinations the offspring can have.

4 Copy the male parent's alleles into the boxes beneath them.

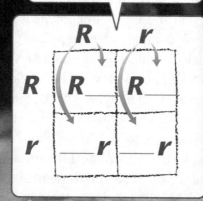

3 Copy the female parent's alleles into the boxes to their right. The first one is done for you.

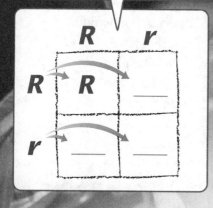

✏️

🔁 **Identify the Main Idea** In your own words, describe what a Punnet square shows you about combinations of alleles.

_____

_____

_____

_____

_____

Relating Punnett Squares to Mendel Mendel did not know about alleles. But a Punnett square shows why he got the results he saw in the F_2 generations. Plants with alleles *RR* would have round seeds. So would plants with alleles *Rr*. Only plants with alleles *rr* would have wrinkled seeds.

Do the Quick Lab *Coin Crosses.*

🔑 **Assess Your Understanding**

1a. Review What is probability?

_____

_____

8.3

b. Apply Concepts What is the probability that a cross between a hybrid pea plant with round seeds and one with wrinkled seeds will produce offspring with wrinkled seeds? (Draw a Punnett square on other paper to find the answer.)

_____

8.3

got it?

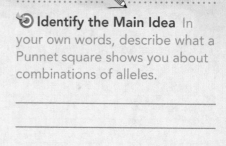

○ **I get it!** Now I know that the combination of alleles parents can pass to offspring _____

_____

○ **I need extra help with** _____

Go to MY SCIENCE 🔄 COACH *online for help with this subject.*

8.3

477

8.3 core standard Understand the predictability of characteristics being passed from parents to offspring.

8.NS.8 Analyze data, using appropriate mathematical manipulation as required, and use it to identify patterns and make inferences based on these patterns.

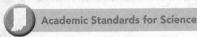

What Are Phenotype and Genotype?

Two terms that geneticists use are **phenotype** (FEE noh typ) and **genotype** (JEE noh typ). **An organism's phenotype is its physical appearance, or visible traits. An organism's genotype is its genetic makeup, or alleles.** In other words, genotype is an organism's alleles. Phenotype is how a trait looks or is expressed.

To compare phenotype and genotype, look at **Figure 2.** The allele for smooth pea pods (*S*) is dominant over the allele for pinched pea pods (*s*). All the plants with at least one *S* allele have the same phenotype. That is, they all produce smooth pods. However, these plants can have two different genotypes—*SS* or *Ss*. If you were to look at the plants with smooth pods, you would not be able to tell the difference between those that have the genotype *SS* and those with the genotype *Ss*. The plants with pinched pods, on the other hand, would all have the same phenotype—pinched pods—as well as the same genotype—*ss*.

Geneticists use two additional terms to describe an organism's genotype. An organism that has two identical alleles for a trait is said to be **homozygous** (hoh moh ZY gus) for that trait. A smooth-pod plant that has the alleles *SS* and a pinched-pod plant with the alleles *ss* are both homozygous. An organism that has two different alleles for a trait is **heterozygous** (het ur oh ZY gus) for that trait. A smooth-pod plant with the alleles *Ss* is heterozygous. Recall that Mendel used the term *hybrid* to describe heterozygous pea plants.

Vocabulary Suffixes The suffix *-ous* means "having." Circle this suffix in the highlighted terms *homozygous* and *heterozygous* in the paragraph at the right. These terms describe the organism as having

____

____

____

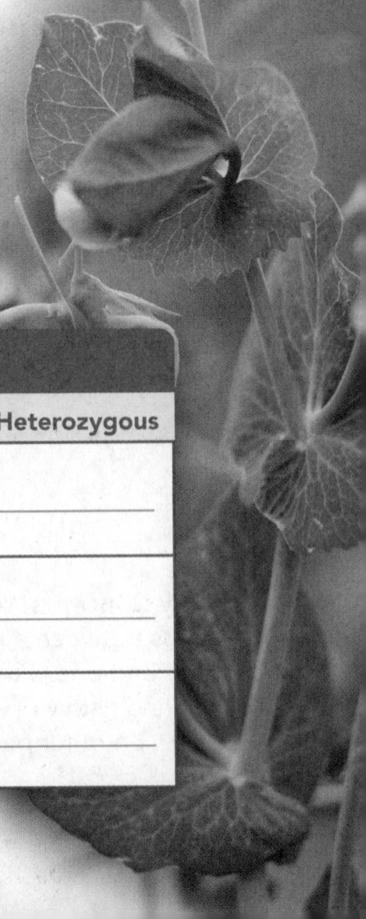

FIGURE 2

Describing Inheritance

An organism's phenotype is its physical appearance. Its genotype is its genetic makeup. 8.NS.8

Based on what you have read, answer these questions.

1. **Classify** Fill in the missing information in the table.
2. **Interpret Tables** How many genotypes are there for the smooth-pod phenotype?

____

Phenotypes and Genotypes

Phenotype	Genotype	Homozygous or Heterozygous
Smooth pods	____	______________
Smooth pods	____	______________
Pinched pods	____	______________

apply it!

Mendel's principles of heredity apply to many other organisms. For example, in guinea pigs, black fur color (*B*) is dominant over white fur color (*b*). Suppose a pair of black guinea pigs produces several litters of pups during their lifetimes. The graph shows the phenotypes of the pups. Write a title for the graph.

1 Read Graphs How many black pups were produced? How many white pups were produced?

_____

2 Infer What are the possible genotypes of the offspring?

_____

3 Draw Conclusions What can you conclude about the genotypes of the parent guinea pigs? Explain your answer.

_____

_____

_____

_____

8.NS.8

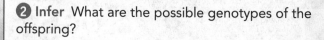

Bar graph titled (blank). Y-axis: Number of Pups, from 0 to 80. X-axis: Phenotype of Offspring — Black pups (about 65), White pups (about 15).

Do the Lab Investigation
Make the Right Call!

🔑 Assess Your Understanding

2a. Relate Cause and Effect Explain how two organisms can have the same phenotype but different genotypes.

_____

_____

_____

8.3

b. CHALLENGE In their lifetimes, two guinea pigs produce 40 black pups and 40 white pups. On a separate paper, make a Punnett square and find the likely genotypes of these parents.

_____

8.3

got it?

○ **I get it!** Now I know that phenotype and

genotype are terms that describe _____

_____

_____

_____

○ I need extra help with _____

Go to MY SCIENCE COACH *online for help with this subject.*

8.3

Patterns of Inheritance

🗝 **How Are Most Traits Inherited?**

8.3, 8.3.5, 8.NS.1, 8.NS.8

🗝 **How Do Genes and the Environment Interact?**

8.3.5

my PLANET DIARY for Indiana

BLOG

Posted by: Chelsey

Location: Monrovia, IN

I have this genetic inheritance trait called "TAR Syndrome." It is where the forearm is short and clubbed. My little sister and I are the only two people that I know that have it. No one knows where it comes from. Sometimes it is hard to do some things like touching my toes. I have to bend my knees to do that. If an object is too high up I have to get a chair to reach it. I also cannot hold a lot of things at one time. But, if I try very hard, I can do it. That is my inheritance and I'm proud of it.

Do the Inquiry Warm-Up *Observing Traits.*

Discuss the question below with a partner. Then write your answer.

What traits or characteristics do you have that resemble those of your relatives?

_____

_____

_____

_____

_____

▷ PLANET DIARY Go to **Planet Diary** to learn more about patterns of inheritance.

How Are Most Traits Inherited?

The traits that Mendel studied are controlled by genes with only two possible alleles. These alleles are either dominant or recessive. Pea flower color is either purple or white. Peas are either yellow or green. Can you imagine if all traits were like this? If people were either short or tall? If cats were either black or yellow?

Studying two-allele traits is a good place to begin learning about genetics. But take a look around at the variety of living things in your surroundings. As you might guess, most traits do not follow such a simple pattern of inheritance. 🗝 **Most traits are the result of complex patterns of inheritance.** Four complex patterns of inheritance are described in this lesson.

Vocabulary
- incomplete dominance
- codominance • multiple alleles
- polygenic inheritance

Skills
- Reading: Compare and Contrast
- Inquiry: Interpret Data

Incomplete Dominance Some traits result from a pattern of inheritance known as incomplete dominance. **Incomplete dominance** occurs when one allele is only partially dominant. For example, look at **Figure 1.** The flowers shown are called snapdragons. A cross between a plant with red flowers and one with white flowers produces pink offspring.

Snapdragons with alleles *RR* produce a lot of red color in their flowers. It's no surprise that their flowers are red. A plant with two white alleles (*WW*) produces no red color. Its flowers are white. Both types of alleles are written as capital letters because neither is totally dominant. If a plant has alleles *RW*, only enough color is produced to make the flowers just a little red. So they look pink.

Codominance The chickens in **Figure 1** show a different pattern of inheritance. **Codominance** occurs when both alleles for a gene are expressed equally. In the chickens shown, neither black feathers nor white feathers are dominant. All the offspring of a black hen and a white rooster have both black and white feathers.

Here, F^B stands for the allele for black feathers. F^W stands for the allele for white feathers. The letter *F* tells you the trait is feathers. The superscripts *B* for black and *W* for white tell you the color.

FIGURE 1 ·······························

Other Patterns of Inheritance
Many crosses do not follow the patterns Mendel discovered.

✏ **Apply Concepts** Fill in the missing pairs of alleles. 8.NS.8

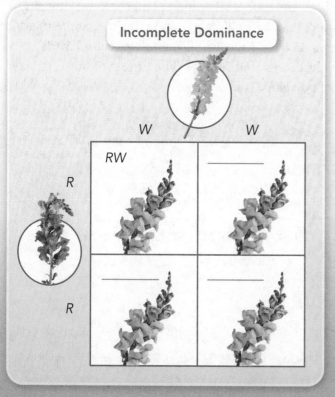

Incomplete Dominance

	W	W
R	RW	_____
R	_____	_____

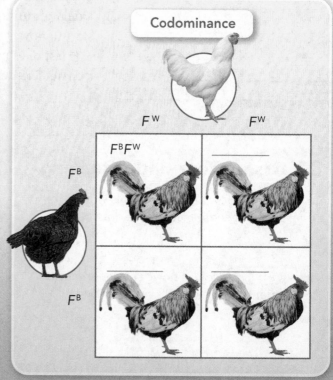

Codominance

	F^W	F^W
F^B	$F^B F^W$	_____
F^B	_____	_____

apply it!

An imaginary insect called the blingwing has three alleles for wing color: R (red), B (blue), and Y (yellow).

1 List If an organism can inherit only two alleles for a gene, what are the six possible allele pairs for wing color in blingwings? One answer is given.

RB, _____

_____

2 ⚠ **Interpret Data** Suppose the three alleles are codominant. What wing color would each pair of alleles produce? One answer is given.

RB: purple _____

_____

_____

_____

_____

8.NS.1, 8.NS.8

Multiple Alleles Some genes have **multiple alleles,** which means that three or more possible alleles determine the trait. Remember that an organism can only inherit two alleles for a gene—one from each parent. Even if there are four, five, or more possible alleles, an individual can only have two. However, more genotypes can occur with multiple alleles than with just two alleles. For example, four alleles control the color of fur in some rabbits. Depending on which two alleles a rabbit inherits, its coat color can range from brownish gray to all white.

Polygenic Inheritance The traits that Mendel studied were each controlled by a single gene. **Polygenic inheritance** occurs when more than one gene affects a trait. The alleles of the different genes work together to produce these traits.

Polygenic inheritance results in a broad range of phenotypes, like human height or the time it takes for a plant to flower. Imagine a field of sunflowers that were all planted the same day. Some might start to flower after 45 days. Most will flower after around 60 days. The last ones might flower after 75 days. The timing of flowering is a characteristic of polygenic traits.

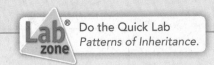

Do the Quick Lab
Patterns of Inheritance.

🔑 Assess Your Understanding

1a. Describe How are the symbols written for alleles that share incomplete dominance?

_____

8.3, 8.3.5

b. CHALLENGE How is polygenic inheritance different from the patterns described by Mendel?

_____

_____

8.3, 8.3.5

got it?

O **I get it!** Now I know that most traits are

produced by _____

_____

O **I need extra help with** _____

Go to MY SCIENCE ⑤ COACH *online for help with this subject.* 8.3, 8.3.5

How Do Genes and the Environment Interact?

You were not born knowing how to skateboard, but maybe you can skateboard now. Many traits are learned, or acquired. Unlike inherited traits, acquired traits are not carried by genes or passed to offspring. Although inherited traits are determined by genes, they also can be affected by factors in the environment. The phenotypes you observe in an organism result both from genes and from interactions of the organism with its environment.

Inherited and Acquired Traits Humans are born with inherited traits, such as vocal cords and tongues that allow for speech. But humans are not born speaking Spanish, or Mandarin, or English. The languages that a person speaks are acquired traits. Do you have a callus on your finger from writing with your pencil? That is an acquired trait. Skills you learn and physical changes that occur, such as calluses and haircuts, are aquired traits. See if you can tell the inherited traits from the acquired traits in **Figure 2**.

Academic Standards for Science

8.3.5 Identify and describe the difference between inherited traits and physical and behavioral traits that are acquired or learned.
8.NS.8 Analyze data.

FIGURE 2 ·····························

Inherited or Acquired?
Which traits shown are carried in the genes, and which are not?

✎ **Classify** Identify each trait shown as inherited or acquired.   8.NS.8

Their heights

Dyed hair color

Fish body color

These hedge shapes

Her freckles

Genes and the Environment

Think again about sunflowers. Genes control when the plants flower. But sunlight, temperature, soil nutrients, and water also affect a plant's flowering time. 🔑 **Environmental factors can influence the way genes are expressed.** Like sunflowers, you have factors in your environment that can affect how your genes are expressed. For example, you may have inherited the ability to play a musical instrument. But without an opportunity to learn, you may never develop the skill.

Some environmental factors can change an organism's genes. For example, tobacco smoke and other pollutants can affect genes in a person's body cells in a way that may result in lung cancer and other cancers. Still other genetic changes happen by chance.

Changes in body cells cannot be passed to offspring. Only changes in the sex cells—eggs and sperm—can be passed to offspring. Not all genetic changes have negative effects. Genetic change in sex cells is an important source of life's variety.

Compare and Contrast
Underline two sentences that tell how changes to genes in body cells differ from changes to genes in egg and sperm cells.

FIGURE 3

> **INTERACTIVE ART** The traits you see in organisms result from their genes and from interactions of genes with the environment.

✏️ **Summarize** Match the terms in the word bank with the examples shown.

8.NS.8

Word Bank

Incomplete dominance	Dominant and recessive traits
Environmental factors	Polygenic inheritance
Multiple alleles	Codominance
Acquired traits	

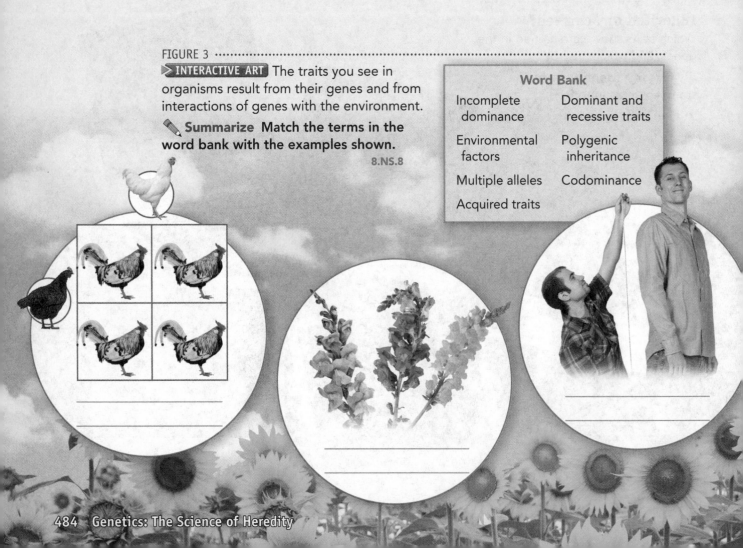

Do the Quick Lab *Is It All in the Genes?*

Assess Your Understanding

2a. Review Only genetic changes in (sex cells/ body cells) can be passed to offspring. 8.3.5

b. Describe Give one example of how environmental factors affect gene expression.

8.3.5

c. Why don't offspring always look like their parents?

8.3.5

got it?

○ **I get it!** Now I know that the environment can affect ______

○ I need extra help with ______

Go to **MY SCIENCE COACH** *online for help with this subject.* 8.3.5

Chromosomes and Inheritance

UNLOCK THE BIG ?

🔑 **How Are Chromosomes, Genes, and Inheritance Related?**
8.3.3, 8.3.4, 8.NS.2, 8.NS.8

🔑 **What Happens During Meiosis?**
8.3.2, 8.3.3, 8.3.4, 8.NS.8

🔑 **How Do Sexual and Asexual Reproduction Compare?**
8.3.1, 8.3.2, 8.3.3, 8.3.7, 8.NS.1, 8.NS.8, 8.NS.11

MY PLANET DIARY

CAREER

Chromosome Sleuth

Finding answers about how chromosomes relate to disease is one job of genetic technologists. These scientists analyze chromosomes from cells. The analysis may pinpoint genetic information that can cause disease or other health problems. In their work, genetic technologists use microscopes, computer-imaging photography, and lab skills. They report data that are used in research and in treating patients affected by genetic diseases.

Communicate Answer these questions. Then discuss Question 2 with a partner.

1. Describe a method that genetic technologists use to pursue a scientific explanation.

_____

_____

_____

_____

2. If you were a genetic technologist, what would you like to research?

_____

_____

_____

> PLANET DIARY Go to **Planet Diary** to learn more about genetic technologists.

Lab zone® Do the Inquiry Warm-Up *Which Chromosome Is Which?*

Vocabulary
• meiosis

Skills
- Reading: Relate Cause and Effect
- Inquiry: Design Experiments

How Are Chromosomes, Genes, and Inheritance Related?

Mendel's work showed that genes exist. (Remember that he called them "factors.") But scientists in the early twentieth century did not know what structures in cells contained genes. The search for the answer was something like a mystery story. The story could be called "The Clue in the Grasshopper's Cells."

At the start of the 1900s, Walter Sutton, an American geneticist, studied the cells of grasshoppers. He wanted to understand how sex cells (sperm and eggs) form. Sutton focused on how the chromosomes moved within cells during the formation of sperm and eggs. He hypothesized that chromosomes are the key to learning how offspring have traits similar to those of their parents.

> **Academic Standards for Science**
>
> **8.3.3** Explain that genetic information is transmitted from parents to offspring mostly by chromosomes.
>
> **8.3.4** Understand the relationship between deoxyribonucleic acid (DNA), genes, and chromosomes.
>
> **8.NS.2** Plan investigations independently.
>
> **8.NS.8** Analyze data.

apply it!

⚠ **Design Experiments** Different types of organisms have different numbers of chromosomes, and some organisms are easier to study than others. Suppose you are a scientist studying chromosomes and you have to pick an organism from those shown below to do your work. Which one would you pick and why?

_____

_____

_____

_____

8.NS.2

did you **know?**

The organism with the highest known number of chromosomes is a plant in the fern family. The netted adderstongue fern has more than 1,200 chromosomes!

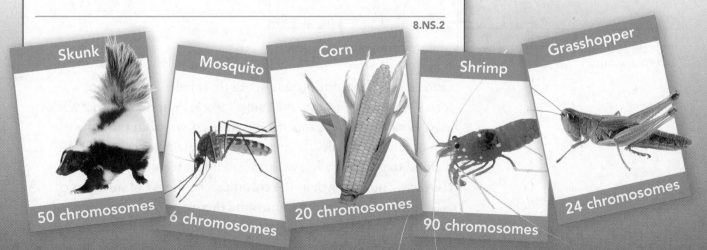

Skunk — 50 chromosomes

Mosquito — 6 chromosomes

Corn — 20 chromosomes

Shrimp — 90 chromosomes

Grasshopper — 24 chromosomes

Chromosomes and Inheritance Sutton needed evidence to support his hypothesis. Look at **Figure 1** to see how he found this evidence in grasshopper cells. To his surprise, he discovered that grasshopper sex cells have exactly half the number of chromosomes found in grasshopper body cells.

Chromosome Pairs Sutton observed what happened when a sperm cell and an egg cell joined. The fertilized egg that formed had 24 chromosomes. It had the same number of chromosomes as each parent. These 24 chromosomes existed as 12 pairs. One chromosome in each pair came from the male parent. The other chromosome came from the female parent.

FIGURE 1 ·······················

Paired Up

Sutton studied grasshopper cells through a microscope. He concluded that genes are carried on chromosomes.

✎ **Relate Text and Visuals**
Answer the questions in the spaces provided. 8.NS.8

❶ Body Cell

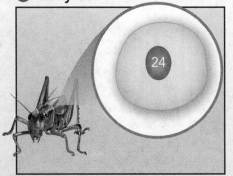

Each grasshopper body cell has 24 chromosomes.

❷ Sex Cells

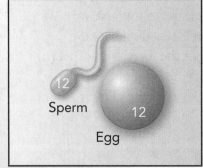

Sutton found that grasshopper sex cells each have 12 chromosomes.

1. How does the number of chromosomes in grasshopper sex cells compare to the number in body cells?

_____
_____
_____
_____

❸ Fertilization

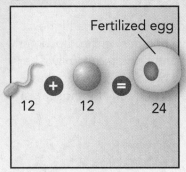

The fertilized egg cell has 24 chromosomes.

❹ Grasshopper Offspring

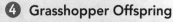
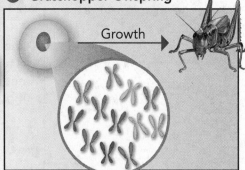

The 24 chromosomes exist as 12 pairs.

2. How is the inheritance of chromosomes similar to what you know about alleles?

_____
_____
_____
_____

Genes on Chromosomes Recall that alleles are different forms of a gene. Because of Mendel's work, Sutton knew that alleles exist in pairs in an organism. One allele comes from the female parent. The other allele comes from the male parent. Sutton realized that paired alleles are carried on paired chromosomes. His idea is now known as the chromosome theory of inheritance.

🔑 **According to the chromosome theory of inheritance, genes pass from parents to their offspring on chromosomes.**

A Lineup of Genes

The body cells of humans contain 46 chromosomes that form 23 pairs. Chromosomes are made up of many genes joined together like beads on a string. Although you have only 23 pairs of chromosomes, your body cells each contain between 20,000 and 25,000 genes. Genes control traits.

Figure 2 shows a pair of chromosomes from an organism. One chromosome is from the female parent. The other chromosome is from the male parent. Notice that each chromosome has the same genes. The genes are lined up in the same order on both chromosomes. However, the alleles for some of the genes are not identical. For example, one chromosome has allele *A*, and the other chromosome has allele *a*. As you can see, this organism is heterozygous for some traits and homozygous for others.

↻ Relate Cause and Effect

Suppose gene A on the left chromosome is damaged and no longer functions. What form of the trait would show? Why?

_____

_____

_____

_____

_____

FIGURE 2 ·······················

A Pair of Chromosomes   8.NS.8

Chromosomes in a pair may have different alleles for some genes and the same alleles for others.

✎ **Interpret Diagrams** For each pair of alleles, tell whether the organism is homozygous or heterozygous. The first two answers are shown.

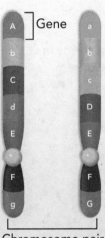

Gene

Chromosome pair

Heterozygous

Homozygous

_____

_____

_____

_____

Do the Quick Lab *Chromosomes and Inheritance.*

☞ Assess Your Understanding

1a. Describe When two grasshopper sex cells join, the chromosome number in the new cell is (half/double) the number in the sex cells.

8.3.3, 8.3.4

b. Summarize Describe the arrangement of genes on a pair of chromosomes.

_____

_____

_____

8.3.3, 8.3.4

c. Relate Evidence and Explanation How do Sutton's observations support the chromosome theory of inheritance?

_____

_____

_____

_____

8.3.3, 8.3.4

got it? ··

○ **I get it!** Now I know that genes are passed from parents to offspring _____

○ **I need extra help with** _____

Go to MY SCIENCE ⬤ COACH *online for help with this subject.*   8.3.3, 8.3.4

What Happens During Meiosis?

How do sex cells end up with half the number of chromosomes as body cells? The answer to this question is a form of cell division called meiosis. **Meiosis** (my OH sis) is the process by which the number of chromosomes is reduced by half as sex cells form. You can trace the events of meiosis in **Figure 3**. Here, the parent cell has four chromosomes arranged in two pairs. 🔑 **During meiosis, the chromosome pairs separate into two different cells. The sex cells that form later have only half as many chromosomes as the other cells in the organism.**

FIGURE 3 ···

Meiosis

During meiosis, a cell produces sex cells with half the number of chromosomes.

✎ **Interpret Diagrams** Fill in the missing terms in the spaces provided, and complete the diagram.

8.NS.8

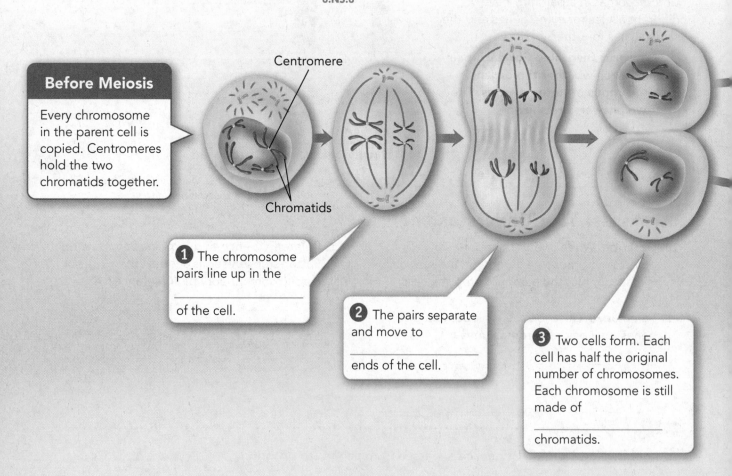

Before Meiosis

Every chromosome in the parent cell is copied. Centromeres hold the two chromatids together.

Centromere

Chromatids

❶ The chromosome pairs line up in the

_____

of the cell.

❷ The pairs separate and move to

_____

ends of the cell.

❸ Two cells form. Each cell has half the original number of chromosomes. Each chromosome is still made of

_____

chromatids.

During meiosis, a cell divides into two cells. Then each of these cells divides again, forming a total of four cells. The chromosomes duplicate only before the first cell division.

Each of the four sex cells shown below receives two chromosomes—one chromosome from each pair in the original cell. When two sex cells join at fertilization, the new cell that forms has the full number of chromosomes. In this case, the number is four. The organism that grows from this cell got two of its chromosomes from one parent and two from the other parent.

did you
know?..................

Researchers at Florida State University have found evidence that a single protein may control how chromosomes separate during meiosis. They are trying to figure out whether taking action during meiosis can prevent the development of some genetic disorders.

5 The centromeres split, and the _____ separate. They become single chromosomes and move to opposite ends of the cell.

4 In each cell, the _____ move to the center.

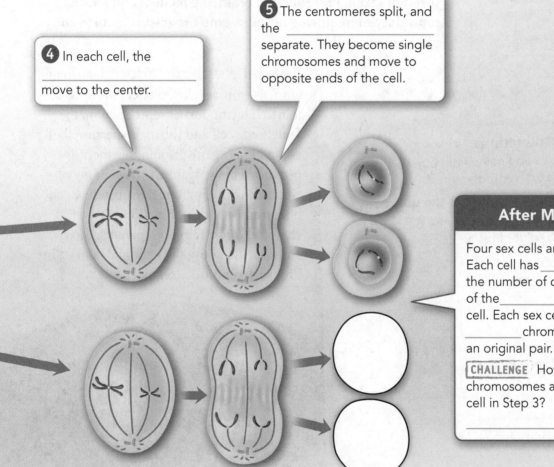

After Meiosis

Four sex cells are produced. Each cell has _____ the number of chromosomes of the _____ cell. Each sex cell has only _____ chromosome from an original pair.

[CHALLENGE] How many chromosomes are in each cell in Step 3?

_____
8.NS.8

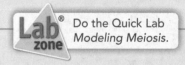
Lab zone®   Do the Quick Lab
Modeling Meiosis.

🔑 **Assess Your Understanding**

got it? ....

O **I get it!** Now I know that during meiosis, the number of chromosomes_____

O I need extra help with _____

Go to MY SCIENCE 💬 COACH *online for help with this subject.*

8.3.2, 8.3.3, 8.3.4

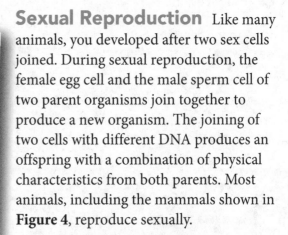

Academic Standards for Science

8.3.1 Explain that reproduction is the mechanism by which all organisms transmit genetic information.

8.3.2 Compare and contrast the transmission of genetic information in sexual and asexual reproduction.

8.3.3 Explain that genetic information is transmitted from parents to offspring mostly by chromosomes.

8.3.7 Recognize and explain that small genetic differences between parent and offspring can accumulate in successive generations.

8.NS.1 Make predictions based on research or prior knowledge.

8.NS.8 Analyze data.

8.NS.11 Communicate findings.

How Do Sexual and Asexual Reproduction Compare?

You now know that sexual reproduction through meiosis starts with the joining of two sex cells. As a result, offspring receive chromosomes (and DNA, or genetic material) from both sexes. Recall that some organisms can reproduce asexually. In many of these organisms, asexual reproduction takes place through mitosis. During mitosis, a parent cell divides into two new cells. No new genetic material is introduced during mitosis. **DNA transfer through sexual reproduction requiring meiosis and asexual reproduction requiring mitosis equip organisms in different ways for survival.**

Sexual Reproduction Like many animals, you developed after two sex cells joined. During sexual reproduction, the female egg cell and the male sperm cell of two parent organisms join together to produce a new organism. The joining of two cells with different DNA produces an offspring with a combination of physical characteristics from both parents. Most animals, including the mammals shown in **Figure 4**, reproduce sexually.

FIGURE 4 ·······························

Sexual Reproduction

8.NS.8

These wolf cubs and guinea pig pups are products of sexual reproduction.

✎ **Use the photos to answer the questions.**

1. Interpret Photos How do the offspring in each photo differ from their parent?

_____

_____

_____

2. Explain Why do the parent and the offspring look different?

_____

_____

_____

_____

Asexual Reproduction During asexual reproduction, one parent produces a new organism identical to itself. This new organism receives an exact copy of the parent's DNA. Some animals, including sponges, jellyfish, and worms, reproduce asexually. The hydra, shown in **Figure 5**, reproduces asexually through budding. In budding, a new animal grows out of the parent and breaks off. Some animals reproduce asexually by dividing in two.

Comparing Asexual and Sexual Reproduction

Both sexual and asexual reproduction offer survival advantages and disadvantages. An advantage of asexual reproduction is that one parent can quickly produce many identical offspring. But a major disadvantage is that offspring have the same DNA as the parent. The offspring have no variation from the parent and may not survive changes in the environment. In contrast, sexual reproduction has the advantage of producing offspring with new combinations of DNA. These offspring may have characteristics that help them survive under unfavorable conditions. However, a disadvantage of sexual reproduction is that it requires finding a mate, and the development of offspring takes a longer time.

FIGURE 5 ·····················

A Chip off the Old Block

Budding is the most common form of asexual reproduction for this hydra, a type of cnidarian.

✎ **Relate Text to Visuals** How does this photo show asexual reproduction?

_____

_____

_____

_____

_____

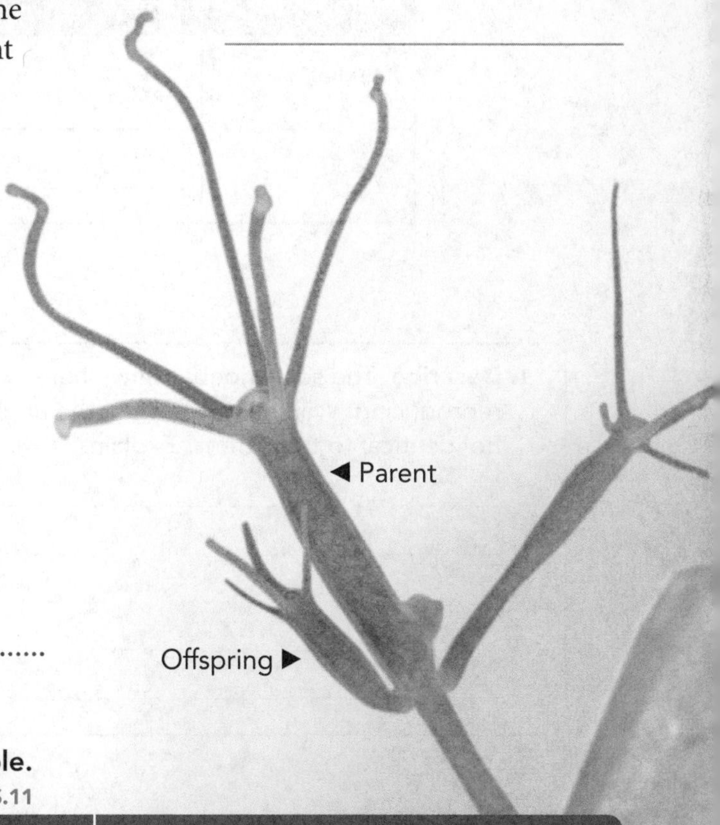

◀ Parent

Offspring ▶

FIGURE 6 ····················

Asexual and Sexual Reproduction

Compare and Contrast Write an advantage and a disadvantage of each type of reproduction in the table.

8.NS.11

	Asexual Reproduction	Sexual Reproduction
Advantage		
Disadvantage		

EXPLORE
THE BIG
?

Same or *Different?*

Why don't offspring always look like their parents?

FIGURE 7 ···

▶ ART IN MOTION Offspring don't always look like their parents. The type of reproduction and genes determine why this is so.

✎ **Review** Fill in the table to review the two types of reproduction. Then complete the tasks that go with each photo.

Type of Reproduction	Number of Parents	Mitosis or Meiosis	Offspring DNA Compared to Parent(s)	How Offspring Looks Compared to Parent(s)
Asexual	_____	_____	_____	_____
Sexual	_____	_____	_____	_____

1. Describe The soil amoeba shown here is reproducing. Will the offspring of the amoeba be identical to the parent? Explain.

_____

_____

_____

_____

Soil amoeba reproducing

2. Predict In rabbits, the allele for black fur (*B*) is dominant over the allele for white fur (*b*). Is it possible for the two rabbits shown below to produce a white offspring? Draw a Punnett square to justify your answer.

3. Interpret Tables Suppose both of the rabbits have the genotype *Bb*. What is the probability that an offspring will have white fur? What is the probability that it will have black fur?

_____

_____

_____

8.NS.1, 8.NS.8, 8.NS.11

 Do the Quick Lab *Types of Reproduction.*

🔑 Assess Your Understanding

2a. Define (Sexual/Asexual) reproduction involves the joining of sperm and egg.

8.3.1, 8.3.2, 8.3.3

b. Compare and Contrast The offspring of (sexual/asexual) reproduction have a better chance of surviving changes in the environment than the offspring of (sexual/asexual) reproduction. 8.3.1, 8.3.2, 8.3.3

c. CHALLENGE In rare cases, female sharks born in captivity that have never been exposed to male sharks have become pregant. Is this an example of asexual or sexual reproduction?

_____

_____

_____

_____

8.3.1, 8.3.2, 8.3.3

**d. ANSWER THE BIG ? ** Why don't offspring always look like their parents?

_____

_____

_____

_____

_____

_____

8.3.1, 8.3.2, 8.3.3

got it? •

○ **I get it!** Now I know that organisms are equipped for survival in different ways as a result of_____

_____

_____

○ **I need extra help with** _____

Go to **MY SCIENCE ⓢ COACH** *online for help with this subject.* 8.3.1, 8.3.2, 8.3.3

Advances in Genetics

UNLOCK THE BIG

🔑 **How Can Organisms Be Produced With Desired Traits?**

8.3.5, 8.NS.8

my planet Diary

FUN FACT

Zorses, Zonies, and Zedonks

Most people can tell the difference between a zebra and a horse. But would you be able to tell the difference among a zorse, a zony, and a zedonk? All three types of animals are zebroids, or zebra hybrids. These animals result when a zebra mates with a horse, a pony, or a donkey. Zebroids do not usually occur in nature. They generally result when people cross them on purpose. People may have first crossed zebras and horses in an effort to develop disease-resistant transportation animals for use in Africa. Zebras are resistant to African sleeping sickness. It was hoped that zorses, the offspring of zebras and horses, would have this resistance.

Communicate Discuss these questions with a classmate. Write your answers below.

1. Why may zebras and horses have been first crossed by people?

_____

_____

2. If zebras and horses do not usually mate in nature, should people intentionally cross them? Why or why not?

_____

_____

_____

_____

> PLANET DIARY Go to **Planet Diary** to learn more about advances in genetics.

 Do the Inquiry Warm-Up *What Do Fingerprints Reveal?*

Vocabulary
- selective breeding • inbreeding • hybridization
- clone • genetic engineering • gene therapy

Skills
- Reading: Ask Questions
- Inquiry: Draw Conclusions

How Can Organisms Be Produced With Desired Traits?

Unless you are an identical twin, your DNA is different from everyone else's. Because of advances in genetics, DNA evidence can show many things, such as family relationships or the ability to produce organisms with desirable traits. **Selective breeding, cloning, and genetic engineering are three different methods for developing organisms with desired traits.**

Selective Breeding The process of selecting organisms with desired traits to be parents of the next generation is called **selective breeding.** Thousands of years ago, in what is now Mexico, the food that we call corn was developed in this way. Every year, farmers saved seeds from the healthiest plants that produced the best food. In the spring, they planted only those seeds. This process was repeated over and over. In time, farmers developed plants that produced better corn. People have used selective breeding with many types of plants and animals. Two techniques for selective breeding are inbreeding and hybridization.

Academic Standards for Science

8.3.5 Identify and describe the difference between inherited traits and physical and behavioral traits that are acquired or learned.

8.NS.8 Analyze data and use it to identify patterns and make inferences based on these patterns.

Ask Questions Before you read this lesson, preview the red headings. In the graphic organizer below, ask a question for each heading. As you read, write answers to your questions.

Question	Answer
What is selective breeding?	Selective breeding is

Vocabulary High-Use Academic Words Use the word *resistant* to explain how hybridization can be useful.

_____

_____

_____

_____

_____

Inbreeding The technique of **inbreeding** involves crossing two individuals that have similar desirable characteristics. Suppose a male and a female golden retriever are both friendly and have the same coloring. Their offspring will probably also have those qualities. Inbreeding produces organisms that are genetically very similar. When inbred organisms are mated, the chance of their offspring inheriting two recessive alleles increases. This can lead to genetic disorders. For example, inherited hip problems are common in golden retrievers and other types of inbred dogs.

Hybridization In **hybridization** (hy brid ih ZAY shun), breeders cross two genetically different individuals. Recall that a hybrid organism has two different alleles for a trait. The hybrid organism that results is bred to have the best traits from both parents. For example, a farmer might cross corn that produces many kernels with corn that is resistant to disease. The farmer is hoping to produce a hybrid corn plant with both of the desired traits. Roses and other types of flowers are also commonly crossed.

apply it!

Since the late eighteenth century, gardeners and plant breeders have used hybridization to develop roses with certain characteristics.

❶ **Observe** Look at each rose below. One characteristic for each flower is given to you. List any other observable characteristics you see.

❷ **Draw Conclusions** Based on the characteristics of the two roses, draw with colored pencils or describe what you think the hybrid offspring will look like. Name the flower and list its characteristics.

Parent A

fragrant

_____

_____

_____

Parent B

survives cold temperatures

_____

_____

_____

Hybrid name:_____

_____

_____

_____

8.NS.8

do the math!

Changing Rice Production

This data table shows how worldwide rice production changed between 1965 and 2005. New hybrid varieties of rice plants are one factor that has affected the amount of rice produced.

Year	Yield
1965	2.04
1970	2.38
1975	2.52
1980	2.75
1985	3.26
1990	3.53
1995	3.66
2000	3.89
2005	4.09

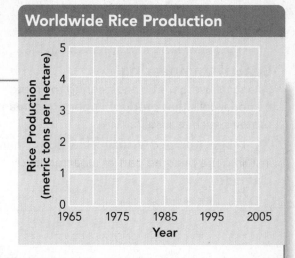

Worldwide Rice Production

① Graph Plot the data from the table and draw a line graph.

② Interpret Data What is the approximate difference between rice production in 1965 and 2005? _____

③ CHALLENGE What other factors might help account for the difference in rice production between 1965 and 2005?

_____

_____

_____

8.NS.8

Cloning

Cloning For some organisms, such as the dog shown in **Figure 1,** a technique called cloning can be used to produce offspring with desired traits. A **clone** is an organism that has exactly the same genes as the organism from which it was produced. It isn't hard to clone some kinds of plants such as African violets. Just cut a stem from one plant and put the stem in soil. Water it, and soon you will have a whole new plant. The new plant is genetically identical to the plant from which the stem was cut.

Genetic Engineering Geneticists have developed another powerful technique for producing organisms with desired traits. In this process, called **genetic engineering,** genes from one organism are transferred into the DNA of another organism. Genetic engineering can produce medicines and improve food crops.

FIGURE 1 ··

Cloning

This puppy, Lancelot Encore, is thought to be the first commercially cloned puppy in the United States. His owners paid $150,000 to have him cloned in South Korea.

✎ **Make Judgments** Would you pay $150,000 to clone a pet? Why or why not?

_____

_____

FIGURE 2 ·······························

Genetic Engineering

Scientists use genetic engineering to create bacterial cells that produce important human proteins such as insulin.

✎ **Relate Text and Visuals** How does a human insulin gene become part of a bacterium's plasmid?

_____

_____

_____

_____

_____

_____

_____

❶ Small rings of DNA, or plasmids, can be found in some bacterial cells.

❷ Scientists remove the plasmid. An enzyme cuts open the plasmid and removes the human insulin gene from its chromosome.

❸ The human insulin gene attaches to the open ends of the plasmid to form a closed ring.

❹ Some bacterial cells take up the plasmids that have the insulin gene.

❺ When the cells reproduce, the new cells will contain copies of the "engineered" plasmid. The foreign gene directs the cells to produce human insulin.

Genetic Engineering in Bacteria One type of bacterium is genetically engineered to produce a human protein called insulin. Many people with diabetes need insulin injections. Bacteria have a single DNA molecule in the cytoplasm. Some bacterial cells also contain small circular pieces of DNA called plasmids. You can see how scientists insert the DNA for the human insulin gene into the plasmid of a bacterium in **Figure 2.** Once the gene is inserted into the plasmid, the bacterial cell and all of its offspring will contain this human gene. As a result, the bacteria produce the protein that the human gene codes for—in this case, insulin. Because bacteria can reproduce quickly, large amounts of insulin can be produced in a short time.

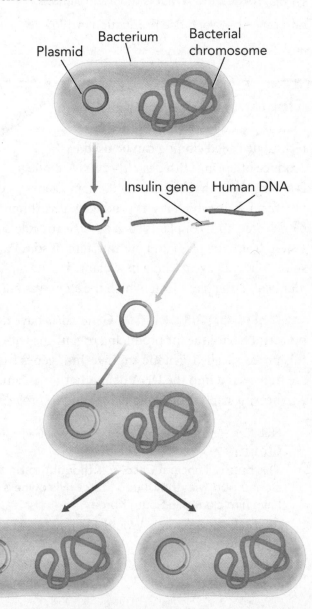

Plasmid   Bacterium   Bacterial chromosome

Insulin gene   Human DNA

Genetic Engineering in Other Organisms

Scientists can also use genetic engineering techniques to insert genes into animals. For example, human genes can be inserted into the cells of cows. The cows then produce milk containing the human protein coded by the gene. Scientists have used this technique to produce the blood-clotting protein needed by people with hemophilia.

Genes have also been inserted into the cells of plants, such as tomatoes and rice. Some of the genes enable the plants to survive in cold temperatures or in poor soil. Other genetically engineered crops can resist insect pests or contain more nutrients.

Gene Therapy Someday it may be possible to use genetic engineering to correct some genetic disorders in humans. This process, called gene therapy, will involve inserting copies of a gene directly into a person's cells. For example, doctors may be able to treat hemophilia by replacing the defective allele on the X chromosome. The inserted gene would provide the body the correct instructions to clot blood normally.

Concerns About Genetic Engineering

Some people are concerned about the long-term effects of genetic engineering. For example, some people think that genetically engineered crops may not be entirely safe. People fear that these crops may harm the environment or cause health problems in humans. To address such concerns, scientists are studying the effects of genetic engineering.

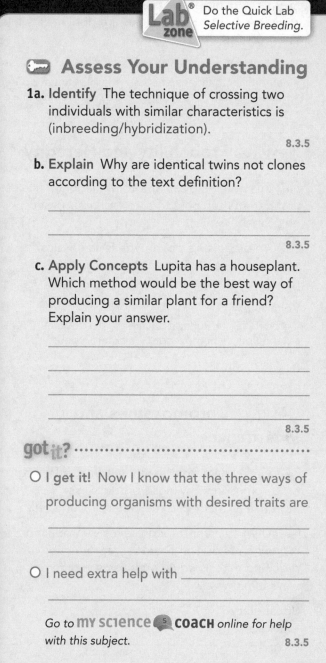

FIGURE 3 ·····················
> ART IN MOTION **Glow Cats**
A fluorescent protein was added to the cells of the cat below. This protein allows the cat to glow red when exposed to ultraviolet light. The cat above lacks this protein.

Lab zone® Do the Quick Lab *Selective Breeding.*

🔑 Assess Your Understanding

1a. Identify The technique of crossing two individuals with similar characteristics is (inbreeding/hybridization).

8.3.5

b. Explain Why are identical twins not clones according to the text definition?

_____

_____

8.3.5

c. Apply Concepts Lupita has a houseplant. Which method would be the best way of producing a similar plant for a friend? Explain your answer.

_____

_____

_____

_____

8.3.5

got it? ·····························

○ **I get it!** Now I know that the three ways of producing organisms with desired traits are

_____

_____

○ **I need extra help with** _____

_____

Go to **my science** 🔵ˢ **coach** *online for help with this subject.*

8.3.5

12 Study Guide

Offspring inherit different forms of genes called _____ from each parent. Traits are affected by patterns of inheritance and interactions with the _____.

LESSON 1 What Is Heredity?

8.3.3, 8.NS.1, 8.NS.8

🔑 In all of his crosses, Mendel found that only one form of the trait appeared in the F_1 generation. However, in the F_2 generation, the "lost" form of the trait always reappeared in about one fourth of the plants.

🔑 An organism's traits are controlled by the alleles it inherits from its parents. Some alleles are dominant, while other alleles are recessive.

Vocabulary
- heredity • trait • genetics • fertilization • purebred
- gene • allele • dominant allele • recessive allele • hybrid

Tall   ✕   Short

LESSON 2 Probability and Heredity

8.3, 8.NS.1, 8.NS.8

🔑 In a genetic cross, the combination of alleles that parents can pass to an offspring is based on probability.

🔑 An organism's phenotype is its physical appearance, or visible traits. An organism's genotype is its genetic makeup, or alleles.

Vocabulary
- probability • Punnett square • phenotype
- genotype • homozygous • heterozygous

LESSON 3 Patterns of Inheritance

8.3, 8.3.5, 8.NS.1, 8.NS.8

🔑 Most traits are the result of complex patterns of inheritance.

🔑 Environmental factors can influence the way genes are expressed.

Vocabulary
- incomplete dominance
- codominance
- multiple alleles
- polygenic inheritance

LESSON 4 Chromosomes and Inheritance

8.3.1, 8.3.2, 8.3.3, 8.3.4, 8.3.7, 8.NS.1, 8.NS.2, 8.NS.8, 8.NS.11

🔑 Genes pass from parents to their offspring on chromosomes. Meiosis produces sex cells that have half as many chromosomes as body cells.

🔑 DNA transfer through sexual reproduction requiring meiosis and asexual reproduction requiring mitosis equip organisms in different ways for survival.

Vocabulary
- meiosis

LESSON 5 Advances in Genetics

8.3.5, 8.NS.8

🔑 Selective breeding, cloning, and genetic engineering are three methods for developing organisms with desired traits.

Vocabulary
- selective breeding
- inbreeding
- hybridization
- clone
- genetic engineering
- gene therapy

Review and Assessment

LESSON 1 **What Is Heredity?**

1. Different forms of a gene are called

   a. alleles.   **b.** hybrids.

   c. genotypes.   **d.** chromosomes.

                               8.3.3

2. _____ is the scientific

study of heredity.

                               8.3.3

3. **Explain** Mendel crossed two pea plants: one with green pods and one with yellow pods. The F_1 generation all had green pods. What color pods did the F_2 generation have? Explain your answer.

_____

_____

_____

_____

                               8.3.3

4. **Predict** The plant below is purebred for height (tall). Write the alleles of this plant. In any cross for height, what kind of offspring will this plant produce? Why?

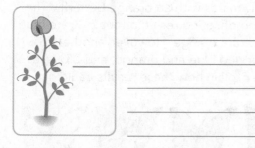

_____

_____

_____

_____

_____

                 8.3.3, 8.NS.1

5. **Compare and Contrast** How do dominant alleles and recessive alleles differ?

_____

_____

_____

_____

                               8.3.3

6. **Write About It** Write a diary entry as if you are Gregor Mendel. You may describe any part of his experiences, experiments, or observations.

                               8.3.3

LESSON 2 **Probability and Heredity**

7. Which of the following represents a heterozygous genotype?

   a. *YY*   **b.** *yy*

   c. *Yy*   **d.** $Y^H Y^H$

                               8.3

8. An organism's _____

is the way its genotype is expressed.

                               8.3

9. **Make Models** Fill in the Punnett square below to show a cross between two guinea pigs that are heterozygous for coat color. *B* is for black coat color, and *b* is for white coat color.

                               8.3

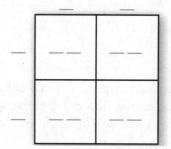

LESSON 3 **Patterns of Inheritance**

10. Which of the following terms describes a pattern of inheritance in which one allele is only partially dominant?

   a. codominance   **b.** acquired traits

   c. multiple alleles   **d.** incomplete dominance

                           8.3, 8.3.5

11. Traits that have three or more phenotypes may

be the result of _____ alleles.

                           8.3, 8.3.5

12. **Compare and Contrast** How is codominance different from incomplete dominance?

_____

_____

_____

_____

_____

                           8.3, 8.3.5

LESSON 4 Chromosomes and Inheritance

13. Genes are carried from parents to offspring on structures called

   a. alleles.   **b.** chromosomes.

   c. phenotypes.   **d.** genotypes.

                                       8.3.3, 8.3.4

14. The process of _____ results in the formation of sex cells.

                                       8.3.1, 8.3.2

15. Summarize What did Walter Sutton discover about the relationship between allelles and chromosomes?

_____

_____

_____

                                       8.3.3, 8.3.4

16. Calculate If an organism's body cells have 12 chromosomes, how many chromosomes will the sex cells have? Explain your answer.

_____

_____

_____

_____

_____

                          8.3.3, 8.3.4, 8.NS.8

17. Sequence What happens before meiosis?

_____

_____

_____

                                         8.3.1, 8.3.2

18. Apply Concepts Use the events of meiosis to explain why a sex cell normally does not receive both chromosomes from a pair.

_____

_____

_____

_____

                                       8.3.1, 8.3.2

LESSON 5 Advances in Genetics

19. An organism that has the same genes as the organism that produced it is called a

   a. clone.   **b.** hybrid.

   c. genome.   **d.** pedigree.

                                         8.3.5

20. Inbreeding and hybridization are two different types of _____

                                         8.3.5

21. **Write About It** Suppose that you are giving a presentation about genetic engineering to a group of people who are not familiar with the topic. Write a short speech that includes a definition of genetic engineering, a description of how it is used, and an explanation of some of the concerns about its use.

                                       8.3.5

APPLY THE BIG ?

Why don't offspring always look like their parents?

22. A species of butterfly has three alleles for wing color: blue, orange, and pale yellow. A blue butterfly mates with an orange butterfly. The following offspring result: about 25% are blue and 25% are orange. However, another 25% are speckled blue and orange, and 25% are yellow. Explain how these results could occur.

Offspring of blue butterfly and orange butterfly

_____

_____

_____

_____

_____

                                       8.3.1, 8.3.3

Indiana ISTEP+ Practice

Multiple Choice

Circle the letter of the best answer.

1. The Punnett square below shows a cross between two pea plants, each with round seeds. What is the missing genotype in the empty square?

	R	R
R	RR	
r	Rr	Rr

   A. rr
   B. rR
   C. Rr
   D. RR

   8.3.3

2. A particular trait has multiple alleles: A, B, and C. How many different genotypes are possible?

   A. 2
   B. 3
   C. 4
   D. 6

   8.3.3, 8.3.4

3. Inserting a human gene into a bacterial plasmid is an example of

   A. inbreeding.
   B. selective breeding.
   C. DNA fingerprinting.
   D. genetic engineering.

   8.3.5

4. For a particular plant, leaf texture is either fuzzy or smooth. A purebred fuzzy plant is crossed with a purebred smooth plant. All offspring are smooth. Which sentence best describes the alleles for this trait?

   A. Fuzzy is dominant over smooth.
   B. Smooth is dominant over fuzzy.
   C. The alleles are codominant.
   D. The alleles have incomplete dominance.

   8.3.3, 8.3.4

Constructed Response

Write your answer to Question 5 on the lines below.

5. Describe an example of an acquired trait.

   _____

   _____

   _____

   8.3.5

Extended Response

Use the diagram below and your knowledge of genetics to answer Question 6. Write your answer on a separate piece of paper.

A. 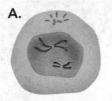   B.   C.

6. One of the cells shown is a parent cell about to undergo meiosis. Another cell is in the process of meiosis. A third cell is a sex cell that results from meiosis. Identify which cell is which, and explain your reasoning.

   8.3.1, 8.3.2, 8.3.3

Everyday Science

Nature
VS.
Nurture

In 1990, the Monterey Bay Aquarium in Monterey, California, released a young otter into the wild. Wildlife rehabilitators at the aquarium raised the otter and taught her how to find food. But, because she was used to receiving food and affection from people at the aquarium, she did not know to avoid other humans. After the otter pestered some local divers, she had to be returned to live at the aquarium.

So, which behaviors do animals learn, and which behaviors "just come naturally"? Actually, the line between inherited behaviors and learned behaviors is rarely clear. Although wild otters are naturally shy around humans, the otter at the Monterey Bay Aquarium had learned to expect food and affection from humans. As a result, wildlife rehabilitators commonly use puppets or animal costumes to keep the animals they care for from becoming too familiar with humans.

▼ This photograph shows a pair of otters, one of the species wildlife rehabilitators try to reintroduce into the wild.

Design It Choose a species, such as deer, otter, or panda, that is raised in captivity and returned to the wild. Design a rehabilitation activity to help orphaned animals learn a skill that they will need to survive in the wild. Explain the features of your rehabilitation activity to your class.

8.3.5, 8.NS.2, 8.DP.1, 8.DP.2, 8.DP.4

Seeing Spots

You would probably recognize a Dalmatian if you saw one—Dalmatians typically have white coats with distinctive black or brown spots. Spots are a defining characteristic of the Dalmatian breed. These spots can be large or small, but all Dalmatians have them.

In Dalmatians, spots are a dominant trait. When two Dalmatians breed, each parent contributes a gene for spots. The trait for spots is controlled by one set of genes with only two possible alleles. No matter how many puppies are in a litter, they will all develop spots.

But what if a Dalmatian breeds with another dog that isn't a Dalmatian? While the puppies won't develop the distinctive Dalmatian pattern, they will have spots, because the allele for spots is dominant. Some puppies will have many tiny spots and some will have large patches! Dalmatians, like leopards, cannot change their spots.

Newborn Dalmatian puppies are white—their spots develop when the puppies are about a week old. ▼

Predict It! Dalmatians' spots may be black or liver (brown), but never both on the same dog. Liver is a recessive allele. Use a Punnett square to predict the color of the spots on the offspring of a liver Dalmatian and a black Dalmatian with a recessive liver allele. Display your prediction on a poster.

8.3.3, 8.NS.1, 8.NS.2, 8.NS.8 8.NS.11

APPENDIX A

The Design Process

Engineers are people who use scientific and technological knowledge to solve practical problems. To design new products, engineers usually follow the process described here, even though they may not follow these steps in the same order each time.

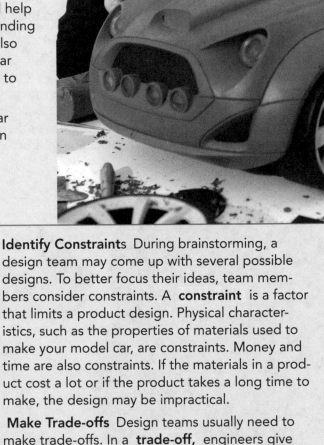

Lab zone®
Do the Indiana Design Project
Building a House

Identify a Need

Before engineers begin designing a new product, they must first identify the need they are trying to meet or the problem they want to solve. For example, suppose you are a member of a design team in a company that makes model cars. Your team has identified a need: a model car that is inexpensive and easy to assemble.

Research the Problem

Engineers often begin by gathering information that will help them with their new design. This research may include finding articles in books, magazines, or on the Internet. It may also involve talking to other engineers who have solved similar problems. Engineers often perform experiments related to the product they want to design.

For your model car, you could look at cars that are similar to the one you want to design. You might do research on the Internet. You could also test some materials to see whether they will work well in a model car.

Design a Solution

Brainstorm Ideas When engineers design new products, they usually work in teams. Design teams often hold brainstorming meetings in which any team member can contribute ideas. **Brainstorming** is a creative process in which one team member's suggestions often spark ideas in other group members. Brainstorming can lead to new approaches to solving a design problem.

Document the Process As the design team works, its members document, or keep a record of, the process. Having access to documentation enables others to repeat, or replicate, the process in the future. Design teams document their research sources, ideas, lists of materials, and so on because any part of the process may be a helpful resource later.

Identify Constraints During brainstorming, a design team may come up with several possible designs. To better focus their ideas, team members consider constraints. A **constraint** is a factor that limits a product design. Physical characteristics, such as the properties of materials used to make your model car, are constraints. Money and time are also constraints. If the materials in a product cost a lot or if the product takes a long time to make, the design may be impractical.

Make Trade-offs Design teams usually need to make trade-offs. In a **trade-off,** engineers give up one benefit of a proposed design in order to obtain another. In designing your model car, you might have to make trade-offs. For example, you might decide to give up the benefit of sturdiness in order to obtain the benefit of lower cost.

Select a Solution After considering the constraints and trade-offs of the possible designs, engineers then select one idea to develop further. That idea represents the solution that the team thinks best meets the need or solves the problem that was identified at the beginning of the process. The decision includes selecting the materials that will be used in the first attempt to build a product.

Create, Test, and Evaluate a Prototype

Once the team has chosen a design plan, the engineers build a prototype. A **prototype** is a working model used to test a design. Engineers evaluate the prototype to see whether it meets the goal. They must determine whether it works well, is easy to operate, is safe to use, and holds up to repeated use.

Part of the evaluation includes collecting data in the form of measurements. For example, think of your model car. Once you decide how to build your prototype, what would you want to know about it? You might want to measure how much baggage it could carry or how its shape affects its speed.

Troubleshoot and Redesign

Few prototypes work perfectly, which is why they need to be tested. Once a design team has tested a prototype, the members analyze the results and identify any problems. The team then tries to **troubleshoot,** or fix the design problems. Troubleshooting allows the team to redesign the prototype to improve on how well the solution meets the need.

Communicate the Solution

A team needs to communicate the final design to the people who will manufacture and use the product. To do this, teams may use sketches, detailed drawings, computer simulations, and word descriptions. The team may also present the evidence that was collected when the prototype was tested. This evidence may include mathematical representations, such as graphs and data tables, that support the choice for the final design.

Academic Standards for Science

The Design Process

8.DP.1 Identify a need or problem to be solved.

8.DP.2 Brainstorm potential solutions.

8.DP.3 Document the design throughout the entire design process so that it can be replicated in a portfolio/notebook with drawings including labels.

8.DP.4 Select a solution to the need or problem.

8.DP.5 Select the most appropriate materials to develop a solution that will meet the need.

8.DP.6 Create the solution through a prototype.

8.DP.7 Test and evaluate how well the solution meets the goal.

8.DP.8 Evaluate and test the design using measurement.

8.DP.9 Present evidence using mathematical representations (graphs, data tables).

8.DP.10 Communicate the solution including evidence using mathematical representations (graphs, data tables), drawings or prototypes.

8.DP.11 Redesign to improve the solution based on how well the solution meets the need.

Science, Engineering and Technology

8.4 Core Standard: Identify the appropriate materials to be used to solve a problem based on their specific properties and characteristics.

8.4.1 Understand how the strength of attractive forces between particles in a material helps to explain many physical properties of the material, such as why different materials exist as gases, liquids or solids at a given temperature.

8.4.2 Rank the strength of attractions between the particles of room-temperature materials.

8.4.3 Investigate the properties (mechanical, chemical, electrical, thermal, magnetic, and optical) of natural and engineered materials.

Periodic Table of the Elements

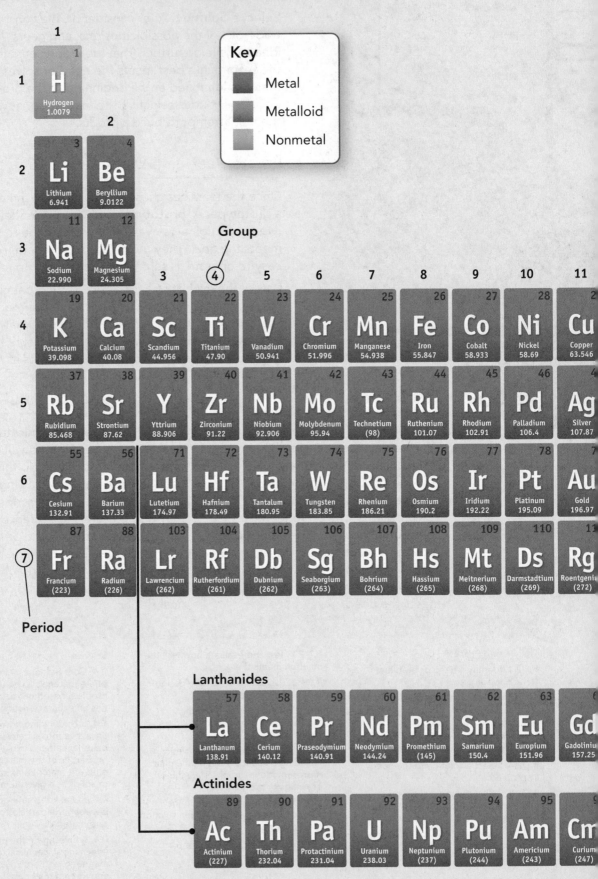

Key

Metal
Metalloid
Nonmetal

Group

Period

Lanthanides

Actinides

Many periodic tables include a zigzag line that separates the metals from the nonmetals. Metalloids, found on either side of the line, share properties of both metals and nonmetals.

18

| | | | | | 2 He Helium 4.0026 |

13 **14** **15** **16** **17**

| 5 B Boron 10.81 | 6 C Carbon 12.011 | 7 N Nitrogen 14.007 | 8 O Oxygen 15.999 | 9 F Fluorine 18.998 | 10 Ne Neon 20.179 |

| 13 Al Aluminum 26.982 | 14 Si Silicon 28.086 | 15 P Phosphorus 30.974 | 16 S Sulfur 32.06 | 17 Cl Chlorine 35.453 | 18 Ar Argon 39.948 |

12

| 30 Zn Zinc 65.38 | 31 Ga Gallium 69.72 | 32 Ge Germanium 72.59 | 33 As Arsenic 74.922 | 34 Se Selenium 78.96 | 35 Br Bromine 79.904 | 36 Kr Krypton 83.80 |

| 48 Cd Cadmium 112.41 | 49 In Indium 114.82 | 50 Sn Tin 118.69 | 51 Sb Antimony 121.75 | 52 Te Tellurium 127.60 | 53 I Iodine 126.90 | 54 Xe Xenon 131.30 |

| 80 Hg Mercury 200.59 | 81 Tl Thallium 204.37 | 82 Pb Lead 207.2 | 83 Bi Bismuth 208.98 | 84 Po Polonium (209) | 85 At Astatine (210) | 86 Rn Radon (222) |

| 112 (277) | 113 (284) | 114 (289) | 115 (288) | 116 (292) | | 118 (294) |

The discoveries of elements 112 and above have not yet been officially confirmed.

Atomic masses in parentheses are those of the most stable isotopes.

| 65 Tb Terbium 158.93 | 66 Dy Dysprosium 162.50 | 67 Ho Holmium 164.93 | 68 Er Erbium 167.26 | 69 Tm Thulium 168.93 | 70 Yb Ytterbium 173.04 |

| 97 Bk Berkelium (247) | 98 Cf Californium (251) | 99 Es Einsteinium (252) | 100 Fm Fermium (257) | 101 Md Mendelevium (258) | 102 No Nobelium (259) |

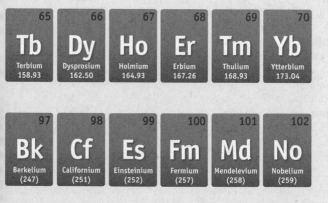

List of Chemical Elements

Name	Symbol	Atomic Number	Atomic Mass†	Name	Symbol	Atomic Number	Atomic Mass†
Actinium	Ac	89	(227)	Mendelevium	Md	101	(258)
Aluminum	Al	13	26.982	Mercury	Hg	80	200.59
Americium	Am	95	(243)	Molybdenum	Mo	42	95.94
Antimony	Sb	51	121.75	Neodymium	Nd	60	144.24
Argon	Ar	18	39.948	Neon	Ne	10	20.179
Arsenic	As	33	74.922	Neptunium	Np	93	(237)
Astatine	At	85	(210)	Nickel	Ni	28	58.71
Barium	Ba	56	137.33	Niobium	Nb	41	92.906
Berkelium	Bk	97	(247)	Nitrogen	N	7	14.007
Beryllium	Be	4	9.0122	Nobelium	No	102	(259)
Bismuth	Bi	83	208.98	Osmium	Os	76	190.2
Bohrium	Bh	107	(264)	Oxygen	O	8	15.999
Boron	B	5	10.81	Palladium	Pd	46	106.4
Bromine	Br	35	79.904	Phosphorus	P	15	30.974
Cadmium	Cd	48	112.41	Platinum	Pt	78	195.09
Calcium	Ca	20	40.08	Plutonium	Pu	94	(244)
Californium	Cf	98	(251)	Polonium	Po	84	(209)
Carbon	C	6	12.011	Potassium	K	19	39.098
Cerium	Ce	58	140.12	Praseodymium	Pr	59	140.91
Cesium	Cs	55	132.91	Promethium	Pm	61	(145)
Chlorine	Cl	17	35.453	Protactinium	Pa	91	231.04
Chromium	Cr	24	51.996	Radium	Ra	88	(226)
Cobalt	Co	27	58.933	Radon	Rn	86	(222)
Copper	Cu	29	63.546	Rhenium	Re	75	186.21
Curium	Cm	96	(247)	Rhodium	Rh	45	102.91
Darmstadtium	Ds	110	(269)	Roentgenium	Rg	111	(272)
Dubnium	Db	105	(262)	Rubidium	Rb	37	85.468
Dysprosium	Dy	66	162.50	Ruthenium	Ru	44	101.07
Einsteinium	Es	99	(252)	Rutherfordium	Rf	104	(261)
Erbium	Er	68	167.26	Samarium	Sm	62	150.4
Europium	Eu	63	151.96	Scandium	Sc	21	44.956
Fermium	Fm	100	(257)	Seaborgium	Sg	106	(263)
Fluorine	F	9	18.998	Selenium	Se	34	78.96
Francium	Fr	87	(223)	Silicon	Si	14	28.086
Gadolinium	Gd	64	157.25	Silver	Ag	47	107.87
Gallium	Ga	31	69.72	Sodium	Na	11	22.990
Germanium	Ge	32	72.59	Strontium	Sr	38	87.62
Gold	Au	79	196.97	Sulfur	S	16	32.06
Hafnium	Hf	72	178.49	Tantalum	Ta	73	180.95
Hassium	Hs	108	(265)	Technetium	Tc	43	(98)
Helium	He	2	4.0026	Tellurium	Te	52	127.60
Holmium	Ho	67	164.93	Terbium	Tb	65	158.93
Hydrogen	H	1	1.0079	Thallium	Tl	81	204.37
Indium	In	49	114.82	Thorium	Th	90	232.04
Iodine	I	53	126.90	Thulium	Tm	69	168.93
Iridium	Ir	77	192.22	Tin	Sn	50	118.69
Iron	Fe	26	55.847	Titanium	Ti	22	47.90
Krypton	Kr	36	83.80	Tungsten	W	74	183.85
Lanthanum	La	57	138.91	Uranium	U	92	238.03
Lawrencium	Lr	103	(262)	Vanadium	V	23	50.941
Lead	Pb	82	207.2	Xenon	Xe	54	131.30
Lithium	Li	3	6.941	Ytterbium	Yb	70	173.04
Lutetium	Lu	71	174.97	Yttrium	Y	39	88.906
Magnesium	Mg	12	24.305	Zinc	Zn	30	65.38
Manganese	Mn	25	54.938	Zirconium	Zr	40	91.22
Meitnerium	Mt	109	(268)				

†Numbers in parentheses give the mass number of the most stable isotope.

GLOSSARY

A

abyssal plain A smooth, nearly flat region of the deep ocean floor. (205)
llanura abisal Región llana, casi plana, de la cuenca oceánica profunda.

accuracy How close a measurement is to the true or accepted value. (56)
exactitud Cuán cerca está una medida del valor verdadero o aceptado.

acid rain Rain or another form of precipitation that is more acidic than normal, caused by the release of molecules of sulfur dioxide and nitrogen oxide into the air. (373)
lluvia ácida Lluvia u otra forma de precipitación que es más ácida de lo normal, debido a la contaminación del aire con moléculas de dióxido de azufre y óxido de nitrógeno.

adaptation An inherited behavior or physical characteristic that helps an organism survive and reproduce in its environment. (443)
adaptación Comportamiento o característica física hereditaria que le permite a un organismo sobrevivir y reproducirse en su ambiente.

air mass A huge body of air that has similar temperature, humidity, and air pressure at any given height. (281)
masa de aire Gran cuerpo de aire que tiene temperatura, humedad y presión similares en todos sus puntos.

air pressure The pressure caused by the weight of a column of air pushing down on an area. (227)
presión de aire Presión causada por el peso de una columna de aire en un área.

alkali metal An element in Group 1 of the periodic table. (110)
metal alcalino Elemento en el Grupo 1 de la tabla periódica.

alkaline earth metal An element in Group 2 of the periodic table. (110)
metal alcalinotérreo Elemento en el Grupo 2 de la tabla periódica.

alleles The different forms of a gene. (471)
alelos Diferentes formas de un gen.

altitude Elevation above sea level. (230)
altitud Elevación sobre el nivel del mar.

analyzing Evaluating data to reach a conclusion about an experiment. (8)
analizar Evaluar datos para llegar a una conclusión acerca de un experimento.

anemometer An instrument used to measure wind speed. (250)
anemómetro Instrumento que se usa para medir la velocidad del viento.

aneroid barometer An instrument that measures changes in air pressure without using a liquid. (229)
barómetro aneroide Instrumento que mide los cambios en la presión del aire sin usar líquidos.

anomalous data Data that do not fit with the rest of a data set. (59)
datos anómalos Información que no encaja con los otros datos de un conjunto de datos.

anticyclone A high-pressure center of dry air. (286)
anticiclón Centro de aire seco de alta presión.

aquaculture The practice of raising fish and other water-dwelling organisms for food. (335)
acuicultura Técnica del cultivo de peces y otros organismos acuáticos para consumo humano.

asexual reproduction A reproductive process that involves only one parent and produces offspring that are genetically identical to the parent. (407)
reproducción asexual Proceso reproductivo que consiste de un solo reproductor y que produce individuos que son genéticamente idénticos al reproductor.

atmosphere The relatively thin layer of gases that form Earth's outermost layer. (222)
atmósfera Capa de gases relativamente delgada que forma la capa exterior de la Tierra.

atom The basic particle from which all elements are made; the smallest particle of an element that has the properties of that element. (91)
átomo Partícula básica de la que todos los elementos están formados; partícula más pequeña de un elemento, que tiene las propiedades de ese elemento.

atomic mass The average mass of all the isotopes of an element. (99)
masa atómica Promedio de la masa de todos los isótopos de un elemento.

atomic number The number of protons in the nucleus of an atom. (96)
número atómico Número de protones en el núcleo de un átomo.

autotroph An organism that is able to capture energy from sunlight or chemicals and use it to produce its own food. (411)
autótrofo Organismo capaz de capturar y usar la energía solar o de sustancias químicas para producir su propio alimento.

GLOSSARY

B

barometer An instrument used to measure changes in air pressure. (228)
barómetro Instrumento que se usa para medir cambios de la presión del aire.

bedrock Rock that makes up Earth's crust; also the solid rock layer beneath the soil. (358)
lecho rocoso Roca que compone la corteza terrestre; también, la capa sólida de roca debajo del suelo.

bias A subjective belief that affects a person's attitude toward something; an error in the design of an experiment that affects the results of the experiment. (22)
predisposición Creencia subjetiva que afecta la actitud de una persona acerca de algo; un error en el diseño de un experimento que afecta los resultados del experimento.

binomial nomenclature The classification system in which each organism is given a unique, two-part scientific name indicating its genus and species. (416)
nomenclatura binaria Sistema de clasificación en el que cada organismo tiene un nombre científico específico de dos partes que indica el género y la especie.

biodegradable Capable of being broken down by bacteria and other decomposers. (366)
biodegradable Sustancia que las bacterias y otros descomponedores pueden descomponer.

biodiversity The total number of different species on Earth, including those on land, in the water, and in the air. (336)
biodiversidad Número total de especies diferentes que habitan la Tierra, incluyendo especies terrestres, marinas y del aire.

blizzard A snowstorm with prolonged winds of 56 kilometers per hour or greater and blowing snow that reduces visibility. (289)
nevasca Tormenta de nieve con vientos prolongados de 56 km por hora o más y caídas de nieve en ráfagas que reducen la visibilidad.

brainstorming A process in which group members freely suggest any creative solutions that come to mind. (508)
lluvia de ideas Proceso mediante el cual los miembros de un grupo sugieren libremente cualquier solución creativa que se les ocurre.

branching tree diagram A diagram that shows probable evolutionary relationships among organisms and the order in which specific characteristics may have evolved. (427)
árbol ramificado Diagrama que muestra las relaciones evolucionarias probables entre los organismos y el orden en que ciertas características específicas podrían haber evolucionado.

C

captive breeding The mating of animals in zoos or wildlife preserves. (343)
reproducción en cautiverio Apareamiento de animales en zoológicos y reservas naturales.

cell The basic unit of structure and function in living things. (406)
célula Unidad básica de la estructura y función de todos los seres vivos.

chemical bond The force of attraction that holds two atoms together. (135)
enlace químico Fuerza de atracción que mantiene juntos a dos átomos.

chemical change A change in which one or more substances combine or break apart to form new substances. (158)
cambio químico Cambio en el cual una o más sustancias se combinan o se descomponen para formar sustancias nuevas.

chemical equation A short, easy way to show a chemical reaction, using symbols. (164)
ecuación química Forma corta y sencilla de mostrar una reacción química usando símbolos.

chemical formula Symbols that show the elements in a compound and the ratio of atoms. (144)
fórmula química Símbolos que muestran los elementos de un compuesto y la cantidad de átomos.

chemical symbol A one- or two-letter representation of an element. (101)
símbolo químico Representación con una o dos letras de un elemento.

chlorofluorocarbons Human-made gases containing chlorine and fluorine (also called CFCs) that are the main cause of ozone depletion. (376)
clorofluorocarbonos Gases generados por el hombre, que contienen cloro y fluor (también llamados CFC) y que son la causa principal del deterioro de la capa de ozono.

cirrus Wispy, feathery clouds made of ice crystals that form at high levels. (272)
cirros Nubes que parecen plumas o pinceladas y que están formadas por cristales de hielo que se crean a grandes alturas.

classification The process of grouping things based on their similarities. (415)
clasificación Proceso de agrupar cosas según sus semejanzas.

classifying The process of grouping together items that are alike in some way. (6)
clasificar Proceso de agrupar objetos con algún tipo de semejanza.

clear-cutting The process of cutting down all the trees in an area at once. (332)
tala total Proceso de cortar simultáneamente todos los árboles de un área.

climate The average annual conditions of temperature, precipitation, winds, and clouds in an area. (208)
clima Condiciones promedio anuales de temperatura, precipitación, viento y nubosidad de un área.

clone An organism that is genetically identical to the organism from which it was produced. (499)
clon Organismo genéticamente idéntico al organismo del que proviene.

closed system A system in which no matter is allowed to enter or leave. (169)
sistema cerrado Sistema en el cual la materia no puede entrar ni salir.

codominance A situation in which both alleles for a gene are expressed equally. (481)
codominancia Situación en la que ambos alelos de un gen se manifiestan de igual manera.

coefficient A number in front of a chemical formula in an equation that indicates how many molecules or atoms of each reactant and product are involved in a reaction. (171)
coeficiente En un ecuación, número delante de una fórmula química que indica cuántas moléculas o átomos de cada reactante y producto intervienen en una reacción.

condensation The change in state from a gas to a liquid. (266)
condensación Cambio del estado gaseoso al estado líquido.

conduction The transfer of thermal energy from one particle of matter to another. (246)
conducción Transferencia de energía térmica de una partícula de materia a otra.

conservation The practice of using less of a resource so that it can last longer. (325)
conservación Práctica que consiste en reducir el uso de un recurso para prolongar su duración.

constraint Any factor that limits a design. (508)
restricción Cualquier factor que limita un diseño.

continental (air mass) A dry air mass that forms over land. (281)
masa de aire continental Masa de aire seco que se forma sobre la Tierra.

continental shelf A gently sloping, shallow area of the ocean floor that extends outward from the edge of a continent. (204)
plataforma continental Área poco profunda con pendiente suave en la cuenca oceánica que se extiende desde los márgenes de un continente.

continental slope A steep incline of the ocean floor leading down from the edge of the continental shelf. (204)
talud continental Región de la cuenca oceánica con pendiente empinada que baja del borde de la plataforma continental.

controlled experiment An experiment in which only one variable is manipulated at a time. (22)
experimento controlado Experimento en el cual sólo se manipula una variable a la vez.

convection The transfer of thermal energy by the movement of a fluid. (246)
convección Transferencia de energía térmica por el movimiento de un líquido.

convection current The movement of a fluid, caused by differences in temperature, that transfers heat from one part of the fluid to another. (247)
corriente de convección Movimiento de un líquido ocasionado por diferencias de temperatura y que transfiere calor de un área del líquido a otra.

convergent evolution The process by which unrelated organisms evolve similar characteristics. (429)
evolución convergente Proceso por el cual organismos no relacionados exhiben una evolución de características similares.

Coriolis effect The effect of Earth's rotation on the direction of winds and currents. (207)
efecto Coriolis Efecto de la rotación de la Tierra sobre la dirección de los vientos y las corrientes.

corrosion The gradual wearing away of a metal element due to a chemical reaction. (109)
corrosión Desgaste progresivo de un elemento metal debido a una reacción química.

covalent bond A chemical bond formed when two atoms share electrons. (149)
enlace covalente Enlace químico que se forma cuando dos átomos comparten electrones.

GLOSSARY

crystal A solid in which the atoms are arranged in a pattern that repeats again and again. (146)
cristal Cuerpo sólido en el que los átomos siguen un patrón que se repite una y otra vez.

cumulus Fluffy, white clouds, usually with flat bottoms, that look like rounded piles of cotton. (272)
cúmulos Nubes blancas, normalmente con la parte inferior plana, que parecen grandes masas de algodón esponjosas y redondas.

current A large stream of moving water that flows through the oceans. (207)
corriente Gran volumen de agua que fluye por los océanos.

cyclone A swirling center of low air pressure. (286)
ciclón Centro de un remolino de aire de baja presión.

D
---

data Facts, figures, and other evidence gathered through observations. (12)
dato Hechos, cifras u otra evidencia reunida por medio de observaciones.

decomposition A chemical reaction that breaks down compounds into simpler products. (174)
descomposición Reacción química que descompone los compuestos en productos más simples.

density The measurement of how much mass of a substance is contained in a given volume. (50)
densidad Medida de la masa de una sustancia que tiene un volumen dado.

dependent variable The factor that changes as a result of changes to the independent variable in an experiment; also called responding variable. (21)
variable dependiente Factor que cambia a causa de los cambios de la variable independiente de un experimento; también se denomina variable de respuesta.

desertification The advance of desert-like conditions into areas that previously were fertile; caused by overfarming, overgrazing, drought, and climate change. (360)
desertificación Paso de condiciones desérticas a áreas que eran fértiles; resulta de la agricultura descontrolada, el uso exagerado de los pastos, las sequías y los cambios climáticos.

development The process of change that occurs during an organism's life to produce a more complex organism. (407)
desarrollo Proceso de cambio que ocurre durante la vida de un organismo, mediante el cual se crea un organismo más complejo.

dew point The temperature at which condensation begins. (271)
punto de rocío Temperatura a la que comienza la condensación.

diatomic molecule A molecule consisting of two atoms. (118)
molécula diatómica Molécula que tiene dos átomos.

divide A ridge of land that separates one watershed from another. (195)
divisoria Elevación de terreno que separa una cuenca hidrográfica de otra.

dominant allele An allele whose trait always shows up in the organism when the allele is present. (471)
alelo dominante Alelo cuyo rasgo siempre se manifiesta en el organismo, cuando el alelo está presente.

double bond A chemical bond formed when atoms share two pairs of electrons. (150)
enlace doble Enlace químico formado cuando los átomos comparten dos pares de electrones.

drought A long period of low precipitation. (279)
sequía Período prolongado de baja precipitación.

ductile A term used to describe a material that can be pulled out into a long wire. (108)
dúctil Término usado para describir un material que se puede estirar hasta crear un alambre largo.

E
---

ecological footprint The amount of land and water that individuals use to meet their resource needs and to absorb the wastes that they produce. (324)
espacio ecológico Cantidad de tierra y agua que los individuos usan para cubrir sus necesidades y absorber sus desechos.

El Niño An abnormal climate event that occurs every two to seven years in the Pacific Ocean, causing changes in winds, currents, and weather patterns for one to two years. (209)
El Niño Suceso climático anormal que se presenta cada dos a siete años en el océano Pacífico y que causa cambios de vientos, corrientes y patrones meteorológicos que duran uno o dos años.

electrical conductivity The ability of an object to carry electric current. (108)
conductividad eléctrica Capacidad de un objeto para cargar corriente eléctrica.

electron A tiny, negatively charged particle that moves around the outside of the nucleus of an atom. (92)
electrón Partícula pequeña de carga negativa que se mueve alrededor del núcleo de un átomo.

electron dot diagram A representation of the valence electrons in an atom, using dots. (135)
esquema de puntos por electrones Representación del número de electrones de valencia de un átomo, usando puntos.

electromagnetic wave A wave that can transfer electric and magnetic energy through the vacuum of space. (238)
onda electromagnética Onda que puede transferir energía eléctrica y magnética a través del vacío del espacio.

emissions Pollutants that are released into the air. (371)
gases contaminantes Contaminantes liberados al aire.

empirical evidence Data and observations that are collected through scientific processes and that explain a particular observation. (12)
evidencia empírica Datos y observaciones que se recopilan a través de procesos científicos y que explican una observación particular.

endangered species A species in danger of becoming extinct in the near future. (341)
especie en peligro de extinción Especie que corre el riesgo de desaparecer en el futuro próximo.

endothermic reaction A reaction that absorbs energy. (162)
reacción endotérmica Reacción que absorbe energía.

energy level A region of an atom in which electrons of the same energy are likely to be found. (94)
nivel de energía Región de un átomo en la que es probable que se encuentren electrones con la misma energía.

environmental science The study of the natural processes that occur in the environment and how humans can affect them. (318)
ciencias del medio ambiente Estudio de los procesos naturales que ocurren en el medio ambiente y de cómo los seres humanos pueden afectarlos.

erosion The process by which water, ice, wind, or gravity moves weathered particles of rock and soil. (359)
erosión Proceso por el cual el agua, el hielo, el viento o la gravedad desplazan partículas desgastadas de roca y suelo.

estimate An approximation of a number based on reasonable assumptions. (55)
estimación Aproximación de un número basada en conjeturas razonables.

eukaryote An organism whose cells contain a nucleus. (424)
eucariota Organismo cuyas células contienen un núcleo.

eutrophication The buildup over time of nutrients in freshwater lakes and ponds that leads to an increase in the growth of algae. (198)
eutroficación Acumulación gradual de nutrientes en lagos y estanques de agua dulce que produce un aumento en el crecimiento de algas.

evacuate Moving away temporarily from an area about to be affected by severe weather. (296)
evacuar Desalojar temporalmente un área que será afectada por mal tiempo.

evaporation The process by which molecules at the surface of a liquid absorb enough energy to change to a gas. (190)
evaporación Proceso mediante el cual las moléculas en la superficie de un líquido absorben suficiente energía para pasar al estado gaseoso.

evidence Observations and conclusions that have been repeated. (29)
evidencia Observaciones y conclusiones que se han repetido.

evolution Change over time; the process by which modern organisms have descended from ancient organisms. (426)
evolución Cambios a través del tiempo; proceso por el cual los organismos modernos se originaron a partir de organismos antiguos.

exosphere The outer layer of the thermosphere. (237)
exósfera Capa externa de la termósfera.

exothermic reaction A reaction that releases energy, usually in the form of heat. (162)
reacción exotérmica Reacción que libera energía generalmente en forma de calor.

exponential growth Growth pattern in which individuals in a population reproduce at a constant rate, so that the larger a population gets, the faster it grows. (327)
crecimiento exponencial Patrón de crecimiento en el cual los individuos de una población se reproducen a una tasa constante, de modo que mientras más aumenta la población, más rápido crece ésta.

GLOSSARY

extinction The disappearance of all members of a species from Earth. (341)
extinción Desaparición de la Tierra de todos los miembros de una especie.

F

feedback Output that changes a system or allows the system to adjust itself. (69)
retroalimentación Salida que cambia un sistema o permite que éste se ajuste.

fertilization The process in sexual reproduction in which an egg cell and a sperm cell join to form a new cell. (469)
fertilización Proceso de la reproducción sexual en el que un óvulo y un espermatozoide se unen para formar una nueva célula.

fertilizer A substance that provides nutrients to help crops grow better. (359)
fertilizante Sustancia que proporciona nutrientes para ayudar a que crezcan mejor los cultivos.

field Any area outside of the laboratory. (75)
campo Cualquier área fuera del laboratorio.

fishery An area with a large population of valuable ocean organisms. (334)
pesquería Área con una gran población de organismos marinos aprovechables.

flood An overflowing of water in a normally dry area. (278)
inundación Ocupación de agua en un área que habitualmente permanece seca.

fossil The preserved remains or traces of an organism that lived in the past. (441)
fósil Restos o vestigios conservados de un organismo que vivió en el pasado.

fossil fuel Coal, oil, or natural gas that forms over millions of years from the remains of ancient organisms; burned to release energy. (390)
combustible fósil Carbón, petróleo o gas natural que se forma a lo largo de millones de años a partir de los restos de organismos antiguos; se queman para liberar energía.

front The boundary where unlike air masses meet but do not mix. (283)
frente Límite donde se encuentran, pero no se mezclan, masas de aire diferentes.

G

gene A sequence of DNA that determines a trait and is passed from parent to offspring. (340)
gen Secuencia de ADN que determina un rasgo y que se pasa de los progenitores a los hijos.

gene therapy The process of changing a gene to treat a medical disease or disorder. An absent or faulty gene is replaced by a normal working gene. (501)
terapia genética Proceso que consiste en cambiar un gen para tratar una enfermedad o un trastorno médico. El gen ausente o defectuoso se cambia por un gen con función normal.

genetic engineering The transfer of a gene from the DNA of one organism into another organism, in order to produce an organism with desired traits. (499)
ingeniería genética Transferencia de un gen desde el ADN de un organismo a otro, para producir un organismo con los rasgos deseados.

genetics The scientific study of heredity. (469)
genética Ciencia que estudia la herencia.

genotype An organism's genetic makeup, or allele combinations. (478)
genotipo Composición genética de un organismo, es decir, las combinaciones de los alelos.

genus A classification grouping that consists of a number of similar, closely related species. (416)
género Clase de agrupación que consiste de un número de especies similares y estrechamente relacionadas.

global warming A gradual increase in the average temperature of the atmosphere, thought to be caused by an increase in greenhouse gases from human activities. (390)
calentamiento global Aumento gradual de la temperatura promedio de la atmósfera cuya causa se piensa que es el aumento de emisiones de gases de efecto invernadero ocasionados por actividades humanas.

global winds Winds that blow steadily from specific directions over long distances. (252)
vientos globales Vientos que soplan constantemente desde direcciones específicas por largas distancias.

gradualism Pattern of evolution characterized by the slow and steady accumulation of small genetic changes over long periods of time. (456)
gradualismo Evolución de una especie por medio de la acumulación lenta pero continua de cambios genéticos a través de largos períodos de tiempo.

graph A picture of information from a data table; shows the relationship between variables. (63)
gráfica Representación visual de la información de una tabla de datos; muestra la relación entre las variables.

greenhouse effect The trapping of heat near a planet's surface by certain gases in the planet's atmosphere. (243)
efecto invernadero Retención de calor cerca de la superficie de un planeta debido a la presencia de ciertos gases en la atmósfera.

greenhouse gases Gases in the atmosphere that trap energy. (389)
gases de efecto invernadero Gases presentes en la atmósfera que atrapan la energía.

groundwater Water that fills the cracks and spaces in underground soil and rock layers. (189)
aguas freáticas Agua que llena las grietas y huecos de las capas subterráneas de tierra y roca.

group Elements in the same vertical column of the periodic table; also called family. (105)
grupo Elementos en la misma columna vertical de la tabla periódica; también llamado familia.

H

habitat An environment that provides the things a specific organism needs to live, grow, and reproduce. (187)
hábitat Medio que provee lo que un organismo específico necesita para vivir, crecer y reproducirse.

habitat destruction The loss of a natural habitat. (342)
destrucción del habitat Pérdida de un hábitat natural.

habitat fragmentation The breaking of a habitat into smaller, isolated pieces. (342)
fragmentación del hábitat Desintegración de un hábitat en porciones aisladas más pequeñas.

halogen An element found in Group 17 of the periodic table. (119)
halógeno Elemento del Grupo 17 de la tabla periódica.

hazardous waste A material that can be harmful if it is not properly disposed of. (368)
desecho peligroso Material que puede ser dañino si no se elimina adecuadamente.

heat The transfer of thermal energy from a warmer object to a cooler object. (246)
calor Transferencia de energía térmica de un cuerpo más cálido a uno menos cálido.

heredity The passing of traits from parents to offspring. (468)
herencia Transmisión de rasgos de padres a hijos.

heterotroph An organism that cannot make its own food and gets food by consuming other living things. (411)
heterótrofo Organismo que no puede producir sus propios alimentos y que se alimenta al consumir otros seres vivos.

heterozygous Having two different alleles for a particular gene. (478)
heterocigoto Que tiene dos alelos distintos para un gen particular.

homeostasis The condition in which an organism's internal environment is kept stable in spite of changes in the external environment. (413)
homeostasis Condición en la que el medio ambiente interno de un organismo se mantiene estable a pesar de cambios en el medio ambiente externo.

homologous structure Structures that are similar in different species and that have been inherited from a common ancestor. (452)
estructuras homólogas Estructuras parecidas de especies distintas y que se han heredado de un antepasado común.

homozygous Having two identical alleles for a particular gene. (478)
homocigoto Que tiene dos alelos idénticos para un gen particular.

humidity The amount of water vapor in a given volume of air. (268)
humedad Cantidad de vapor de agua en cierto volumen de aire.

hurricane A tropical storm that has winds of about 119 kilometers per hour or higher. (292)
huracán Tormenta tropical que tiene vientos de cerca de 119 kilómetros por hora o más.

hybrid An offspring of crosses that has two different alleles for a trait. (472)
híbrido Descendiente de cruces que tiene dos alelos distintos para un rasgo.

GLOSSARY

hybridization A selective breeding method that involves crossing different individuals to bring together the best traits from both parents. (498)
hibridación Técnica reproductiva en la que se cruzan individuos distintos para reunir los mejores rasgos de ambos progenitores.

hypothesis A possible explanation for a set of observations or answer to a scientific question; must be testable. (20)
hipótesis Explicación posible de un conjunto de observaciones o respuesta a una pregunta científica; se debe poder poner a prueba.

I

inbreeding A selective breeding method in which two individuals with similar sets of alleles are crossed. (498)
endogamia Técnica reproductiva en la que se cruzan dos individuos con conjuntos de alelos parecidos.

incineration The burning of solid waste. (363)
incineración Quema de desechos sólidos.

incomplete dominance A situation in which one allele is not completely dominant over another allele. (481)
dominancia incompleta Situación en la que un alelo no es completamente dominante sobre el otro.

independent variable The one factor that a scientist changes during an experiment; also called manipulated variable. (21)
variable independiente El único factor que un científico altera durante un experimento; también se denomina variable manipulada.

inferring The process of making an inference, an interpretation based on observations and prior knowledge. (6)
inferir Proceso de hacer una inferencia; interpretación basada en observaciones y conocimientos previos.

infrared radiation Electromagnetic waves with wavelengths that are longer than visible light but shorter than microwaves. (239)
radiación infrarroja Ondas electromagnéticas con longitudes de onda más largas que la luz visible, pero más cortas que las microondas.

input Material, energy, or information that goes into a system. (68)
entrada Material, energía o informacion que se agrega a un sistema.

International System of Units (SI) A system of units used by scientists to measure the properties of matter. (45)
Sistema Internacional de Unidades (SI) Sistema de unidades que los científicos usan para medir las propiedades de la materia.

ion An atom or group of atoms that has become electrically charged. (141)
ión Átomo o grupo de átomos que está cargado eléctricamente.

ionic bond The attraction between oppositely charged ions. (142)
enlace iónico Atracción entre iones con cargas opuestas.

ionic compound A compound that consists of positive and negative ions. (142)
compuesto iónico Compuesto que tiene iones positivos y negativos.

ionosphere The lower part of the thermosphere. (237)
ionósfera Parte inferior de la termósfera.

isobar A line on a weather map that joins places that have the same air pressure. (301)
isobara Línea en un mapa del tiempo que une lugares que tienen la misma presión de aire.

isotherm A line on a weather map that joins places that have the same temperature. (301)
isoterma Línea en un mapa del tiempo que une lugares que tienen la misma temperatura.

isotope An atom with the same number of protons and a different number of neutrons from other atoms of the same element. (97)
isótopo Átomo con el mismo número de protones y un número diferente de neutrones que otros átomos del mismo elemento.

J

jet streams Bands of high-speed winds about 10 kilometers above Earth's surface. (283)
corrientes de viento en chorro Bandas de vientos de alta velocidad a unos 10 kilómetros sobre la superficie de la Tierra.

K

keystone species A species that influences the survival of many other species in an ecosystem. (337)
especie clave Especie que tiene un impacto en la supervivencia de muchas otras especies de un ecosistema.

L

La Niña A climate event in the eastern Pacific Ocean in which surface waters are colder than normal. (209)
la Niña Fenómeno climático que ocurre en la parte este del océano Pacífico, en el cual las aguas superficiales están más fías que lo normal.

land breeze The flow of air from land to a body of water. (251)
brisa terrestre Flujo de aire desde la tierra a una masa de agua.

land reclamation The process of restoring land to a more natural, productive state. (361)
recuperación de la tierra Proceso que consiste en restaurar la tierra y llevarla a un estado productivo más natural.

latitude The distance in degrees north or south of the equator. (254)
latitud Distancia en grados al norte o al sur del ecuador.

law of conservation of mass The principle that the total amount of matter is neither created nor destroyed during any chemical or physical change. (168)
ley de conservación de la masa Principio que establece que la cantidad total de materia no se crea ni se destruye durante cambios químicos o físicos.

leachate Polluted liquid produced by water passing through and dissolving chemicals from buried wastes in a landfill. (364)
lixiviado Líquido contaminado producido por el agua que pasa por y disuelve químicos provenientes de desechos bajo la tierra y en rellenos sanitarios.

lightning A sudden spark, or energy discharge, caused when electrical charges jump between parts of a cloud, between nearby clouds, or between a cloud and the ground. (291)
rayo Chispa repentina o descarga de energía causada por cargas eléctricas que saltan entre partes de una nube, entre nubes cercanas o entre una nube y la tierra.

linear graph A line graph in which the data points yield a straight line. (64)
gráfica lineal Gráfica en la cual los puntos de los datos forman una línea recta.

litter The very top layer of fertile soil made of dead leaves and grass. (358)
mantillo Capa superior del suelo fértil, que está formada por hojas y pasto muertos.

local winds Winds that blow over short distances. (251)
vientos locales Vientos que soplan en distancias cortas.

luster The way a mineral reflects light from its surface. (108)
lustre Manera en la que un mineral refleja la luz en su superficie.

M

malleable A term used to describe material that can be hammered or rolled into flat sheets. (108)
maleable Término usado para describir materiales que se pueden convertir en láminas planas por medio de martillazos o con un rodillo.

maritime (air mass) A humid air mass that forms over oceans. (281)
masa de aire marítima Masa de aire húmedo que se forma sobre los océanos.

mass A measure of how much matter is in an object. (48)
masa Medida de cuánta materia hay en un cuerpo.

mass number The sum of protons and neutrons in the nucleus of an atom. (97)
número de masa Suma de los protones y neutrones en el núcleo de un átomo.

mean The numerical average of a set of data. (58)
media Promedio numérico de un conjunto de datos.

median The middle number in a set of data. (58)
mediana Número del medio de un conjunto de datos.

meiosis The process that occurs in the formation of sex cells (sperm and egg) by which the number of chromosomes is reduced by half. (490)
meiosis Proceso durante la formación de las células sexuales (espermatozoide y óvulo) por el cual el número de cromosomas se reduce a la mitad.

meniscus The curved upper surface of a liquid in a column of liquid. (49)
menisco Superficie superior curva de un líquido en una columna de líquido.

GLOSSARY

mercury barometer An instrument that measures changes in air pressure, consisting of a glass tube partially filled with mercury, with its open end resting in a dish of mercury. (228)
barómetro de mercurio Instrumento que mide los cambios de presión del aire; es un tubo de vidrio parcialmente lleno de mercurio con su extremo abierto posado sobre un recipiente con mercurio.

mesosphere The layer of Earth's atmosphere immediately above the stratosphere. (236)
mesósfera Capa de la atmósfera de la Tierra inmediatamente sobre la estratósfera.

metal A class of elements characterized by physical properties that include shininess, malleability, ductility, and conductivity. (107)
metal Clase de elementos caracterizados por propiedades físicas que incluyen brillo, maleabilidad, ductilidad y conductividad.

metabolism The combination of chemical reactions through which an organism builds up or breaks down materials. (406)
metabolismo Combinación de reacciones químicas mediante las cuales un organismo compone o descompone la materia.

metalloid An element that has some characteristics of both metals and nonmetals. (121)
metaloide Elemento que tiene algunas características de los metales y de los no metales.

meteorologists Scientists who study the causes of weather and try to predict it. (299)
meteorólogos Científicos que estudian las causas del tiempo e intentan predecirlo.

metric system A system of measurement based on the number 10. (45)
sistema métrico Sistema de medidas basado en el número 10.

mid-ocean ridge An undersea mountain chain where new ocean floor is produced; a divergent plate boundary under the ocean. (205)
cordillera oceánica central Cadena montañosa submarina donde se produce el nuevo suelo oceánico; borde de placa divergente bajo el oceáno.

mode The number that appears most often in a list of numbers. (58)
moda Número que aparece con más frecuencia en una lista de números.

model A representation of a complex object or process, used to help people understand a concept that they cannot observe directly. (67)
modelo Representación de un objeto o proceso complejo que se usa para explicar un concepto que no se puede observar directamente.

molecular compound A compound that is composed of molecules. (151)
compuesto molecular Compuesto que tiene moléculas.

molecule A neutral group of two or more atoms held together by covalent bonds. (149)
molécula Grupo neutral de dos o más átomos unidos por medio de enlaces covalentes.

multicellular Consisting of many cells. (406)
multicelular Que se compone de muchas células.

multiple alleles Three or more possible alleles of a gene that determine a trait. (482)
alelo múltiple Tres o más alelos posibles del gen que determina un rasgo.

municipal solid waste Waste produced in homes, businesses, schools and in a community. (363)
desechos sólidos urbanos Desechos generados en los hogares, los negocios, las escuelas y las comunidades.

N

natural resource Anything naturally occuring in the environment that humans use. (316)
recurso natural Cualquier elemento natural en el medio ambiente que el ser humano usa.

natural selection The process by which organisms that are best adapted to their environment are most likely to survive and reproduce. (446)
selección natural Proceso por el cual los organismos que se adaptan mejor a su ambiente tienen mayor probabilidad de sobrevivir y reproducirse.

neutron A small particle in the nucleus of the atom, with no electrical charge. (95)
neutrón Partícula pequeña en el núcleo del átomo, que no tiene carga eléctrica.

noble gas An element in Group 18 of the periodic table. (120)
gas noble Elemento del Grupo 18 de la tabla periódica.

nonlinear graph A line graph in which the data points do not fall along a straight line. (64)
gráfica no lineal Gráfica lineal en la que los puntos de datos no forman una línea recta.

nonmetal An element that lacks most of the properties of a metal. (115)
no metal Elemento que carece de la mayoría de las propiedades de un metal.

nonpoint source A widely spread source of pollution that is difficult to link to a specific point of origin. (317)
fuente dispersa Fuente muy extendida de contaminación que es difícil vincular a un punto de origen específico.

nonpolar bond A covalent bond in which electrons are shared equally. (153)
enlace no polar Enlace covalente en el que los electrones se comparten por igual.

nonrenewable resource A natural resource that is not replaced in a useful time frame. (322)
recurso no renovable Recurso natural que no se restaura, en un período relativamente corto, una vez se utiliza.

nucleus The central core of an atom which contains protons and neutrons. (93)
núcleo Parte central del átomo que contiene los protones y los neutrones.

nutrient depletion The situation that arises when more soil nutrients are used than the decomposers can supply. (359)
agotamiento de nutrientes Situación que se produce cuando se usan más nutrientes del suelo de lo que los descomponedores pueden proporcionar.

open system A system in which matter can enter from or escape to the surroundings. (169)
sistema abierto Sistema en el que la materia puede escapar a sus alrededores o entrar desde ahí.

opinion An idea about a situation that is not supported by evidence. (29)
opinión Idea sobre una situación que la evidencia no sustenta.

organism A living thing. (405)
organismo Un ser vivo.

outlier An abnormal or irregular data point; a point on a graph that is clearly not part of the trend. (64)
valor atípico Punto de datos anormal o irregular; punto en una gráfica que se aleja demasiado de los valores esperados.

output Material, energy, result, or product that comes out of a system. (68)
salida Material, energía, resultado o producto que un sistema produce.

ozone A form of oxygen that has three oxygen atoms in each molecule instead of the usual two; toxic to organisms where it forms near Earth's surface. (372)
ozono Forma de oxígeno que tiene tres átomos de oxígeno en cada molécula, en vez de dos; donde se forma en la superficie terrestre, es tóxico para los organismos.

ozone layer The layer of the upper atmosphere that contains a higher concentration of ozone than the rest of the atmosphere. (375)
capa de ozono Capa superior de la atmósfera que contiene una concentración mayor de ozono que el resto de la atmósfera.

O

objective reasoning Reasoning that is based on evidence. (14)
razonamiento objetivo Razonamiento basado en la evidencia.

observing The process of using one or more of your senses to gather information. (5)
observar Proceso de usar uno o más de tus sentidos para reunir información.

occluded Cut off, as in a front where a warm air mass is caught between two cooler air masses. (285)
ocluido Aislado o cerrado, como un frente donde una masa de aire cálido queda atrapada entre dos masas de aire más frío.

P

percent error A calculation used to determine how accurate, or close to the true value, an experimental value really is. (60)
error porcentual Cálculo usado para determinar cuán exacto, o cercano al valor verdadero, es realmente un valor experimental.

period A horizontal row of elements in the periodic table. (104)
período Fila horizontal de los elementos de la tabla periódica.

periodic table An arrangement of the elements showing the repeating pattern of their properties. (100)
tabla periódica Configuración de los elementos que muestra el patrón repetido de sus propiedades.

GLOSSARY

pesticide A chemical that kills insects and other crop-destroying organisms. (382)
pesticida Químico usado para matar insectos y otros organismos que destruyen los cultivos.

phenotype An organism's physical appearance, or visible traits. (478)
fenotipo Apariencia física, o rasgos visibles, de un organismo.

photochemical smog A brownish thick haze that is a mixture of ozone and other chemicals formed when pollutants react with sunlight. (372)
neblina tóxica fotoquímica Nubosidad gruesa de color marrón, resultado de la mezcla del ozono y otras sustancias químicas que se forman cuando los contaminantes reaccionan a la luz del sol.

physical change A change that alters the form or appearance of a material but does not make the material into another substance. (158)
cambio físico Cambio que altera la forma o apariencia de un material, pero que no convierte el material en otra sustancia.

poaching Illegal killing or removal of wildlife from their habitats. (342)
caza ilegal Matanza o eliminación de la fauna silvestre de su hábitat.

point source A specific source of pollution that can be identified. (317)
fuente localizada Fuente específica de contaminación que puede identificarse.

polar (air mass) A cold air mass that forms north of 50° north latitude or south of 50° south latitude and has high air pressure. (281)
masa de aire polar Masa de aire frío que se forma al norte de los 50° de latitud norte o al sur de los 50° de latitud sur y que tiene presión alta.

polar bond A covalent bond in which electrons are shared unequally. (153)
enlace polar Enlace covalente en el que los electrones se comparten de forma desigual.

pollutant A substance that causes pollution. (364)
contaminante Sustancia que provoca contaminación.

pollution Contamination of Earth's land, water, or air. (317)
polución Contaminación del suelo, el agua o el aire de la Tierra.

polyatomic ion An ion that is made of more than one atom. (142)
ión poliatómico Ión formado por más de un átomo.

polygenic inheritance The inheritance of traits that are controlled by two or more genes, such as height in humans. (482)
herencia poligénica Herencia de los rasgos controlados por dos o más genes, como la altura en los seres humanos.

precipitate A solid that forms from a solution during a chemical reaction. (160)
precipitado Sólido que se forma de una solución durante una reacción química.

precipitation Any form of water that falls from clouds and reaches Earth's surface as rain, snow, sleet, or hail. (191)
precipitación Cualquier forma del agua que cae de las nubes y llega a la superficie de la tierra como lluvia, nieve, aguanieve o granizo.

precision How close a group of measurements are to each other. (56)
precisión Cuán cerca se encuentran un grupo de medidas.

predicting The process of forecasting what will happen in the future based on past experience or evidence. (7)
predecir Proceso de pronosticar lo que va a suceder en el futuro, basándose en evidencia o experiencias previas.

probability A number that describes how likely it is that a particular event will occur. (475)
probabilidad Número que describe cuán probable es que ocurra un suceso.

process A sequence of actions in a system. (68)
proceso Secuencia de acciones en un sistema.

product A substance formed as a result of a chemical reaction. (158)
producto Sustancia formada como resultado de una reacción química.

prokaryotes A unicellular organism that lacks a nucleus and some other cell structures. (423)
procariota Organismo unicelular que carece de un núcleo y otras estructuras celulares.

protons Small, positively charged particles that are found in the nucleus of an atom. (93)
protones Partículas pequeñas de carga positiva que se encuentran en el núcleo de un átomo.

prototype A working model used to test a design. (508)
prototipo Modelo funcional usado para probar un diseño.

pseudoscience A set of beliefs that may make use of science but whose conclusions and predictions are not based on observation, objective reasoning, or scientific evidence. (15)
pseudociencia Conjunto de creencias que pueden basarse en la ciencia, pero cuyas conclusiones no se derivan de la observación, el razonamiento objetivo o evidencia científica.

psychrometer An instrument used to measure relative humidity. (268)
psicrómetro Instrumento que se usa para medir la humedad relativa.

punctuated equilibrium Pattern of evolution in which long stable periods are interrupted by brief periods of more rapid change. (457)
equilibrio puntual Patrón de la evolución en el que los períodos largos estables son interrumpidos por breves períodos de cambio rápido.

Punnett square A chart that shows all the possible combinations of alleles that can result from a genetic cross. (476)
cuadrado de Punnett Tabla que muestra todas las combinaciones posibles de los alelos que se pueden derivar de un cruce genético.

purebred An offspring of many generations that has the same form of a trait. (469)
raza pura Descendiente de varias generaciones que tienen los mismos rasgos.

Q

qualitative observation An observation that deals with characteristics that cannot be expressed in numbers. (5)
observación cualitativa Observación que se centra en las características que no se pueden expresar con números.

quantitative observation An observation that deals with a number or amount. (5)
observación cuantitativa Observación que se centra en un número o cantidad.

R

radiation The transfer of energy by electromagnetic waves. (239)
radiación Transferencia de energía por medio de ondas magnéticas.

radon A colorless, odorless, radioactive gas. (374)
radón Gas radioactivo que no tiene color ni olor.

rain gauge An instrument used to measure precipitation. (275)
pluviómetro Instrumento que se usa para medir la precipitación.

range The difference between the greatest value and the least value in a set of data. (58)
rango Diferencia entre el mayor y el menor valor de un conjunto de datos.

reactant A substance that enters into a chemical reaction. (158)
reactante Sustancia que interviene en una reacción química.

reactivity The ease and speed with which an element combines, or reacts, with other elements and compounds. (109)
reactividad Facilidad y rapidez con las que un elemento se combina, o reacciona, con otros elementos y compuestos.

recessive allele An allele that is hidden whenever the dominant allele is present. (471)
alelo recesivo Alelo que se no manifiesta cuando el alelo dominante está presente.

recycling The process of reclaiming and reusing raw materials. (365)
reciclaje Proceso de recuperar y volver a usar materias primas.

relative humidity The percentage of water vapor in the air compared to the maximum amount of water vapor that air can contain at a particular temperature. (268)
humedad relativa Porcentaje de vapor de agua del aire comparado con la cantidad máxima de vapor de agua que puede contener el aire a una temperatura particular.

renewable resource A resource that is either always available or is naturally replaced in a relatively short time. (321)
recurso renovable Recurso que está siempre disponible o que es restituido de manera natural en un período relativamente corto.

repeated trial A repetition of an experiment to gather additional data and determine whether the experiment's results support the hypothesis. (24)
prueba repetida Repetición de un experimento para recopilar datos adicionales y determinar si los resultados de un experimento sustentan la hipótesis.

GLOSSARY

replacement A reaction in which one element replaces another in a compound or when two elements in different compounds trade places. (174)
sustitución Reacción en la que un elemento reemplaza a otro en un compuesto o en la que se intercambian dos elementos de diferentes compuestos.

replication The process by which a cell makes a copy of the DNA in its nucleus before cell division. (25)
replicación Proceso en el que la célula copia el ADN de su núcleo antes de la división celular.

reservoir A lake that stores water for human use. (197)
embalse Lago que almacena agua para el uso humano.

response An action or change in behavior that occurs as a result of a stimulus. (407)
respuesta Acción o cambio del comportamiento que ocurre como resultado de un estímulo.

S

salinity The total amount of dissolved salts in a water sample. (201)
salinidad Cantidad total de sales disueltas en una muestra de agua.

sanitary landfill A landfill that holds nonhazardous waste such as municipal solid waste, construction debris, and some agricultural and industrial wastes. (364)
relleno sanitario Vertedero que contiene desechos que no son peligrosos, como desechos sólidos municipales, de construcción y algunos tipos de desechos industriales y resultantes de la agricultura.

scattering Reflection of light in all directions. (241)
dispersión Reflexión de la luz en todas las direcciones.

science A way of learning about the natural world through observations and logical reasoning; leads to a body of knowledge. (5)
ciencia Estudio del mundo natural a través de observaciones y del razonamiento lógico; conduce a un conjunto de conocimientos.

scientific explanation A generalization that makes sense of observations by using logical reasoning. (26)
explicación científica Generalización que usa el razonamiento lógico para darle sentido a las observaciones.

scientific inquiry The ongoing process of discovery in science; the diverse ways in which scientists study the natural world and propose explanations based on evidence they gather. (19)
indagación científica Proceso continuo de descubrimiento en la ciencia; diversidad de métodos con los que los científicos estudian el mundo natural y proponen explicaciones del mismo basadas en la evidencia que reúnen.

scientific literacy The knowledge and understanding of scientific terms and principles required for evaluating information, making personal decisions, and taking part in public affairs. (29)
conocimiento científico Conocimiento y comprensión de los términos y principios científicos necesarios para evaluar información, tomar decisiones personales y participar en actividades públicas.

scientific theory A well-tested explanation for a wide range of observations or experimental results. (444)
teoría científica Explicación comprobada de una gran variedad de observaciones o resultados de experimentos.

sea breeze The flow of cooler air from over an ocean or lake toward land. (251)
brisa marina Flujo de aire frío procedente de un océano o lago hacia la costa.

seamount A steep-sided volcanic mountain rising from the deep-ocean floor. (204)
montaña marina Montaña muy inclinada de origen volcánico cuya base es el fondo del mar.

sediment Small, solid pieces of material that come from rocks or the remains of organisms; earth materials deposited by erosion. (383)
sedimento Trozos pequeños y sólidos de materiales que provienen de las rocas o de los restos de organismos; materiales terrestres depositados por la erosión.

selective breeding Method of breeding that allows only those organisms with desired traits to produce the next generation. (497)
cruce selectivo Técnica reproductiva por medio de la cual sólo los organismos con rasgos deseados producen la próxima generación.

selective cutting The process of cutting down only some tree species in an area. (332)
tala selectiva Proceso que consiste en cortar solo algunas especies de árboles de un área.

semiconductor A substance that can conduct electric current under some conditions. (121)
semiconductor Sustancia que puede conducir una corriente eléctrica bajo ciertas condiciones.

sewage The water and human wastes that are washed down sinks, toilets, and showers. (382)
aguas residuales Agua y desechos humanos que son desechados por lavamanos, servicios sanitarios y duchas.

sexual reproduction A reproductive process that involves two parents that combine their genetic material to produce a new organism which differs from both parents. (407)
reproducción sexual Proceso de reproducción que involucra a dos reproductores que combinan su material genético para producir un nuevo organismo que es distinto a los dos reproductores.

shared derived characteristic A characteristic or trait, such as fur, that the common ancestor of a group had and passed on to its descendants. (427)
característica derivada compartida Característica o rasgo, como el pelaje, del ancestro común de un grupo que éste pasa a sus descendientes.

significant figures All the digits in a measurement that have been measured exactly, plus one digit whose value has been estimated. (57)
cifras significativas En una medida, todos los dígitos que se han medido con exactitud, más un dígito cuyo valor se ha estimado.

skepticism An attitude of doubt. (11)
escepticismo Actitud de duda.

sonar A system that uses reflected sound waves to locate and determine the distance to objects under water. (204)
sónar Sistema que usa ondas sonoras reflejadas para detectar y localizar objetos bajo agua.

species A group of similar organisms that can mate with each other and produce offspring that can also mate and reproduce. (416)
especie Grupo de organismos semejantes que pueden cruzarse y producir descendencia fértil.

spontaneous generation The mistaken idea that living things arise from nonliving sources. (408)
generación espontánea Idea equivocada de que los seres vivos surgen de fuentes inertes.

stimulus Any change or signal in the environment that can make an organism react in some way. (407)
estimulante Droga que acelera los procesos del cuerpo.

storm A violent disturbance in the atmosphere. (289)
tormenta Alteración violenta en la atmósfera.

storm surge A "dome" of water that sweeps across the coast where a hurricane lands. (293)
marejadas "Cúpula" de agua que se desplaza a lo largo de la costa donde aterriza un huracán.

stratosphere The second-lowest layer of Earth's atmosphere. (235)
estratósfera Segunda capa de la atmósfera de la Tierra.

stratus Clouds that form in flat layers and often cover much of the sky. (273)
estratos Nubes que aparecen como capas planas y que a menudo cubren gran parte del cielo.

subjective reasoning Reasoning that is based on personal feelings or personal values. (14)
razonamiento subjetivo Razonamiento basado en los sentimientos o los valores personales.

subscript A number in a chemical formula that tells the number of atoms in a molecule or the ratio of elements in a compound. (144)
subíndice Número en una fórmula química que indica el número de átomos que tiene una molécula o la razón de elementos en un compuesto.

subsoil The layer of soil below topsoil that has less plant and animal matter than topsoil and contains mostly clay and other minerals. (358)
subsuelo Capa de suelo debajo del suelo superior que tiene menos materia de plantas y animales que el suelo superior, y que principalmente contiene arcilla y otros minerales.

sustainable use The use of a resource in ways that maintain the resource at a certain quality for a certain period of time. (324)
uso sostenible Uso de un recurso que permite que ese recurso mantenga cierta calidad por un período de tiempo determinado.

sustainable yield An amount of a renewable resource that can be harvested regularly without reducing the future supply. (333)
rendimiento sostenible Cantidad de un recurso renovable que puede ser recolectado constantemente sin reducir el abastecimiento futuro.

synthesis A chemical reaction in which two or more simple substances combine to form a new, more complex substance. (174)
síntesis Reacción química en la que dos o más sustancias simples se combinan y forman una sustancia nueva más compleja.

GLOSSARY

system A group of related parts that work together to perform a function or produce a result. (68)
sistema Grupo de partes relacionadas que trabajan conjuntamente para realizar una función o producir un resultado.

--- T ---

taxonomy The scientific study of how living things are classified. (415)
taxonomía Estudio científico de cómo se clasifican los seres vivos.

temperature How hot or cold something is; a measure of the average energy of motion of the particles of a substance; the measure of the average kinetic energy of the particles of a substance. (244)
temperatura Cuán caliente o frío es algo; medida de la energía de movimiento promedio de las partículas de una sustancia; medida de la energía cinética promedio de las partículas de una sustancia.

temperature inversion A condition in which a layer of warm air traps polluted air close to Earth's surface. (372)
inversión térmica Condición en la que una capa de aire caliente atrapa aire contaminado cerca de la superficie de la Tierra.

thermal conductivity The ability of an object to transfer heat. (108)
conductividad térmica Capacidad de un objeto para transferir calor.

thermal energy The total kinetic and potential energy of all the particles of an object. (245)
energía térmica Energía cinética y potencial total de las partículas de un cuerpo.

thermometer An instrument used to measure temperature. (245)
termómetro Instrumento que se usa para medir la temperatura.

thermosphere The outermost layer of Earth's atmosphere. (237)
termósfera Capa exterior de la atmósfera de la Tierra.

threatened species A species that could become endangered in the near future. (341)
especie amenazada Especie que puede llegar a estar en peligro de extinción en el futuro próximo.

thunderstorm A small storm often accompanied by heavy precipitation and frequent thunder and lightning. (290)
tronada Pequeña tormenta acompañada de fuertes precipitaciones y frecuentes rayos y truenos.

topsoil The crumbly, topmost layer of soil made up of clay and other minerals and humus (nutrients and decaying plant and animal matter). (358)
suelo superior Capa superior desmenuzable del suelo formada por arcilla, otros minerales y humus (nutrientes y materia orgánica de origen vegetal y animal).

tornado A rapidly whirling, funnel-shaped cloud that reaches down to touch Earth's surface. (294)
tornado Nube con forma de embudo que gira rápidamente y que desciende hasta tocar la superficie terrestre.

trade-off An exchange in which one benefit is given up in order to obtain another. (508)
sacrificar una cosa por otra Intercambio en el que se renuncia a un beneficio para obtener otro.

trait A specific characteristic that an organism can pass to its offspring through its genes. (468)
rasgo Característica específica que un organismo puede transmitir a sus descendientes a través de los genes.

transition metal One of the elements in Groups 3 through 12 of the periodic table. (111)
metal de transición Uno de los elementos de los Grupos 3 a 12 de la tabla periódica.

transpiration The process by which water is lost through a plant's leaves. (190)
transpiración Proceso por el cual las hojas de una planta pierden agua.

trench A deep, steep-sided canyon in the ocean floor. (204)
fosa Cañón profundo, de lados empinados, en el suelo oceánico.

tributary A stream or river that flows into a larger river. (193)
afluente Río o arroyo que desemboca en un río más grande.

triple bond A chemical bond formed when atoms share three pairs of electrons. (150)
enlace triple Enlace químico formado cuando los átomos comparten tres pares de electrones.

tropical (air mass) A warm air mass that forms in the tropics and has low air pressure. (281)
masa de aire tropical Masa de aire templado que se forma en los trópicos y cuya presión atmosférica es baja.

troposphere The lowest layer of Earth's atmosphere. (234)
troposfera Capa más inferior de la atmósfera de la Tierra.

troubleshooting The process of analyzing a design problem and finding a way to fix it. (508)
solución de problemas Proceso por el cual se analiza un problema de diseño y se halla una forma de solucionarlo.

U

ultraviolet radiation Electromagnetic waves with wavelengths that are shorter than visible light but longer than X-rays. (239)
radiación ultravioleta Ondas electromagnéticas con longitudes de onda más cortas que la luz visible, pero más largas que los rayos X.

unicellular Made of a single cell. (406)
unicelular Compuesto por una sola célula.

V

valence electrons The electrons that are in the highest energy level of an atom and that are involved in chemical bonding. (135)
electrones de valencia Electrones que tienen el nivel más alto de energía de un átomo y que intervienen en los enlaces químicos.

variation Any difference between individuals of the same species. (447)
variación Cualquier diferencia entre individuos de la misma especie.

volume The amount of space that matter occupies. (49)
volumen Cantidad de espacio que ocupa la materia.

W

water cycle The continual movement of water among Earth's atmosphere, oceans, and land surface through evaporation, condensation, and precipitation. (190)
ciclo del agua Circulación continua del agua por la atmósfera, los océanos y la superficie de la Tierra mediante la evaporación, la condensación y la precipitación.

water vapor Water in the form of a gas. (224)
vapor de agua Agua en forma de gas.

watershed The land area that supplies water to a river system. (194)
cuenca hidrográfica Área de terreno que suministra agua a un sistema fluvial.

weather The condition of Earth's atmosphere at a particular time and place. (222)
tiempo meteorológico Condición de la atmósfera terrestre en un momento y lugar determinado.

weight A measure of the force of gravity acting on an object. (48)
peso Medida de la fuerza de gravedad que actúa sobre un objeto.

wind The horizontal movement of air from an area of high pressure to an area of lower pressure. (249)
viento Movimiento horizontal de aire de un área de alta presión a una de menor presión.

wind-chill factor A measure of cooling combining temperature and wind speed. (250)
factor de enfriamiento por viento Medida del enfriamiento que combina la temperatura y la velocidad del viento.

INDEX

INDEX

Page numbers for key terms are printed in **boldface** type.

INDEX

Page numbers for key terms are printed in **boldface** type.

ACKNOWLEDGMENTS

Staff Credits

The people who made up the *Interactive Science* team—representing composition services, core design digital and multimedia production services, digital product development, editorial, editorial services, manufacturing, and production—are listed below:

Jan Van Aarsen, Samah Abadir, Ernie Albanese, Chris Anton, Zareh Artinian, Bridget Binstock, Suzanne Biron, Niki Birbilis, MJ Black, Nancy Bolsover, Stacy Boyd, Jim Brady, Katherine Bryant, Michael Burstein, Pradeep Byram, Jessica Chase, Jonathan Cheney, Arthur Ciccone, Allison Cook-Bellistri, Rebecca Cottingham, AnnMarie Coyne, Bob Craton, Chris Deliee, Paul Delsignore, Michael Di Maria, Diane Dougherty, Kristen Ellis, Kelly Engel, Theresa Eugenio, Amanda Ferguson, Jorgensen Fernandez, Kathryn Fobert, Alicia Franke, Louise Gachet, Julia Gecha, Mark Geyer, Steve Gobbell, Paula Gogan-Porter, Jeffrey Gong, Sandra Graff, Robert M. Graham, Adam Groffman, Lynette Haggard, Christian Henry, Karen Holtzman, Susan Hutchinson, Sharon Inglis, Marian Jones, Sumy Joy, Sheila Kanitsch, Courtenay Kelley, Chris Kennedy, Toby Klang, Greg Lam, Russ Lappa, Margaret LaRaia, Ben Leveillee, Thea Limpus, Charles Luey, Dotti Marshall, Kathy Martin, Robyn Matzke, John McClure, Mary Beth McDaniel, Krista McDonald, Tim McDonald, Rich McMahon, Cara McNally, Bernadette McQuilkin, Melinda Medina, Angelina Mendez, Maria Milczarek, Claudi Mimo, Mike Napieralski, Deborah Nicholls, Dave Nichols, William Oppenheimer, Jodi O'Rourke, Ameer Padshah, Lorie Park, Celio Pedrosa, Jonathan Penyack, Linda Zust Reddy, Jennifer Reichlin, Stephen Rider, Charlene Rimsa, Walter Rodriguez, Stephanie Rogers, Marcy Rose, Rashid Ross, Anne Rowsey, Logan Schmidt, Amanda Seldera, Laurel Smith, Nancy Smith, Ted Smykal, Emily Soltanoff, Cindy Strowman, Dee Sunday, Barry Tomack, Elizabeth Tustian, Patricia Valencia, Ana Sofia Villaveces, Stephanie Wallace, Amanda Watters, Christine Whitney, Brad Wiatr, Heidi Wilson, Heather Wright, Rachel Youdelman.

Photography

All otherwise unacknowledged photos are copyright © 2011 Pearson Education.

Cover, Front and Back

Cardinal, John Cancalosi/Peter Arnold Images/Photolibrary New York; **leaves,** Pixtal Images/Photolibrary New York.

Front Matter

Page vi monument, Carroteater/Shutterstock; **vii barn,** Visions LLC/Photolibrary New York; **vi–vii fields,** Alexey Stiop/Alamy; **vii flag,** Stacey Lynn Payne; **vii cardinal,** Tom Vezo/Peter Arnold Images/Photolibrary New York; **viii,** Chris Sattlberger/Digital Vision/Getty Images; **ix,** Stephen Dalton/Minden Pictures; **x,** Tom Schierlitz/Getty Images; **xi,** Javier Trueba/Madrid Scientific Films; **xii,** Pete Saloutos/Corbis; **xiii,** LOOK Die Bildagentur der Fotografen GmbH/Alamy; **xiv,** Eric Nguyen/Photo Researchers, Inc.; **xv,** Shin Yoshino/Minden Pictures; **xvi,** Benedict Luxmoore/Arcaid/Corbis; **xvii,** Chris Newbert/Minden Pictures; **xviii,** Chris Newbert/Minden Pictures; **xix,** Blickwinkel/Alamy; **xxi laptop,** iStockphoto; **xxiii br,** JupiterImages/Getty Images; **xxvi laptop,** iStockphoto; **xxviii l,** Comstock/JupiterUnlimited; **xviii r,** Kevin Fleming/Corbis; **xxix l,** M. Claye/Photo Researchers, Inc.; **xxix r,** Shin Yoshino/Minden Pictures; **xxx l,** Jeffrey L. Rotman/Corbis; **xxx r,** Mark turner/Garden Picture; **xxxi,** ZSSD/SuperStock.

Chapter 1

Pages xxix l, M. Claye/Photo Researchers, Inc.; **xxxii–001 spread,** Robert Postma/AGE Fotostock; **3 t,** Mark Humphrey/AP Images; **3 tm,** Edgewater Media/Shutterstock; **3 b,** Daniel Templeton/Alamy; **3 bm,** Richard Haynes; **4 m,** Copyright 2006 by The National Academy of Sciences of the USA; **4 tr,** Science Source/Photo Researchers, Inc.; **5 inset,** Inga Spence/Getty Images; **5 bkgrnd,** Tom & Pat Leeson/Photo Researchers, Inc.; **6 tl,** W.D. Brush/USDA-NRCS PLANTS Database; **7 bl,** Thomas Mangelsen/Minden Pictures; **8–9 spread,** Mark Humphrey/AP Images; **10 m,** Indianapolis Recorder Collection, Indiana Historical Society; **14 b,** Edgewater Media/Shutterstock; **15 bkgrnd,** Babak Tafreshi/Photo Researchers, Inc.; **16 tr,** *Untitled* (1920), George Grosz. Oil on canvas. Collection Kunstsammlung Nordrhein-Westfalen, Duesseldorf, Germany/Photo by Erich Lessing/Art Resource, New York/Artwork copyright Estate of George Grosz/Licensed by VAGA, New York, NY; **17 m,** Walter C. Jaap/Sustainable Seas/R. Halley/Courtesy of USGS; **19 b,** Navnit/Shutterstock; **20 m,** Radius Images/Photolibrary New York; **21 br,** Sam Yu/The Frederick News-Post/AP Images; **24 bkgrnd,** Patrick LaRoque/First Light Associated Photographers/Photolibrary New York; **26 bl,** Tim Fitzharris/Minden Pictures; **27 spread,** John Dominis/Index Stock Imagery/Photolibrary New York; **29 r,** Daniel Templeton/Alamy; **29 l,** John Short/Jupiter Images; **31 m,** Inspirestock/Jupiter Images; **32–33 spread,** imagebroker/Alamy; **34 b,** John Short/Jupiter Images; **34 m,** Navnit/Shutterstock; **34 t,** Science Source/Photo Researchers, Inc.; **36,** Barrie Rokeach/Alamy.

Chapter 1 Feature

Page 38, Explorer/Photo Researchers, Inc.

Chapter 2

Pages 40–41 spread, NASA Langley Research Center (NASA-LaRC); **43 t,** Paul Burns/Getty Images; **43 tm,** Stem Jems/Photo Researchers, Inc.; **43 bm,** J. I. Alvarez-Hamelin, M. Beiró, L. Dall'Asta, A. Barrat, A. Vespignani; http://xavier.informatics.indiana.edu/lanet-vi/ http://sourceforge.net/projects/lanet-vi/; **45 br,** Zhao Jianwei/Imaginechina/AP Images; **46 t,** Image Source/Getty Images; **47 tr,** Stephen Dalton/Minden Pictures; **47 bkgrnd,** Barry Mansell/Nature Picture Library; **48 bl,** Paul Burns/Getty Images; **49 m,** Image100/SuperStock; **51 spread,** Kenneth Morris/ASP-Covered Images/Zuma Press; **52 b,** Tue Nam Ton/Contra Costa Newspapers/Zuma Press; **52 tl,** Olga Lipatova/Shutterstock; **54 inset,** NOAA; **54 bkgrnd,** Erik Zobrist/NOAA Restoration Center; **55 tr,** Amazon Images/Alamy; **55 br,** Stem Jems/Photo Researchers, Inc.; **56 b,** Richard Haynes; **57 r,** Lukasz Kwapien/iStockphoto.com; **58 t,** Andy Levin/Alamy; **58–59 bkgrnd,** imagebroker/Alamy; **58–59 bkgrnd,** imagebroker/Alamy; **59 r,** Melvyn Longhurst/Alamy; **60 m,** Science & Society Picture Library/Getty Images; **62 b,** Bernd Vogel/Corbis; **63 b,** Chris Parypa/Alamy; **64–65 spread,** Bill Curtsinger/National Geographic Stock; **65 tr,** Valery Rizzo/

ACKNOWLEDGMENTS

Marano/U.S. Navy; **200–201 bkgrnd,** Marevision Marevision/ AGE Fotostock/Photolibrary New York; **203 t,** Chris Newbert/ Minden Pictures; **203 l,** Emory Kristof and Alvin Chandler/ National Geographic Stock; **203 m,** Courtesy of Deep Flight Hawkes Ocean Technologies; **205 t,** U.S. Navy News Photo; **206,** Dr. W. James Ingraham, Jr/National Oceanic and Atmospheric Administration (NOAA); **207 bl,** Dr. W. James Ingraham, Jr./National Oceanic and Atmospheric Administration (NOAA); **207 mr,** Dr. W. James Ingraham, Jr./ National Oceanic and Atmospheric Administration (NOAA); **208 inset,** Eitan Simanor/Robert Harding World Imagery; **208 bkgrnd,** Chris Wattie/Reuters; **209 t,** Goddard Space Flight Center Scientific Visualization Studio/NASA; **209 b,** Goddard Space Flight Center Scientific Visualization Studio/ NASA; **211 tr,** J-C Vaillant/Photononstop/Photolibrary New York.

Chapter 5 Feature
Page 216 bkgrnd, Kevin Schafer/Alamy; **216 t,** Dave King/ Dorling Kindersley; **217,** Brian J. Skerry/National Geographic Stock.

Chapter 6
Pages 218–219 spread, Corbis/Kevin Fleming; **221 t,** Bettmann/Corbis; **221 m1,** Van D. Bucher/Photo Researchers, Inc.; **221 m2,** David Wall/Alamy; **221 b,** Norma Cornes/ Shutterstock; **222,** Charles D. Winters/Photo Researchers, Inc.; **223 bkgrnd,** Bettmann/Corbis; **224 t,** Sean Randall/ iStockphoto; **224 b,** Digital Vision/Alamy; **225,** GSFC Lab for Atmospheres/NASA; **226,** Check Six/Getty Images; **229 t,** Van D. Bucher/Photo Researchers, Inc.; **232,** Melissa McManus/ Getty Images; **233,** David Wall/Alamy; **236 t,** LOOK Die Bildagentur der Fotografen GmbH/Alamy; **239 bkgrnd,** Aqua Image/Alamy; **241 l,** Ermin Gutenberger/iStockphoto; **241 m1,** Mark Yuill/iStockphoto; **241 m2,** Ideeone/ iStockphoto; **241 r,** Jason Major/iStockphoto; **244,** Helle Bro Clemmensen/iStockphoto; **246 inset,** Mikhail Kokhanchikov/ iStockphoto.com; **246–247 bkgrnd,** Xavi Arnau/iStockphoto; **248–249 bkgrnd,** Norma Cornes/Shutterstock, Inc.; **250** Geri Lavrov/Alamy; **251,** Harris Shiffman/Shutterstock; **256,** GSFC Lab for Atmospheres/NASA.

Chapter 6 Feature
Page 260, NASA; **261 t,** Stefano Bianchetti/Corbis; **261 b,** LPI/NASA.

Chapter 7
Pages 262–263 spread, Eric Nguyen/Photo Researchers, Inc.; **265 m1,** John Howard/Photo Researchers, Inc.; **265 m2,** Gene Rhoden/Still Pictures; **267 bkgrnd,** Jeremy Horner/ Corbis; **270 spread,** Reimar/Alamy; **274,** Adam Jones/Alamy; **276 bl,** Liz Leyden/iStockphoto; **276 br,** John Howard/ Photo Researchers, Inc.; **276 tr,** Tom King/Alamy; **276 tl,** Don Johnston/AGE Fotostock/Photolibrary New York; **277 inset,** Matthias Hauser/Imagebroker/Alamy; **278 bkgrnd,** Tom Pennington/Fort Worth Star-Telegram/MCT; **279,** Paul S. Howell/Getty Images; **280,** Digital Vision/Getty Images; **283,** Gene Rhoden/Still Pictures; **288,** AP Images; **290,** Peter Menzel/Photo Researchers, Inc.; **291,** King Wu/iStockphoto; **293 tr,** Joe Raedle/Getty Images; **293 tl,** Goddard Space Flight Center Scientific Visualization Studio/NASA; **293 bl,**

Goddard Space Flight Center Scientific Visualization Studio/ NASA; **295,** John Sleezer/Kansas City Star/MCT; **296,** Donna McWilliam/AP Images; **297 l,** Chris Mampe/iStockphoto; **298 inset,** Courtesy of Mish Michaels; **298 bkgrnd,** Tom Sibley/Corbis; **299 b,** Frans Lanting/Corbis; **300 r,** David Parker/Photo Researchers, Inc.; **300 l,** NASA/Photo Researchers, Inc.; **300 m,** Paul Rapson/Science Photo Library; **304 br,** David Parker/Photo Researchers, Inc.

Chapter 7 Feature
Page 308 bkgrnd, Brian Cosgrove/Dorling Kindersley; **308 inset,** NASA.

Chapter 8
Pages 310–311 spread, Kent Gilbert/AP Images; **313 t,** Mark Bolton/Photolibrary New York; **313 inset,** C Squared Studios/Photodisc/Getty Images; **313 m1,** C Squared Studios/ Photodisc/Getty Images; **314,** Copyright Brenna Hernandez/ Shedd Aqua/SeaPics; **315,** Frank Krahmer/Masterfile; **316,** Yvon-Lemanour/Photolibrary New York; **317,** Steve Schapiro/ Corbis; **318 bkgrnd,** Dennis Macdonald/Photolibrary New York; **318 inset,** Mark Bolton/Photolibrary New York; **320 bkgrnd,** AP Images; **320 inset,** Derek Dammann/ iStockphoto; **322 tl,** C Squared Studios/Photodisc/Getty Images; **322 tl,** C Squared Studios/Photodisc/Getty Images; **323 ml,** Liba Taylor/Corbis; **323 mr,** Alfred Cheng Jin / Reuters/Landov; **323 bl,** Roger Ressmeyer/Corbis; **326 t,** Andreas Koschate/Photolibrary New York; **326 b,** London Scientific Films/Oxford Scientific/Photolibrary New York; **328–329 spread,** Digital Vision/Photolibrary New York; **330 bkgrnd,** Yann Arthus-Bertrand/Corbis; **331,** Matthew Gonzalez/iStockphoto; **331 ml,** Nick Schlax/iStockphoto; **331 m,** javier fontanella/iStockphoto; **331 mr,** Anna Yu/ iStockphoto; **331 bl,** Plainview/iStockphoto; **331 bm,** iStockphoto; **331 br,** Long Ha/iStockphoto; **334 bkgrnd,** Alaska Stock/AGE Fotostock; **335,** Edward.J.Westmacott/ Alamy; **336 b,** Jerome Whittingham/iStockphoto; **337 bl,** Burke/Triolo Productions/Brand X/Corbis; **337 bm,** Pete Oxford/Minden Pictures; **337 br,** PhotographerOlympus/ iStockphoto; **337 t,** iStockphoto; **337 mr,** iStockphoto; **339,** Kiamsoon/iStockphoto; **340,** StockFood America/Buntrock; **341 t,** Copyright 2007 James D. Watt/Image Quest Marine; **341 mr,** Courtesy of the National Tropical Botanical Garden; **341 ml,** Betsy Gange/Hawaii Department of Land and Natural Resources/AP Images; **343 tl,** Markus Botzek/Zefa/Corbis; **343 tm,** Tom Lazar/Animals Animals Enterprises; **343 tl,** Konrad Wothe/Minden Pictures; **343 bl,** Thomas Wiewandt; **343 bm,** Courtesy of Operation Migration; **343 br,** Copyright 2005 Jason Hahn; **344,** Nevio Doz/Marka/AGE Fotostock; **346,** Burke/Triolo Productions/Brand X/Corbis; XXX Sonny T. Senser/AGE Fotostock.

Chapter 8 Feature
Page 350 bkgrnd, VStock/Alamy; **351 t,** MPI/Getty Images; **351 b,** Courtesy of Melissa Scanlan.

Chapter 9
Pages 352–353 spread, Benedict Luxmoore/Arcaid/ Corbis; **355 t,** Dorling Kindersley; **356,** Creatas/SuperStock; **357 m,** G. Brad Lewis/Science Faction; **357 b,** Ron Chapple/ Corbis; **357 t,** Dorling Kindersley; **358,** Dorling Kindersley;

Chapter 12

Pages 464–465 spread, ZSSD/SuperStock; **467 t,** Timothy Large/iStockphoto.com; **467 ml,** Frank Krahmer/Getty Images; **467 m,** Burke/Triolo/Jupiter Unlimited; **467 mr,** Burke/Triolo/Jupiter Unlimited; **468 bkgrnd,** Bettmann/Corbis; **468 inset,** Wally Eberhart/Getty Images; **470 bkgrnd,** Andrea Jones/Alamy; **473 tl,** Herman Eisenbeiss/Photo Researchers, Inc.; **473 tr,** WildPictures/Alamy; **473 bkgrnd,** Monika Gniot/Shutterstock; **474 inset,** J. Pat Carter/AP Images; **474 bkgrnd,** National Oceanic and Atmospheric Administration (NOAA); **475 bkgrnd,** Brand X/Jupiter Images; **476–477 bkgrnd,** Monika Gniot/Shutterstock; **478–479 bkgrnd,** Alexandra Grablewski/Jupiter Images; **479 l,** Timothy Large/iStockphoto.com; **479 r,** Jomann/Dreamstime.com; **481 ml,** Mike Dunning/Dorling Kindersley; **481 ml,** Burke/Triolo/Jupiter Unlimted; **481 tl,** Burke/Triolo/Jupiter Unlimited; **481 bl,** Frank Krahmer/Getty Images; **481 tr,** CreativeAct-Animals Series/Alamy; **481 br,** Dorling Kindersley; **482 r,** Jay Brousseau/Getty Images; **482 l,** Geoff Dann/Dorling Kindersley; **483 tl,** Radius Images/Photolibrary New York; **483 bl,** Randy Faris/Corbis; **483 tm,** Stuart McClymont/Getty Images; **483 tr,** Blickwinkel/Alamy; **483 bm,** Michael Melford/Getty Images; **483 br,** Naile Goelbasi/Getty Images; **483 t,** Luis Carlos Torres/iStockphoto.com; **484 l,** Mike Dunning/Dorling Kindersley; **484 mr,** Burke/Triolo/Jupiter Unlimited; **484 r,** Radius Images/Photolibrary New York; **484 t1,** CreativeAct-Animals series/Alamy; **484 t2,** Dorling Kindersley; **484 mr,** Burke/Triolo/Jupiter Unlimited; **484 ml,** Frank Krahmer/Getty Images; **484–485 bkgrnd,** Tomas Bercic/iStockphoto.com; **485 b,** Joel Sartore/Getty Images; **485 m,** Stuart McClymont/Getty Images; **486 br,** Phototake NYC; **486 l,** Phototake NYC; **487 r,** proxyminder/iStockphoto.com; **487 l,** Eric Isselée/iStockphoto.com; **487 m1,** Frank Greenaway/Dorling Kindersley; **487 m,** Cathleen Clapper/iStockphoto.com; **492 l,** Paul Bricknell/Dorling Kindersley; **492 r,** Konrad Wothe/Minden Pictures; **494 inset,** Biophoto Associates/Photo Researchers, Inc.; **494–495 bkgrnd,** Miguel Salmeron/Getty Images; **495 inset,** Isifa Image Service S.R.O./Alamy; **496 inset,** Udo Richter/AFP/Getty Images; **496–497 bkgrnd,** Anke van Wyk/Shutterstock; **499,** Splashnews/Newscom; **501 bkgrnd,** Yonhap/Choi Byung-kil/AP Images; **502,** Blickwinkel/Alamy.

Chapter 12 Feature

Page 506, We Shoot/Alamy; **507,** Dorling Kindersley.

Appendix

Pages 508–509 foreground, Eckehard Schulz/AP Images; **bkgrnd,** Car Culture/Corbis.